GROB

# BASIC ELECTRONICS

## EIGHTH EDITION

## Bernard Grob

**Glencoe McGraw-Hill**

New York, New York    Columbus, Ohio    Woodland Hills, California    Peoria, Illinois

**IN MEMORY OF RUTH**

## TO THE STUDENT

*Basic Electronics,* Eighth Edition, has been split into two convenient books. This set divides the original text into two logical parts. Book 1 contains the Survey chapter and Chapters 1 through 15, which cover all the material on direct current. Book 2 contains the remainder of the book—Chapters 16 to 32, which cover alternating current and an introduction to electronics.

For the convenience of the student, the glossary and appendixes are included in both Book 1 and Book 2. To facilitate reference to the supplemental materials and to maintain continuity between the volumes, the page numbering system has been kept as it appears in the single-volume textbook. For instance, the text of Book 1 is numbered through page 412, with the appendixes beginning on the next page, numbered 955. The text of Book 2 is numbered from page 414 through 954, and the appendixes continue on page 955.

Photo credits appear on page 1010, which is hereby made part of this copyright page.

**The Library of Congress has cataloged *Basic Electronics,* Eighth Edition, as follows:**
Grob, Bernard.
    Basic electronics / Bernard Grob.—8th ed.
      p.    cm.
    Includes bibliographical references and index.
    ISBN 0-02-802253-X
    1. Electronics.  I. Title.
TK7816.G75  1997
621.3—dc21                      96-39669
                                          CIP

*Glencoe/McGraw-Hill*
*A Division of The McGraw-Hill Companies*

**Basic Electronics, Eighth Edition, Book 2, Chapters 16 to 32**

Send all inquiries to:
Glencoe/McGraw-Hill
936 Eastwind Drive
Westerville, Ohio 43081

ISBN 0-02-802265-3

 2 3 4 5 6 7 8 9  027  02 01 00 99 98 97

# CONTENTS

PREFACE   vii

CHAPTER 16   ALTERNATING VOLTAGE AND
            CURRENT   414
16-1   Alternating Current Applications   416
16-2   Alternating-Voltage Generator   417
16-3   The Sine Wave   420
16-4   Alternating Current   423
16-5   Voltage and Current Values for a Sine Wave
       424
16-6   Frequency   427
16-7   Period   428
16-8   Wavelength   430
16-9   Phase Angle   423
16-10  The Time Factor in Frequency and Phase
       436
16-11  Alternating Current Circuits with Resistance
       437
16-12  Nonsinusoidal AC Waveforms   440
16-13  Harmonic Frequencies   442
16-14  The 60-Hz AC Power Line   442
16-15  Motors and Generators   445
16-16  Three-Phase AC Power   447
Summary and Review   450
REVIEW: CHAPTERS 13 TO 16   456

CHAPTER 17   CAPACITANCE   458

17-1   How Charge Is Stored in the Dielectric 460
17-2   Charging and Discharging a Capacitor   461
17-3   The Farad Unit of Capacitance   463
17-4   Typical Capacitors   468
17-5   Electrolytic Capacitors   472

17-6   Capacitor Coding   474
17-7   Parallel Capacitances   481
17-8   Series Capacitances   481
17-9   Stray Capacitive and Inductive Effects   483
17-10  Energy in Electrostatic Field of Capacitance
       485
17-11  Troubles in Capacitors   487
Summary and Review   490

CHAPTER 18   CAPACITIVE REACTANCE   496

18-1   Alternating Current in a Capacitive Circuit
       498
18-2   The Amount of $X_C$ Equals $1/(2\pi fC)$   499
18-3   Series or Parallel Capacitive Reactances   503
18-4   Ohm's Law Applied to $X_C$   504
18-5   Applications of Capacitive Reactance   505
18-6   Sine-Wave Charge and Discharge Current
       506
Summary and Review   511

CHAPTER 19   CAPACITIVE CIRCUITS   516

19-1   Sine-Wave $v_C$ Lags $i_C$ by 90°   518
19-2   $X_C$ and $R$ in Series   519
19-3   $RC$ Phase-Shifter Circuit   522
19-4   $X_C$ and $R$ in Parallel   524
19-5   RF and AF Coupling Capacitors   527
19-6   Capacitive Voltage Dividers   528
19-7   The General Case of Capacitive Current $i_C$
       530
Summary and Review   531
REVIEW: CHAPTERS 17 TO 19   537

## CHAPTER 20   INDUCTANCE   540

20-1   Induction by Alternating Current   542
20-2   Self-Inductance $L$   543
20-3   Self-Induced Voltage $v_L$   546
20-4   How $v_L$ Opposes a Change in Current   547
20-5   Mutual Inductance $L_M$   548
20-6   Transformers   552
20-7   Transformer Ratings   558
20-8   Impedance Transformation   563
20-9   Core Losses   567
20-10  Types of Cores   568
20-11  Variable Inductance   569
20-12  Inductances in Series or Parallel   570
20-13  Stray Inductance   573
20-14  Energy in Magnetic Field of Inductance   573
20-15  Troubles in Coils   575
Summary and Review   577

## CHAPTER 21   INDUCTIVE REACTANCE   584

21-1   How $X_L$ Reduces the Amount of $I$   586
21-2   $X_L = 2\pi fL$   587
21-3   Series or Parallel Inductive Reactances   591
21-4   Ohm's Law Applied to $X_L$   592
21-5   Applications of $X_L$ for Different Frequencies   593
21-6   Waveshape of $v_L$ Induced by Sine-Wave Current   594
Summary and Review   599

## CHAPTER 22   INDUCTIVE CIRCUITS   604

22-1   Sine-Wave $i_L$ Lags $v_L$ by 90°   606
22-2   $X_L$ and $R$ in Series   607
22-3   Impedance $Z$ Triangle   610
22-4   $X_L$ and $R$ in Parallel   613
22-5   $Q$ of a Coil   617
22-6   AF and RF Chokes   619
22-7   The General Case of Inductive Voltage   621
Summary and Review   624

## CHAPTER 23   RC AND L/R TIME CONSTANTS   630

23-1   Response of Resistance Alone   632
23-2   $L/R$ Time Constant   632
23-3   High Voltage Produced by Opening an $RL$ Circuit   634
23-4   $RC$ Time Constant   636
23-5   $RC$ Charge and Discharge Curves   639
23-6   High Current Produced by Short-circuiting $RC$ Circuit   640
23-7   $RC$ Waveshapes   642
23-8   Long and Short Time Constants   644
23-9   Charge and Discharge with Short $RC$ Time Constant   645
23-10  Long Time Constant for $RC$ Coupling Circuit   647
23-11  Universal Time Constant Graph   648
23-12  Comparison of Reactance and Time Constant   653
Summary and Review   655
REVIEW: CHAPTERS 20 TO 23   661

## CHAPTER 24   ALTERNATING CURRENT CIRCUITS   664

24-1   AC Circuits with Resistance but No Reactance   666
24-2   Circuits with $X_L$ Alone   667
24-3   Circuits with $X_C$ Alone   668
24-4   Opposite Reactances Cancel   669
24-5   Series Reactance and Resistance   671
24-6   Parallel Reactance and Resistance   674
24-7   Series-Parallel Reactance and Resistance   676
24-8   Real Power   677
24-9   AC Meters   680
24-10  Wattmeters   681
24-11  Summary of Types of Ohms in AC Circuits   682
24-12  Summary of Types of Phasors in AC Circuits   683
Summary and Review   686

## CHAPTER 25   COMPLEX NUMBERS FOR AC CIRCUITS   690

25-1   Positive and Negative Numbers   692
25-2   The $j$ Operator   692
25-3   Definition of a Complex Number   694
25-4   How Complex Numbers Are Applied to AC Circuits   695

25-5  Impedance in Complex Form   696
25-6  Operations with Complex Numbers   698
25-7  Magnitude and Angle of a Complex Number   700
25-8  Polar Form of Complex Numbers   701
25-9  Converting Polar to Rectangular Form   703
25-10 Complex Numbers in Series AC Circuits   705
25-11 Complex Numbers in Parallel AC Circuits   708
25-12 Combining Two Complex Branch Impedances   710
25-13 Combining Complex Branch Currents   711
25-14 Parallel Circuit with Three Complex Branches   712
Summary and Review   715
REVIEW: CHAPTERS 24 AND 25   720


CHAPTER 26   RESONANCE   722

26-1  The Resonance Effect   724
26-2  Series Resonance   725
26-3  Parallel Resonance   728
26-4  Resonant Frequency $f_r = 1/(2\pi\sqrt{LC})$   732
26-5  $Q$ Magnification Factor of Resonant Circuit   736
26-6  Bandwidth of Resonant Circuit   740
26-7  Tuning   744
26-8  Mistuning   746
26-9  Analysis of Parallel Resonant Circuits   747
26-10 Damping of Parallel Resonant Circuits   749
26-11 Choosing $L$ and $C$ for a Resonant Circuit   751
Summary and Review   752


CHAPTER 27   FILTERS   758

27-1  Examples of Filtering   760
27-2  Direct Current Combined with Alternating Current   760
27-3  Transformer Coupling   763
27-4  Capacitive Coupling   764
27-5  Bypass Capacitors   767
27-6  Filter Circuits   770
27-7  Low-Pass Filters   771
27-8  High-Pass Filters   773
27-9  Analyzing Filter Circuits   774

27-10 Decibels and Frequency Response Curves   784
27-11 Resonant Filters   791
27-12 Interference Filters   794
Summary and Review   795
REVIEW: CHAPTERS 26 AND 27   801


CHAPTER 28   ELECTRONIC DEVICES   804

28-1  Semiconductors   806
28-2  The PN Junction   811
28-3  Semiconductor Diodes   816
28-4  PNP and NPN Transistors   818
28-5  Field-Effect Transistor (FET)   823
28-6  Testing Diodes and Thyristors   827
Summary and Review   830


CHAPTER 29   ELECTRONIC CIRCUITS   834

29-1  Analog and Digital Signals   836
29-2  Amplifier Gain   838
29-3  Characteristics of Amplifier Circuits   841
29-4  Oscillators   847
29-5  Multivibrators   850
29-6  Modulation   853
29-7  Diode Rectifiers   857
29-8  Troubleshooting the DC Supply Voltage   860
Summary and Review   864


CHAPTER 30   TRANSISTOR AMPLIFIERS   868

30-1  Circuit Configurations   870
30-2  Class A, B, or C Operation   873
30-3  Analysis of Common-Emitter (CE) Amplifier   875
30-4  Collector Characteristic Curves   879
30-5  Letter Symbols for Transistors   881
30-6  FET Amplifiers   882
30-7  Troubleshooting Amplifier Circuits   884
Summary and Review   888
REVIEW: CHAPTERS 28 TO 30   890


CHAPTER 31   DIGITAL ELECTRONICS   892

31-1  Comparing Binary and Decimal Numbers   894

31-2   Decimal to Binary Conversion   896
31-3   Hexadecimal Numbers   896
31-4   Binary Coded Decimal System   900
31-5   The ASCII Code   901
31-6   Logic Gates, Symbols, and Truth Tables   902
31-7   Boolean Algebra   906
31-8   DeMorgan's Theorem   909
31-9   Active HIGH/Active LOW Terminology   912
31-10  Treating Unused Inputs on Logic Gates   914
31-11  Combinational Logic Circuits   915
31-12  Flip-Flops   918
31-13  Binary Counters   922
31-14  New Logic Symbols   925
Summary and Review   927

CHAPTER 32   INTEGRATED CIRCUITS   932

32-1   Operational Amplifiers and Their Characteristics   934
32-2   Op Amp Circuits   941
Summary and Review   950
REVIEW: CHAPTERS 31 AND 32   953

Appendix A Electrical Symbols and Abbreviations   955
Appendix B Solder and the Soldering Process   957
Appendix C Schematic Symbols   964
Appendix D Using the Oscilloscope   966
Glossary   981
Answers to Self-Tests   988
Answers to Odd-Numbered Problems and Critical Thinking Problems   992
Index   1002

# PREFACE

*Basic Electronics,* now in its eighth edition, is intended for students taking their first course in the fundamentals of electricity and electronics. The book is written for the beginning student, who is assumed to have no prior knowledge of the technical aspects of the subject. The prerequisites for using this book include an understanding of basic algebra and some trigonometry. In many schools, it will be possible to take a basic algebra-trigonometry course concurrently with the use of this book in a course covering the fundamental concepts of dc and ac theory.

The primary focus of this revision was a very careful review of its content and layout. Many additions, deletions, and reordering of topics have occurred as a direct result of an extensive survey sent to electronics instructors all across the country. For current users of the book, the additions and changes will be easy to identify throughout the book.

**ORGANIZATION**    The book begins with a chapter entitled "Survey of Electronics." This chapter provides a brief overview of the history of the development of electronics, describes a variety of career opportunities available in electronics, explains the most common components used in electronics, and identifies some of the most common types of equipment used by professionals in the electronics field. Following the "Survey of Electronics" chapter, the book provides complete and comprehensive coverage of the subjects which form the real fundamentals of basic electronics. Beginning with the atomic nature of electricity in Chapter 1, the topics progress through a study of resistors, Ohm's law, series and parallel circuits, series-parallel circuits, voltage and current dividers, dc meters, Kirchhoff's laws and network theorems, conductors and insulators, batteries, magnetism, magnetic units, electromagnetic induction, alternating voltage and current, capacitance, capacitive reactance, capacitive circuits, inductance, inductive reactance, inductive circuits, *RC* and *L/R* time constants, ac circuits, complex numbers, resonance, and filters.

Current users of the book will notice that the chapters on capacitance, capacitive reactance, and capacitive circuits now precede the chapters on inductance, inductive reactance, and inductive circuits. This change has been made as a result of the previously mentioned survey that was sent to electronics instructors. If they wish, instructors may choose to cover the chapters on inductance prior to those on capacitance.

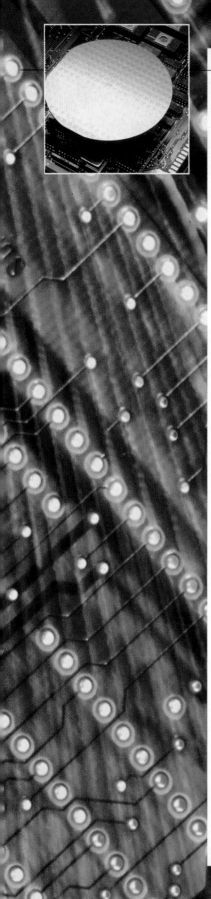

In this edition, several changes have been made in Chapter 2, "Resistors." There is expanded coverage of both carbon and metal film resistors and the five-band resistor color code. Also new to this chapter is coverage of surface-mount resistors and zero-ohm resistors. These additions reflect the most state-of-the-art coverage available on resistors in any basic textbook covering dc and ac theory.

In Chapter 11, "Conductors and Insulators," more information on switches has been added. In Chapter 15, "Electromagnetic Induction," a new section on electromechanical relays has been added.

In Chapter 17, "Capacitance," new and updated material regarding the coding system used with a wide variety of types of capacitors has been added. Also new to this chapter is the coverage of surface-mount capacitors and the coding systems used with them. In Chapter 20, "Inductance," new material covers impedance matching and the many ratings associated with transformers. In Chapter 23, "*RC* and *L/R* Time Constants," new information on differentiation and integration is included. In Chapter 27, "Filters," a wealth of new information, on phase angles, calculating cutoff frequency and output voltage, decibels, and frequency response curves, now appears.

The last five chapters of the book provide a basic introduction to semiconductor theory, diodes, transistors, amplifiers, oscillators, modulation, rectifier circuits, circuit configurations, class of operation, troubleshooting, number systems, basic logic gates, Boolean algebra, flip-flops, counters, op amp characteristics, and op amp circuits. The coverage of op amp circuits has been expanded in response to the survey.

Following the text chapters are four appendixes: Appendix A, "Electrical Symbols and Abbreviations," Appendix B, "Solder and the Soldering Process," Appendix C, "Schematic Symbols," and Appendix D, "Using the Oscilloscope." The appendixes are followed by a glossary, answers to self-tests, answers to odd-numbered chapter problems and critical thinking problems, and an index.

**CHAPTER LAYOUT**   Each chapter begins with a brief introduction of the topic, a list of important terms, chapter objectives (new to this edition), and a list of the sections appearing within the chapter. Within each chapter, test-point questions are given at the end of each section. This provides the student with a quick means of checking his or her understanding of the material in that section. At the end of each chapter are the following items: summary, self-test, questions, problems, and critical thinking questions. Like the chapter objectives, the critical thinking questions are new to the eighth edition. It should be noted that new problems have been added to each chapter. The answers to the test-point questions appear at the end of each chapter.

Step-by-step solutions of typical problems dealing with a particular concept are generously provided in every chapter of the book. Where appropriate, typical calculator keystroke routines are provided as an additional aid to the student. The illustrative examples are highlighted so that students can access them more readily.

**ANCILLARY PACKAGE**    The following supplements are available to adopters of Grob *Basic Electronics:*

- *Problems in Grob Basic Electronics:* This book, written by Mitchel E. Schultz, provides students and instructors with a source of hundreds of practical problems for self-study, homework assignments, tests, and review. Each chapter contains a number of solved illustrative problems demonstrating, step-by-step, how representative problems on a particular topic are solved. Following the solved problems are sets of problems for the students to solve.

- *Experiments in Grob Basic Electronics:* This book, written by Frank Pugh and Wes Ponick, provides students and instructors with 67 easy-to-follow laboratory experiments. The experiments range from an introduction to laboratory equipment to an experiment on operational amplifiers. All experiments have been student-tested to ensure their effectiveness.

- *Mathematics for Grob Basic Electronics:* This book, written by Bernard Grob, provides students with the basic math skills needed to solve problems in the text, *Grob Basic Electronics.* Included are chapters on algebra, trigonometry, the basics of computer mathematics, and a new chapter on complex numbers for ac circuits.

- *Instructor's Productivity Center for Grob Basic Electronics, Eighth Edition:* This package includes a Windows-based test generator, a math tutorial, and a Power Point presentation for every chapter of the text. It also includes a graphics file of the circuits in the text. These files can be used for tests or presentations. The optional Group Instruction software, developed by HyperGraphics, can be accessed directly from the IPC. An optional Electronics Workbench file of the circuits in *Basic Electronics* is also available.

- *Instructor's Annotated Edition for Grob Basic Electronics, Eighth Edition:* This book includes teaching hints and scheduling suggestions for the instructor and career information for students. Much of this material has been given in the margin of this text for the instructor's ease of reference while teaching a class. Answers to test-point questions, which appear in the student's text, are also included in the margin of this version, produced especially for the instructor.

- *Instructor's Manual for Grob Basic Electronics, Eighth Edition:* This book provides the instructor with answers to all the questions and problems in the text and in its supplements, *Problems in Grob Basic Electronics, Experiments in Grob Basic Electronics,* and *Mathematics for Grob Basic Electronics.*

Bernard Grob

# CREDITS AND ACKNOWLEDGMENTS

The author would like to thank those individuals who responded to the survey which was sent out long before this book was revised. Their comments and suggestions provided the information needed to make this the most up-to-date book available on electricity and electronics. The author would also like to thank the reviewers listed below who painstakingly examined every sentence, example, and problem for accuracy prior to the publication of the eighth edition.

In addition, the author would like to thank the highly professional staff at Glencoe in Columbus, Ohio—especially Brian Mackin for his patience, hard work, and understanding during the long period of the manuscript preparation. My thanks also go to Mitchel Schultz for his help on this project. Finally, it is a pleasure to thank my wife, Sylvia, for her help in preparing the manuscript.

Tim Beecher
Wisconsin Indianhead Technical College
Superior, WI

Jack Berger
ITT Technical Institute
Murray, UT

B. J. Tobias Boydell
Seva Electronics
Burford, Ontario, Canada

Patrick J. Chalmers
ITT Technical Institute
Matteson, IL

Michael Fairbanks
ITT Technical Institute
Nashville, TN

Richard L. Green
ITT Technical Institute
Maitland, FL

Rich Hassler
ITT Technical Institute
Youngstown, OH

William M. Hessmiller
QRS Corporation
Dunmore, PA

Barry Hoy
ITT Technical Institute
Norfolk, VA

Arnold Kroeger
Hillsborough Community College
Tampa, FL

James A. McQuoid
ITT Technical Institute
San Antonio, TX

Jim Myers
Wallace Community College
Selma, AL

Tony Richardson
ITT Technical Institute
Strongsville, OH

T. Randall Riggs
ITT Technical Institute
Tampa, FL

Gregg Richley
ITT Technical Institute
Youngstown, OH

Victor Rozeboom
Burlington, NC

John Ryan
ITT Technical Institute
Knoxville, TN

Dan Siddall
ITT Technical Institute
Boise, ID

Mike Siemion
Madison Area Technical College
Madison, WI

William H. Sims III
ITT Technical Institute
Jacksonville, FL

Pat Thomason
Patterson State Technical
College
Montgomery, AL

Bryon K. Van Beek
Courtesy Communications
Spokane, WA

# CHAPTER 16

# ALTERNATING VOLTAGE AND CURRENT

This chapter begins the analysis of alternating voltage, as used for the 120-Vac power line, and the alternating current that the voltage produces in an ac circuit. Alternating voltage reverses in polarity and amplitude periodically with time. One cycle includes two alternations in polarity. The number of cycles per second is the frequency whose unit is the hertz (Hz). One hertz is equal to one cycle per second (1 Hz = 1 cps). The ac power line frequency is standardized at 60 Hz in the United States.

For an ac voltage:

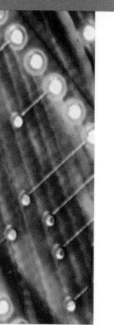

1. The *V* reverses polarity at a specific rate. Consider one terminal of the ac source positive at a given time, with respect to the other terminal. A little later in time, the positive terminal will become negative to reverse the polarity of the ac output voltage. The polarity reversals are continuously repeated at a regular rate.
2. For either polarity, the ac voltage varies in amplitude. In fact, the voltage must vary from a maximum value to zero in order to be ready for the next polarity reversal.

The alternating current that results has the following features:

1. The *I* reverses in direction with the polarity reversal in *V*.
2. The amplitude of *I* varies with the changing values of voltage.

The ac waveform with its polarity reversals and amplitude variations is very important in electronics because the many audio, radio, and video signals are examples of ac voltages.

# CHAPTER OBJECTIVES

*Upon completion of this chapter, you should be able to:*

- *Understand* how a sine wave of alternating voltage is generated.
- *Calculate* the instantaneous value of a sine wave.
- *Define* the following values for a sine wave: peak, peak-to-peak, root-mean-square, and average.
- *Calculate* the rms, average, and peak-to-peak values of a sine wave when the peak value is known.
- *Define* the terms *frequency* and *period* and list the units of each.
- *Calculate* the wavelength when the frequency is known.
- *Understand* the concept of phase angles.
- *Understand* the makeup of a nonsinusoidal waveform.
- Define the term *harmonics*.
- *Understand* the 60-Hz ac power line and the basics of residential house wiring.

## IMPORTANT TERMS IN THIS CHAPTER

| | | |
|---|---|---|
| alternation | field winding | sawtooth wave |
| alternator | frequency | sine wave |
| armature | harmonic | sinusoid |
| average value | hertz | slip rings |
| brushes | octave | square wave |
| commutator | peak value | three-phase power |
| cycle | phase angle | wavelength |
| delta connections | phasor | wye connections |
| effective value | rms value | |

## TOPICS COVERED IN THIS CHAPTER

16-1 Alternating Current Applications
16-2 Alternating-Voltage Generator
16-3 The Sine Wave
16-4 Alternating Current
16-5 Voltage and Current Values for a Sine Wave
16-6 Frequency
16-7 Period
16-8 Wavelength
16-9 Phase Angle
16-10 The Time Factor in Frequency and Phase
16-11 Alternating Current Circuits with Resistance
16-12 Nonsinusoidal AC Waveforms
16-13 Harmonic Frequencies
16-14 The 60-Hz AC Power Line
16-15 Motors and Generators
16-16 Three-Phase AC Power

# 16-1 ALTERNATING CURRENT APPLICATIONS

Figure 16-1 shows the output from an ac voltage generator, with the reversals between positive and negative polarities and the variations in amplitude. In Fig. 16-1a, the waveform shown simulates an ac voltage as it would appear on the screen of an oscilloscope, which is an important test instrument for ac voltages. The oscilloscope shows a picture of any ac voltage connected to its input terminals, while indicating the amplitude. The details of how to use the oscilloscope for ac voltage measurements are explained in App. D, "Using the Oscilloscope."

In Fig. 16-1b, the graph of the ac waveform shows how the output from the generator in Fig. 16-1c varies with respect to time. Assume that this graph shows V at terminal 2 with respect to terminal 1. Then the voltage at terminal 1 corresponds to the zero axis in the graph as the reference level. At terminal 2, the output voltage has positive amplitude variations from zero up to the peak value and down to zero. All these voltage values are with respect to terminal 1. After a half-cycle, the voltage at terminal 2 becomes negative, still with respect to the other terminal. Then the same voltage variations are repeated at terminal 2, but they have negative polarity compared to the reference level. It should be noted that if we take the voltage at terminal 1 with terminal 2 as the reference, the waveform in Fig. 16-1b would have the same shape but be inverted in polarity. The negative half-cycle would come first, but it does not matter which is first or second.

The characteristic of varying values is the reason why ac circuits have so many uses. For instance, a transformer can operate only with alternating current, to step up or step down an ac voltage. The reason is that the changing current produces changes in its associated magnetic field. This application is just an example of inductance L in ac circuits, where the changing magnetic flux of a varying current can produce induced voltage. The details of inductance are explained in Chaps. 20, 21, and 22.

A similar but opposite effect in ac circuits is capacitance C. The capacitance is important with the changing electric field of a varying voltage. Just as L has

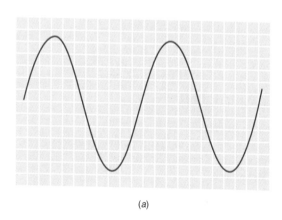

(a)

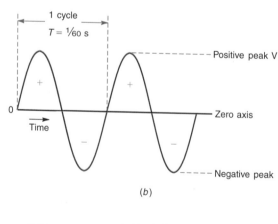

(b)

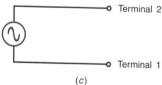

(c)

FIG. 16-1   Waveform of ac power-line voltage with frequency of 60 Hz. Two cycles are shown. (a) Oscilloscope readout. (b) Details of waveform and alternating polarities. (c) Symbol for an ac voltage source.

an effect with alternating current, $C$ has an effect which depends on alternating voltage. The details of capacitance are explained in Chaps. 17, 18, and 19.

The $L$ and $C$ are additional factors, besides resistance $R$, in the operation of ac circuits. It should be noted that $R$ is the same for either a dc or an ac circuit. However, the effects of $L$ and $C$ depend on having an ac source. The rate at which the ac variations occur, which determines the frequency, allows a greater or lesser reaction by $L$ and $C$. Therefore, the effect is different for different frequencies. One important application is a resonant circuit with $L$ and $C$ which is tuned to a particular frequency. Tuning in radio and television stations are applications of resonance in an $LC$ circuit.

In general, electronic circuits are combinations of $R$, $L$, and $C$, with both direct current and alternating current. The audio, video, and radio signals are ac voltages and currents. However, the amplifiers that use transistors need dc voltages in order to conduct any current at all. The resulting output of an amplifier circuit, therefore, consists of direct current with a superimposed ac signal. More details of amplifiers are explained in Chap. 29, "Electronic Circuits."

# 16-2 ALTERNATING-VOLTAGE GENERATOR

We can define an ac voltage as one that continuously varies in magnitude and periodically reverses in polarity. In Fig. 16-1, the variations up and down on the waveform show the changes in magnitude. The zero axis is a horizontal line across the center. Then voltages above the center have positive polarity, while the values below center are negative.

Figure 16-2 illustrates how such a voltage waveform is produced by a rotary generator. The conductor loop rotates through the magnetic field to generate the induced ac voltage across its open terminals. The magnetic flux shown here is vertical, with lines of force down in the plane of the paper.

In Fig. 16-2a the loop is in its horizontal starting position in a plane perpendicular to the paper. When the loop rotates counterclockwise, the two longer conductors move around a circle. Note that in the flat position shown, the two long conductors of the loop move vertically up or down but parallel to the vertical flux lines. In this position, motion of the loop does not induce a voltage because the conductors are not cutting across the flux.

When the loop rotates through the upright position in Fig. 16-2b, however, the conductors cut across the flux, producing maximum induced voltage. The shorter connecting wires in the loop do not have any appreciable voltage induced in them.

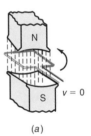

(a)

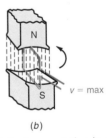

(b)

FIG. 16-2 Loop rotating in magnetic field to produce induced voltage $v$ with alternating polarities. (a) Loop conductors moving parallel to magnetic field results in zero voltage. (b) Loop conductors cutting across magnetic field produce maximum induced voltage.

Each of the longer conductors has opposite polarity of induced voltage because the conductor at the top is moving to the left while the bottom conductor is moving to the right. The amount of voltage varies from zero to maximum as the loop moves from a flat position to upright, where it can cut across the flux. Also, the polarity at the terminals of the loop reverses as the motion of each conductor reverses during each half-revolution.

With one revolution of the loop in a complete circle back to the starting position, therefore, the induced voltage provides a potential difference $v$ across the loop, varying in the same way as the wave of voltage shown in Fig. 16-1. If the loop rotates at the speed of 60 revolutions per second, the ac voltage will have the frequency of 60 Hz.

**THE CYCLE**  One complete revolution of the loop around the circle is a *cycle*. In Fig. 16-3, the generator loop is shown in its position at each quarter-turn during one complete cycle. The corresponding wave of induced voltage also goes through one cycle. Although not shown, the magnetic field is from top to bottom of the page as in Fig. 16-2.

At position A in Fig. 16-3, the loop is flat and moves parallel to the magnetic field, so that the induced voltage is zero. Counterclockwise rotation of the loop moves the dark conductor to the top at position B, where it cuts across the field to produce maximum induced voltage. The polarity of the induced voltage here makes the open end of the dark conductor positive. This conductor at the top is cutting across the flux from right to left. At the same time, the opposite conductor below is moving from left to right, causing its induced voltage to have opposite polarity. Therefore, maximum induced voltage is produced at this time across the two open ends of the loop. Now the top conductor is positive with respect to the bottom conductor.

In the graph of induced voltage values below the loop in Fig. 16-3, the polarity of the dark conductor is shown with respect to the other conductor. Positive voltage is shown above the zero axis in the graph. As the dark conductor

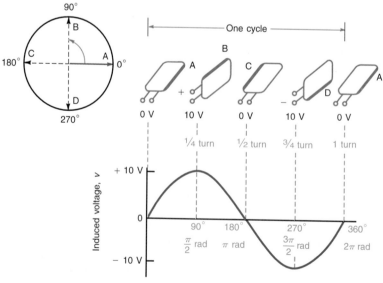

**FIG. 16-3**  One cycle of alternating voltage generated by rotating loop. Magnetic field, not shown here, is directed from top to bottom, as in Fig. 16-2.

rotates from its starting position parallel to the flux toward the top position, where it cuts maximum flux, more and more induced voltage is produced, with positive polarity.

When the loop rotates through the next quarter-turn, it returns to the flat position shown in C, where it cannot cut across flux. Therefore, the induced voltage values shown in the graph decrease from the maximum value to zero at the half-turn, just as the voltage was zero at the start. The half-cycle of revolution is called an *alternation.*

The next quarter-turn of the loop moves it to the position shown at D in Fig. 16-3, where the loop cuts across the flux again for maximum induced voltage. Note, however, that here the dark conductor is moving left to right at the bottom of the loop. This motion is reversed from the direction it had when it was at the top, moving right to left. Because the direction of motion is reversed during the second half-revolution, the induced voltage has opposite polarity, with the dark conductor negative. This polarity is shown as negative voltage, below the zero axis. The maximum value of induced voltage at the third quarter-turn is the same as at the first quarter-turn but with opposite polarity.

When the loop completes the last quarter-turn in the cycle, the induced voltage returns to zero as the loop returns to its flat position at A, the same as at the start. This cycle of values of induced voltage is repeated as the loop continues to rotate, with one complete cycle of voltage values, as shown, for each circle of revolution.

Note that zero at the start and zero after the half-turn of an alternation are not the same. At the start, the voltage is zero because the loop is flat, but the dark conductor is moving upward in the direction that produces positive voltage. After one half-cycle, the voltage is zero with the loop flat, but the dark conductor is moving downward in the direction that produces negative voltage. After one complete cycle, the loop and its corresponding waveform of induced voltage are the same as at the start. *A cycle can be defined, therefore, as including the variations between two successive points having the same value and varying in the same direction.*

**ANGULAR MEASURE**   Because the cycle of voltage in Fig. 16-3 corresponds to rotation of the loop around a circle, it is convenient to consider parts of the cycle in angles. The complete circle includes 360°. One half-cycle, or one alternation, is 180° of revolution. A quarter-turn is 90°. The circle next to the loop positions in Fig. 16-3 illustrates the angular rotation of the dark conductor as it rotates counterclockwise from 0 to 90 to 180° for one half-cycle, then to 270° and returning to 360° to complete the cycle. Therefore, one cycle corresponds to 360°.

**RADIAN MEASURE**   In angular measure it is convenient to use a specific unit angle called the *radian* (abbreviated rad), which is an angle equal to 57.3°. Its convenience is due to the fact that a radian is the angular part of the circle that includes an arc equal to the radius *r* of the circle, as shown in Fig. 16-4. The circumference around the circle equals $2\pi r$. A circle includes $2\pi$ rad, then, as each radian angle includes one length *r* of the circumference. Therefore, one cycle equals $2\pi$ rad.

As shown in the graph in Fig. 16-3, divisions of the cycle can be indicated by angles in either degrees or radians. The comparison between degrees and radians can be summarized as follows:

Zero degrees is also zero radians
$360° = 2\pi$ rad
$180° = \frac{1}{2} \times 2\pi$ rad $= \pi$ rad
$90° = \frac{1}{2} \times \pi$ rad $= \pi/2$ rad
$270° = 180° + 90°$ or $\pi$ rad $+ \pi/2$ rad $= 3\pi/2$ rad

The constant $2\pi$ in circular measure is numerically equal to 6.2832. This is double the value of 3.1416 for $\pi$. The Greek letter $\pi$ (pi) is used to represent the ratio of the circumference to the diameter for any circle, which always has the numerical value of 3.1416. The fact that $2\pi$ rad is 360° can be shown as $2 \times 3.1416 \times 57.3° = 360°$ for a complete cycle.

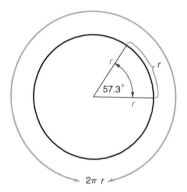

**FIG. 16-4**   One radian (rad) is the angle equal to 57.3°. The complete circle with 360° includes $2\pi$ rad.

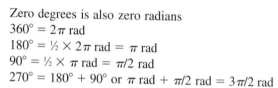

**TEST-POINT QUESTION 16-2**

Answers at end of chapter.

Refer to Fig. 16-3.
**a.** How much is the induced voltage at $\pi/2$ rad?
**b.** How many degrees are in a complete cycle?

## 16-3 THE SINE WAVE

The voltage waveform in Figs. 16-1 and 16-3 is called a *sine wave, sinusoidal wave,* or *sinusoid* because the amount of induced voltage is proportional to the sine of the angle of rotation in the circular motion producing the voltage. The sine is a trigonometric function* of an angle; it is equal to the ratio of the opposite side to the hypotenuse in a right triangle. This numerical ratio increases from zero for 0° to a maximum value of 1 for 90° as the side opposite the angle becomes larger.

The voltage waveform produced by the circular motion of the loop is a sine wave, because the induced voltage increases to a maximum at 90°, when the loop is vertical, in the same way that the sine of the angle of rotation increases to a maximum at 90°. The induced voltage and sine of the angle correspond for the full 360° of the cycle. Table 16-1 lists the numerical values of the sine for several important angles, to illustrate the specific characteristics of a sine wave.

## TABLE 16-1   VALUES IN A SINE WAVE

| ANGLE $\theta$ | | SIN $\theta$ | LOOP VOLTAGE |
|---|---|---|---|
| DEGREES | RADIANS | | |
| 0 | 0 | 0 | Zero |
| 30 | $\dfrac{\pi}{6}$ | 0.500 | 50% of maximum |
| 45 | $\dfrac{\pi}{4}$ | 0.707 | 70.7% of maximum |
| 60 | $\dfrac{\pi}{3}$ | 0.866 | 86.6% of maximum |
| 90 | $\dfrac{\pi}{2}$ | 1.000 | Positive maximum value |
| 180 | $\pi$ | 0 | Zero |
| 270 | $\dfrac{3\pi}{2}$ | −1.000 | Negative maximum value |
| 360 | $2\pi$ | 0 | Zero |

Notice that the sine wave reaches ½ its maximum value in 30°, which is only ⅓ of 90°. This fact means that the sine wave has a sharper slope of changing values when the wave is near the zero axis, compared with the more gradual changes near the maximum value.

The instantaneous value of a sine-wave voltage for any angle of rotation is expressed by the formula

▶   $v = V_M \sin \theta$ (16-1)

where $\theta$ (Greek letter *theta*) is the angle, sin is the abbreviation for its sine, $V_M$ is the maximum voltage value, and $v$ is the instantaneous value of voltage at angle $\theta$.

---

*More details are given in B. Grob, *Mathematics for Basic Electronics*, Glencoe/McGraw-Hill, Columbus, Ohio.

## Example

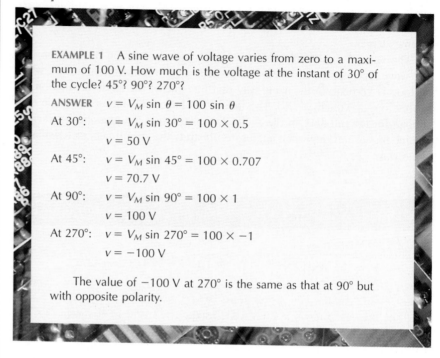

**EXAMPLE 1** A sine wave of voltage varies from zero to a maximum of 100 V. How much is the voltage at the instant of 30° of the cycle? 45°? 90°? 270°?

**ANSWER** $v = V_M \sin \theta = 100 \sin \theta$

At 30°: $v = V_M \sin 30° = 100 \times 0.5$

$v = 50$ V

At 45°: $v = V_M \sin 45° = 100 \times 0.707$

$v = 70.7$ V

At 90°: $v = V_M \sin 90° = 100 \times 1$

$v = 100$ V

At 270°: $v = V_M \sin 270° = 100 \times -1$

$v = -100$ V

The value of $-100$ V at 270° is the same as that at 90° but with opposite polarity.

To do the problems in Example 1 you must either refer to a table of trigonometric functions or use a scientific calculator that has trig functions. With the calculator, be sure it is set for degrees, not radians or grad units. To find the value of the sine function, just punch in the number for angle $\theta$ in degrees and push the (SIN) key to see the values of sin $\theta$ on the display.

Applying this procedure to Formula (16-1), find the value of sin $\theta$ and multiply by the peak value $V_M$. Specifically, for the first problem in Example 1 with $V_M$ of 100 and $\theta$ of 30°, first punch in 30 on the calculator. Next press the (SIN) key to see 0.5 on the display, which is sin 30°. Then push the multiplication (×) key, punch in 100 for $V_M$, and press the (=) key for the final answer of 50. The same method is used for all the other values of angle $\theta$.

Between zero at 0° and maximum at 90° the amplitudes of a sine wave increase exactly as the sine value for the angle of rotation. These values are for the first quadrant in the circle, that is, 0° to 90°. From 90° to 180°, in the second quadrant, the values decrease as a mirror image of the first 90°. The values in the third and fourth quadrants, from 180° to 360°, are exactly the same as 0° to 180° but with opposite sign. At 360° the waveform is back to 0° to repeat its values every 360°.

In summary, the characteristics of the sine-wave ac waveform are:

1. The cycle includes 360° or $2\pi$ rad.
2. The polarity reverses each half-cycle.
3. The maximum values are at 90° and 270°.
4. The zero values are at 0° and 180°.
5. The waveform changes its values the fastest when it crosses the zero axis.
6. The waveform changes its values the slowest when it is at its maximum value. The values must stop increasing before they can decrease.

A perfect example of the sine-wave ac waveform is the 60-Hz power-line voltage in Fig. 16-1.

A sine-wave voltage has a peak value of 170 V. What is its value at

**a.** 30°?

**b.** 45°?

**c.** 90°?

# 16-4 ALTERNATING CURRENT

When a sine wave of alternating voltage is connected across a load resistance, the current that flows in the circuit is also a sine wave. In Fig. 16-5, let the sine-wave voltage at the left in the diagram be applied across $R$ of 100 $\Omega$. The resulting sine wave of alternating current is shown at the right in the diagram. Note that the frequency is the same for $v$ and $i$.

During the first alternation of $v$ in Fig. 16-5, terminal 1 is positive with respect to terminal 2. Since the direction of electron flow is from the negative side of $v$, through $R$, and back to the positive side of $v$, current flows in the direction indicated by arrow A for the first half-cycle. This direction is taken as the positive direction of current in the graph for $i$, corresponding to positive values of $v$.

The amount of current is equal to $v/R$. If several instantaneous values are taken, when $v$ is zero, $i$ is zero; when $v$ is 50 V, $i$ equals 50 V/100, or 0.5 A; when $v$ is 100 V, $i$ equals 100 V/100, or 1 A. For all values of applied voltage with positive polarity, therefore, the current is in one direction, increasing to its maximum value and decreasing to zero, just like the voltage.

On the next half-cycle, the polarity of the alternating voltage reverses. Then terminal 1 is negative with respect to terminal 2. With reversed voltage polarity, current flows in the opposite direction. Electron flow is from terminal 1 of the voltage source, which is now the negative side, through $R$, and back to terminal 2. This direction of current, as indicated by arrow B in Fig. 16-5, is negative.

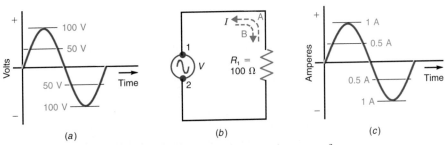

**FIG. 16-5** A sine wave of alternating voltage applied across $R$ produces a sine wave of alternating current in the circuit. (*a*) Waveform of applied voltage. (*b*) AC circuit. Note the symbol for sine-wave generator V. (*c*) Waveform of current in the circuit.

The negative values of $i$ in the graph have the same numerical values as the positive values in the first half-cycle, corresponding to the reversed values of applied voltage. As a result, the alternating current in the circuit has sine-wave variations corresponding exactly to the sine-wave alternating voltage.

Only the waveforms for $v$ and $i$ can be compared. There is no comparison between relative values, because the current and voltage are different quantities.

It is important to note that the negative half-cycle of applied voltage is just as useful as the positive half-cycle in producing current. The only difference is that the reversed polarity of voltage produces the opposite direction of current.

Furthermore, the negative half-cycle of current is just as effective as the positive values when heating the filament to light a bulb. With positive values, electrons flow through the filament in one direction. Negative values produce electron flow in the opposite direction. In both cases, electrons flow from the negative side of the voltage source, through the filament, and return to the positive side of the source. For either direction, the current heats the filament. The direction does not matter, since it is just the motion of electrons against resistance that produces power dissipation. In short, resistance $R$ has the same effect in reducing $I$ for either direct current or alternating current.

## TEST-POINT QUESTION 16-4

Answers at end of chapter.

Refer to Fig. 16-5.
**a.** When $v$ is 70.7 V, how much is $i$?
**b.** How much is $i$ at 30°?

# 16-5 VOLTAGE AND CURRENT VALUES FOR A SINE WAVE

Since an alternating sine wave of voltage or current has many instantaneous values through the cycle, it is convenient to define specific magnitudes for comparing one wave with another. The peak, average, and root-mean-square (rms) values can be specified, as indicated in Fig. 16-6. These values can be used for either current or voltage.

**PEAK VALUE**   This is the maximum value $V_M$ or $I_M$. For example, specifying that a sine wave has a peak value of 170 V states the highest value the sine wave reaches. All other values during the cycle follow a sine wave. The peak value applies to either the positive or the negative peak.

In order to include both peak amplitudes, the *peak-to-peak* (p-p) *value* may be specified. For the same example, the peak-to-peak value is 340 V, double the peak value of 170 V, since the positive and negative peaks are symmetrical. It should be noted, though, that the two opposite peak values cannot occur at the same time. Furthermore, in some waveforms the two peaks are not equal.

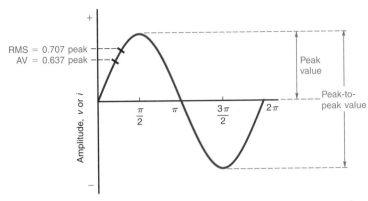

FIG. 16-6  Definitions of important amplitude values for a sine wave of voltage or current.

**AVERAGE VALUE**  This is an arithmetic average of all the values in a sine wave for one alternation, or half-cycle. The half-cycle is used for the average because over a full cycle the average value is zero, which is useless for comparison purposes. If the sine values for all angles up to 180°, for one alternation, are added and then divided by the number of values, this average equals 0.637. These calculations are shown in Table 16-2.

Since the peak value of the sine function is 1 and the average equals 0.637, then

▶  Average value = 0.637 × peak value                    **(16-2)**

**TABLE 16-2  DERIVATION OF AVERAGE AND RMS VALUES FOR A SINE-WAVE ALTERNATION**

| INTERVAL | ANGLE $\theta$ | SIN $\theta$ | $(\text{SIN } \theta)^2$ |
|:---:|:---:|:---:|:---:|
| 1 | 15° | 0.26 | 0.07 |
| 2 | 30° | 0.50 | 0.25 |
| 3 | 45° | 0.71 | 0.50 |
| 4 | 60° | 0.87 | 0.75 |
| 5 | 75° | 0.97 | 0.93 |
| 6 | 90° | 1.00 | 1.00 |
| 7* | 105° | 0.97 | 0.93 |
| 8 | 120° | 0.87 | 0.75 |
| 9 | 135° | 0.71 | 0.50 |
| 10 | 150° | 0.50 | 0.25 |
| 11 | 165° | 0.26 | 0.07 |
| 12 | 180° | 0.00 | 0.00 |
| | Total | 7.62 | 6.00 |
| | Average voltage: $\dfrac{7.62}{12} = 0.635\dagger$ | | RMS value: $\sqrt{6/12} = \sqrt{0.5} = 0.707$ |

*For angles between 90 and 180°, sin $\theta$ = sin (180° − $\theta$).
†More intervals and precise values are needed to get the exact average of 0.637.

With a peak of 170 V, for example, the average value is $0.637 \times 170$ V, which equals approximately 108 V.

**ROOT-MEAN-SQUARE, OR EFFECTIVE, VALUE**  The most common method of specifying the amount of a sine wave of voltage or current is by relating it to dc voltage and current that will produce the same heating effect. This is called its *root-mean-square* value, abbreviated rms. The formula is

▶  rms value $= 0.707 \times$ peak value  (16-3)

or

▶  $V_{rms} = 0.707 V_{max}$  and  $I_{rms} = 0.707 I_{max}$

With a peak of 170 V, for example, the rms value is $0.707 \times 170$, or 120 V, approximately. This is a voltage of the commercial ac power line, which is always given in rms value.

It is often necessary to convert from rms to peak value. This can be done by inverting Formula (16-3), as follows:

▶  Peak $= \dfrac{1}{0.707} \times$ rms $= 1.414 \times$ rms  (16-4)

or

▶  $V_{max} = 1.414 V_{rms}$  and  $I_{max} = 1.414 I_{rms}$

Dividing by 0.707 is the same as multiplying by 1.414.

For example, the commercial power-line voltage with an rms value of 120 V has a peak value of $120 \times 1.414$, which equals 170 V, approximately. Its peak-to-peak value is $2 \times 170$, or 340 V, which is double the peak value. As a formula,

▶  Peak-to-peak value $= 2.828 \times$ rms value  (16-5)

The factor 0.707 for rms value is derived as the square root of the average (mean) of all the squares of the sine values. If we take the sine for each angle in the cycle, square each value, add all the squares, divide by the number of values added to obtain the average square, and then take the square root of this mean value, the answer is 0.707. These calculations are shown in Table 16-2 for one alternation from 0° to 180°. The results are the same for the opposite alternation.

The advantage of the rms value derived in terms of the squares of the voltage or current values is that it provides a measure based on the ability of the sine wave to produce power, which is $I^2R$ or $V^2/R$. As a result, the rms value of an alternating sine wave corresponds to the same amount of direct current or voltage in heating power. An alternating voltage with an rms value of 120 V, for instance, is just as effective in heating the filament of a light bulb as 120 V from a steady dc voltage source. For this reason, the rms value is also called the *effective* value.

Unless indicated otherwise, all sine-wave ac measurements are in rms values. The capital letters $V$ and $I$ are used, corresponding to the symbols for dc values. As an example, $V = 120$ V for the ac power-line voltage.

The ratio of the rms to average values is the *form factor*. For a sine wave, this ratio is 0.707/0.637 = 1.11.

Note that sine waves can have different amplitudes but still follow the sinusoidal waveform. Figure 16-7 compares a low-amplitude voltage with a high-amplitude voltage. Although different in amplitude, they are both sine waves. In each wave, the rms value = 0.707 × peak value.

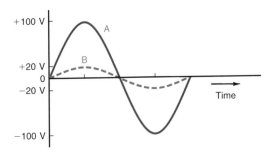

FIG. 16-7 Waveforms A and B have different amplitudes, but they are both sine waves.

## TEST-POINT QUESTION 16-5

Answers at end of chapter.
a. Convert 170 V peak to rms value.
b. Convert 10 V rms to peak value.
c. Convert 1 V rms to peak-to-peak value.

## 16-6 FREQUENCY

The number of cycles per second is the *frequency,* with the symbol *f*. In Fig. 16-3, if the loop rotates through 60 complete revolutions, or cycles, during 1 s, the frequency of the generated voltage is 60 cps, or 60 Hz. You see only one cycle of the sine waveform, instead of 60 cycles, because the time interval shown here is ⅟₆₀ s. Note that the factor of time is involved. More cycles per second means a higher frequency and less time for one cycle, as illustrated in Fig. 16-8. Then the changes in values are faster for higher frequencies.

A complete cycle is measured between two successive points that have the same value and direction. In Fig. 16-8 the cycle is between successive points where the waveform is zero and ready to increase in the positive direction. Or the cycle can be measured between successive peaks.

On the time scale of 1 s, waveform *a* goes through one cycle; waveform *b* has much faster variations, with four complete cycles during 1 s. Both waveforms are sine waves, even though each has a different frequency.

In comparing sine waves, the amplitude has no relation to frequency. Two waveforms can have the same frequency with different amplitudes (Fig. 16-7), the same amplitude but different frequencies (Fig. 16-8), or different amplitudes and frequencies. The amplitude indicates how much the voltage or current is, while the frequency indicates the time rate of change of the amplitude variations, in cycles per second.

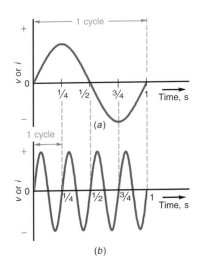

FIG. 16-8 Number of cycles per second is the frequency in hertz (Hz) units. (*a*) *f* = 1 Hz. (*b*) *f* = 4 Hz.

**FREQUENCY UNITS**   The unit called the *hertz* (Hz), named after H. Hertz, is used for cycles per second. Then 60 cps = 60 Hz. All the metric prefixes can be used. As examples:

$$1 \text{ kilocycle per second} = 1 \times 10^3 \text{ Hz} = 1 \text{ kHz}$$

$$1 \text{ megacycle per second} = 1 \times 10^6 \text{ Hz} = 1 \text{ MHz}$$

$$1 \text{ gigacycle per second} = 1 \times 10^9 \text{ Hz} = 1 \text{ GHz}$$

**AUDIO AND RADIO FREQUENCIES**   The entire frequency range of alternating voltage or current from 1 Hz to many megahertz can be considered in two broad groups: audio frequencies (AF) and radio frequencies (RF). *Audio* is a Latin word meaning "I hear." The audio range includes frequencies that can be heard in the form of sound waves by the human ear. This range of audible frequencies is approximately 16 to 16,000 Hz.

The higher the frequency, the higher the pitch or tone of the sound. High audio frequencies, about 3000 Hz and above, can be considered to provide *treble* tone. Low audio frequencies, about 300 Hz and below, provide *bass* tone.

Loudness is determined by amplitude. The greater the amplitude of the AF variation, the louder is its corresponding sound.

Alternating current and voltage above the audio range provide RF variations, since electrical variations of high frequency can be transmitted by electromagnetic radio waves. Examples of frequency allocations are given in Table 16-3.

**SONIC AND ULTRASONIC FREQUENCIES**   These terms refer to sound waves, which are variations in pressure generated by mechanical vibrations, rather than electrical variations. The velocity of transmission for sound waves equals 1130 ft/s, through dry air at 20°C. Sound waves above the audible range of frequencies are called *ultrasonic* waves. The range of frequencies for ultrasonic applications, therefore, is from 16,000 Hz up to several megahertz. Sound waves in the audible range of frequencies below 16,000 Hz can be considered *sonic* or sound frequencies, reserving *audio* for electrical variations that can be heard when converted to sound waves.

---

### TEST-POINT QUESTION 16-6

Answers at end of chapter.
**a.** What is the frequency of the bottom waveform in Fig. 16-8?
**b.** Convert 1605 kHz to megahertz.

---

## 16-7 PERIOD

The amount of time it takes to go through one cycle is called the *period*. Its symbol is *T* for time. With a frequency of 60 Hz, as an example, the time for one cycle is 1/60 s. Therefore, the period is 1/60 s in this case. The frequency and period are reciprocals of each other:

## TABLE 16-3 EXAMPLES OF COMMON FREQUENCIES

| FREQUENCY | USE |
|---|---|
| 60 Hz | AC power line |
| 50–15,000 Hz | Audio equipment |
| 535–1605 kHz* | AM radio band |
| 54–60 MHz | TV channel 2 |
| 88–108 MHz | FM radio band |

*Expanded to 1705 kHz in 1991.

▶ $$T = \frac{1}{f} \quad \text{or} \quad f = \frac{1}{T}$$ (16-6)

The higher the frequency, the shorter the period. In Fig. 16-8a, the period for the wave, with a frequency of 1 Hz, is 1 s, while the higher-frequency wave of 4 Hz in Fig. 16-8b has the period of ¼ s for a complete cycle.

**UNITS OF TIME**  The second is the basic unit, but for higher frequencies and shorter periods, smaller units of time are convenient. Those used most often are:

$$T = 1 \text{ millisecond} = 1 \text{ ms} = 1 \times 10^{-3} \text{ s}$$
$$T = 1 \text{ microsecond} = 1 \text{ } \mu s = 1 \times 10^{-6} \text{ s}$$
$$T = 1 \text{ nanosecond} = 1 \text{ ns} = 1 \times 10^{-9} \text{ s}$$

These units of time for period are reciprocals of the corresponding units for frequency. The reciprocal of frequency in kilohertz gives the period $T$ in milliseconds; the reciprocal of megahertz is microseconds; the reciprocal of gigahertz is nanoseconds.

## Example

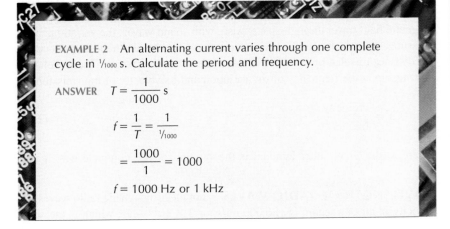

**EXAMPLE 2**  An alternating current varies through one complete cycle in $\frac{1}{1000}$ s. Calculate the period and frequency.

ANSWER  $T = \dfrac{1}{1000}$ s

$$f = \frac{1}{T} = \frac{1}{\frac{1}{1000}}$$

$$= \frac{1000}{1} = 1000$$

$f = 1000$ Hz or 1 kHz

---

### TEST-POINT QUESTION 16-7

Answers at end of chapter.
**a.** $T = \frac{1}{400}$ s. Calculate $f$.
**b.** $f = 400$ Hz. Calculate $T$.

## 16-8 WAVELENGTH

When a periodic variation is considered with respect to distance, one cycle includes the *wavelength*, which is the length of one complete wave or cycle (Fig. 16-9). For example, when a radio wave is transmitted, variations in the electromagnetic field travel through space. Also, with sound waves, the variations in air pressure corresponding to the sound wave move through air. In these applications, the distance traveled by the wave in one cycle is the wavelength. The wavelength depends upon the frequency of the variation and its velocity of transmission:

$$\blacktriangleright \qquad \lambda = \frac{\text{velocity}}{\text{frequency}} \qquad \qquad \textbf{(16-7)}$$

where $\lambda$ (the Greek letter lambda) is the symbol for one complete wavelength.

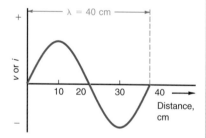

**FIG. 16-9** Wavelength $\lambda$ is the distance traveled by the wave in one cycle.

**WAVELENGTH OF RADIO WAVES**   For electromagnetic radio waves, the velocity in air or vacuum is 186,000 mi/s, or $3 \times 10^{10}$ cm/s, which is the speed of light. Therefore,

$$\blacktriangleright \quad \lambda \text{ (cm)} = \frac{3 \times 10^{10} \text{ cm/s}}{f \text{(Hz)}} \qquad\qquad \textbf{(16-8)}$$

Note that the higher the frequency is, the shorter the wavelength. For instance, the short-wave radio broadcast band of 5.95 to 26.1 MHz includes higher frequencies than the standard radio broadcast band of 535 to 1605 kHz.

## Example

**EXAMPLE 4**  Calculate $\lambda$ for a radio wave with $f$ of 30 GHz.

**ANSWER**  $\lambda = \dfrac{3 \times 10^{10} \text{ cm/s}}{30 \times 10^9 \text{ Hz}} = \dfrac{3}{30} \times 10 \text{ cm}$

$\qquad\qquad = 0.1 \times 10$

$\qquad \lambda = 1 \text{ cm}$

Such short wavelengths are called *microwaves*. This range includes $\lambda$ of 1 m or less, for frequencies of 300 MHz or more.

**EXAMPLE 5**  The length of a TV antenna is $\lambda/2$ for radio waves with $f$ of 60 MHz. What is the antenna length in centimeters and feet?

**ANSWER**

**a.**  $\lambda = \dfrac{3 \times 10^{10} \text{ cm/s}}{60 \times 10^6 \text{ Hz}} = \dfrac{1}{20} \times 10^4 \text{ cm}$

$\qquad = 0.05 \times 10^4$

$\quad \lambda = 500 \text{ cm}$

Then, $\lambda/2 = {}^{500}/_2 = 250 \text{ cm}.$

**b.**  Since 2.54 cm = 1 in.,

$\qquad \lambda/2 = \dfrac{250 \text{ cm}}{2.54 \text{ cm/in.}} = 98.4 \text{ in.}$

$\qquad \lambda/2 = \dfrac{98.4 \text{ in.}}{12 \text{ in./ft}} = 8.2 \text{ ft}$

**EXAMPLE 6**  For the 6-m band used in amateur radio, what is the corresponding frequency?

**ANSWER**  The formula $\lambda = v/f$ can be inverted

$$f = \frac{v}{\lambda}$$

Then

$$f = \frac{3 \times 10 \text{ cm/s}}{6 \text{ m}} = \frac{3 \times 10^{10} \text{ cm/s}}{6 \times 10^2 \text{ cm}}$$

$$= \frac{3}{6} \times 10^8 = 0.5 \times 10^8 \text{ Hz}$$

$$f = 50 \times 10^6 \text{ Hz} \quad \text{or} \quad 50 \text{ MHz}$$

**WAVELENGTH OF SOUND WAVES**   The velocity of sound waves is much lower, compared with that of radio waves, because sound waves result from mechanical vibrations rather than electrical variations. For average conditions the velocity of sound waves in air equals 1130 ft/s. To calculate the wavelength, therefore,

▶ $$\lambda = \frac{1130 \text{ ft/s}}{f \text{ Hz}}$$

(16-9)

This formula can also be used for ultrasonic waves. Although their frequencies are too high to be audible, ultrasonic waves are still sound waves rather than radio waves.

*Example*

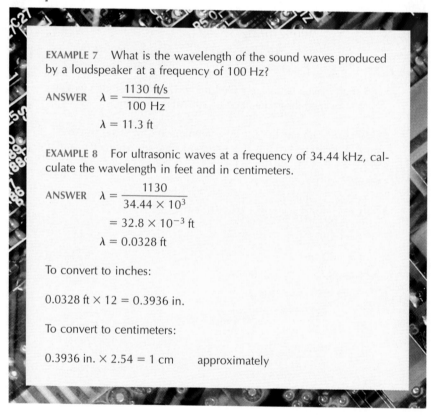

EXAMPLE 7   What is the wavelength of the sound waves produced by a loudspeaker at a frequency of 100 Hz?

ANSWER   $\lambda = \dfrac{1130 \text{ ft/s}}{100 \text{ Hz}}$

$\lambda = 11.3$ ft

EXAMPLE 8   For ultrasonic waves at a frequency of 34.44 kHz, calculate the wavelength in feet and in centimeters.

ANSWER   $\lambda = \dfrac{1130}{34.44 \times 10^3}$

$= 32.8 \times 10^{-3}$ ft

$\lambda = 0.0328$ ft

To convert to inches:

$0.0328 \text{ ft} \times 12 = 0.3936$ in.

To convert to centimeters:

$0.3936 \text{ in.} \times 2.54 = 1$ cm      approximately

Note that the 34.44 kHz sound waves in this example have the same wavelength (1 cm) as the 30 GHz radio waves in Example 4. The reason is that radio waves have a much higher velocity than sound waves.

<hr>

## TEST-POINT QUESTION 16-8

Answers at end of chapter.

Answer True or False.
**a.** The higher the frequency, the shorter the wavelength $\lambda$.
**b.** The higher the frequency, the longer the period $T$.
**c.** The velocity of propagation for radio waves in free space is $3 \times 10^{10}$ cm/s.

# 16-9 PHASE ANGLE

Referring back to Fig. 16-3, suppose that the generator started its cycle at point B, where maximum voltage output is produced, instead of starting at the point of zero output. If we compare the two cases, the two output voltage waves would be as shown in Fig. 16-10. Each is the same waveform of alternating voltage, but wave B starts at maximum, while wave A starts at zero. The complete cycle of wave B through 360° takes it back to the maximum value from which it started. Wave A starts and finishes its cycle at zero. With respect to time, therefore, wave B is ahead of wave A in its values of generated voltage. The amount it leads in time equals one quarter-revolution, which is 90°. This angular difference is the phase angle between waves B and A. Wave B leads wave A by the phase angle of 90°.

The 90° phase angle between waves B and A is maintained throughout the complete cycle and in all successive cycles, as long as they both have the same frequency. At any instant of time, wave B has the value that A will have 90° later. For instance, at 180° wave A is at zero, but B is already at its negative maximum value, where wave A will be later at 270°.

In order to compare the phase angle between two waves, they must have the same frequency. Otherwise, the relative phase keeps changing. Also, they must have sine-wave variations, as this is the only kind of waveform that is measured in angular units of time. The amplitudes can be different for the two waves, although they are shown the same here. We can compare the phase of two voltages, two currents, or a current with a voltage.

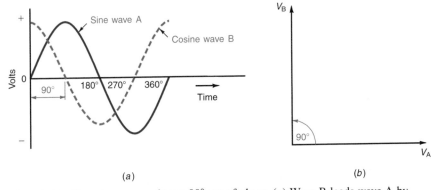

(a)                    (b)

**FIG. 16-10**   Two sine-wave voltages 90° out of phase. (a) Wave B leads wave A by 90°. (b) Corresponding phasors $V_B$ and $V_A$ for the two sine-wave voltages with phase angle $\theta = 90°$. The right angle shows quadrature phase.

**THE 90° PHASE ANGLE**   The two waves in Fig. 16-10 represent a sine wave and a cosine wave 90° out of phase with each other. The 90° phase angle means that one has its maximum amplitude when the other is at zero value. Wave A starts at zero, corresponding to the sine of 0°, has its peak amplitude at 90 and 270°, and is back to zero after one cycle of 360°. Wave B starts at its peak value, corresponding to the cosine of 0°, has its zero value at 90 and 270°, and is back to the peak value after one cycle of 360°.

However, wave B can also be considered a sine wave that starts 90° before wave A in time. This phase angle of 90° for current and voltage waveforms has many applications in sine-wave ac circuits with inductance or capacitance.

The sine and cosine waveforms really have the same variations, but displaced by 90°. In fact, both waveforms are called *sinusoids*. The 90° angle is called *quadrature phase*.

**PHASE-ANGLE DIAGRAMS**    To compare phases of alternating currents and voltages, it is much more convenient to use phasor diagrams corresponding to the voltage and current waveforms, as shown in Fig. 16-10b. The arrows here represent the phasor quantities corresponding to the generator voltage.

A phasor is a quantity that has magnitude and direction. The length of the arrow indicates the magnitude of the alternating voltage, in rms, peak, or any ac value as long as the same measure is used for all the phasors. The angle of the arrow with respect to the horizontal axis indicates the phase angle.

The terms *phasor* and *vector* are used for a quantity that has direction, requiring an angle to specify the value completely. However, a vector quantity has direction in space, while a phasor quantity varies in time. As an example of a vector, a mechanical force can be represented by a vector arrow at a specific angle, with respect to either the horizontal or vertical direction.

For phasor arrows, the angles shown represent differences in time. One sinusoid is chosen as the reference. Then the timing of the variations in another sinusoid can be compared to the reference by means of the angle between the phasor arrows.

The phasor corresponds to the entire cycle of voltage, but is shown only at one angle, such as the starting point, since the complete cycle is known to be a sine wave. Without the extra details of a whole cycle, phasors represent the alternating voltage or current in a compact form that is easier for comparing phase angles.

In Fig. 16-10b, for instance, the phasor $V_A$ represents the voltage wave A, with a phase angle of 0°. This angle can be considered as the plane of the loop in the rotary generator where it starts with zero output voltage. The phasor $V_B$ is vertical to show the phase angle of 90° for this voltage wave, corresponding to the vertical generator loop at the start of its cycle. The angle between the two phasors is the phase angle.

The symbol for a phase angle is $\theta$ (the Greek letter theta). In Fig. 16-10, as an example, $\theta = 90°$.

**PHASE-ANGLE REFERENCE**    The phase angle of one wave can be specified only with respect to another as reference. How the phasors are drawn to show the phase angle depends on which phase is chosen as the reference. Generally, the reference phasor is horizontal, corresponding to 0°. Two possibilities are shown in Fig. 16-11. In Fig. 16-11a the voltage wave A or its phasor $V_A$ is the reference. Then the phasor $V_B$ is 90° counterclockwise. This method is standard practice, using counterclockwise rotation as the positive direction for angles. Also, a leading angle is positive. In this case, then, $V_B$ is 90° counterclockwise from the reference $V_A$ to show that wave B leads wave A by 90°.

However, wave B is shown as the reference in Fig. 16-11b. Now $V_B$ is the horizontal phasor. In order to have the same phase angle, $V_A$ must be 90° clockwise, or −90° from $V_B$. This arrangement shows that negative angles, clockwise from the 0° reference, are used to show a lagging phase angle. The reference determines whether the phase angle is considered leading or lagging in time.

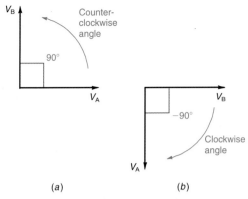

FIG. 16-11 Leading and lagging phase angles for 90°. (*a*) When phasor $V_A$ is the horizontal reference, phasor $V_B$ leads by 90°. (*b*) When phasor $V_B$ is the horizontal reference, phasor $V_A$ lags by −90°.

The phase is not actually changed by the method of showing it. In Fig. 16-11, $V_A$ and $V_B$ are 90° out of phase, and $V_B$ leads $V_A$ by 90° in time. There is no fundamental difference whether we say $V_B$ is ahead of $V_A$ by +90° or $V_A$ is behind $V_B$ by −90°.

Two waves and their corresponding phasors can be out of phase by any angle, either less or more than 90°. For instance, a phase angle of 60° is shown in Fig. 16-12. For the waveforms in Fig. 16-12*a*, wave D is behind C by 60° in time. For the phasors in Fig. 16-12*b* this lag is shown by the phase angle of −60°.

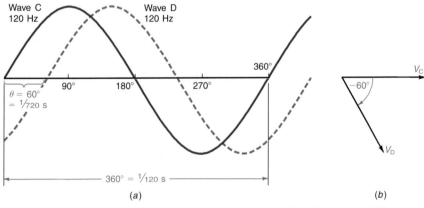

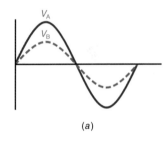

FIG. 16-12 Phase angle of 60° is the time for 60/360 or 1/6 of the cycle. (*a*) Waveforms. (*b*) Phasor diagram.

**IN-PHASE WAVEFORMS** A phase angle of 0° means the two waves are in phase (Fig. 16-13).

**OUT-OF-PHASE WAVEFORMS** An angle of 180° means opposite phase, or the two waveforms are exactly out of phase (Fig. 16-14). Then the amplitudes are opposing.

FIG. 16-13 Two waveforms in phase, or the phase angle is 0°. (*a*) Waveforms. (*b*) Phasor diagram.

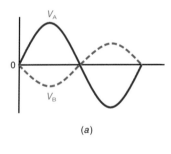

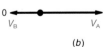

FIG. 16-14 Two waveforms out of phase or in opposite phase, with phase angle of 180°. (*a*) Waveforms. (*b*) Phasor diagram.

Answers at end of chapter.

Give the phase angle in
**a.** Fig. 16-10.
**b.** Fig. 16-12.
**c.** Fig. 16-13.

# 16-10 THE TIME FACTOR IN FREQUENCY AND PHASE

It is important to remember that the waveforms we are showing are just graphs drawn on paper. The physical factors represented are variations in amplitude, usually on the vertical scale, with respect to equal intervals on the horizontal scale, which can represent either distance or time. To show wavelength, as in Fig. 16-9, the cycles of amplitude variations are plotted against distance or length units. To show frequency, the cycles of amplitude variations are shown with respect to time in angular measure. The angle of 360° represents the time for one cycle, or the period $T$.

As an example of how frequency involves time, a waveform with stable frequency is actually used in electronic equipment as a clock reference for very small units of time. Assume a voltage waveform with the frequency of 10 MHz. The period $T$ is 0.1 $\mu$s. Every cycle is repeated at 0.1-$\mu$s intervals, therefore. When each cycle of voltage variations is used to indicate time, then, the result is effectively a clock that measures 0.1-$\mu$s units. Even smaller units of time can be measured with higher frequencies. In everyday applications, an electric clock connected to the power line keeps correct time because it is controlled by the exact frequency of 60 Hz.

Furthermore, the phase angle between two waves of the same frequency indicates a specific difference in time. As an example, Fig. 16-12 shows a phase angle of 60°, with wave C leading wave D. They both have the same frequency of 120 Hz. The period $T$ for each wave then is $\frac{1}{120}$ s. Since 60° is one-sixth of the complete cycle of 360°, this phase angle represents one-sixth of the complete period of $\frac{1}{120}$ s. Multiplying $\frac{1}{6} \times \frac{1}{120}$, the answer is $\frac{1}{720}$ s for the time corresponding to the phase angle of 60°. If we consider wave D lagging wave C by 60°, this lag is a time delay of $\frac{1}{720}$ s.

More generally, the time for a phase angle $\theta$ can be calculated as

$$\blacktriangleright \quad t = \frac{\theta}{360} \times \frac{1}{f} \tag{16-10}$$

where $f$ is in Hz, $\theta$ is in degrees, and $t$ is in seconds.

The formula gives the time of the phase angle as its proportional part of the total period of one cycle. For the example of $\theta$ equal to 60° with $f$ at 120 Hz,

$$t = \frac{\theta}{360} \times \frac{1}{f}$$

$$= \frac{60}{360} \times \frac{1}{120} = \frac{1}{6} \times \frac{1}{120}$$

$$t = \frac{1}{720} \text{ s}$$

---

**TEST-POINT QUESTION 16-10**

Answers at end of chapter.
**a.** In Fig. 16-12, how much time corresponds to 180°?
**b.** For two waves with the frequency of 1 MHz, how much time is the phase angle of 36°?

## 16-11 ALTERNATING CURRENT CIRCUITS WITH RESISTANCE

An ac circuit has an ac voltage source. Note the symbol in Fig. 16-15 used for any source of sine-wave alternating voltage. This voltage connected across an external load resistance produces alternating current of the same waveform, frequency, and phase as the applied voltage.

The amount of current equals $V/R$ by Ohm's law. When $V$ is an rms value, $I$ is also an rms value. For any instantaneous value of $V$ during the cycle, the value of $I$ is for the corresponding instant of time.

In an ac circuit with only resistance, the current variations are in phase with the applied voltage, as shown in Fig. 16-15b. This in-phase relationship between $V$ and $I$ means that such an ac circuit can be analyzed by the same methods used for dc circuits, since there is no phase angle to consider. Circuit components that have $R$ alone include resistors, the filaments of light bulbs, and heating elements.

**DID YOU KNOW?**

Automatic car airbags work on the closing of a simple electric circuit using magnets and metal balls.

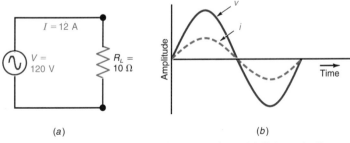

FIG. 16-15   An ac circuit with resistance $R$ alone. (*a*) Schematic diagram. (*b*) Waveforms.

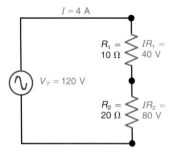

**FIG. 16-16** Series ac circuit with resistance only.

The calculations in ac circuits are generally in rms values, unless noted otherwise. In Fig. 16-15a, for example, the 120 V applied across the 10-Ω $R_L$ produces rms current of 12 A. The calculations are

$$I = \frac{V}{R_L} = \frac{120\ \text{V}}{10\ \Omega} = 12\ \text{A}$$

Furthermore, the rms power dissipation is $I^2R$, or

$$P = 144 \times 10 = 1440\ \text{W}$$

**SERIES AC CIRCUIT WITH $R$**    In Fig. 16-16, $R_T$ is 30 Ω, equal to the sum of 10 Ω for $R_1$ plus 20 Ω for $R_2$. The current in the series circuit is

$$I = \frac{V}{R_T} = \frac{120\ \text{V}}{30\ \Omega} = 4\ \text{A}$$

The 4-A current is the same in all parts of the series circuit. This principle applies for either an ac or a dc source.

Next, we can calculate the series voltage drops in Fig. 16-16. With 4 A through the 10-Ω $R_1$, its $IR$ voltage drop is

$$V_1 = I \times R_1 = 4\ \text{A} \times 10\ \Omega = 40\ \text{V}$$

The same 4 A through the 20-Ω $R_2$ produces an $IR$ voltage drop of 80 V. The calculations are

$$V_2 = I \times R_2 = 4\ \text{A} \times 20\ \Omega = 80\ \text{V}$$

Note that the sum of 40 V for $V_1$ and 80 V for $V_2$ in series equals the 120 V applied.

**PARALLEL AC CIRCUIT WITH $R$**    In Fig. 16-17, the 10-Ω $R_1$ and 20-Ω $R_2$ are in parallel across the 120-V ac source. Therefore, the voltage across the parallel branches is the same as the applied voltage.

Each branch current, then, is equal to 120 V divided by the branch resistance. The branch current for the 10-Ω $R_1$ is

$$I_1 = \frac{120\ \text{V}}{10\ \Omega} = 12\ \text{A}$$

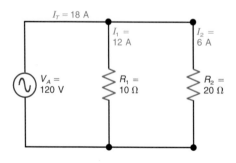

**FIG. 16-17** Parallel ac circuit with resistance only.

The same 120 V is across the 20-$\Omega$ branch with $R_2$. Its branch current is

$$\blacktriangleright \quad I_2 = \frac{120 \text{ V}}{20 \ \Omega} = 6 \text{ A}$$

The total line current $I_T$ is $12 + 6 = 18$ A, or the sum of the branch currents.

**SERIES-PARALLEL AC CIRCUIT WITH R**   See Fig. 16-18. The 20-$\Omega$ $R_2$ and 20-$\Omega$ $R_3$ are in parallel, for an equivalent bank resistance of 20/2 or 10 $\Omega$. This 10-$\Omega$ bank is in series with the 20-$\Omega$ $R_1$ in the main line, for a total of 30 $\Omega$ for $R_T$ across the 120-V source. Therefore, the main line current produced by the 120-V source is

$$I_T = \frac{V}{R_T} = \frac{120 \text{ V}}{30 \ \Omega} = 4 \text{ A}$$

The voltage drop across $R_1$ in the main line is calculated as

$$V_1 = I_T \times R_1 = 4 \text{ A} \times 20 \ \Omega = 80 \text{ V}$$

Subtracting this 80-V drop from the 120 V of the source, the remaining 40 V is across the bank of $R_2$ and $R_3$ in parallel. Since the branch resistances are equal, the 4-A $I_T$ divides equally, with 2 A in $R_2$ and 2 A in $R_3$. The branch currents can be calculated as

$$I_2 = \frac{40 \text{ V}}{20 \ \Omega} = 2 \text{ A}$$

$$I_3 = \frac{40 \text{ V}}{20 \ \Omega} = 2 \text{ A}$$

Note that the 2 A for $I_2$ and 2 A for $I_3$ in parallel branches add to equal the 4-A current in the main line.

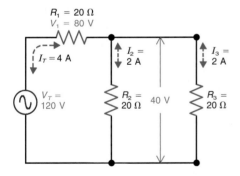

**FIG. 16-18**   Series-parallel ac circuit with resistance only.

---

**TEST-POINT QUESTION 16-11**

Answers at end of chapter.

Calculate $R_T$ in
**a.** Fig. 16-16.
**b.** Fig. 16-17.
**c.** Fig. 16-18.

The sine wave is the basic waveform for ac variations for several reasons. This waveform is produced by a rotary generator, as the output is proportional to the angle of rotation. In addition, electronic oscillator circuits with inductance and capacitance naturally produce sine-wave variations.

Because of its derivation from circular motion, any sine wave can be analyzed in terms of angular measure, either in degrees from 0 to 360° or in radians from 0 to $2\pi$ rad.

Another feature of a sine wave is its basic simplicity, as the rate of change for the amplitude variations corresponds to a cosine wave which is similar but 90° out of phase. The sine wave is the only waveform that has this characteristic of a rate of change with the same waveform as the original changes in amplitude.

In many electronic applications, however, other waveshapes are important. Any waveform that is not a sine or cosine wave is a *nonsinusoidal waveform*. Common examples are the square wave and sawtooth wave in Fig. 16-19.

With nonsinusoidal waveforms, for either voltage or current, there are important differences and similarities to consider. Note the following comparisons with sine waves.

1.  In all cases, the cycle is measured between two points having the same amplitude and varying in the same direction. The period is the time for one cycle. In Fig. 16-19, $T$ for any of the waveforms is 4 $\mu$s and the corresponding frequency is $1/T$, equal to ¼ MHz, or 0.25 MHz.
2.  Peak amplitude is measured from the zero axis to the maximum positive or negative value. However, peak-to-peak amplitude is better for measuring nonsinusoidal waveshapes because they can have unsymmetrical peaks, as in Fig. 16-19*d*. For all the waveforms shown here, though, the peak-to-peak (p–p) amplitude is 20 V.
3.  The rms value 0.707 of maximum applies only to sine waves, as this factor is derived from the sine values in the angular measure used only for the sine waveform.
4.  Phase angles apply only to sine waves, as angular measure is used only for sine waves. Note that the horizontal axis for time is divided into angles for the sine wave in Fig. 16-19*a*, but there are no angles shown for the nonsinusoidal waveshapes.
5.  All the waveforms represent ac voltages. Positive values are shown above the zero axis, with negative values below the axis.

The sawtooth wave in Fig. 16-19*b* represents a voltage that slowly increases, with a uniform or linear rate of change, to its peak value, and then drops sharply to its starting value. This waveform is also called a *ramp voltage*. It is also often referred to as a *time base* because of its constant rate of change.

Note that one complete cycle includes the slow rise and the fast drop in voltage. In this example, the period $T$ for a complete cycle is 4 $\mu$s. Therefore, these sawtooth cycles are repeated at the frequency of ¼ MHz, which equals 0.25 MHz. The sawtooth waveform of voltage or current is often used for horizontal deflection of the electron beam in the cathode-ray tube (CRT) for oscilloscopes and TV receivers.

The square wave in Fig. 16-19*c* represents a switching voltage. First, the 10-V peak is instantaneously applied in positive polarity. This voltage remains

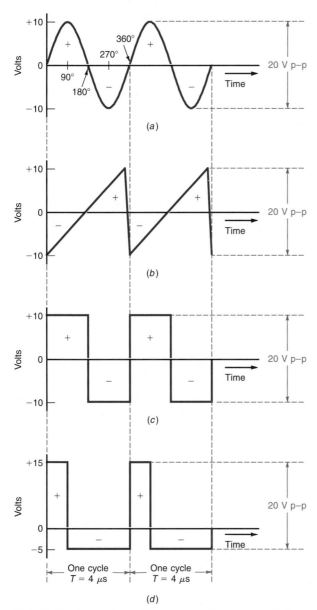

**FIG. 16-19** Comparison of sine wave with nonsinusoidal waveforms. Two cycles shown. (*a*) Sine wave. (*b*) Sawtooth wave. (*c*) Symmetrical square wave. (*d*) Unsymmetrical rectangular wave or pulse waveform

on for 2 $\mu$s, which is one half-cycle. Then the voltage is instantaneously reduced to zero and applied in reverse polarity for another 2 $\mu$s. The complete cycle then takes 4 $\mu$s, and the frequency is ¼ MHz.

The rectangular waveshape in Fig. 16-19*d* is similar, but the positive and negative half-cycles are not symmetrical, either in amplitude or in time. However, the frequency is the same 0.25 MHz and the peak-to-peak amplitude is the same 20 V, as in all the waveshapes. This waveform shows pulses of voltage or current, repeated at a regular rate.

Answers at end of chapter.
**a.** In Fig. 16-19$c$, for how much time is the waveform at $+10$ V?
**b.** In Fig. 16-19$d$, what voltage is the positive peak amplitude?

## 16-13 HARMONIC FREQUENCIES

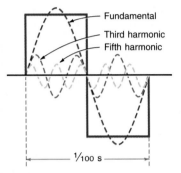

FIG. 16-20 Fundamental and harmonic frequencies for an example of a 100-Hz square wave.

Consider a repetitive nonsinusoidal waveform, such as a 100-Hz square wave. Its fundamental rate of repetition is 100 Hz. Exact multiples of the fundamental frequency are called *harmonic frequencies.* The second harmonic is 200 Hz, the third harmonic is 300 Hz, etc. Even multiples are even harmonics, while odd multiples are odd harmonics.

Harmonics are useful in analyzing distorted sine waves or nonsinusoidal waveforms. Such waveforms consist of a pure sine wave at the fundamental frequency plus harmonic frequency components. For example, Fig. 16-20 illustrates how a square wave corresponds to a fundamental sine wave with odd harmonics. Typical audio waveforms include odd and even harmonics. It is the harmonic components that make one source of sound different from another with the same fundamental frequency.

A common unit for frequency multiples is the *octave,* which is a range of 2:1. Doubling the frequency range—from 100 to 200 Hz, from 200 to 400 Hz, and from 400 to 800 Hz, as examples—raises the frequency by one octave. The reason for this name is that an octave in music includes eight consecutive tones, for double the frequency. One-half the frequency is an octave lower.

Another unit for representing frequency multiples is the decade. A decade corresponds to a 10:1 range in frequencies such as 100 Hz to 1 kHz and 30 kHz to 300 kHz.

Answers at end of chapter.
**a.** What frequency is the fourth harmonic of 12 MHz?
**b.** Give the frequency one octave above 220 Hz.

## 16-14 THE 60-HZ AC POWER LINE

Practically all homes in the United States are supplied alternating voltage between 115 and 125 V rms, at a frequency of 60 Hz. This is a sine-wave voltage produced by a rotary generator. The electricity is distributed by high voltage power lines from the generating station and reduced to the lower voltages used in the home. Here the incoming voltage is wired to all the wall outlets and electrical equipment in parallel. The 120-V source of commercial electricity is the *60-Hz power line* or the *mains,* indicating it is the main line for all the parallel branches.

**ADVANTAGES** The incoming electric service to residences is normally given as 120 V rms. With an rms value of 120 V, the ac power is equivalent to 120-V dc power in heating effect. If the value were higher, there would be more danger of a fatal electric shock. Lower voltages would be less efficient in supplying power.

Higher voltage can supply electric power with less $I^2R$ loss, since the same power is produced with less $I$. Note that the $I^2R$ power loss increases as the square of the current. For applications where large amounts of power are used such as central air-conditioners and clothes dryers, a line voltage of 240 V is often used.

The advantage of ac over dc power is greater efficiency in distribution from the generating station. Alternating voltages can easily be stepped up by means of a transformer, with very little loss, but a transformer cannot operate on direct current. The reason is that a transformer needs the varying magnetic field produced by an ac voltage.

Using a transformer, the alternating voltage at the generating station can be stepped up to values as high as 500 kV for high-voltage distribution lines. These high-voltage lines supply large amounts of power with much less current and less $I^2R$ loss, compared with a 120-V line. At the home, the lower voltage required is supplied by a step-down transformer. The step-up and step-down characteristics of a transformer refer to the ratio of voltages across the input and output connections.

The frequency of 60 Hz is convenient for commercial ac power. Much lower frequencies would require much bigger transformers because larger windings would be necessary. Also, too low a frequency for alternating current in a lamp could cause the light to flicker. For the opposite case, too high a frequency results in excessive iron-core heating in the transformer because of eddy currents and hysteresis losses. Based on these factors, 60 Hz is the frequency of the ac power line in the United States. However, the frequency of the ac power mains in England and most European countries is 50 Hz.

**THE 60-HZ FREQUENCY REFERENCE** All power companies in the United States, except those in Texas, are interconnected in a grid that maintains the ac power-line frequency between 59.98 and 60.02 Hz. The frequency is compared with the time standard provided by the Bureau of Standards radio station WWV at Fort Collins, Colorado. As a result the 60-Hz power-line frequency is maintained accurate to $\pm 0.033$ percent. This accuracy makes the power-line voltage a good secondary standard for checking frequencies based on 60 Hz.

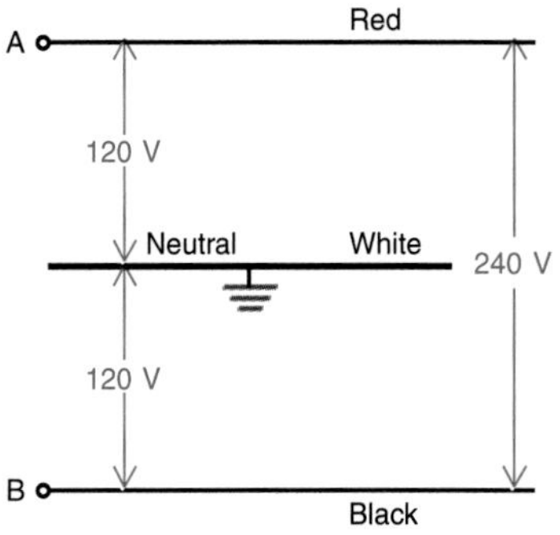

**RESIDENTIAL WIRING** Most homes have at the electrical service entrance the three-wire power lines illustrated in Fig. 16-21. The three wires, including the grounded neutral, can be used for either 240 or 120 V single phase. The 240 V at the residence is stepped down from the high-voltage distribution lines.

Note the color coding for the wiring in Fig. 16-21. The grounded neutral is white, or bare wire is used. Each high side can use any color except white or green, but usually they use black* or red. White is reserved for the neutral wire, and green is reserved for grounding.

FIG. 16-21 Three-wire, single-phase power lines that can provide either 240 or 120 V.

---

*It should be noted that in electronic equipment black is the color-coded wiring used for chassis-ground returns. However, in electric power work, black wire is used for high-side connections.

From either the red or black high side to the neutral, 120 V is available for separate branch circuits to the lights and outlets. Across the red and black wires, 240 V is available for high-power appliances. This three-wire service with a grounded neutral is called the *Edison system.*

The electrical service is commonly rated for 100 A. At 240 V, then, the power available is $100 \times 240 = 24,000$ W, or 24 kW.

The main wires to the service entrance, where the power enters the house, are generally No. 4 to 8 gage. Sizes 6 and heavier are always stranded wire. The 120-V branch circuits, usually rated at 15 A or 20 A, use No. 12 or 14 gage wire. Each branch has its own fuse or circuit breaker. A main switch is usually included to cut off all power from the service entrance.

The neutral wire is grounded at the service entrance to a water pipe or a metal rod driven into the earth, which is *ground*. All 120-V branches must have one side connected to the grounded neutral. White wire is used for these connections. In addition, all the metal boxes for outlets, switches, and lights must have a continuous ground to each other and to the neutral. The wire cable usually has a bare wire for this grounding of the boxes.

Cables commonly used are armored sheath with the trade name BX and non-metallic flexible cable with the trade name Romex. Each has two or more wires for the neutral, high-side connections, and grounding. Both cables contain an extra bare wire for grounding. Rules and regulations for residential wiring are governed by local electrical codes. These are usually based on the National Electrical Code published by the National Fire Protection Association.

**GROUNDING**    In ac power distribution systems, grounding is the practice of connecting one side of the power line to earth or ground. The purpose is safety, in two ways. First is protection against dangerous electric shock. Also, the power distribution lines are protected against excessive high voltage, particularly from lightning. If the system is struck by lightning, excessive current in the grounding system will energize a cutout device to deenergize the lines.

The grounding in the power distribution system means that it is especially important to have grounding for the electric wiring at the residence. For instance, suppose that an electric appliance such as a clothes dryer does not have its metal case grounded. An accidental short circuit in the equipment can connect the metal frame to the "hot" side of the ac power line. Then the frame has voltage with respect to earth ground. If somebody touches the frame and has a return to ground, the result is a dangerous electric shock. With the case grounded, however, the accidental short circuit blows the fuse or circuit breaker to cut off the power.

In normal operation, the electric circuits function the same way with or without the ground, but the grounding is an important safety precaution. Figure 16-22 shows two types of plug connectors for the ac power line that help in providing protection because they are polarized with respect to the ground connections. Although an ac voltage does not have any fixed polarity, the plugs ensure grounding of the chassis or frame of equipment connected to the power line. In Fig. 16-22a, the plug has two blades for the 120-V line but the wider blade will fit only the side of the outlet that is connected to the neutral wire. This wiring is standard practice. For the three-prong plug in Fig. 16-22b, the rounded pin is for a separate grounding wire, usually color coded green.

In some cases, there may be leakage of current from the "hot" side of the power line to ground. A leakage current of 5 mA or more is considered danger-

(a)                                                                                          (b)

**FIG. 16-22** Plug connectors polarized for ground connection to an ac power line. (a) Wider blade connects to neutral. (b) Rounded pin connects to ground.

ous. The ground-fault circuit interrupter (GCFI) shown in Fig. 16-23 is a device that can sense excessive leakage current and open the circuit as a protection against shock hazard.

It may be of interest to note that with high-fidelity audio equipment, the lack of proper grounding can cause a hum to be heard in the sound. The hum is usually not any safety problem but it still is undesirable.

**TEST-POINT QUESTION 16-14**

Answers at end of chapter.

Answer True or False.
**a.** The 120 V of the ac power line is a peak-to-peak value.
**b.** The frequency of the ac power-line voltage is 60 Hz ± 0.033 percent.
**c.** In Fig. 16-21 the voltage between black and white wires is 120 V.
**d.** The color code for grounding wires is green.

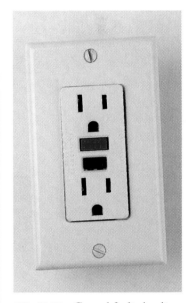

**FIG. 16-23** Ground-fault circuit interrupter (GFCI).

# 16-15 MOTORS AND GENERATORS

A generator converts mechanical energy into electric energy; a motor does the opposite, converting electricity into rotary motion. The main parts in the assembly of motors and generators are essentially the same (Fig. 16-24).

**ARMATURE** In a generator, the armature connects to the external circuit to provide the generator output voltage. In a motor, it connects to the electrical source that drives the motor. The armature is often constructed in the form of a drum, using many conductor loops for increased output. In Fig. 16-24 the rotating armature is the *rotor* part of the assembly.

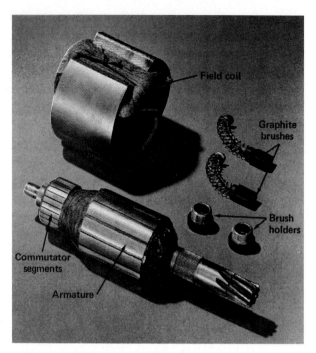

FIG. 16-24 Main parts of a dc motor.

**FIELD WINDING**   This electromagnet provides the flux cut by the rotor. In a motor, current for the field is produced by the same source that supplies the armature. In a generator, the field current may be obtained from a separate exciter source, or from its own armature output. Residual magnetism in the iron yoke of the field allows this *self-excited generator* to start.

The field coil may be connected in series with the armature, in parallel, or in a series-parallel *compound winding*. When the field winding is stationary, it is the *stator* part of the assembly.

**SLIP RINGS**   In an ac machine, two or more slip rings or *collector rings* enable the rotating loop to be connected to the stationary wire leads for the external circuit.

**BRUSHES**   These graphite connectors are spring-mounted to brush against the spinning rings on the rotor. The stationary external leads are connected to the brushes for connection to the rotating loop. Constant rubbing slowly wears down the brushes, and they must be replaced after they are worn.

**COMMUTATOR**   A dc machine has a commutator ring instead of the slip rings. As shown in Fig. 16-24, the commutator ring has segments, with one pair for each loop in the armature. Each of the commutator segments is insulated from the others by mica.

The commutator converts the ac machine to dc operation. In a generator, the commutator segments reverse the loop connections to the brushes every half-cycle to maintain a constant polarity of output voltage. For a dc motor, the commutator segments allow the dc source to produce torque in one direction.

Brushes are necessary with a commutator ring. The two stationary brushes contact opposite segments on the rotating commutator. Graphite brushes are used for very low resistance.

**ALTERNATING CURRENT INDUCTION MOTOR**   This type, for alternating current only, does not have any brushes. The stator is connected directly to the ac source. Then alternating current in the stator winding induces current in the rotor without any physical connection between them. The magnetic field of the current induced in the rotor reacts with the stator field to produce rotation. Alternating-current induction motors are economical and rugged, without any troublesome brush arcing.

With a single-phase source, however, a starting torque must be provided for an ac induction motor. One method uses a starting capacitor in series with a separate starting coil. The capacitor supplies an out-of-phase current just for starting, and then is switched out. Another method of starting uses shaded poles. A solid copper ring on the main field pole makes the magnetic field unsymmetrical to allow starting.

The rotor of an ac induction motor may be wire-wound or the squirrel-cage type. This rotor is constructed with a frame of metal bars.

**UNIVERSAL MOTOR**   This type operates on either alternating or direct current because the field and armature are in series. Its construction is like that of a dc motor, with the rotating armature connected to a commutator and brushes. The universal motor is commonly used for small machines such as portable drills and food mixers.

**ALTERNATORS**   Alternating current generators are alternators. For large power requirements, the alternator usually has a rotating field, while the armature is the stator.

---

### TEST-POINT QUESTION 16-15

Answers at end of chapter.

Answer True or False.
**a.** In Fig. 16-24 the commutator segments are on the armature.
**b.** Motor brushes are made of graphite because of its very low resistance.
**c.** A starting capacitor is used with dc motors that have small brushes.

## 16-16 THREE-PHASE AC POWER

In an alternator with three generator windings equally spaced around the circle, the windings will produce output voltages 120° out of phase with each other. The three-phase output is illustrated by the sine-wave voltages in Fig. 16-25a and the corresponding phasors in Fig. 16-25b. The advantage of three-phase ac voltage is more efficient distribution of power. Also, ac induction motors are self-start-

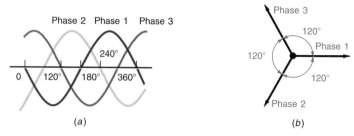

FIG. 16-25 Three-phase alternating voltage or current with 120° between each phase. (*a*) Sine waves. (*b*) Phasor diagram.

ing with three-phase alternating current. Finally, the ac ripple is easier to filter in the rectified output of a dc power supply.

In Fig. 16-26*a*, the three windings are in the form of a Y, also called *Wye* or *star* connections. All three coils are joined at one end, with the opposite ends for the output terminals A, B, and C. Note that any pair of terminals is across two coils in series. Each coil has 120 V. The voltage output across any two output terminals is 120 × 1.73 = 208 V, because of the 120° phase angle.

In Fig. 16-26*b*, the three windings are connected in the form of a *delta* (Δ). Any pair of terminals is across one generator winding. The output then is 120 V. However, the other coils are in a parallel branch. Therefore, the current capacity to the line is increased by the factor 1.73.

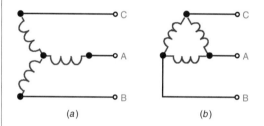

(*a*)  (*b*)

FIG. 16-26 Types of connections for three-phase power. (*a*) Wye or Y. (*b*) Delta or Δ.

In Fig. 16-27, the center point of the Y is used for a fourth line, as the neutral wire in the three-phase power distribution system. This way, power is avail-

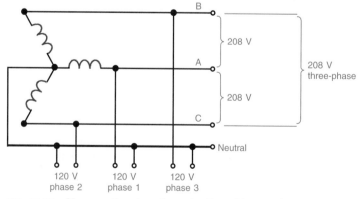

FIG. 16-27 Y connections to a four-wire line with neutral.

able either at 208 V three phase or 120 V single phase. Note that the three-phase voltage is 208 V, not the 240 V in the Edison single-phase system. From terminal A, B, or C to the neutral line in Fig. 16-27, the output is 120 V across one coil. This 120 V single-phase power is used in conventional lighting circuits. However, across terminals AB, BC, or CA, without the neutral, the output is 208 V for three-phase induction motors or other circuits that need three-phase power. Although illustrated here for the 120-V 60-Hz power line, it should be noted that three-phase connections are commonly used for higher voltages.

---

### TEST-POINT QUESTION 16-16

Answers at end of chapter.
**a.** What is the angle between three-phase voltages?
**b.** For the Y in Fig. 16-26a how much is $V_{AC}$ or $V_{AB}$?

# 16 SUMMARY AND REVIEW

- Alternating voltage continuously varies in magnitude and reverses in polarity. When alternating voltage is applied across a load resistance, the result is alternating current in the circuit.
- A complete set of values repeated periodically is one cycle of the ac waveform. The cycle can be measured from any one point on the wave to the next successive point having the same value and varying in the same direction. One cycle includes 360° in angular measure, or $2\pi$ rad.
- The rms value of a sine wave is $0.707 \times$ peak value.
- The peak amplitude, at 90° and 270° in the cycle, is $1.414 \times$ rms value.
- The peak-to-peak value is double the peak amplitude, or $2.828 \times$ rms for a symmetrical ac waveform.
- The average value is $0.637 \times$ peak value.
- The frequency equals the number of cycles per second. One cps is 1 Hz. The audio-frequency (AF) range is 16 to 16,000 Hz. Higher frequencies up to 300,000 MHz are radio frequencies (RF).
- The amount of time for one cycle is the period $T$. The period and frequency are reciprocals: $T = 1/f$, or $f = 1/T$. The higher the frequency, the shorter the period.
- Wavelength $\lambda$ is the distance a wave travels in one cycle. The higher the frequency, the shorter the wavelength. The wavelength also depends on the velocity at which the wave travels: $\lambda = v/f$ where $v$ is velocity of the wave and $f$ is the frequency.
- Phase angle is the angular difference in time between corresponding values in the cycles for two waveforms of the same frequency.
- When one sine wave has its maximum value while the other is at zero, the two waves are 90° out of phase. Two waveforms with zero phase angle between them are in phase; a 180° phase angle means opposite phase.
- The length of a phasor arrow indicates amplitude, while the angle corresponds to the phase. Leading phase is shown by counterclockwise angles.
- Sine-wave alternating voltage $V$ applied across a load resistance $R$ produces alternating current $I$ in the circuit. The current has the same waveform, frequency, and phase as the applied voltage because of the resistive load. The amount of $I = V/R$.
- The sawtooth wave and square wave are two common examples of nonsinusoidal waveforms. The amplitudes of these waves are usually measured in peak-to-peak value.
- Harmonic frequencies are exact multiples of the fundamental frequency.
- The ac voltage used in residences range from 115 to 125 V rms with a frequency of 60 Hz. The nominal voltage is usually given as 120 V.
- For residential wiring, the three-wire single-phase Edison system shown in Fig. 16-21 is used to provide either 120 or 240 V.
- In a motor, the rotating armature connects to the power line. The stator field coils provide the magnetic flux cut by the armature as it is forced to rotate. A generator has the opposite effect; it converts mechanical energy into electrical output.

- A dc motor has commutator segments contacted by graphite brushes for the external connections to the power source. An ac induction motor does not have brushes.
- In three-phase power, each phase angle is 120°. For the Y connections in Fig. 16-26a, each pair of output terminals has output of $120 \times 1.73 = 208$ V. This voltage is known as the line-to-line voltage.

## SELF-TEST

### ANSWERS AT BACK OF BOOK.

Answer True or False.

1. An ac voltage varies in magnitude and reverses in polarity.
2. A dc voltage always has one polarity.
3. Sine-wave alternating current flows in a load resistor with a sine-wave voltage applied.
4. When two waves are 90° out of phase, one has its peak value when the other is at zero.
5. When two waves are in phase, they have their peak values at the same time.
6. The positive peak of a sine wave cannot occur at the same time as the negative peak.
7. The angle of 90° is the same as $\pi$ rad.
8. A period of 2 $\mu$s corresponds to a higher frequency than $T$ of 1 $\mu$s.
9. A wavelength of 2 ft corresponds to a lower frequency than a wavelength of 1 ft.
10. When we compare the phase between two waveforms, they must have the same frequency.

Fill in the missing answers.

11. For the rms voltage of 10 V, the peak-to-peak value is _____ V.
12. With 120 V rms across 100 $\Omega$ $R_L$, the rms current equals _____ A.
13. For a peak value of 100 V, the rms value is _____ V.
14. The wavelength of a 1000-kHz radio wave is _____ cm.
15. The period of a 1000-kHz voltage is _____ ms.
16. The period of $\frac{1}{60}$ s corresponds to a frequency of _____ Hz.
17. The frequency of 100 MHz corresponds to a period of _____ $\mu$s.
18. The square wave in Fig. 16-19c has the frequency of _____ MHz.
19. The rms voltage for the sine wave in Fig. 16-19a is _____ V.
20. The ac voltage across $R_2$ in Fig. 16-18 is _____ V.
21. For an audio signal with a $T$ of 0.001 s, its frequency is _____ Hz.
22. For the 60-Hz ac power-line voltage, the third harmonic is _____ Hz.
23. For a 10-V average value, the rms value is _____ V.
24. For a 340-V p–p value, the rms value is _____ V.
25. An audio signal that produces four cycles in the time it takes for one cycle of ac voltage from the power line has the frequency of _____ Hz.
26. In Fig. 16-21, the voltage between the red and black wires is _____ V.
27. In Fig. 16-25, the angle between the three phases is _____ degrees.
28. In Fig. 16-26a, the voltage between terminals B and C is _____ V.

## QUESTIONS

1. (a) Define an alternating voltage. (b) Define an alternating current. (c) Why does ac voltage applied across a load resistance produce alternating current in the circuit?
2. (a) State two characteristics of a sine wave of voltage. (b) Why does the rms value of $0.707 \times$ peak value apply just to sine waves?
3. Draw two cycles of an ac sawtooth voltage waveform with a peak-to-peak amplitude of 40 V. Do the same for a square wave.
4. Give the angle, in degrees and radians, for each of the following: one cycle, one half-cycle, one quarter-cycle, three quarter-cycles.
5. The peak value of a sine wave is 1 V. How much is its average value? Rms value? Effective value? Peak-to-peak value?
6. State the following ranges in Hz: (a) audio frequencies; (b) radio frequencies; (c) standard AM radio broadcast band; (d) FM broadcast band; (e) VHF band; (f) microwave band.
7. Make a graph with two waves, one with a frequency of 500 kHz and the other with 1000 kHz. Mark the horizontal axis in time, and label each wave.
8. Draw the sine waves and phasor diagrams to show (a) two waves 180° out of phase; (b) two waves 90° out of phase.
9. Give the voltage value for the 60-Hz ac line voltage with an rms value of 120 V at each of the following times in a cycle: 0°, 30°, 45°, 90°, 180°, 270°, 360°.
10. (a) The phase angle of 90° equals how many radians? (b) For two sine waves 90° out of phase with each other, compare their amplitudes at 0°, 90°, 180°, 270°, and 360°.
11. Tabulate the sine and cosine values every 30° from 0 to 360° and draw the corresponding sine wave and cosine wave.
12. Draw a graph of the values for $(\sin \theta)^2$ plotted against $\theta$ for every 30° from 0 to 360°.
13. Why is the wavelength of an ultrasonic wave at 34.44 kHz the same 1 cm as for the much higher frequency radio wave at 30 GHz?
14. Draw the sine waves and phasors to show wave $V_1$ leading wave $V_2$ by 45°.
15. Why are amplitudes for nonsinusoidal waveforms generally measured in peak-to-peak values, rather than rms or average value?
16. Define harmonic frequencies, giving numerical values.
17. Define one octave, with an example of numerical values.
18. Which do you consider more important for applications of alternating current—the polarity reversals or the variations in value?
19. Define the following parts in the assembly of motors: (a) armature rotor; (b) field stator; (c) collector rings; (d) commutator segments.
20. Show diagrams of Y and Δ connections for three-phase ac power.

## PROBLEMS

**ANSWERS TO ODD-NUMBERED PROBLEMS AT BACK OF BOOK.**

1. The 60-Hz power-line voltage of 120 V is applied across a resistance of 20 Ω. (a) How much is the rms current in the circuit? (b) What is the frequency of the current? (c) What is the

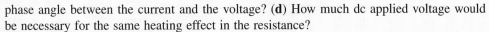

phase angle between the current and the voltage? (**d**) How much dc applied voltage would be necessary for the same heating effect in the resistance?

2. What is the frequency for the following ac variations? (**a**) 10 cycles in 1 s; (**b**) 1 cycle in $\frac{1}{10}$ s; (**c**) 50 cycles in 1 s; (**d**) 50 cycles in $\frac{1}{2}$ s; (**e**) 50 cycles in 5 s.

3. Calculate the time delay for a phase angle of 45° at the frequency of (**a**) 500 Hz; (**b**) 2 MHz.

4. Calculate the period $T$ for the following frequencies: (**a**) 500 Hz; (**b**) 5 MHz; (**c**) 5 GHz.

5. Calculate the frequency for the following periods: (**a**) 0.05 s; (**b**) 5 ms; (**c**) 5 $\mu$s; (**d**) 5 ns.

6. Refer to Fig. 16-18; calculate the $I^2R$ power dissipated in $R_1$, $R_2$, and $R_3$.

7. Give the plus and minus peak values for each wave in Fig. 16-19a to d.

8. An ac circuit has a 5-M$\Omega$ resistor $R_1$ in series with a 10-M$\Omega$ resistor $R_2$ across a 200-V source. Calculate $I$, $V_1$, $V_2$, $P_1$, and $P_2$.

9. The two resistors in Prob. 8 are connected in parallel. Calculate $I_1$, $I_2$, $V_1$, $V_2$, $P_1$, and $P_2$.

10. A series-parallel ac circuit has two branches across the 60-Hz 120-V power line. One branch has a 10-$\Omega$ $R_1$ in series with a 20-$\Omega$ $R_2$. The other branch has a 10-M$\Omega$ $R_3$ in series with a 20-M$\Omega$ $R_4$. Find $V_1$, $V_2$, $V_3$, and $V_4$.

11. How much $I$ does a 300-W 120-V bulb take from a 120-V 60-Hz line?

12. In Fig. 16-28, calculate $V_{rms}$, period $T$, and frequency $f$.

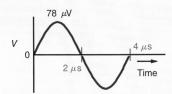

FIG. 16-28   Sine wave for Prob. 12.

13. A sine-wave ac voltage has a rms value of 19.2 V. (**a**) Find the peak value. (**b**) What is the instantaneous value at 50° of the cycle?

14. In Fig. 16-29, calculate $I$, $V_1$, $V_2$, and $V_3$.

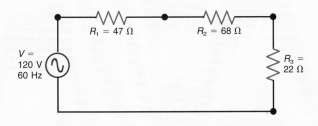

FIG. 16-29   Circuit diagram for Prob. 14.

15. In Fig. 16-30, calculate $I_1$, $I_2$, $I_3$, and $I_T$.

16. A 5-$\Omega$ $R$ in a circuit connected to the ac power line has $I$ of 1.17 A. Calculate the power dissipated in the resistor.

17. Convert to peak-to-peak voltage the following rms values of sine-wave ac signal voltage: (**a**) 164 $\mu$V; (**b**) 3.49 mV; (**c**) 12.48 mV.

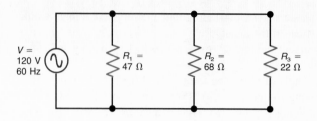

$V = $ 120 V 60 Hz

$R_1 = 47\ \Omega$  $R_2 = 68\ \Omega$  $R_3 = 22\ \Omega$

**FIG. 16-30** Circuit diagram for Prob. 15.

18. Convert to rms voltage the following peak-to-peak values of sine-wave ac signal voltage: **(a)** 462.5 $\mu$V; **(b)** 9.84 mV; **(c)** 35.19 mV.

19. **(a)** What size $R_S$ is needed to drop 120 V from the ac power line to 9 V with a load current of 14 mA? **(b)** Calculate the power dissipated in $R_S$.

20. Do the same as in Prob. 19 but for a load current of 1.2 A.

21. A sine wave of voltage has an average value of 38.22 V. Calculate the waveform's: **(a)** rms value; **(b)** peak value; **(c)** peak-to-peak value.

22. A sine wave of voltage has an instantaneous value of 24 V at $\theta = 60°$. Calculate the waveform's value at $\theta = 270°$.

23. List the first four harmonics of 7.5 MHz. Also, identify each harmonic as being either an even or odd multiple of the fundamental frequency.

24. Calculate the wavelength $\lambda$ in meters for the following radio frequencies: **(a)** 1.875 MHz; **(b)** 3.75 MHz; **(c)** 7.5 MHz; **(d)** 15 MHz; **(e)** 20 MHz; **(f)** 30 MHz.

25. Calculate the wavelength $\lambda$ in feet for the following sound wave frequencies: **(a)** 10 Hz; **(b)** 50 Hz; **(c)** 250 Hz; **(d)** 1 kHz; **(e)** 15 kHz; **(f)** 20 kHz.

26. List the frequency three decades above 100 Hz.

27. Raising the frequency of 400 Hz by two octaves corresponds to what frequency?

28. What is the frequency three octaves below 40 kHz?

29. Two waveforms, A and B, each have a frequency of 10 kHz. If waveform A reaches its maximum positive value 6.25 $\mu$s after waveform B, calculate the phase-angle difference between the two waveforms.

30. Draw the phase-angle diagram for Prob. 29. Represent waveform A as $V_A$ and waveform B as $V_B$. Use $V_A$ as the reference phasor.

31. Calculate the period $T$ of a radio wave whose wavelength $\lambda$ is 2 m.

## CRITICAL THINKING

1. The electrical length of an antenna is to be one-half wavelength long at a frequency $f$ of 7.2 MHz. Calculate the length of the antenna in: **(a)** feet; **(b)** centimeters.

2. A transmission line has a length $l$ of 7.5 m. What is its electrical wavelength at 10 MHz?

3. The total length of an antenna is 120 ft. At what frequency is the antenna one-half wavelength long?

4. A cosine wave of current has an instantaneous amplitude of 45 mA at $\theta = \pi/3$ rad. Calculate the waveform's instantaneous amplitude at $\theta = 3\pi/2$ rad.

**16-1**  a. T
     b. F
     c. T

**16-2**  a. 10 V
     b. 360°

**16-3**  a. 85 V
     b. 120 V
     c. 170 V

**16-4**  a. 0.707 A
     b. 0.5 A

**16-5**  a. 120 V rms
     b. 14.14 V peak
     c. 2.8 V p–p

**16-6**  a. 4 Hz
     b. 1.605 MHz

**16-7**  a. 400 Hz
     b. $\frac{1}{400}$ s

**16-8**  a. T
     b. F
     c. T

**16-9**  a. 90°
     b. 60°
     c. 0°

**16-10**  a. $\frac{1}{240}$ s
      b. 0.1 $\mu$s

**16-11**  a. 30 $\Omega$
      b. 6.67 $\Omega$
      c. 30 $\Omega$

**16-12**  a. 2 $\mu$s
      b. 15 V

**16-13**  a. 48 MHz
      b. 440 Hz

**16-14**  a. F
      b. T
      c. T
      d. T

**16-15**  a. T
      b. T
      c. F

**16-16**  a. 120°
      b. 208 V

# REVIEW: CHAPTERS 13 TO 16

## SUMMARY

- Iron, nickel, and cobalt are magnetic materials. Magnets have a north pole and a south pole at opposite ends. Opposite poles attract; like poles repel.
- A magnet has an invisible, external magnetic field. This magnetic flux is indicated by field lines. The direction of field lines outside the magnet is from north pole to south pole.
- An electromagnet has an iron core that becomes magnetized when current flows in the coil winding.
- Magnetic units are defined in Tables 13-1 and 14-2.
- Continuous magnetization and demagnetization of an iron core by means of alternating current causes hysteresis losses, which increase with higher frequencies.
- Current in a conductor has an associated magnetic field with circular lines of force in a plane perpendicular to the wire.
- Motor action results from the net force of two fields that can aid or cancel. The direction of the resultant force is from the stronger field to the weaker.
- The motion of flux cutting across a perpendicular conductor generates an induced emf.
- Faraday's law of induced voltage states that $v = N \, d\phi/dt$.
- Lenz' law states that an induced voltage must have the polarity that opposes the change causing the induction.
- Alternating voltage varies in magnitude and reverses in polarity.
- One cycle includes the values between points having the same value and varying in the same direction. The cycle includes 360°, or $2\pi$ rad.
- Frequency $f$ equals the cycles per second (cps). One cps = 1 Hz.
- Period $T$ is the time for one cycle. It equals $1/f$. When $f$ is in cycles per second, $T$ is in seconds.
- Wavelength $\lambda$ is the distance a wave travels in one cycle. $\lambda = v/f$.
- The rms, or effective value, of a sine wave equals 0.707 × peak value. Or the peak value equals 1.414 × rms value. The average value equals 0.637 × peak value.
- Phase angle $\theta$ is the angular difference between corresponding values in the cycles for two sine waves of the same frequency. The angular difference can be expressed in time based on the frequency of the waves.
- Phasors, similar to vectors, indicate the amplitude and phase angle of alternating voltage or current. The length of the phasor is the amplitude, while the angle is the phase.
- The square wave and sawtooth wave are common examples of nonsinusoidal waveforms.
- Direct current motors generally use commutator segments with graphite brushes. Alternating current motors are usually the induction type without brushes.

- House wiring uses three-wire single-phase power with a frequency of 60 Hz. The voltages for house wiring are 120 V to the grounded neutral and 240 V across the two high sides.
- Three-phase ac power has three legs 120° out of phase. A Y connection, with 120 V across each phase, has 208 V available across each two legs.

## REVIEW SELF-TEST

### ANSWERS AT BACK OF BOOK.

Choose (*a*), (*b*), (*c*), or (*d*).

1. Which of the following statements is true? (*a*) Alnico is commonly used for electromagnets. (*b*) Paper cannot affect magnetic flux because it is not a magnetic material. (*c*) Iron is generally used for permanent magnets. (*d*) Ferrites have lower permeability than air or vacuum.

2. Hysteresis losses (*a*) are caused by high-frequency alternating current in a coil with an iron core; (*b*) generally increase with direct current in a coil; (*c*) are especially important with permanent magnets that have a steady magnetic field; (*d*) cannot be produced in an iron core, because it is a conductor.

3. A magnetic flux of 25,000 lines through an area of 5 $cm^2$ results in (*a*) 5 lines of flux; (*b*) 5000 Mx of flux; (*c*) flux density of 5000 G; (*d*) flux density corresponding to 25,000 A.

4. If 10 V is applied across a relay coil with 100 turns having 2 Ω of resistance, the total force producing magnetic flux in the circuit is (*a*) 10 Mx; (*b*) 50 G; (*c*) 100 Oe; (*d*) 500 A · t.

5. The ac power-line voltage of 120 V rms has a peak value of (*a*) 100 V; (*b*) 170 V; (*c*) 240 V; (*d*) 338 V.

6. Which of the following can produce the most induced voltage? (*a*) 1-A direct current; (*b*) 50-A direct current; (*c*) 1-A 60-Hz alternating current; (*d*) 1-A 400-Hz alternating current.

7. Which of the following has the highest frequency? (*a*) $T = \frac{1}{1000}$ s; (*b*) $T = \frac{1}{60}$ s; (*c*) $T = 1$ s; (*d*) $T = 2$ s.

8. Two waves of the same frequency have opposite phase when the phase angle between them is (*a*) 0°; (*b*) 90°; (*c*) 360°; (*d*) $\pi$ rad.

9. The 120-V 60-Hz power-line voltage is applied across a 120-Ω resistor. The current equals (*a*) 1 A, peak value; (*b*) 120 A, peak value; (*c*) 1 A, rms value; (*d*) 5 A, rms value.

10. When an alternating voltage reverses in polarity, the current it produces (*a*) reverses in direction; (*b*) has a steady dc value; (*c*) has a phase angle of 180°; (*d*) alternates at 1.4 times the frequency of the applied voltage.

## REFERENCES

Adams, J. E., and G. Rockmaker: *Industrial Electricity—Principles and Practices,* Glencoe/McGraw-Hill, Columbus, Ohio.

Petruzella, F. D.: *Industrial Electronics*, Glencoe/McGraw-Hill, Columbus, Ohio.

# CHAPTER 17

# CAPACITANCE

Capacitance is the ability of a dielectric to store electric charge. The more the charge that is stored for a given voltage, the higher the value of capacitance. Its symbol is $C$ and the unit is the farad (F), named after Michael Faraday.

A capacitor consists of an insulator (also called a dielectric) between two conductors. The conductors make it possible to apply voltage across the insulator. Different types of capacitors are manufactured for specific values of $C$. They are named according to the dielectric. Common types are air, ceramic, mica, paper, film, and electrolytic capacitors. Capacitors used in electronic circuits are small and economical.

The most important property of a capacitor is its ability to block a steady dc voltage, while passing ac signals. The higher the frequency is, the less the opposition for ac voltages.

Capacitors are a common source of troubles because they can either have an open at the conductors or a short circuit through the dielectric. These troubles are described here, including the method of checking a capacitor with an ohmmeter, even though a capacitor is actually an insulator.

# CHAPTER OBJECTIVES

*Upon completion of this chapter, you should be able to:*

- *Understand* how charge is stored in the dielectric of a capacitor.
- *Understand* how a capacitor charges and discharges.
- *Define* the farad unit of capacitance.
- *List* the physical factors affecting the capacitance of a capacitor.
- *List* several types of capacitors and the characteristics of each.
- *Understand* how an electrolytic capacitor is constructed.
- *Understand* how capacitors are coded.
- *Calculate* the total capacitance of parallel connected capacitors.
- *Calculate* the equivalent capacitance of series connected capacitors.
- *Calculate* the energy stored in a capacitor.
- *Understand* how an ohmmeter can be used to test a capacitor.

# IMPORTANT TERMS IN THIS CHAPTER

| | | |
|---|---|---|
| aluminum capacitor | electrostatic induction | shelf life of capacitors |
| capacitor charge and discharge | farad (F) unit | stored charge |
| ceramic capacitor | film capacitor | stray capacitance |
| chip capacitor | ganged capacitors | tantalum capacitor |
| coding of capacitors | leakage resistance | testing of capacitors |
| dielectric constant | mica capacitor | tuning capacitor |
| distributed capacitance | Mylar capacitor | |
| electrolytic capacitor | paper capacitor | |

# TOPICS COVERED IN THIS CHAPTER

| | | | | |
|---|---|---|---|---|
| **17-1** | How Charge Is Stored in the Dielectric | **17-7** | Parallel Capacitances | |
| **17-2** | Charging and Discharging a Capacitor | **17-8** | Series Capacitances | |
| **17-3** | The Farad Unit of Capacitance | **17-9** | Stray Capacitive and Inductive Effects | |
| **17-4** | Typical Capacitors | **17-10** | Energy in Electrostatic Field of Capacitance | |
| **17-5** | Electrolytic Capacitors | | | |
| **17-6** | Capacitor Coding | **17-11** | Troubles in Capacitors | |

# 17-1 HOW CHARGE IS STORED IN THE DIELECTRIC

It is possible for dielectric materials such as air or paper to hold an electric charge because free electrons cannot flow through an insulator. However, the charge must be applied by some source. In Fig. 17-1$a$, the battery can charge the capacitor shown. With the dielectric contacting the two conductors connected to the potential difference $V$, electrons from the voltage source accumulate on the side of the capacitor connected to the negative terminal of $V$. The opposite side of the capacitor connected to the positive terminal of $V$ loses electrons.

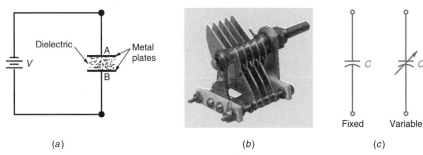

FIG. 17-1   Capacitance stores the charge in the dielectric between two conductors. ($a$) Structure. ($b$) Air-dielectric variable capacitor. Length is 2 in. ($c$) Schematic symbols for fixed and variable capacitors.

As a result, the excess of electrons produces a negative charge on one side of the capacitor, while the opposite side has a positive charge. As an example, if $6.25 \times 10^{18}$ electrons are accumulated, the negative charge equals 1 coulomb (C). The charge on only one plate need be considered, as the number of electrons accumulated on one plate is exactly the same as the number taken from the opposite plate.

What the voltage source does is simply redistribute some electrons from one side of the capacitor to the other. This process is called *charging* the capacitor. Charging continues until the potential difference across the capacitor is equal to the applied voltage. Without any series resistance, the charging is instantaneous. Practically, however, there is always some series resistance. This charging current is transient, or temporary, as it flows only until the capacitor is charged to the applied voltage. Then there is no current in the circuit.

The result is a device for storing charge in the dielectric. Storage means that the charge remains even after the voltage source is disconnected. The measure of how much charge can be stored is the capacitance $C$. More charge stored for a given amount of applied voltage means more capacitance. Components made to provide a specified amount of capacitance are called *capacitors,* or by their old name *condensers.*

Electrically, then, capacitance is the ability to store charge. Physically, a capacitor consists simply of two conductors separated by an insulator. For example, Fig. 17-1$b$ shows a capacitor using air for the dielectric between the metal plates. There are many types with different dielectric materials, including paper, mica, and ceramics, but the schematic symbols shown in Fig. 17-1$c$ apply to all capacitors.

## ABOUT

## ELECTRONICS

Magnets made out of organic materials could be used in optical disks and components in computers, mobile phones, TVs, motors, generators, and data storage. Circuits can make use of ceramic magnets that do not conduct electricity.

**ELECTRIC FIELD IN THE DIELECTRIC**   Any voltage has a field of electric lines of force between the opposite electric charges. The electric field corresponds to the magnetic lines of force of the magnetic field associated with electric current.* What a capacitor does is concentrate the electric field in the dielectric between the plates. This concentration corresponds to a magnetic field concentrated in the turns of a coil. The only function of the capacitor plates and wire conductors is to connect the voltage source $V$ across the dielectric. Then the electric field is concentrated in the capacitor, instead of being spread out in all directions.

**ELECTROSTATIC INDUCTION**   The capacitor has opposite charges because of electrostatic induction by the electric field. Electrons that accumulate on the negative side of the capacitor provide electric lines of force that repel electrons from the opposite side. When this side loses electrons, it becomes positively charged. The opposite charges induced by an electric field correspond to the idea of opposite poles induced in magnetic materials by a magnetic field.

---

### TEST-POINT QUESTION 17-1

Answers at end of chapter.
**a.** In a capacitor, is the electric charge stored in the dielectric or in the metal plates?
**b.** What is the unit of capacitance?

## 17-2 CHARGING AND DISCHARGING A CAPACITOR

Charging and discharging are the two main effects of capacitors. Applied voltage puts charge in the capacitor. The accumulation of charge results in a buildup of potential difference across the capacitor plates. When the capacitor voltage equals the applied voltage, there is no more charging. The charge remains in the capacitor, with or without the applied voltage connected.

The capacitor discharges when a conducting path is provided across the plates, without any applied voltage. Actually, it is only necessary that the capacitor voltage be more than the applied voltage. Then the capacitor can serve as voltage source, temporarily, to produce discharge current in the discharge path. The capacitor discharge continues until the capacitor voltage drops to zero or is equal to the applied voltage.

**APPLYING THE CHARGE**   In Fig. 17-2a, the capacitor is neutral with no charge because it has not been connected to any source of applied voltage and there is no electrostatic field in the dielectric. Closing the switch in Fig. 17-2b, however, allows the negative battery terminal to repel free electrons in the

---

*Electric and magnetic fields are compared in Fig. 14-6 on page 383.

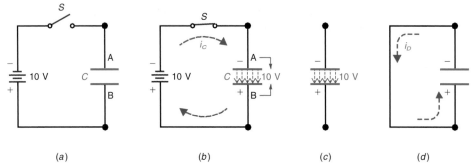

**FIG. 17-2** Storing electric charge in a capacitance. (*a*) Capacitor without any charge. (*b*) Battery charges capacitor to applied voltage of 10 V. (*c*) Stored charge remains in capacitor, providing 10 V without the battery. (*d*) Discharging the capacitor.

conductor to plate A. At the same time, the positive terminal attracts free electrons from plate B. The side of the dielectric at plate A accumulates electrons because they cannot flow through the insulator, while plate B has an equal surplus of protons.

Remember that the opposite charges have an associated potential difference, which is the voltage across the capacitor. The charging process continues until the capacitor voltage equals the battery voltage, which is 10 V in this example. Then no further charging is possible because the applied voltage cannot make free electrons flow in the conductors.

Note that the potential difference across the charged capacitor is 10 V between plates A and B. There is no potential difference from each plate to its battery terminal, however, which is the reason why the capacitor stops charging.

**STORING THE CHARGE** The negative and positive charges on opposite plates have an associated electric field through the dielectric, as shown by the dotted lines in Figs. 17-2*b* and 17-2*c*. The direction of these electric lines of force is shown repelling electrons from plate B, making this side positive. It is the effect of electric lines of force through the dielectric that results in storage of the charge. The electric field distorts the molecular structure so that the dielectric is no longer neutral. The dielectric is actually stressed by the invisible force of the electric field. As evidence, the dielectric can be ruptured by a very intense field with high voltage across the capacitor.

The result of the electric field, then, is that the dielectric has charge supplied by the voltage source. Since the dielectric is an insulator that cannot conduct, the charge remains in the capacitor even after the voltage source is removed, as illustrated in Fig. 17-2*c*. You can now take this charged capacitor by itself out of the circuit, and it still has 10 V across the two terminals.

**DISCHARGING** The action of neutralizing the charge by connecting a conducting path across the dielectric is called *discharging* the capacitor. In Fig. 17-2*d*, the wire between plates A and B is a low-resistance path for discharge current. With the stored charge in the dielectric providing the potential difference, 10 V is available to produce discharge current. The negative plate repels electrons, which are attracted to the positive plate through the wire, until the positive and negative charges are neutralized. Then there is no net charge. The capacitor is completely discharged, the voltage across it equals zero, and there is no discharge current. Now the capacitor is in the same uncharged condition as in Fig. 17-2a. It can be charged again, however, by a source of applied voltage.

**NATURE OF THE CAPACITANCE**    A capacitor has the ability to store the amount of charge necessary to provide a potential difference equal to the charging voltage. If 100 V were applied in Fig. 17-2, the capacitor would charge to 100 V.

The capacitor charges to the applied voltage because, when the capacitor voltage is less, it takes on more charge. As soon as the capacitor voltage equals the applied voltage, no more charging current can flow. *Note that any charge or discharge current flows through the conducting wires to the plates but not through the dielectric.*

**CHARGE AND DISCHARGE CURRENTS**    In Fig. 17-2b, $i_C$ is in the opposite direction from $i_D$ in Fig. 17-2d. In both cases the current shown is electron flow. However, $i_C$ is charging current to the capacitor and $i_D$ is discharge current from the capacitor. The charge and discharge currents must always be in opposite directions. In Fig. 17-2b, the negative plate of C accumulates electrons from the voltage source. In Fig. 17-2d, the charged capacitor serves as a voltage source to produce electron flow around the discharge path.

More charge and discharge current result with a higher value of C for a given amount of voltage. Also, more V produces more charge and discharge current with a given amount of capacitance. However, the value of C does not change with the voltage, as the amount of C depends on the physical construction of the capacitor.

---
**TEST-POINT QUESTION 17-2**
---

Answers at end of chapter.

Refer to Fig. 17-2.
**a.** If the applied voltage were 14.5 V, how much would the voltage be across C after it has charged?
**b.** How much is the voltage across C after it is completely discharged?
**c.** Can the capacitor be charged again after it is discharged?

# 17-3 THE FARAD UNIT OF CAPACITANCE

With more charging voltage, the electric field is stronger and more charge is stored in the dielectric. The amount of charge Q stored in the capacitance is therefore proportional to the applied voltage. Also, a larger capacitance can store more charge. These relations are summarized by the formula

▶    $Q = CV$    coulombs    **(17-1)**

where Q is the charge stored in the dielectric in coulombs (C), and V is the voltage across the plates of the capacitor, and C is the capacitance in farads.

The $C$ is a physical constant, indicating the capacitance in terms of how much charge can be stored for a given amount of charging voltage. When one coulomb is stored in the dielectric with a potential difference of one volt, the capacitance is one *farad*.

Practical capacitors have sizes in millionths of a farad, or smaller. The reason is that typical capacitors store charge of microcoulombs or less. Therefore, the common units are

$$1 \text{ microfarad} = 1 \ \mu\text{F} = 1 \times 10^{-6} \text{ F}$$
$$1 \text{ nanofarad} = 1 \text{ nF} = 1 \times 10^{-9} \text{ F}$$
$$1 \text{ picofarad} = 1 \text{ pF} = 1 \times 10^{-12} \text{ F}$$

Although traditionally it has not been used, the nanofarad unit of capacitance is gaining acceptance in the electronics industry.

## Example

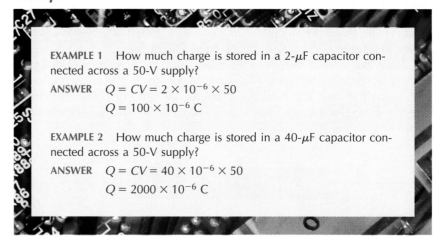

**EXAMPLE 1**   How much charge is stored in a 2-$\mu$F capacitor connected across a 50-V supply?

**ANSWER**   $Q = CV = 2 \times 10^{-6} \times 50$
$\qquad\qquad Q = 100 \times 10^{-6} \text{ C}$

**EXAMPLE 2**   How much charge is stored in a 40-$\mu$F capacitor connected across a 50-V supply?

**ANSWER**   $Q = CV = 40 \times 10^{-6} \times 50$
$\qquad\qquad Q = 2000 \times 10^{-6} \text{ C}$

Note that the larger capacitor stores more charge for the same voltage, in accordance with the definition of capacitance as the ability to store charge.

The factors in $Q = CV$ can be inverted to

$$C = \frac{Q}{V} \tag{17-2}$$

or

$$V = \frac{Q}{C} \tag{17-3}$$

For all three formulas, the basic units are volts for $V$, coulombs for $Q$, and farads for $C$. Note that the formula $C = Q/V$ actually defines one farad of capacitance as one coulomb of charge stored for one volt of potential difference. The letter $C$ (in italic, or slanted, type) is the symbol for capacitance. The same letter C (in roman, or upright, type) is the abbreviation for coulomb unit of charge. The difference between C and $C$ will be made clearer in the examples that follow.

# Example

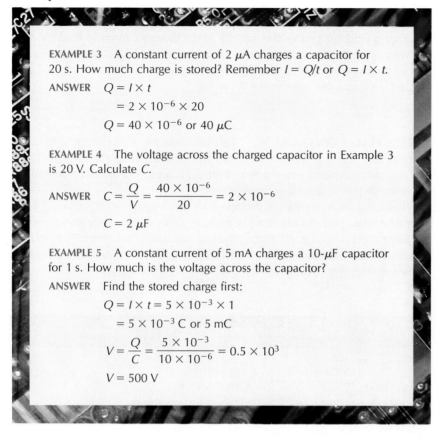

**EXAMPLE 3** A constant current of 2 $\mu$A charges a capacitor for 20 s. How much charge is stored? Remember $I = Q/t$ or $Q = I \times t$.

**ANSWER**
$$Q = I \times t$$
$$= 2 \times 10^{-6} \times 20$$
$$Q = 40 \times 10^{-6} \text{ or } 40 \ \mu C$$

**EXAMPLE 4** The voltage across the charged capacitor in Example 3 is 20 V. Calculate $C$.

**ANSWER**
$$C = \frac{Q}{V} = \frac{40 \times 10^{-6}}{20} = 2 \times 10^{-6}$$
$$C = 2 \ \mu F$$

**EXAMPLE 5** A constant current of 5 mA charges a 10-$\mu$F capacitor for 1 s. How much is the voltage across the capacitor?

**ANSWER** Find the stored charge first:
$$Q = I \times t = 5 \times 10^{-3} \times 1$$
$$= 5 \times 10^{-3} \text{ C or 5 mC}$$
$$V = \frac{Q}{C} = \frac{5 \times 10^{-3}}{10 \times 10^{-6}} = 0.5 \times 10^{3}$$
$$V = 500 \text{ V}$$

**LARGER PLATE AREA INCREASES CAPACITANCE**  As illustrated in Fig. 17-3, when the area of each plate is doubled, the capacitance in Fig. 17-3*b* stores twice the charge of Fig. 17-3*a*. The potential difference in both cases is still 10 V. This voltage produces a given strength of electric field. A larger plate area, however, means that more of the dielectric surface can contact each plate, allowing more lines of force through the dielectric between the plates and less flux leakage outside the dielectric. Then the field can store more charge in the dielectric. The result of larger plate area is more charge stored for the same applied voltage, which means the capacitance is larger.

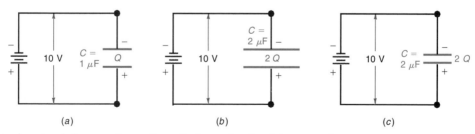

(a)　　　　　　(b)　　　　　　(c)

**FIG. 17-3** Increasing stored charge and capacitance by increasing the plate area and decreasing the distance between plates. (*a*) Capacitance of 1 $\mu$F. (*b*) A 2-$\mu$F capacitance with twice the plate area and the same distance. (*c*) A 2-$\mu$F capacitance with one-half the distance and the same plate area.

**THINNER DIELECTRIC INCREASES CAPACITANCE**   As illustrated in Fig. 17-3c, when the distance between plates is reduced one-half, the capacitance stores twice the charge of Fig. 17-3a. The potential difference is still 10 V, but its electric field has greater flux density in the thinner dielectric. Then the field between opposite plates can store more charge in the dielectric. With less distance between the plates, the stored charge is greater for the same applied voltage, which means the capacitance is greater.

**DIELECTRIC CONSTANT $K_\epsilon$**   This indicates the ability of an insulator to concentrate electric flux. Its numerical value is specified as the ratio of flux in the insulator compared with the flux in air or vacuum. The dielectric constant of air or vacuum is 1, since it is the reference.

Mica, for example, has an average dielectric constant of 6, meaning it can provide a density of electric flux six times as great as that of air or vacuum for the same applied voltage and equal physical size. Insulators generally have a dielectric constant $K_\epsilon$ greater than 1, as listed in Table 17-1. Higher values of $K_\epsilon$ allow greater values of capacitance.

**TABLE 17-1   DIELECTRIC MATERIALS\***

| MATERIAL | DIELECTRIC CONSTANT $K_\epsilon$ | DIELECTRIC STRENGTH, V/MIL |
|---|---|---|
| Air or vacuum | 1 | 20 |
| Aluminum oxide | 7 | |
| Ceramics | 80–1200 | 600–1250 |
| Glass | 8 | 335–2000 |
| Mica | 3–8 | 600–1500 |
| Oil | 2–5 | 275 |
| Paper | 2–6 | 1250 |
| Plastic film | 2–3 | |
| Tantalum oxide | 25 | |

\*Exact values depend on the specific composition of different types.

It should be noted that the aluminum oxide and tantalum oxide listed in Table 17-1 are used for the dielectric in electrolytic capacitors. Also, plastic film is often used instead of paper for the rolled-foil type of capacitor.

The dielectric constant for an insulator is actually its *relative permittivity,* with the symbol $\epsilon_r$ or $K_\epsilon$, indicating the ability to concentrate electric flux. This factor corresponds to relative permeability, with the symbol $\mu_r$ or $K_m$, for magnetic flux. Both $\epsilon_r$ and $\mu_r$ are pure numbers without units, as they are just ratios.\*

---

\*The absolute permittivity $\epsilon_0$ is $8.854 \times 10^{-12}$ F/m, in SI units, for electric flux in air or vacuum. This value corresponds to an absolute permeability $\mu_0$ of $4\pi \times 10^{-7}$ H/m, in SI units, for magnetic flux in air or vacuum.

These physical factors for a parallel-plate capacitor are summarized by the formula

$$\blacktriangleright \quad C = K_\epsilon \times \frac{A}{d} \times 8.85 \times 10^{-12} \text{ F} \qquad\qquad \textbf{(17-4)}$$

where $A$ is the area in square meters of either plate, $d$ is the distance in meters between plates, $K_\epsilon$ is the dielectric constant, or relative permittivity, as listed in Table 17-1, and $C$ is capacitance in farads. The constant factor $8.85 \times 10^{-12}$ is the absolute permittivity of air or vacuum, in SI, since the farad is an SI unit.

## Example

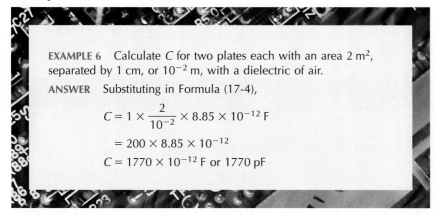

**EXAMPLE 6**  Calculate $C$ for two plates each with an area 2 m$^2$, separated by 1 cm, or $10^{-2}$ m, with a dielectric of air.

**ANSWER**  Substituting in Formula (17-4),

$$C = 1 \times \frac{2}{10^{-2}} \times 8.85 \times 10^{-12} \text{ F}$$

$$= 200 \times 8.85 \times 10^{-12}$$

$$C = 1770 \times 10^{-12} \text{ F or } 1770 \text{ pF}$$

This value means the capacitor can store $1770 \times 10^{-12}$ C of charge with 1 V. Note the relatively small capacitance, in picofarad units, with the extremely large plates of 2 m$^2$, which is really the size of a table or a desktop.

If the dielectric used is paper with a dielectric constant of 6, then $C$ will be six times greater. Also, if the spacing between plates is reduced by one-half to 0.5 cm, the capacitance will be doubled. It should be noted that practical capacitors for electronic circuits are much smaller than this parallel-plate capacitor. They use a very thin dielectric, with a high dielectric constant, and the plate area can be concentrated in a small space.

**DIELECTRIC STRENGTH**  Table 17-1 also lists breakdown-voltage ratings for typical dielectrics. Dielectric strength is the ability of a dielectric to withstand a potential difference without arcing across the insulator. This voltage rating is important because rupture of the insulator provides a conducting path through the dielectric. Then it cannot store charge, because the capacitor has been short-circuited. Since the breakdown voltage increases with greater thickness, capacitors with higher voltage ratings have more distance between the plates. This increased distance reduces the capacitance, however, all other factors remaining the same.

Answers at end of chapter.

**a.** A capacitor charged to 100 V has 1000 $\mu$C of charge. How much is $C$?

**b.** A mica capacitor and ceramic capacitor have the same physical dimensions. Which has more $C$?

## 17-4 TYPICAL CAPACITORS

Commercial capacitors are generally classified according to the dielectric. Most common are air, mica, paper, plastic film, and ceramic capacitors, plus the electrolytic type. Electrolytic capacitors use a molecular-thin oxide film as the dielectric, resulting in large capacitance values in little space. These types are compared in Table 17-2 and discussed in the sections that follow.

**TABLE 17-2   TYPES OF CAPACITORS**

| DIELECTRIC | CONSTRUCTION | CAPACITANCE | BREAKDOWN, V |
|---|---|---|---|
| Air | Meshed plates | 10–400 pF | 400 (0.02-in. air gap) |
| Ceramic | Tubular | 0.5–1600 pF | 500–20,000 |
|  | Disk | 1 pF to 1 $\mu$F |  |
| Electrolytic | Aluminum | 1–6800 $\mu$F | 10–450 |
|  | Tantalum | 0.047 to 330 $\mu$F | 6–50 |
| Mica | Stacked sheets | 10–5000 pF | 500–20,000 |
| Paper | Rolled foil | 0.001–1 $\mu$F | 200–1600 |
| Plastic film | Foil or metalized | 100 pF to 100 $\mu$F | 50–600 |

Except for electrolytic capacitors, capacitors can be connected to a circuit without regard to polarity, since either side can be the more positive plate. Electrolytic capacitors are marked to indicate the side that must be connected to the positive or negative side of the circuit. *It should be noted that it is the polarity of the charging source that determines the polarity of the capacitor voltage.* Failure to observe the correct polarity can damage the dielectric and lead to the complete destruction of the capacitor.

**MICA CAPACITORS**   Thin mica sheets as the dielectric are stacked between tinfoil sections for the conducting plates to provide the required capacitance. Alternate strips of tinfoil are connected together and brought out as one terminal for one set of plates, while the opposite terminal connects to the other set of interlaced plates. The construction is shown in Fig. 17-4a. The entire unit is generally in a molded Bakelite case. Mica capacitors are often used for small capacitance values of about 10 to 5000 pF; their length is ¾ in. or less with about ⅛-in. thickness. A typical mica capacitor is shown in Fig. 17-4b.

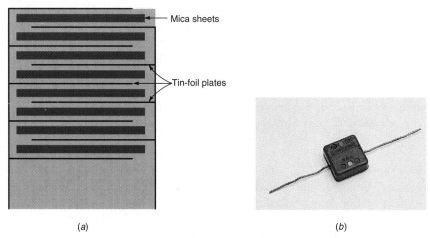

Mica sheets

Tin-foil plates

(a)                                                         (b)

FIG. 17-4   Mica capacitor. (a) Physical construction. (b) Example of a mica capacitor.

**PAPER CAPACITORS**   In this construction, shown in Fig. 17-5a, two rolls of tinfoil conductor separated by a paper dielectric are rolled into a compact cylinder. Each outside lead connects to its roll of tinfoil as a plate. The entire cylinder is generally placed in a cardboard container coated with wax or encased in plastic. Paper capacitors are often used for medium capacitance values of 0.001 to 1.0 $\mu$F, approximately. The physical size for 0.05 $\mu$F is typically 1 in. long with ⅜-in. diameter. A paper capacitor is shown in Fig. 17-5b.

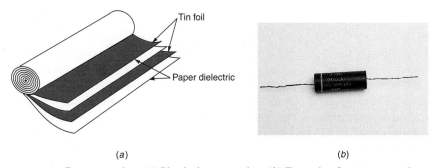

Tin foil

Paper dielectric

(a)                                                         (b)

FIG. 17-5   Paper capacitor. (a) Physical construction. (b) Example of a paper capacitor.

A black or a white band at one end of a paper capacitor indicates the lead connected to the outside foil. This lead should be used for the ground or low-potential side of the circuit to take advantage of shielding by the outside foil. There is no required polarity, however, since the capacitance is the same no matter which side is grounded. It should also be noted that in the schematic symbol for $C$ the curved line usually indicates the low-potential side of the capacitor.

**FILM CAPACITORS** Film capacitors are constructed much like paper capacitors except that the paper dielectric is replaced with a plastic film such as polypropylene, polystrene, polycarbonate, or polyethelene terepthalate (Mylar). There are two main types of film capacitors: the foil type and the metallized type. The foil type uses sheets of metal foil, such as aluminum or tin, for its conductive plates. The metallized type is constructed by depositing (spraying) a thin layer of metal, such as aluminum or zinc, on the plastic film. The sprayed-on metal serves as the plates of the capacitor. The advantage of the metallized type over the foil type is that the metallized type is much smaller for a given capacitance value and breakdown voltage rating. The reason is that the metallized type has much thinner plates due to the fact that they are sprayed on. Another advantage of the metallized type is that they are self-healing. This means that if the dielectric is punctured, due to exceeding its breakdown voltage rating, the capacitor is not damaged permanently. Instead the capacitor heals itself. This is not true of the foil type.

Film capacitors are very temperature stable and are therefore used frequently in circuits that require very stable capacitance values. Some examples are radio frequency oscillators and timer circuits. Film capacitors are available with values ranging from about 100 pF to 100 $\mu$F. Figure 17-6 shows a typical film capacitor.

**FIG. 17-6** Film capacitor.

**CERAMIC CAPACITORS** The ceramic materials used in ceramic capacitors are made from earth fired under extreme heat. By using titanium dioxide or one of several types of silicates, very high values of dielectric constant, $K_E$, can be obtained. Most ceramic capacitors come in disk form, as shown in Fig. 17-7. In the disk form, silver is deposited on both sides of the ceramic dielectric to form the capacitor plates. Ceramic capacitors are available with values of 1 pF (or less) up to about 1 $\mu$F. The wide range of values is possible because the dielectric constant $K_E$ can be tailored to provide almost any desired value of capacitance.

It should be noted that ceramic capacitors are also available in forms other than disk form. Some ceramic capacitors are available with axial leads and use a color code similar to that of a resistor.

**FIG. 17-7** Disk ceramic capacitor.

**SURFACE-MOUNT CAPACITORS** Like resistors, capacitors are also available as surface-mounted components. Surface-mounted capacitors are often called *chip capacitors*. Chip capacitors are constructed by placing a ceramic dielectric material between layers of conductive film which form the capacitor plates. The capacitance is determined by the dielectric constant $K_E$ and the physical area of the plates. Chip capacitors are available in many different sizes. A common size is 0.125 in. long by 0.063 in. wide in various thicknesses. Another common size is 0.080 in. long by 0.050 in. wide in various thicknesses. Figure 17-8 shows two different sizes of chip capacitors. Like chip resistors, chip capacitors have their end electrodes soldered directly to the copper traces of the printed circuit board. Chip capacitors are available with values ranging from a fraction of a picofarad up to several microfarads.

**VARIABLE CAPACITORS** Figure 17-1b shows a variable air capacitor. In this construction, the fixed metal plates connected together form the *stator*. The movable plates connected together on the shaft form the *rotor*. Capacitance is varied by rotating the shaft to make the rotor plates mesh with the stator plates.

They do not touch, however, since air is the dielectric. Full mesh is maximum capacitance. Moving the rotor completely out of mesh provides minimum capacitance.

A common application is the tuning capacitor in radio receivers. When you tune to different stations, the capacitance varies as the rotor moves in or out of mesh. Combined with an inductance, the variable capacitance then tunes the receiver to a different resonant frequency for each station. Usually two or three capacitor sections are *ganged* on one common shaft.

**TEMPERATURE COEFFICIENT** Ceramic capacitors are often used for temperature compensation, to increase or decrease capacitance with a rise in temperature. The temperature coefficient is given in parts per million (ppm) per degree Celsius, with a reference of 25°C. As an example, a negative 750 ppm unit is stated as N750. A positive temperature coefficient of the same value would be stated as P750. Units that do not change in capacitance are labeled NPO.

**CAPACITANCE TOLERANCE** Ceramic disk capacitors for general applications usually have a tolerance of ±20 percent. For closer tolerances, mica or film capacitors are used. These have tolerance values of ±2 to 20 percent. Silver-plated mica capacitors are available with a tolerance of ±1 percent.

The tolerance may be less on the minus side to make sure there is enough capacitance, particularly with electrolytic capacitors, which have a wide tolerance. For instance, a 20-$\mu$F electrolytic with a tolerance of −10 percent, +50 percent may have a capacitance of 18 to 30 $\mu$F. However, the exact capacitance value is not critical in most applications of capacitors for filtering, ac coupling, and bypassing.

**FIG. 17-8** Chip capacitors.

**VOLTAGE RATING OF CAPACITORS** This rating specifies the maximum potential difference that can be applied across the plates without puncturing the dielectric. Usually the voltage rating is for temperatures up to about 60°C. Higher temperatures result in a lower voltage rating. Voltage ratings for general-purpose paper, mica, and ceramic capacitors are typically 200 to 500 V. Ceramic capacitors with ratings of 1 to 20 kV are also available.

Electrolytic capacitors are typically available in 16-, 35-, and 50-V ratings. For applications where a lower voltage rating is permissible, more capacitance can be obtained in a smaller physical size.

The potential difference across the capacitor depends upon the applied voltage and is not necessarily equal to the voltage rating. A voltage rating higher than the potential difference applied across the capacitor provides a safety factor for long life in service. With electrolytic capacitors, however, the actual capacitor voltage should be close to the rated voltage to produce the oxide film that provides the specified capacitance.

The voltage ratings are for dc voltage applied. The breakdown rating is lower for ac voltage because of the internal heat produced by continuous charge and discharge.

**CAPACITOR APPLICATIONS**  In most electronic circuits, a capacitor has dc voltage applied, combined with a much smaller ac signal voltage. The usual function of the capacitor is to block the dc voltage but pass the ac signal voltage, by means of the charge and discharge current. These applications include coupling, bypassing, and filtering for ac signal.

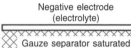

Negative electrode
(electrolyte)

Gauze separator saturated
with electrolyte

Oxide
film

Positive electrode
(aluminum foil)

(*a*)

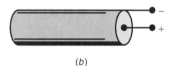

−
+

(*b*)

(*c*)

**FIG. 17-9**  Construction of aluminum electrolytic capacitor. (*a*) Internal electrodes. (*b*) Foil rolled into cartridge. (*c*) Typical capacitor with multiple sections.

# 17-5 ELECTROLYTIC CAPACITORS

Electrolytic capacitors are commonly used for *C* values ranging from about 1 to 6800 $\mu$F, because electrolytics provide the most capacitance in the smallest space with least cost.

**CONSTRUCTION**  Figure 17-9 shows the aluminum-foil type. The two aluminum electrodes are in an electrolyte of borax, phosphate, or carbonate. Between the two aluminum strips, absorbent gauze soaks up electrolyte to provide the required electrolysis that produces an oxide film. This type is considered a wet electrolytic, but it can be mounted in any position.

When dc voltage is applied to form the capacitance in manufacture, the electrolytic action accumulates a molecular-thin layer of aluminum oxide at the junction between the positive aluminum foil and the electrolyte. The oxide film is an insulator. As a result, capacitance is formed between the positive aluminum electrode and the electrolyte in the gauze separator. The negative aluminum electrode simply provides a connection to the electrolyte. Usually, the metal can itself is the negative terminal of the capacitor, as shown in Fig. 17-9*c*.

Because of the extremely thin dielectric film, very large *C* values can be obtained. The area is increased by using long strips of aluminum foil and gauze, which are rolled into a compact cylinder with very high capacitance. For example, an electrolytic capacitor the same size as a 0.1-$\mu$F paper capacitor, but rated at 10 V breakdown, may have 1000 $\mu$F of capacitance or more. Higher voltage ratings, up to 450 V, are available, with typical *C* values up to about 6800 $\mu$F. The very high *C* values usually have lower voltage ratings.

**POLARITY**  Electrolytic capacitors are used in circuits that have a combination of dc voltage and ac voltage. The dc voltage maintains the required polarity across the electrolytic capacitor to form the oxide film. A common application is for electrolytic filter capacitors to eliminate the 60- or 120-Hz ac ripple in a dc power supply. Another use is for audio coupling capacitors in transistor amplifiers. In both these applications, for filtering or coupling, electrolytics are needed for large $C$ with a low-frequency ac component, while the circuit has a dc component for the required voltage polarity. Incidentally, the difference between filtering an ac component out or coupling it into a circuit is only a question of parallel or series connections. The filter capacitors for a power supply are typically 100 to 1000 $\mu$F. Audio capacitors are usually 10 to 47 $\mu$F.

If the electrolytic is connected in opposite polarity, the reversed electrolysis forms gas in the capacitor. It becomes hot and may explode. This is a possibility only with electrolytic capacitors.

**LEAKAGE CURRENT**   The disadvantage of electrolytics, in addition to the required polarization, is their relatively high leakage current compared with other capacitors, since the oxide film is not a perfect insulator. The problem with leakage current in a capacitor is that it allows part of the dc component to be coupled into the next circuit along with the ac component. In the newer electrolytic capacitors, the leakage current is quite small.

**NONPOLARIZED ELECTROLYTICS**   This type is available for applications in circuits without any dc polarizing voltage, as in the 60-Hz ac power line. One application is the starting capacitor for ac motors. A nonpolarized electrolytic actually contains two capacitors, connected internally in series-opposing polarity.

**TANTALUM CAPACITORS**   This is another form of electrolytic capacitor, using tantalum (Ta) instead of aluminum. Titanium (Ti) is also used. Typical tantalum capacitors are shown in Fig. 17-10. They feature:

1.  Larger $C$ in a smaller size
2.  Longer shelf life
3.  Less leakage current

However, tantalum electrolytics cost more than the aluminum type. Methods of construction for tantalum capacitors include the wet-foil type and a solid chip or slug. The solid tantalum is processed in manufacture to have an oxide film as the dielectric. Referring back to Table 17-1, note that tantalum oxide has a dielectric constant of 25, compared with 7 for aluminum oxide.

### TEST-POINT QUESTION 17-5

Answers at end of chapter.

Answer True or False.
**a.** The rating of 1000 $\mu$F at 25 V could be for an electrolytic capacitor.
**b.** Electrolytic capacitors allow more leakage current than a mica capacitor.
**c.** Tantalum capacitors have a longer shelf life than aluminum electrolytics.

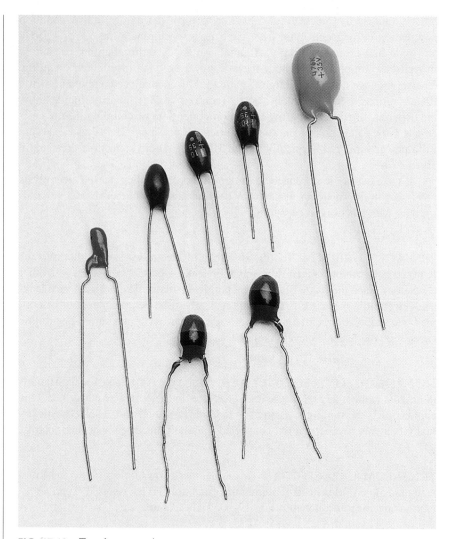

FIG. 17-10   Tantalum capacitors.

## 17-6 CAPACITOR CODING

The value of a capacitor is always specified in either $\mu$F or pF units of capacitance. This is true for all types of capacitors. As a general rule, if a capacitor (other than an electrolytic capacitor) is marked using a whole number such as 33, 220, 680, etc., the capacitance $C$ is in picofarads (pF). Conversely, if a capacitor is labeled using a decimal fraction such as 0.1, 0.047, or 0.0082, the capacitance $C$ is in microfarads ($\mu$F). There are a variety of different ways in which a manufacturer may indicate the value of a capacitor. What follows is an explanation of the most frequently encountered coding systems.

**FILM-TYPE CAPACITORS**   Figure 17-11 shows a popular coding system used with film-type capacitors. The first two numbers printed on the capacitor indicate the first two digits in the numerical value of the capacitance. The third

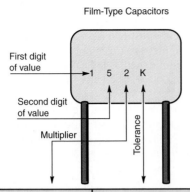

Film-Type Capacitors

First digit of value → 1  5  2  K

Second digit of value

Multiplier

Tolerance

| Multiplier | | Tolerance of Capacitor | | |
|---|---|---|---|---|
| For the Number | Multiplier | Letter | 10 pF or Less | Over 10 pF |
| 0 | 1 | B | ±0.1 pF | |
| 1 | 10 | C | ±0.25 pF | |
| 2 | 100 | D | ±0.5 pF | |
| 3 | 1,000 | F | ±1.0 pF | ±1% |
| 4 | 10,000 | G | ±2.0 pF | ±2% |
| 5 | 100,000 | H | | ±3% |
| 8 | 0.01 | J | | ±5% |
| | | K | | ±10% |
| 9 | 0.1 | M | | ±20% |

Examples:
152K = 15 × 100 = 1500 pF or 0.0015 μF, ±10%
759J = 75 × 0.1 = 7.5 pF, ±5%

*Note:* The letter R may be used at times to signify a decimal point, as in 2R2 = 2.2 (pF or μF).

FIG. 17-11   Film capacitor coding system.

number is the *multiplier,* indicating by what factor the first two digits must be multiplied. The letter at the far right indicates the capacitor's tolerance. With this coding system the capacitance is always in pF units. The capacitor's breakdown voltage rating is usually printed on the body directly below the coded value of capacitance.

## Example

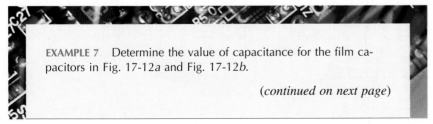

**EXAMPLE 7**   Determine the value of capacitance for the film capacitors in Fig. 17-12a and Fig. 17-12b.

(*continued on next page*)

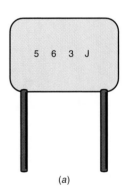

5  6  3  J

(a)

4  7  9  C

(b)

FIG. 17-12   Film capacitors for Example 7.

ANSWER   In Fig. 17-12a, the first two numbers are 5 and 6, respectively, for 56 as the first two digits in the numerical value of the capacitance. The third number, 3, indicates a multiplier of 1000, or 56 × 1000 = 56,000 pF. The letter J indicates a capacitor tolerance of ±5 percent.

In Fig. 17-12b, the first two numbers are 4 and 7, respectively, for 47 as the first two digits in the numerical value of the capacitance. The third number, 9, indicates a fractional multiplier of 0.1, or 47 × 0.1 = 4.7 pF. The letter C indicates a capacitor tolerance of ±0.25 pF.

**DISK CERAMIC CAPACITORS**   Figure 17-13 shows the way in which most disk ceramic capacitors are marked to indicate their capacitance. As you can see, the capacitance is expressed either as a whole number or as a decimal fraction. The type of coding system used depends on the manufacturer. Disk ceramic

Ceramic Disk Capacitors

ABC
100J
NPO

Manufacturer's code
Capacity value
Tolerance
*Working voltage
Temperature range

ABC
.0022
K
1KV
Z5F

*If no voltage marked, generally 500 V dc

Typical Ceramic Disk Capacitor Markings

| Low Temp. | Letter Symbol | High Temp. | Numerical Symbol | Max. Capacitance Change over Temp. Range | Letter Symbol |
|---|---|---|---|---|---|
| +10°C | Z | +45°C | 2 | +1.0% | A |
| −30°C | Y | +65°C | 4 | ±1.5% | B |
| −55°C | X | +85°C | 5 | ±1.1% | C |
| | | +105°C | 6 | ±3.3% | D |
| | | +125°C | 7 | ±4.7% | E |
| | | | | ±7.5% | F |
| | | | | ±10.0% | P |
| | | | | ±15.0% | R |
| | | | | ±22.0% | S |
| | | | | +22%,−33% | T |
| | | | | +22%,−56% | U |
| | | | | +22%,−82% | V |

Temperature Range Identification of
Ceramic Disk Capacitors

| 1st & 2nd Fig. of Capacitance | Multiplier | Numerical Symbol | Tolerance on Capacitance | Letter Symbol |
|---|---|---|---|---|
| | 1 | 0 | | |
| | 10 | 1 | | |
| | 100 | 2 | ±5% | J |
| | 1,000 | 3 | ±10% | K |
| | 10,000 | 4 | ±20% | M |
| | 100,000 | 5 | +100%,−0% | P |
| | | — | +80%,−20% | Z |
| | 0.01 | 8 | | |
| | 0.1 | 9 | | |

Capacity Value and Tolerance of
Ceramic Disk Capacitors

FIG. 17-13   Disk ceramic capacitor coding system.

capacitors are often used for coupling and bypassing ac signals, where it is allowable to have a wide or lopsided tolerance.

## Example

FIG. 17-14   Disk ceramic capacitor for Example 8.

**EXAMPLE 8**   In Fig. 17-14, determine: (**a**) the capacitance value and tolerance; (**b**) the temperature-range identification information.

**ANSWER**   (**a**) Since the capacitance is expressed as a decimal fraction, its value is in microfarads. In this case, $C = 0.047 \ \mu F$. The letter Z, to the right of 0.047, indicates a capacitor tolerance of +80 percent, −20 percent. Notice that the actual capacitance value can be as much as 80 percent above its coded value but only 20 percent below its coded value.

(**b**) The alphanumeric code, Z5V, printed below the capacitance value provides additional capacitor information. Referring to Fig. 17-13, note that the letter Z and number 5 indicate the low and high temperatures of +10°C and +85°C, respectively. The letter V indicates that the maximum capacitance change over the specified temperature range (+10°C to +85°C) is +22 percent, −82 percent. With temperature changes less than the range indicated, the percent change in capacitance will be less than that indicated.

**MICA CAPACITORS**   Mica capacitors are coded using colored dots to indicate the capacitance value in picofarads. Three different coding systems are shown in Fig. 17-16. The color code is best understood through the use of an example.

## Example

**EXAMPLE 9**   Determine the capacitance and tolerance for the capacitor in Fig. 17-15 (refer to Fig. 17-16 on the next page).

**ANSWER**   The dots in the top row are read from left to right, in the direction of the arrow. In the bottom row they are read in the reverse order, from right to left. The first dot at the left in the top row is black, indicating a mica capacitor. The next two color dots are blue and red, for 62 as the first two digits in the numerical value of the capacitance. The next dot, at the far right in the bottom row, is red, indicating a multiplier of 100. Therefore, $C = 62 \times 100 = 6200$ pF. The next dot is gold, indicating a capacitor tolerance of ±5 percent.

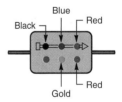

FIG. 17-15   Mica capacitor for Example 9.

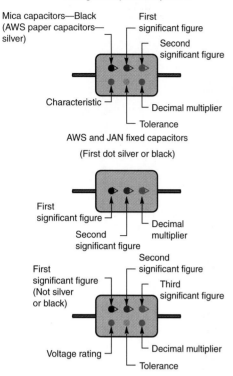

Postage Stamp Mica Capacitors

Mica capacitors—Black
(AWS paper capacitors—
silver)

First
significant figure

Second
significant figure

Characteristic

Decimal multiplier

Tolerance

AWS and JAN fixed capacitors

(First dot silver or black)

First
significant figure

Second
significant figure

Decimal
multiplier

Second
significant figure

First
significant figure
(Not silver
or black)

Third
significant figure

Voltage rating

Decimal multiplier

Tolerance

| Color | Significant Figure | Multiplier | Tolerance (%) | Voltage Rating |
|---|---|---|---|---|
| Black | 0 | 1 | — | — |
| Brown | 1 | 10 | 1 | 100 |
| Red | 2 | 100 | 2 | 200 |
| Orange | 3 | 1,000 | 3 | 300 |
| Yellow | 4 | 10,000 | 4 | 400 |
| Green | 5 | 100,000 | 5 | 500 |
| Blue | 6 | 1,000,000 | 6 | 600 |
| Violet | 7 | 10,000,000 | 7 | 700 |
| Gray | 8 | 100,000,000 | 8 | 800 |
| White | 9 | 1,000,000,000 | 9 | 900 |
| Gold | — | 0.1 | 5 | 1,000 |
| Silver | — | 0.01 | 10 | 2,000 |
| No color | — | — | 20 | 500 |

FIG. 17-16    Three different coding systems used with mica capacitors.

**CHIP CAPACITORS**    Before determining the capacitance value of a chip capacitor, make sure it is a capacitor and not a resistor. Chip capacitors have the following identifiable features:

The body is one solid color, such as off-white, beige, gray, tan, or brown. Also, the end electrodes completely enclose the end of the part.

Three popular coding systems are currently being used by the different manufacturers of chip capacitors. In all three systems, the values represented are in picofarads. One system, shown in Fig. 17-17, uses a two-place system in which a letter indicates the first and second digits of the capacitance value and a number indicates the multiplier (0 to 9). Thirty-three symbols are used to represent the two significant figures. The symbols used include 24 uppercase letters and 9 lowercase letters. In Fig. 17-17, note that J3 represents 22,000 pF.

Another system, shown in Fig. 17-18, also uses two places. In this case, however, values below 100 pF are indicated using two numbers from which the capacitance value is read directly. Values above 100 pF are indicated by a letter and a number as before. In this system, only 24 uppercase letters are used. Also note that the alphanumeric codes in this system are 10 times higher than in the system shown in Fig. 17-17.

Figure 17-19 shows yet another system, in which a single letter or number is used to designate the first two digits in the capacitance value. The multiplier is determined by the color of the letter. In the example shown, an orange-colored W represents a capacitance $C$ of 4.7 pF.

| Value (33 Value Symbols)—Upper and Lowercase Letters | | | | | Multiplier |
|---|---|---|---|---|---|
| A-1.0 | H-2.0 | b-3.5 | f-5.0 | X-7.5 | 0 = × 1.0 |
| B-1.1 | J-2.2 | P-3.6 | T-5.1 | t-8.0 | 1 = × 10 |
| C-1.2 | K-2.4 | Q-3.9 | U-5.6 | Y-8.2 | 2 = × 100 |
| D-1.3 | a-2.5 | d-4.0 | m-6.0 | y-9.0 | 3 = × 1,000 |
| E-1.5 | L-2.7 | R-4.3 | V-6.2 | Z-9.1 | 4 = × 10,000 |
| F-1.6 | M-3.0 | e-4.5 | W-6.8 | | 5 = × 100,000 |
| G-1.8 | N-3.3 | S-4.7 | n-7.0 | | etc. |

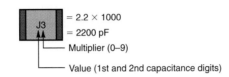

FIG. 17-17 Chip capacitor coding system.

Alternate Two-Place Code
• Values below 100 pF—Value read directly

• Values 100 pF and above—Letter/number code

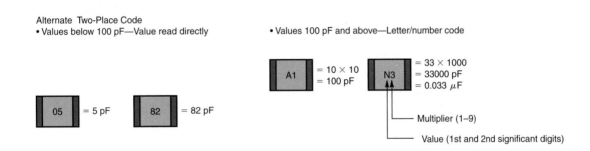

| Value (24 Value Symbols)—Uppercase Letters Only | | | | | Multiplier |
|---|---|---|---|---|---|
| A-10 | F-16 | L-27 | R-43 | W-68 | 1 = × 10 |
| B-11 | G-18 | M-30 | S-47 | X-75 | 2 = × 100 |
| C-12 | H-20 | N-33 | T-51 | Y-82 | 3 = × 1,000 |
| D-13 | J-22 | P-36 | U-56 | Z-91 | 4 = × 10,000 |
| E-15 | K-24 | Q-39 | V-62 | | 5 = × 100,000 etc. |

FIG. 17-18 Chip capacitor coding system.

Standard Single-Place Code

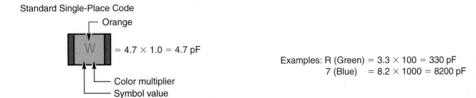

Examples: R (Green) = 3.3 × 100 = 330 pF
7 (Blue) = 8.2 × 1000 = 8200 pF

| Value (24 Value Symbols)—Uppercase Letters and Numerals | | | | | Multiplier (Color) |
|---|---|---|---|---|---|
| A-1.0 | H-1.6 | N-2.7 | V-4.3 | 3-6.8 | Orange = × 1.0 |
| B-1.1 | I-1.8 | O-3.0 | W-4.7 | 4-7.5 | Black = × 10 |
| C-1.2 | J-2.0 | R-3.3 | X-5.1 | 7-8.2 | Green = × 100 |
| D-1.3 | K-2.2 | S-3.6 | Y-5.6 | 9-9.1 | Blue = × 1,000 |
| E-1.5 | L-2.4 | T-3.9 | Z-6.2 | | Violet = × 10,000 |
| | | | | | Red = × 100,000 |

FIG. 17-19 Chip capacitor coding system.

It should be noted that other coding systems are used with chip capacitors; these systems are not covered here. However, the three coding systems shown in this section are the most common systems presently in use.

**TANTALUM CAPACITORS** Tantalum capacitors are frequently coded to indicate their capacitance in picofarads. Figure 17-20 shows how to interpret this system.

Dipped Tantalum Capacitors

| Color | Rated Voltage | Capacitance in Picofarads | | Multiplier |
| | | 1st Figure | 2nd Figure | |
|---|---|---|---|---|
| Black | 4 | 0 | 0 | — |
| Brown | 6 | 1 | 1 | — |
| Red | 10 | 2 | 2 | — |
| Orange | 15 | 3 | 3 | — |
| Yellow | 20 | 4 | 4 | 10,000 |
| Green | 25 | 5 | 5 | 100,000 |
| Blue | 35 | 6 | 6 | 1,000,000 |
| Violet | 50 | 7 | 7 | 10,000,000 |
| Gray | — | 8 | 8 | — |
| White | 3 | 9 | 9 | — |

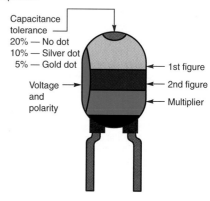

Capacitance
tolerance
20% — No dot
10% — Silver dot
5% — Gold dot

Voltage and polarity

1st figure
2nd figure
Multiplier

**FIG. 17-20** Tantalum capacitor coding system.

## Example

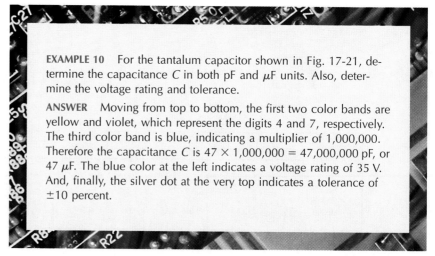

**EXAMPLE 10** For the tantalum capacitor shown in Fig. 17-21, determine the capacitance $C$ in both pF and $\mu$F units. Also, determine the voltage rating and tolerance.

**ANSWER** Moving from top to bottom, the first two color bands are yellow and violet, which represent the digits 4 and 7, respectively. The third color band is blue, indicating a multiplier of 1,000,000. Therefore the capacitance $C$ is 47 × 1,000,000 = 47,000,000 pF, or 47 $\mu$F. The blue color at the left indicates a voltage rating of 35 V. And, finally, the silver dot at the very top indicates a tolerance of ±10 percent.

Silver

Blue

Yellow
Violet
Blue

**FIG. 17-21** Tantalum capacitor for Example 10.

TEST-POINT QUESTION 17-6

Answers at end of chapter.

Answer True or False.
**a.** A disk ceramic capacitor that is marked .01 has a capacitance of 0.01 pF.
**b.** A film capacitor that is marked 224 has a capacitance of 220,000 pF.
**c.** A chip capacitor has a green letter E marked on it. Its capacitance is 150 pF.
**d.** A disk ceramic capacitor is marked .001P. Its tolerance is +100 percent, 0 percent.

# 17-7 PARALLEL CAPACITANCES

Connecting capacitances in parallel is equivalent to adding the plate areas. Therefore, the total capacitance is the sum of the individual capacitances. As illustrated in Fig. 17-22,

▶ $$C_T = C_1 + C_2 + \cdots + \text{etc.}$$ **(17-5)**

A 10-$\mu$F capacitor in parallel with a 5-$\mu$F capacitor, for example, provides a 15-$\mu$F capacitance for the parallel combination. The voltage is the same across the parallel capacitors. Note that adding parallel capacitances is opposite to the case of inductances in parallel, and resistances in parallel.

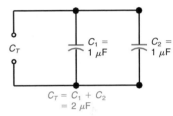

$$C_T = C_1 + C_2 = 2\ \mu\text{F}$$

**FIG. 17-22** Capacitances in parallel.

TEST-POINT QUESTION 17-7

Answers at end of chapter.
**a.** How much is $C_T$ for 0.01 $\mu$F in parallel with 0.02 $\mu$F?
**b.** What $C$ must be connected in parallel with 100 pF to make $C_T$ of 250 pF?

# 17-8 SERIES CAPACITANCES

Connecting capacitances in series is equivalent to increasing the thickness of the dielectric. Therefore, the combined capacitance is less than the smallest individual value. As shown in Fig. 17-23, the combined equivalent capacitance is calculated by the reciprocal formula:

▶ $$\frac{1}{C_{EQ}} = \frac{1}{C_1} + \frac{1}{C_2} + \cdots + \text{etc.}$$ **(17-6)**

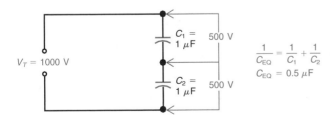

$$\frac{1}{C_{EQ}} = \frac{1}{C_1} + \frac{1}{C_2}$$
$$C_{EQ} = 0.5\ \mu\text{F}$$

**FIG. 17-23** Capacitances in series.

Any of the short-cut calculations for the reciprocal formula apply. For example, the combined capacitance of two equal capacitances of 10 $\mu$F in series is 5 $\mu$F.

Capacitors are used in series to provide a higher working voltage rating for the combination. For instance, each of three equal capacitances in series has one-third the applied voltage.

**DIVISION OF VOLTAGE ACROSS UNEQUAL CAPACITANCES**   In series, the voltage across each $C$ is inversely proportional to its capacitance, as illustrated in Fig. 17-24. The smaller capacitance has the larger proportion of the applied voltage. The reason is that the series capacitances all have the same charge because they are in one current path. With equal charge, a smaller capacitance has a greater potential difference.

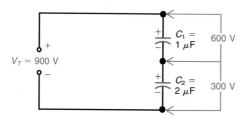

**FIG. 17-24**   With series capacitors, the smaller $C$ has more voltage for the same charge.

We can consider the amount of charge in the series capacitors in Fig. 17-24. Let the charging current be 600 $\mu$A flowing for 1 s. The charge $Q$ equals $I \times t$ or 600 $\mu$C. Both $C_1$ and $C_2$ have $Q$ equal to 600 $\mu$C, as they are in the same series path for charging current.

Although the charge is the same in $C_1$ and $C_2$, they have different voltages because of different capacitance values. For each capacitor $V = Q/C$. For the two capacitors in Fig. 17-24, then:

$$\blacktriangleright \quad V_1 = \frac{Q}{C_1} = \frac{600 \ \mu C}{1 \ \mu F} = 600 \text{ V}$$

$$V_2 = \frac{Q}{C_2} = \frac{600 \ \mu F}{2 \ \mu F} = 300 \text{ V}$$

**CHARGING CURRENT FOR SERIES CAPACITANCES**   The charging current is the same in all parts of the series path, including the junction between $C_1$ and $C_2$, even though this point is separated from the source voltage by two insulators. At the junction, the current is the resultant of electrons repelled by the negative plate of $C_2$ and attracted by the positive plate of $C_1$. The amount of current in the circuit is determined by the equivalent capacitance of $C_1$ and $C_2$ in series. In Fig. 17-24, the equivalent capacitance is $\frac{2}{3}$ $\mu$F.

---

### TEST-POINT QUESTION 17-8

Answers at end of chapter.
**a.** How much is $C_{EQ}$ for two 0.2-$\mu$F capacitors in series?
**b.** With 50 V applied across both, how much is $V_C$ across each capacitor?
**c.** How much is $C_{EQ}$ for 100 pF in series with 50 pF?

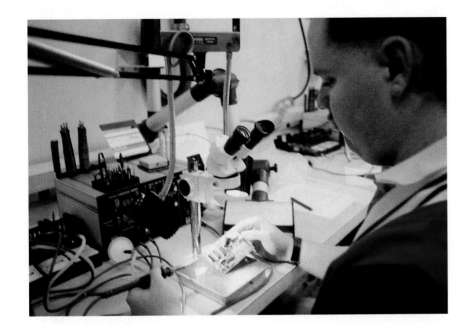

The study of surface-mount technology is on the rise at technical institutes. Here a student at Texas State Technical College in Harlingen, Texas, uses surface-mount laboratory equipment manufactured by PACE Inc.

# 17-9 STRAY CAPACITIVE AND INDUCTIVE EFFECTS

Stray capacitive and inductive effects can occur in all circuits with all types of components. A capacitor has a small amount of inductance in the conductors. A coil has some capacitance between windings. A resistor has a small amount of inductance and capacitance. After all, a capacitance physically is simply an insulator between two conductors having a difference of potential. An inductance is basically just a conductor carrying current.

Actually, though, these stray effects are usually quite small, compared with the concentrated or lumped values of capacitance and inductance. Typical values of stray capacitance may be 1 to 10 pF, while stray inductance is usually a fraction of 1 $\mu$H. For very high radio frequencies, however, when small values of $L$ and $C$ must be used, the stray effects become important. As another example, any wire cable has capacitance between the conductors.

A practical case of problems caused by stray $L$ and $C$ is the example of a long cable used for RF signals. If the cable is rolled in a coil to save space, a serious change in the electrical characteristics of the line will take place. Specifically, for twin-lead or coaxial cable feeding the antenna input to a television receiver, the line should not be coiled, as the added $L$ or $C$ can affect the signal. Any excess line should be cut off, leaving just the little slack that may be needed. This precaution is not so important with audio cables.

**STRAY CIRCUIT CAPACITANCE**  The wiring and the components in a circuit have capacitance to the metal chassis. This stray capacitance $C_S$ is typically 5 to 10 pF. To reduce $C_S$, the wiring should be short, with the leads and components placed high off the chassis. Sometimes, for very high frequencies, the stray capacitance is included as part of the circuit design. Then changing the

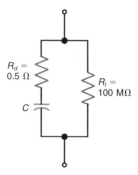

**FIG. 17-25** Equivalent circuit of a capacitor; $R_l$ is leakage resistance and $R_d$ is absorption loss dissipated in dielectric.

placement of components or wiring affects the circuit operation. Such critical *lead dress* is usually specified in the manufacturer's service notes.

**LEAKAGE RESISTANCE OF A CAPACITOR**    Consider a capacitor charged by a dc voltage source. After the charging voltage is removed, a perfect capacitor would keep its charge indefinitely. Because there is no perfect insulator, after a long period of time, however, the charge will be neutralized by a small leakage current through the dielectric and across the insulated case between terminals. For paper, ceramic, and mica capacitors, though, the leakage current is very slight or, inversely, the leakage resistance is very high. As shown in Fig. 17-25, the leakage resistance $R_l$ is indicated by a high resistance in parallel with the capacitance $C$. For paper, ceramic, or mica capacitors $R_l$ is 100 MΩ or more. However, electrolytic capacitors may have a leakage resistance which is much less.

**ABSORPTION LOSSES IN CAPACITORS**    With ac voltage applied to a capacitor, the continuous charge, discharge, and reverse charging action cannot be followed instantaneously in the dielectric. This corresponds to hysteresis in magnetic materials. With a high-frequency charging voltage applied to the capacitor, there may be a difference between the amount of ac voltage applied and the ac voltage stored in the dielectric. The difference can be considered *absorption loss* in the dielectric. With higher frequencies, the losses increase. In Fig. 17-25, the small value of 0.5 Ω for $R_d$ indicates a typical value for paper capacitors. For ceramic and mica capacitors, the dielectric losses are even smaller. These losses need not be considered for electrolytic capacitors because they are generally not used for radio frequencies.

**POWER FACTOR OF A CAPACITOR**    The quality of a capacitor in terms of minimum loss is often indicated by its power factor. The lower the numerical value of the power factor, the better is the quality of the capacitor. Since the losses are in the dielectric, the power factor of the capacitor is essentially the power factor of the dielectric, independent of capacitance value or voltage rating. At radio frequencies, approximate values of power factor are 0.000 for air or vacuum, 0.0004 for mica, about 0.01 for paper, and 0.0001 to 0.03 for ceramics.

The reciprocal of the power factor can be considered the $Q$ of the capacitor, similar to the idea of $Q$ of a coil. For instance, a power factor of 0.001 corresponds to a $Q$ of 1000. A higher $Q$ therefore means better quality for the capacitor.

**INDUCTANCE OF A CAPACITOR**    Capacitors with a coiled construction, particularly paper and electrolytic capacitors, have some internal inductance. The larger the capacitor, the greater is its series inductance. Mica and ceramic capacitors have very little inductance, however, which is why they are generally used for radio frequencies.

For use above audio frequencies, the rolled-foil type of capacitor must have a noninductive construction. This means the start and finish of the foil winding must not be the terminals of the capacitor. Instead, the foil windings are offset. Then one terminal can contact all layers of one foil at one edge, while the opposite edge of the other foil contacts the second terminal. Most rolled-foil capacitors, including the paper and film types, are constructed this way.

**DISTRIBUTED CAPACITANCE OF A COIL**   As illustrated in Fig. 17-26, a coil has distributed capacitance $C_d$ between turns. Note that each turn is a conductor separated from the next turn by an insulator, which is the definition of capacitance. Furthermore, the potential of each turn is different from the next, providing part of the total voltage as a potential difference to charge $C_d$. The result then is the equivalent circuit shown for an RF coil. The $L$ is the inductance and $R_e$ its internal effective ac resistance in series with $L$, while the total distributed capacitance $C_d$ for all the turns is across the entire coil.

Special methods for minimum $C_d$ include *space-wound* coils, where the turns are spaced far apart; the honeycomb or *universal* winding, with the turns crossing each other at right angles; and the *bank winding,* with separate sections called *pies.* These windings are for RF coils. In audio and power transformers, a grounded conductor shield, called a *Faraday screen,* is often placed between windings to reduce capacitive coupling.

**REACTIVE EFFECTS IN RESISTORS**   As illustrated by the high-frequency equivalent circuit in Fig. 17-27, a resistor can include a small amount of inductance and capacitance. For carbon-composition resistors, the inductance is usually negligible. However, approximately 0.5 pF of capacitance across the ends may have an effect, particularly with large resistances used for high radio frequencies. Wire-wound resistors definitely have enough inductance to be evident at radio frequencies. However, special resistors are available with double windings in a noninductive method based on cancellation of opposing magnetic fields.

**CAPACITANCE OF AN OPEN CIRCUIT**   An open switch or a break in a conducting wire has capacitance $C_O$ across the open. The reason is that the open consists of an insulator between two conductors. With a voltage source in the circuit, $C_O$ charges to the applied voltage. Because of the small $C_O$, in the order of picofarads, the capacitance charges to the source voltage in a short time. This charging of $C_O$ is the reason why an open series circuit has the applied voltage across the open terminals. After a momentary flow of charging current, $C_O$ charges to the applied voltage and stores the charge needed to maintain this voltage.

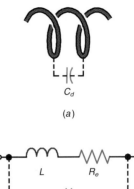

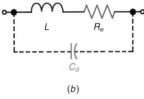

**FIG. 17-26**   Equivalent circuit of an RF coil. (*a*) Distributed capacitance $C_d$ between turns of wire. (*b*) Equivalent circuit.

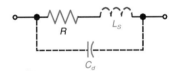

**FIG. 17-27**   High-frequency equivalent circuit of a resistor.

---

**TEST-POINT QUESTION 17-9**

Answers at end of chapter.

Answer True or False.
**a.** A two-wire cable has distributed $C$ between the conductors.
**b.** A coil has distributed $C$ between the turns.
**c.** The leakage resistance of ceramic capacitors is very high.

# 17-10 ENERGY IN ELECTROSTATIC FIELD OF CAPACITANCE

The electrostatic field of the charge stored in the dielectric has electric energy supplied by the voltage source that charges $C$. This energy is stored in the dielectric. The proof is the fact that the capacitance can produce discharge current when the voltage source is removed. The electric energy stored is

▶ Energy = $\mathcal{E}$ = ½ $CV^2$     joules     (17-7)

where $C$ is the capacitance in farads and $V$ is the voltage across the capacitor, and $\mathcal{E}$ is the electric energy in joules. For example, a 1-$\mu$F capacitor charged to 400 V has stored energy equal to

$$\mathcal{E} = \frac{1}{2}\,CV^2 = \frac{1 \times 10^{-6} \times (4 \times 10^2)^2}{2}$$

$$= \frac{1 \times 10^{-6} \times (16 \times 10^4)}{2} = 8 \times 10^{-2}$$

$$\mathcal{E} = 0.08 \text{ J}$$

This 0.08 J of energy is supplied by the voltage source that charges the capacitor to 400 V. When the charging circuit is opened, the stored energy remains as charge in the dielectric. With a closed path provided for discharge, the entire 0.08 J is available to produce discharge current. As the capacitor discharges, the energy is used in producing discharge current. When the capacitor is completely discharged, the stored energy is zero.

The stored energy is the reason why a charged capacitor can produce an electric shock, even when not connected into a circuit. When you touch the two leads of the charged capacitor, its voltage produces discharge current through your body. Stored energy greater than 1 J can be dangerous with a capacitor charged to a voltage high enough to produce an electric shock.

## Example

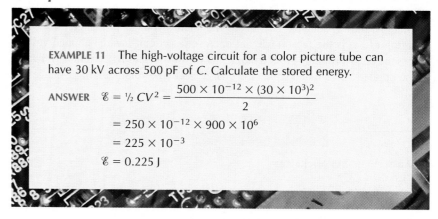

EXAMPLE 11    The high-voltage circuit for a color picture tube can have 30 kV across 500 pF of $C$. Calculate the stored energy.

ANSWER   $\mathcal{E} = \frac{1}{2}\,CV^2 = \dfrac{500 \times 10^{-12} \times (30 \times 10^3)^2}{2}$

$= 250 \times 10^{-12} \times 900 \times 10^6$

$= 225 \times 10^{-3}$

$\mathcal{E} = 0.225$ J

Notice that the energy is less, even with 30 kV, because $C$ is so small.

--- **TEST-POINT QUESTION 17-10** ---

Answers at end of chapter.

Answer True or False.
**a.** The stored energy in $C$ increases with more $V$.
**b.** The stored energy decreases with less $C$.

# 17-11 TROUBLES IN CAPACITORS

Capacitors can become open or short-circuited. In either case, the capacitor is useless because it cannot store charge. A leaky capacitor is equivalent to a partial short circuit where the dielectric gradually loses its insulating properties under the stress of applied voltage, lowering its resistance. A good capacitor has very high resistance of the order of megohms; a short-circuited capacitor has zero ohms resistance, or continuity; the resistance of a leaky capacitor is lower than normal.

**CHECKING CAPACITORS WITH AN OHMMETER**   A capacitor usually can be checked with an ohmmeter. The highest ohms range, such as $R \times$ 1 M$\Omega$, is preferable. Also, disconnect one side of the capacitor from the circuit to eliminate any parallel resistance paths that can lower the resistance. Keep your fingers off the connections, since the body resistance lowers the reading.

As illustrated in Fig. 17-28, the ohmmeter leads are connected across the capacitor. For a good capacitor, the meter pointer moves quickly toward the low-resistance side of the scale and then slowly recedes toward infinity. The reading when the pointer stops moving is the insulation resistance of the capacitor, which is normally very high. For paper, mica, and ceramic capacitors, the resistance can be 500 to 1000 M$\Omega$, or more, which is practically infinite resistance. However, electrolytic capacitors will usually measure a much lower resistance of about 500 k$\Omega$ to 10 M$\Omega$. In all cases, discharge the capacitor before checking with the ohmmeter.

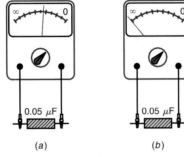

(a)                    (b)

**FIG. 17-28**   Checking a capacitor with an ohmmeter. The $R$ scale is shown right to left, as on a VOM. Use the highest ohms range. (a) Capacitor action as needle is moved by the charging current from the battery in the ohmmeter. (b) Practically infinite leakage resistance reading after the capacitor has been charged.

When the ohmmeter is initially connected, its battery charges the capacitor. This charging current is the reason the meter pointer moves away from infinity, since more current through the ohmmeter means less resistance. Maximum current flows at the first instant of charge. Then the charging current decreases as the capacitor voltage increases toward the applied voltage; therefore, the needle pointer slowly moves toward infinite resistance. Finally, the capacitor is completely charged to the ohmmeter battery voltage, the charging current is zero, and the ohmmeter reads just the small leakage current through the dielectric. This charging effect, called *capacitor action,* shows that the capacitor can store charge, indicating a normal capacitor. It should be noted that both the rise and fall of the

**DID YOU KNOW?**

Flashes far above storm clouds are caused by nitrogen molecules becoming agitated by electron collisions. During the process, lightning sends pulses of energy upward and causes slower changes in the atmosphere's electric field.

meter readings are caused by charging. The capacitor discharges when the meter leads are reversed.

**OHMMETER READINGS** Troubles in a capacitor are indicated as follows:

1. If an ohmmeter reading immediately goes practically to zero and stays there, the capacitor is short-circuited.
2. If the capacitor shows charging, but the final resistance reading is appreciably less than normal, the capacitor is leaky. Such capacitors are particularly troublesome in high-resistance circuits. When checking electrolytics, reverse the ohmmeter leads and take the higher of the two readings.
3. If the capacitor shows no charging action but just reads very high resistance, it may be open. Some precautions must be remembered, however, since very high resistance is a normal condition for capacitors. Reverse the ohmmeter leads to discharge the capacitor, and check it again. In addition, remember that capacitance values of 100 pF, or less, normally have very little charging current for the low battery voltage of the ohmmeter.

**SHORT-CIRCUITED CAPACITORS** In normal service, capacitors can become short-circuited because the dielectric deteriorates with age, usually over a period of years under the stress of charging voltage, especially with higher temperatures. This effect is more common with paper and electrolytic capacitors. The capacitor may become leaky gradually, indicating a partial short circuit, or the dielectric may be punctured, causing a short circuit.

**OPEN CAPACITORS** In addition to the possibility of an open connection in any type of capacitor, electrolytics develop high resistance in the electrolyte with age, particularly at high temperatures. After service of a few years, if the electrolyte dries up, the capacitor will be partially open. Much of the capacitor action is gone, and the capacitor should be replaced.

**LEAKY CAPACITORS** A leaky capacitor reads $R$ less than normal with an ohmmeter. However, dc voltage tests are more definite. In a circuit, the dc voltage at one terminal of the capacitor should not affect the dc voltage at the other terminal.

**SHELF LIFE** Except for electrolytics, capacitors do not deteriorate with age while stored, since there is no applied voltage. Electrolytic capacitors, however, like dry cells, should be used fresh from manufacture. The reason is the wet electrolyte may dry out over a period of time.

**CAPACITOR VALUE CHANGE** All capacitors can change value over time, but some are more prone to change than others. Ceramic capacitors often change value by 10 to 15 percent over the first year, as the ceramic material relaxes. Electrolytics change value from simply sitting, because the electrolytic solution dries out.

**REPLACEMENT CAPACITORS**    Approximately the same $C$ and $V$ ratings should be used when installing a new capacitor. Except for tuning capacitors, the $C$ value is not critical. In most applications the tolerance of capacitors is $-20$ to $+50$ percent. Also, a higher voltage rating can be used. An important exception, however, is the electrolytic capacitor. Then the ratings should be close to the original values for two reasons. First, the specified voltage is needed to form the internal oxide film that provides the required capacitance. Also, too much $C$ may allow excessive charging current in the circuit that charges the capacitor. Remember that electrolytics generally have large values of capacitance.

---

### TEST-POINT QUESTION 17-11

Answers at end of chapter.
a. What is the ohmmeter reading for a shorted capacitor?
b. Does capacitor action with an ohmmeter show the capacitor is good or bad?
c. Which type of capacitor is more likely to develop trouble, mica or electrolytic?

# 17 SUMMARY AND REVIEW

- A capacitor consists of two conductors separated by an insulator, or dielectric. Its ability to store charge is the capacitance $C$. Applying voltage to store charge is called charging the capacitor; short-circuiting the two leads or terminals of the capacitor to neutralize the charge is called discharging the capacitor. Schematic symbols for $C$ are summarized in Fig. 17-29.

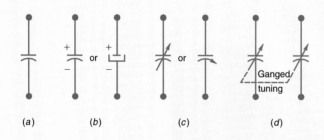

FIG. 17-29    Schematic symbols for types of $C$. (a) Fixed type with air, paper, plastic film, mica, or ceramic dielectric. (b) Electrolytic type, which has polarity. (c) Variable. (d) Ganged variable capacitors on one shaft.

- The unit of capacitance is the farad. One farad of capacitance stores one coulomb of charge with one volt applied. Practical capacitors have much smaller capacitance values, from 1 pF to 1000 $\mu$F. A capacitance of 1 pF is $1 \times 10^{-12}$ F; 1 $\mu$F $= 1 \times 10^{-6}$ F; and 1 nF $= 1 \times 10^{-9}$ F.
- $Q = CV$, where $Q$ is the charge in coulombs, $C$ the capacitance in farads, and $V$ is the potential difference across the capacitor in volts.
- Capacitance increases with larger plate area and less distance between the plates.
- The ratio of charge stored in different insulators to the charge stored in air is the dielectric constant $K_\epsilon$ of the material. Air or vacuum has a dielectric constant of 1.
- The most common types of commercial capacitors are air, plastic film, paper, mica, ceramic, and electrolytic. Electrolytics are the only capacitors that require observing polarity when connecting to a circuit. The different types are compared in Table 17-2.
- Capacitors are coded to indicate their capacitance, in either microfarads ($\mu$F) or picofarads (pF).
- For parallel capacitors, $C_T = C_1 + C_2 + C_3 + \cdots +$ etc.
- For series capacitors, $1/C_{EQ} = 1/C_1 + 1/C_2 + 1/C_3 + \cdots +$ etc.
- The electric field of a capacitance has stored energy $\mathscr{E} = \frac{1}{2} CV^2$, where $V$ is volts, $C$ is in farads, and the electric energy is in joules.
- When checked with an ohmmeter, a good capacitor shows charging current, and then the ohmmeter reading steadies at the insulation resistance. All types except electrolytics normally have a very high insulation resistance of 500 to 1000 M$\Omega$. Electrolytics have more leakage current, with a typical resistance of about 500 k$\Omega$ to 10 M$\Omega$.

**ANSWERS AT BACK OF BOOK.**

Choose (*a*), (*b*), (*c*), or (*d*).

1. A capacitor consists of two (*a*) conductors separated by an insulator; (*b*) insulators separated by a conductor; (*c*) conductors alone; (*d*) insulators alone.
2. A capacitance of 0.02 $\mu$F equals (*a*) $0.02 \times 10^{-12}$ F; (*b*) $0.02 \times 10^{-6}$ F; (*c*) $0.02 \times 10^{6}$ F; (*d*) $200 \times 10^{-12}$ F.
3. A 10-$\mu$F capacitance charged to 10 V has a stored charge equal to (*a*) 10 $\mu$C; (*b*) 100 $\mu$C; (*c*) 200 $\mu$C; (*d*) 1 C.
4. Capacitance increases with (*a*) larger plate area and greater distance between plates; (*b*) smaller plate area and less distance between plates; (*c*) larger plate area and less distance between plates; (*d*) higher values of applied voltage.
5. Which of the following statements is correct? (*a*) Air capacitors have a black band to indicate the outside foil. (*b*) Mica capacitors are available in capacitance values of 1 to 10 $\mu$F. (*c*) Electrolytic capacitors must be connected in the correct polarity. (*d*) Ceramic capacitors must be connected in the correct polarity.
6. Voltage applied across a ceramic dielectric produces an electrostatic field 100 times greater than in air. The dielectric constant $K_\epsilon$ of the ceramic equals (*a*) 33⅓; (*b*) 50; (*c*) 100; (*d*) 10,000.
7. A six-dot mica capacitor color-coded white, red, green, brown, red, and yellow has the capacitance value of (*a*) 25 pF; (*b*) 124 pF; (*c*) 250 pF; (*d*) 925 pF.
8. The combination of two 0.02-$\mu$F 500-V capacitors in series has a capacitance and a working voltage rating of (*a*) 0.01 $\mu$F, 500 V; (*b*) 0.01 $\mu$F, 1000 V; (*c*) 0.02 $\mu$F, 500 V; (*d*) 0.04 $\mu$F, 500 V.
9. The combination of two 0.02-$\mu$F 500-V capacitors in parallel has a capacitance and a working voltage rating of (*a*) 0.01 $\mu$F, 1000 V; (*b*) 0.02 $\mu$F, 500 V; (*c*) 0.04 $\mu$F, 500 V; (*d*) 0.04 $\mu$F, 1000 V.
10. For a good 0.05-$\mu$F paper capacitor, the ohmmeter reading should (*a*) go quickly to 100 $\Omega$, approximately, and remain there; (*b*) show low resistance momentarily and back off to a very high resistance; (*c*) show high resistance momentarily and then a very low resistance; (*d*) not move at all.

## QUESTIONS

1. Define capacitance with respect to physical structure and electrical function. Explain how a two-wire conductor has capacitance.
2. **(a)** What is meant by a dielectric material? **(b)** Name five common dielectric materials. **(c)** Define dielectric flux.
3. Explain briefly how to charge a capacitor. How is a charged capacitor discharged?
4. Define 1 F of capacitance. Convert the following into farads using powers of 10: **(a)** 50 pF; **(b)** 0.001 $\mu$F; **(c)** 0.047 $\mu$F; **(d)** 0.01 $\mu$F; **(e)** 10 $\mu$F.

5. State the effect on capacitance of (a) larger plate area; (b) thinner dielectric; (c) higher value of dielectric constant.

6. Give one reason for your choice of the type of capacitor to be used in the following applications: (a) 80-$\mu$F capacitance for a circuit where one side is positive and the applied voltage never exceeds 150 V; (b) 1.5-pF capacitance for an RF circuit where the required voltage rating is less than 500 V; (c) 5-$\mu$F capacitance for an audio circuit where the required voltage rating is less than 25 V.

7. Give the capacitance value of six-dot mica capacitors color-coded as follows: (a) Black, red, green, brown, black, black. (b) White, green, brown, black, silver, brown. (c) Brown, green, black, red, gold, blue.

8. Draw a diagram showing the least number of 400-V 2-$\mu$F capacitors needed for a combination rated at 800 V with 2 $\mu$F total capacitance.

9. Suppose you are given two identical uncharged capacitors. One is charged to 50 V and connected across the uncharged capacitor. Why will the voltage across both capacitors then be 25 V?

10. Describe briefly how you would check a 0.05-$\mu$F capacitor with an ohmmeter. State the ohmmeter indications for the case of the capacitor being good, short-circuited, or open.

11. Define the following: (a) stray circuit capacitance; (b) distributed capacitance of a coil; (c) leakage resistance of a capacitor; (d) power factor and $Q$ of a capacitor.

12. Give two comparisons between the electric field in a capacitor and the magnetic field in a coil.

13. Give three types of troubles in capacitors.

14. When a capacitor discharges, why is its discharge current in the opposite direction from the charging current?

15. Compare the features of aluminum and tantalum electrolytic capacitors.

16. Why can plastic film be used instead of paper for capacitors?

17. What two factors determine the breakdown voltage rating of a capacitor?

## PROBLEMS

### ANSWERS TO ODD-NUMBERED PROBLEMS AT BACK OF BOOK.

1. How much charge in coulombs is in a 4-$\mu$F capacitor charged to 100 V?

2. A 4-$\mu$F capacitor has 400 $\mu$C of charge. (a) How much voltage is across the capacitor? (b) How much is the voltage across an 8-$\mu$F capacitor with the same 400-$\mu$C charge?

3. A 2-$\mu$F capacitor is charged by a constant 3-$\mu$A charging current for 6 s. (a) How much charge is stored in the capacitor? (b) How much is the voltage across the capacitor?

4. A 1-$\mu$F capacitor $C_1$ and a 10-$\mu$F capacitor $C_2$ are in series with a constant 2-mA charging current. (a) After 4 s, how much charge is in $C_1$ and in $C_2$? (b) How much is the voltage across capacitor $C_1$ and across capacitor $C_2$?

5. Calculate $C$ for a mica capacitor, with $K_\epsilon = 8$, a thickness of 0.02 cm, plates of 6 cm$^2$, and five sections in parallel. (Hint: 1 cm $= 10^{-2}$ m and 1 cm$^2 = 10^{-4}$ m$^2$.)

6. How much capacitance stores 6000 $\mu$C of charge with 150 V applied? The charge of how many electrons is stored? What type of capacitor is this most likely to be?

7. With 100 V across a capacitor, it stores 100 $\mu$C of charge. Then the applied voltage is doubled to 200 V. (a) How much is the voltage across the capacitor? (b) How much charge is stored? (c) How much is its capacitance?

8. Referring to the parallel capacitors in Fig. 17-22, calculate the charge $Q_1$ in $C_1$ and $Q_2$ in $C_2$ with 50 V. How much is the total charge $Q_T$ in both capacitors? Calculate the total capacitance $C_T$ as $Q_T/V$.

9. Calculate the energy in joules stored in (a) a 500-pF capacitor charged to 10 kV; (b) a 1-$\mu$F capacitor charged to 5 kV; (c) a 40-$\mu$F capacitor charged to 400 V.

10. Three capacitors are in series. $C_1$ is 100 pF, $C_2$ is 100 pF, and $C_3$ is 50 pF. Calculate $C_{EQ}$.

11. Calculate $C_T$ for the series-parallel combination of capacitors in Figs. 17-30a and 17-30b.

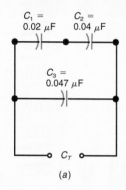

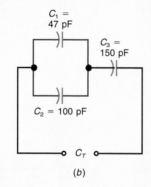

FIG. 17-30   Circuit diagrams for Probs. 11, 13, and 14.

12. What $C$ must be connected in series with 0.47 $\mu$F for an equivalent capacitance of 0.02 $\mu$F? (Hint: Use formulas for parallel $R$).

13. In Fig. 17-30a: (a) Change $C_3$ to 10 pF, and calculate $C_T$ in $\mu$F units; (b) change $C_2$ to 10 pF and calculate $C_T$.

14. In Fig. 17-30b: (a) Change $C_3$ to 100 pF, and calculate $C_T$ in pF units; (b) change $C_1$ to 100 pF and calculate $C_T$ in pF units.

15. Determine the capacitance and tolerance for the capacitors shown in Fig. 17-31.

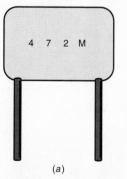

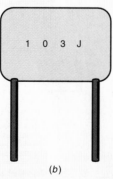

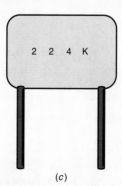

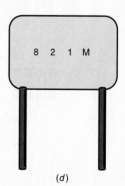

FIG. 17-31   Film and disk ceramic capacitors for Prob. 15. (*continues on next page*)

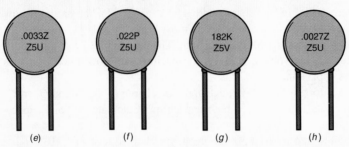

FIG. 17-31 *(continued)* Film and disk ceramic capacitors for Prob. 15.

**16.** Determine the capacitance of each chip capacitor shown in Fig. 17-32. Use the coding system shown in Fig. 17-17.

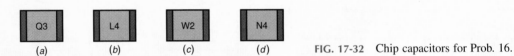

FIG. 17-32 Chip capacitors for Prob. 16.

**17.** Determine the capacitance for each chip capacitor shown in Fig. 17-33. Use the coding system shown in Fig. 17-18.

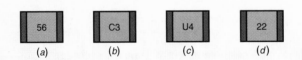

FIG. 17-33 Chip capacitors for Prob. 17.

**18.** Determine the capacitance for each chip capacitor in Fig. 17-34.

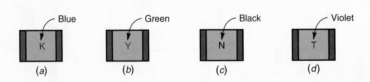

FIG. 17-34 Chip capacitors for Prob. 18.

**19.** Determine the capacitance for each tantalum capacitor in Fig. 17-35.
**20.** Calculate the permissible capacitance range at 25°C for the disk ceramic capacitor in Fig. 17-31e.

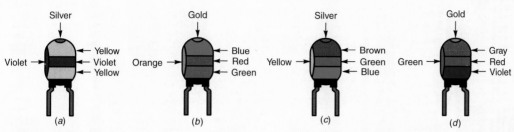

**FIG. 17-35** Tantalum capacitors for Prob. 19.

## CRITICAL THINKING

1. Three capacitors in series have a combined equivalent capacitance, $C_{EQ}$, of 1.6 nF. If $C_1 = 4C_2$ and $C_3 = 20C_1$, calculate the values for $C_1$, $C_2$, and $C_3$.

2. A 100-pF ceramic capacitor has a temperature coefficient $T_C$ of N500. Calculate its capacitance at: (**a**) 75°C; (**b**) 125°C; (**c**) −25°C.

3. (**a**) Calculate the energy stored by a 100-$\mu$F capacitor charged to 100 V. (**b**) If this capacitor is now connected across another 100-$\mu$F capacitor which is uncharged, calculate the total energy stored by both capacitors. (**c**) Is the energy stored by both capacitors in part (**b**) less than the energy stored by the single capacitor in part (**a**)? If yes, where did the energy go?

## ANSWERS TO TEST-POINT QUESTIONS

| | | | | | | | | |
|---|---|---|---|---|---|---|---|---|
| **17-1** | **a.** dielectric | **17-4** | **a.** T | **17-6** | **a.** F | **17-9** | **a.** T | |
| | **b.** farad | | **b.** F | | **b.** T | | **b.** T | |
| **17-2** | **a.** 14.5 V | | **c.** T | | **c.** T | | **c.** T | |
| | **b.** 0 V | | **d.** T | | **d.** T | **17-10** | **a.** T | |
| | **c.** Yes | **17-5** | **a.** T | **17-7** | **a.** 0.03 $\mu$F | | **b.** T | |
| **17-3** | **a.** 10 $\mu$F | | **b.** T | | **b.** 150 pF | **17-11** | **a.** 0 $\Omega$ | |
| | **b.** ceramic | | **c.** T | **17-8** | **a.** 0.1 $\mu$F | | **b.** good | |
| | | | | | **b.** 25 V | | **c.** electrolytic | |
| | | | | | **c.** 33.3 pF | | | |

# CHAPTER 18

# CAPACITIVE REACTANCE

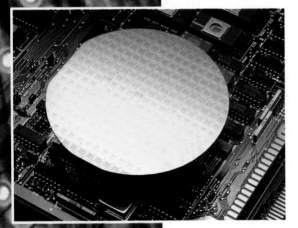

When a capacitor charges and discharges with a varying voltage applied, alternating current can flow. Although there cannot be any current through the dielectric of the capacitor, its charge and discharge produces alternating current in the circuit connected to the capacitor plates. The amount of $I$ that results from the applied sine-wave $V$ depends on the capacitor's capacitive reactance. The symbol for capacitive reactance is $X_C$ and its unit is the ohm. The $X$ in $X_C$ indicates reactance, whereas the subscript $C$ specifies capacitive reactance.

The amount of $X_C$ is a $V/I$ ratio but it can also be calculated as $X_C = 1/(2\pi f C)$ in terms of the value of the capacitance and the frequency of the varying $V$ and $I$. With $f$ and $C$ in the basic units of the hertz and farad, the $X_C$ is in the basic units of ohms. The reciprocal relation in $1/(2\pi f C)$ means that the ohms of $X_C$ decrease for higher frequencies and with more $C$. The reason is that more charge and discharge current results either with more capacitance or faster changes in the applied voltage.

# CHAPTER OBJECTIVES

*Upon completion of this chapter, you should be able to:*

- *Explain* how alternating current can flow in a capacitive circuit.
- *Calculate* the reactance of a capacitor when the frequency and capacitance are known.
- *Calculate* the total capacitive reactance of series connected capacitors.
- *Calculate* the equivalent capacitive reactance of parallel connected capacitors.
- *Explain* how Ohm's law can be applied to capacitive reactance.
- *Calculate* the capacitive current when the capacitance and rate of voltage change are known.

# IMPORTANT TERMS IN THIS CHAPTER

| | | |
|---|---|---|
| capacitive reactance | discharge current | phase angle |
| charge current | inverse relation | series capacitance |
| dc blocking | parallel capacitance | |

# TOPICS COVERED IN THIS CHAPTER

**18-1** Alternating Current in a Capacitive Circuit

**18-2** The Amount of $X_C$ Equals $1/(2\pi fC)$

**18-3** Series or Parallel Capacitive Reactances

**18-4** Ohm's Law Applied to $X_C$

**18-5** Applications of Capacitive Reactance

**18-6** Sine-Wave Charge and Discharge Current

## 18-1 ALTERNATING CURRENT IN A CAPACITIVE CIRCUIT

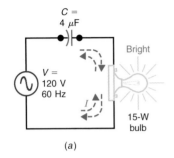

(a)

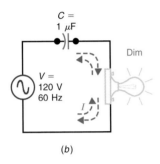

(b)

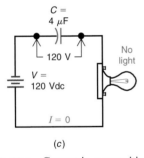

(c)

**FIG. 18-1** Current in a capacitive circuit. (*a*) The 4-$\mu$F capacitor allows enough current *I* to light the bulb brightly. (*b*) Less current with smaller capacitor causes dim light. (*c*) Bulb cannot light with dc voltage applied because a capacitor blocks the direct current.

The fact that current flows with ac voltage applied is demonstrated in Fig. 18-1, where the bulb lights in Fig. 18-1*a* and *b* because of the capacitor charge and discharge current. There is no current through the dielectric, which is an insulator. While the capacitor is being charged by increasing applied voltage, however, the charging current flows in one direction in the conductors to the plates. While the capacitor is discharging, when the applied voltage decreases, the discharge current flows in the reverse direction. With alternating voltage applied, the capacitor alternately charges and discharges.

First the capacitor is charged in one polarity, and then it discharges; next the capacitor is charged in the opposite polarity, and then it discharges again. The cycles of charge and discharge current provide alternating current in the circuit, at the same frequency as the applied voltage. This is the current that lights the bulb.

In Fig. 18-1*a*, the 4-$\mu$F capacitor provides enough alternating current to light the bulb brightly. In Fig. 18-1*b*, the 1-$\mu$F capacitor has less charge and discharge current because of the smaller capacitance, and the light is not so bright. Therefore, the smaller capacitor has more opposition to alternating current as less current flows with the same applied voltage; that is, it has more reactance for less capacitance.

In Fig. 18-1*c*, the steady dc voltage will charge the capacitor to 120 V. Because the applied voltage does not change, though, the capacitor will just stay charged. Since the potential difference of 120 V across the charged capacitor is a voltage drop opposing the applied voltage, no current can flow. Therefore, the bulb cannot light. The bulb may flicker on for an instant as charging current flows when voltage is applied, but this current is only temporary until the capacitor is charged. Then the capacitor has the applied voltage of 120 V, but there is zero voltage across the bulb.

As a result, the capacitor is said to *block* direct current or voltage. In other words, after the capacitor has been charged by a steady dc voltage, there is no current in the dc circuit. All the applied dc voltage is across the charged capacitor, with zero voltage across any series resistance.

In summary, then, this demonstration shows the following points:

1. Alternating current flows in a capacitive circuit with ac voltage applied.
2. A smaller capacitance allows less current, which means more $X_C$ with more ohms of opposition.
3. Lower frequencies for the applied voltage result in less current and more $X_C$. With a steady dc voltage source, which corresponds to a frequency of zero, the opposition of the capacitor is infinite and there is no current. In this case the capacitor is effectively an open circuit.

These effects have almost unlimited applications in practical circuits because $X_C$ depends on frequency. A very common use of a capacitor is to provide little opposition for ac voltage but to block any dc voltage. Another example is to use $X_C$ for less opposition to a high-frequency alternating current, compared with lower frequencies.

**CAPACITIVE CURRENT** The reason why a capacitor allows current to flow in an ac circuit is the alternate charge and discharge. If we insert an ammeter

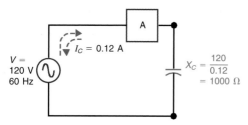

FIG. 18-2    Capacitive reactance $X_C$ is the ratio $V_C/I_C$.

in the circuit, as shown in Fig. 18-2, the ac meter will read the amount of charge and discharge current. In this example $I_C$ is 0.12 A. This current is the same in the voltage source, the connecting leads, and the plates of the capacitor. However, there is no current through the insulator between the plates of the capacitor.

**VALUES FOR $X_C$**    When we consider the ratio of $V_C/I_C$ for the ohms of opposition to the sine-wave current, this value is 120/0.12, which equals 1000 Ω. This 1000 Ω is what we call $X_C$, to indicate how much current can be produced by sine-wave voltage applied to a capacitor. In terms of current, $X_C = V_C/I_C$. In terms of frequency and capacitance, $X_C = 1/(2\pi fC)$.

The $X_C$ value depends on the amount of capacitance and the frequency of the applied voltage. If $C$ in Fig. 18-2 were increased, it could take on more charge for more charging current and then produce more discharge current. Then $X_C$ is less for more capacitance. Also, if the frequency in Fig. 18-2 were increased, the capacitor could charge and discharge faster to produce more current. This action also means $V_C/I_C$ would be less, with more current for the same applied voltage. Therefore, $X_C$ is less for higher frequencies. Reactance $X_C$ can actually have almost any value, from practically zero to almost infinite ohms.

**TEST-POINT QUESTION 18-1**

Answers at end of chapter.

**a.** Which has more reactance, a 0.1- or a 0.5-$\mu$F capacitor, at the same frequency?

**b.** Which allows more charge and discharge current, a 0.1- or a 0.5-$\mu$F capacitor, at the same frequency?

## 18-2 THE AMOUNT OF $X_C$ EQUALS $1/(2\pi fC)$

The effects of frequency and capacitance are included in the formula for calculating the ohms of reactance. The $f$ is in hertz units and $C$ in farads for $X_C$ in ohms. As an example, we can calculate $X_C$ for $C$ of 2.65 $\mu$F and $f$ of 60 Hz. Then

$$X_C = \frac{1}{2\pi fC}$$ (18-1)

$$= \frac{1}{2\pi \times 60 \times 2.65 \times 10^{-6}} = \frac{1}{6.28 \times 159 \times 10^{-6}}$$

$$= 0.00100 \times 10^6$$

$$X_C = 1000 \ \Omega$$

The constant factor $2\pi$, equal to 6.28, indicates the circular motion from which a sine wave is derived. Therefore, the formula for $X_C$ applies only to sine-wave circuits. Remember that $C$ must be in farad units for $X_C$ in ohms. Although $C$ values are usually microfarads ($10^{-6}$) or picofarads ($10^{-12}$), substitute the value of $C$ in farads with the required negative power of 10.

## Example

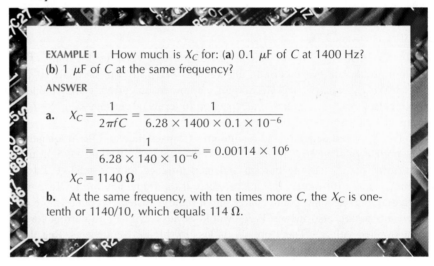

**EXAMPLE 1**   How much is $X_C$ for: (**a**) 0.1 $\mu$F of $C$ at 1400 Hz? (**b**) 1 $\mu$F of $C$ at the same frequency?

**ANSWER**

a.   $X_C = \dfrac{1}{2\pi fC} = \dfrac{1}{6.28 \times 1400 \times 0.1 \times 10^{-6}}$

$$= \frac{1}{6.28 \times 140 \times 10^{-6}} = 0.00114 \times 10^6$$

$$X_C = 1140 \ \Omega$$

b.   At the same frequency, with ten times more $C$, the $X_C$ is one-tenth or 1140/10, which equals 114 $\Omega$.

When using Formula (18-1) with a calculator, probably the best method is to multiply all the factors in the denominator and then take the reciprocal of the total product. To save time, memorize $2\pi$ as $2 \times 3.14 = 6.28$. If your calculator does not have an (EXP) key, keep the powers of 10 separate. Remember that the negative sign of the exponent becomes positive in the reciprocal value. Specifically, for Example 1, the procedure can be as follows:

1. Punch in 6.28 as the numbers for $2\pi$.
2. Press the (×) key and punch in the factor of 1400, then (×) and 0.1.
3. Press the (=) key to see the total product of 879.2.
4. While 879.2 is on the display, press the reciprocal key (1/x). This may require pushing the (2ndF) key first.
5. The reciprocal value is 0.00114.
6. The reciprocal of $10^{-6}$ in the denominator becomes $10^6$ in the numerator.
7. For the final answer, then, move the decimal point six places to the right, as indicated by $10^6$, for the final answer of 1140.

## Example

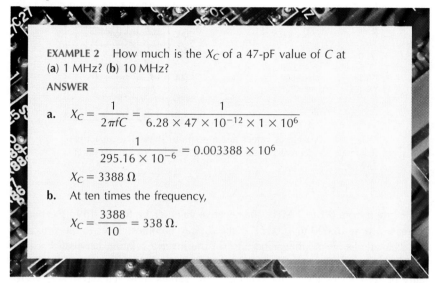

**EXAMPLE 2**  How much is the $X_C$ of a 47-pF value of $C$ at
(a) 1 MHz? (b) 10 MHz?

**ANSWER**

a.  $$X_C = \frac{1}{2\pi fC} = \frac{1}{6.28 \times 47 \times 10^{-12} \times 1 \times 10^6}$$

$$= \frac{1}{295.16 \times 10^{-6}} = 0.003388 \times 10^6$$

$$X_C = 3388 \ \Omega$$

b.  At ten times the frequency,

$$X_C = \frac{3388}{10} = 338 \ \Omega.$$

Note that $X_C$ in Example 2b is one-tenth the value in Example 2a because the $f$ is 10 times greater.

**$X_C$ IS INVERSELY PROPORTIONAL TO CAPACITANCE**  This statement means that $X_C$ increases as the capacitance is decreased. In Fig. 18-3, when $C$ is reduced by the factor of 1/10, from 1.0 to 0.1 $\mu$F, then $X_C$ increases ten times, from 1000 to 10,000 $\Omega$. Also, decreasing $C$ one-half, from 0.2 to 0.1 $\mu$F, doubles $X_C$ from 5000 to 10,000 $\Omega$.

This inverse relation between $C$ and $X_C$ is illustrated by the graph in Fig. 18-3. Note that values of $X_C$ increase downward on the graph, indicating negative reactance that is opposite from inductive reactance. With $C$ increasing to the right, the decreasing values of $X_C$ approach the zero axis of the graph.

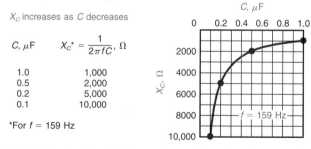

$X_C$ increases as $C$ decreases

| $C$, $\mu$F | $X_C{}^* = \dfrac{1}{2\pi fC}$, $\Omega$ |
|:---:|:---:|
| 1.0 | 1,000 |
| 0.5 | 2,000 |
| 0.2 | 5,000 |
| 0.1 | 10,000 |

*For $f$ = 159 Hz

**FIG. 18-3**  A table of values and a graph to show that capacitive reactance $X_C$ decreases with higher values of $C$. Frequency is constant at 159 Hz.

**$X_C$ IS INVERSELY PROPORTIONAL TO FREQUENCY**  Figure 18-4 illustrates the inverse relationship between $X_C$ and $f$. With $f$ increasing to the right

## ABOUT ELECTRONICS

Blindness from retinal damage affects more than a million people. A new sensor placed within the eye can stimulate the optic nerve to "see" images transmitted to it from a camera on a person's glasses.

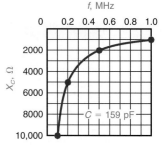

$X_C$ increases as $f$ decreases

| $f$, MHz | $X_C^* = \dfrac{1}{2\pi f C}$, $\Omega$ |
|---|---|
| 1.0 | 1,000 |
| 0.5 | 2,000 |
| 0.2 | 5,000 |
| 0.1 | 10,000 |

*For $C = 159$ pF

**FIG. 18-4** A table of values and a graph to show that capacitive reactance $X_C$ decreases with higher frequencies. $C$ is constant at 159 pF.

in the graph from 0.1 to 1 MHz, the negative value of $X_C$ for the 159-pF capacitor decreases from 10,000 to 1000 $\Omega$ as the $X_C$ curve comes closer to the zero axis.

The graphs are nonlinear because of the inverse relation between $X_C$ and $f$ or $C$. At one end, the curves approach infinitely high reactance for zero capacitance or zero frequency. At the other end, the curves approach zero reactance for infinitely high capacitance or frequency.

**CALCULATING _C_ FROM ITS REACTANCE**     In some applications, it may be necessary to find the value of capacitance required for a desired amount of $X_C$. For this case the reactance formula can be inverted to

▶  $$C = \frac{1}{2\pi f X_C}$$     **(18-2)**

The value of 6.28 for $2\pi$ is still used. The only change from Formula (18-1) is that the $C$ and $X_C$ values are inverted between denominator and numerator on the left and right side of the equation.

### Example

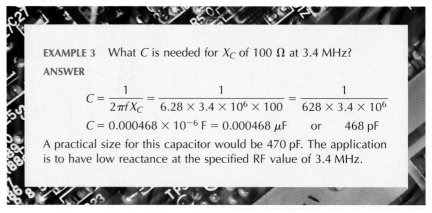

**EXAMPLE 3**     What $C$ is needed for $X_C$ of 100 $\Omega$ at 3.4 MHz?

**ANSWER**

$$C = \frac{1}{2\pi f X_C} = \frac{1}{6.28 \times 3.4 \times 10^6 \times 100} = \frac{1}{628 \times 3.4 \times 10^6}$$

$$C = 0.000468 \times 10^{-6} \text{ F} = 0.000468 \ \mu\text{F}  \quad \text{or} \quad 468 \text{ pF}$$

A practical size for this capacitor would be 470 pF. The application is to have low reactance at the specified RF value of 3.4 MHz.

**CALCULATING FREQUENCY FROM THE REACTANCE**     Another use is to find the frequency at which a capacitor has a specified amount of $X_C$. Again, the reactance formula can be inverted to the form shown in Formula (18-3).

$$f = \frac{1}{2\pi C X_C} \qquad \text{(18-3)}$$

The following example illustrates the use of this formula.

## Example

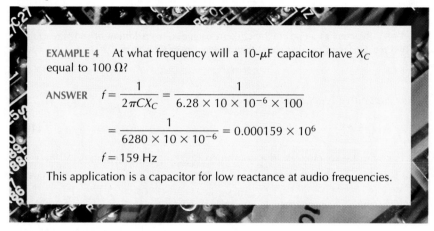

EXAMPLE 4   At what frequency will a 10-$\mu$F capacitor have $X_C$ equal to 100 $\Omega$?

ANSWER   $f = \dfrac{1}{2\pi C X_C} = \dfrac{1}{6.28 \times 10 \times 10^{-6} \times 100}$

$= \dfrac{1}{6280 \times 10 \times 10^{-6}} = 0.000159 \times 10^6$

$f = 159$ Hz

This application is a capacitor for low reactance at audio frequencies.

**SUMMARY OF THE $X_C$ FORMULAS**   Formula (18-1) is the basic form to calculate $X_C$ when $f$ and $C$ are the known values. As another possibility, the value of $X_C$ can be measured as $V_C/I_C$.

   With $X_C$ known, the value of $C$ can be calculated for a specified $f$ by Formula (18-2). Or the $f$ can be calculated with a known value of $C$ by using Formula (18-3).

---

### TEST-POINT QUESTION 18-2

Answers at end of chapter.

The $X_C$ for a capacitor is 400 $\Omega$ at 8 MHz.
**a.** How much is $X_C$ at 16 MHz?
**b.** How much is $X_C$ at 4 MHz?
**c.** Is a smaller or larger $C$ needed for less $X_C$?

# 18-3 SERIES OR PARALLEL CAPACITIVE REACTANCES

Because capacitive reactance is an opposition in ohms, series or parallel reactances are combined in the same way as resistances. As shown in Fig. 18-5a, series capacitive reactances are added arithmetically.

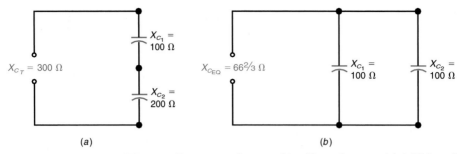

(a)                                            (b)

**FIG. 18-5** Reactances alone combine like resistances. (*a*) Addition of series reactances. (*b*) Two reactances in parallel equal their product over their sum.

*Series capacitive reactance:*

$$X_{C_T} = X_{C_1} + X_{C_2} + \cdots + \text{etc.} \qquad \textbf{(18-4)}$$

For parallel reactances, the combined reactance is calculated by the reciprocal formula, as shown in Fig. 18-5*b*.

*Parallel capacitive reactance:*

$$\frac{1}{X_{C_{EQ}}} = \frac{1}{X_{C_1}} + \frac{1}{X_{C_2}} + \cdots + \text{etc.} \qquad \textbf{(18-5)}$$

In Fig. 18-5*b* the parallel combination of 100 and 200 $\Omega$ is 66⅔ $\Omega$ for $X_{C_{EQ}}$. The combined parallel reactance is less than the lowest branch reactance. Any short cuts for combining parallel resistances also apply to parallel reactances.

Combining capacitive reactances is opposite to the way capacitances are combined. The two procedures are compatible, however, because capacitive reactance is inversely proportional to capacitance. The general case is that ohms of opposition add in series but combine by the reciprocal formula in parallel. This rule applies to resistances, to a combination of inductive reactances alone, or to capacitive reactances alone.

---

### TEST-POINT QUESTION 18-3

Answers at end of chapter.
**a.** How much is $X_{C_T}$ for a 200-$\Omega$ $X_{C_1}$ in series with a 300-$\Omega$ $X_{C_2}$?
**b.** How much is $X_{C_{EQ}}$ for a 200-$\Omega$ $X_{C_1}$ in parallel with a 300-$\Omega$ $X_{C_2}$?

## 18-4 OHM'S LAW APPLIED TO $X_C$

The current in an ac circuit with $X_C$ alone is equal to the applied voltage divided by the ohms of $X_C$. Three examples with $X_C$ are illustrated in Fig. 18-6. In Fig. 18-6*a* there is just one reactance of 100 $\Omega$. The current $I$ then is equal to $V/X_C$, or 100 V/100 $\Omega$, which is 1 A.

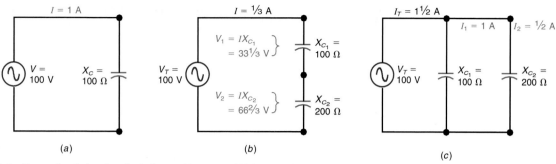

**FIG. 18-6** Example of circuit calculations with $X_C$. (a) With a single $X_C$, the $I = V/X_C$. (b) Sum of series voltage drops equals the applied voltage $V_T$. (c) Sum of parallel branch currents equals total line current $I_T$.

For the series circuit in Fig. 18-6b, the total reactance, equal to the sum of the series reactances, is 300 Ω. Then the current is 100 V/300 Ω, which equals ⅓ A. Furthermore, the voltage across each reactance is equal to its $IX_C$ product. The sum of these series voltage drops equals the applied voltage.

For the parallel circuit in Fig. 18-6c, each parallel reactance has its individual branch current, equal to the applied voltage divided by the branch reactance. The applied voltage is the same across both reactances, since they are all in parallel. In addition, the total line current of 1½ A is equal to the sum of the individual branch currents of 1 and ½ A each. With the applied voltage an rms value, all the calculated currents and voltage drops in Fig. 18-6 are also rms values.

---

### TEST-POINT QUESTION 18-4

Answers at end of chapter.
**a.** In Fig. 18-6b, how much is $X_{C_T}$?
**b.** In Fig. 18-6c, how much is $X_{C_{EQ}}$?

## 18-5 APPLICATIONS OF CAPACITIVE REACTANCE

The general use of $X_C$ is to block direct current but provide low reactance for alternating current. In this way, a varying ac component can be separated from a steady direct current. Furthermore, a capacitor can have less reactance for alternating current of high frequencies, compared with lower frequencies.

Note the following difference in ohms of $R$ and $X_C$. Ohms of $R$ remain the same for dc circuits or ac circuits, whereas $X_C$, depends on the frequency.

If 100 Ω is taken as a desired value of $X_C$, capacitor values can be calculated for different frequencies, as listed in Table 18-1. The $C$ values indicate typical capacitor sizes for different frequency applications. Note that the required $C$ becomes smaller for higher frequencies.

## TABLE 18-1 CAPACITANCE VALUES FOR A REACTANCE OF 100 Ω

| C (APPROX.) | FREQUENCY | REMARKS |
|---|---|---|
| 27 μF | 60 Hz | Power-line and low audio frequency |
| 1.6 μF | 1,000 Hz | Audio frequency |
| 0.16 μF | 10,000 Hz | Audio frequency |
| 1600 pF | 1,000 kHz (RF) | AM radio |
| 160 pF | 10 MHz (HF) | Short-wave radio |
| 16 pF | 100 MHz (VHF) | FM radio |

The 100 Ω of reactance for Table 18-1 is taken as a low $X_C$ in common applications of $C$ as a coupling capacitor, bypass capacitor, or filter capacitor for ac variations. For all these functions, the $X_C$ must be low compared with the resistance in the circuit. Typical values of $C$, then, are 16 to 1600 pF for RF signals and 0.16 to 27 μF for AF signals. The power line frequency of 60 Hz, which is a low audio frequency, requires $C$ values of about 27 μF or more.

---

### TEST-POINT QUESTION 18-5

Answers at end of chapter.

A 20-μF $C$ has 100 Ω of $X_C$ at 60 Hz.
**a.** How much is $X_C$ at 120-Hz?
**b.** How much is $X_C$ at 6 Hz?

## 18-6 SINE-WAVE CHARGE AND DISCHARGE CURRENT

In Fig. 18-7, sine-wave voltage applied across a capacitor produces alternating charge and discharge current. The action is considered for each quarter-cycle. Note that the voltage $v_C$ across the capacitor is the same as the applied voltage

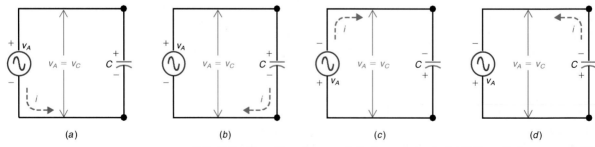

FIG. 18-7 Capacitive charge and discharge currents. (a) Voltage $V_A$ increases positive to charge C. (b) The C discharges as $V_A$ decreases. (c) Voltage $V_A$ increases negative to charge C in opposite polarity. (d) The C discharges as reversed $V_A$ decreases.

$v_A$ at all times because they are in parallel. The values of current $i$, however, depend on the charge and discharge of $C$. When $v_A$ is increasing, it charges $C$ to keep $v_C$ at the same voltage as $v_A$; when $v_A$ is decreasing, $C$ discharges to maintain $v_C$ at the same voltage as $v_A$. When $v_A$ is not changing, there is no charge or discharge current.

During the first quarter-cycle, in Fig. 18-7a, $v_A$ is positive and increasing, charging $C$ in the polarity shown. The electron flow is from the negative terminal of the source voltage, producing charging current in the direction indicated by the arrow for $i$. Next, when the applied voltage decreases during the second quarter-cycle, $v_C$ also decreases by discharging. The discharge current is from the negative plate of $C$ through the source, and back to the positive plate. Note that the discharge current in Fig. 18-7b has the opposite direction from the charge current in Fig. 18-7a.

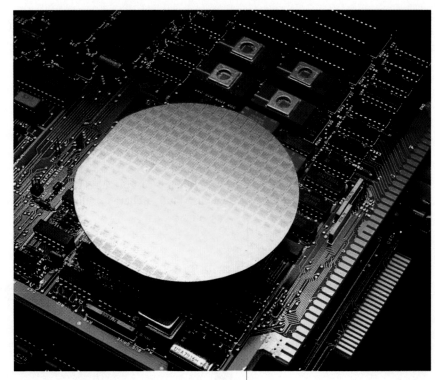

For the third quarter-cycle, in Fig. 18-7c, the applied voltage $v_A$ increases again but in the negative direction. Now $C$ charges again but in reversed polarity. Here the charging current is in the opposite direction from the charge current in Fig. 18-7a but in the same direction as the discharge current in Fig. 18-7b. Finally, the negative applied voltage decreases during the final quarter-cycle in Fig. 18-7d. As a result, $C$ discharges. This discharge current is opposite to the charge current in Fig. 18-7c, but in the same direction as the charge current in Fig. 18-7a.

For the sine wave of applied voltage, therefore, the capacitor provides a cycle of alternating charge and discharge current. Notice that capacitive current flows for either charge or discharge, whenever the voltage changes, for either an increase or decrease. Also, $i$ and $v$ have the same frequency.

**CALCULATING THE VALUES OF $i_C$**   The greater the voltage change, the greater is the amount of capacitive current. Furthermore, a larger capacitor can allow more charge current when the applied voltage increases and produce more discharge current. Because of these factors the amount of capacitive current can be calculated as

▶  $$i_C = C \frac{dv}{dt} \qquad\qquad\qquad \textbf{(18-6)}$$

where $i$ is in amperes, $C$ is in farads, and $dv/dt$ is in volts per second. As an example, suppose that the voltage across a 240-pF capacitor changes by 25 V in 1 $\mu$s. The amount of capacitive current then is

$$i_C = C\frac{dv}{dt} = 240 \times 10^{-12} \times \frac{25}{1 \times 10^{-6}}$$
$$= 240 \times 25 \times 10^{-6} = 6000 \times 10^{-6}$$
$$i_C = 6 \times 10^{-3}\text{ A or 6 mA}$$

Notice how Formula (18-6) is similar to the capacitor charge formula $Q = CV$. When the voltage changes, this $dv/dt$ factor produces a change in the charge $Q$. When the charge moves, this $dq/dt$ change is the current $i_C$. Therefore, $dq/dt$ or $i_C$ is proportional to $dv/dt$. With the constant factor $C$, then, $i_C$ becomes equal to $C(dv/dt)$.

By means of Formula (18-6), then, $i_C$ can be calculated to find the instantaneous value of charge or discharge current when the voltage changes across a capacitor.

## Example

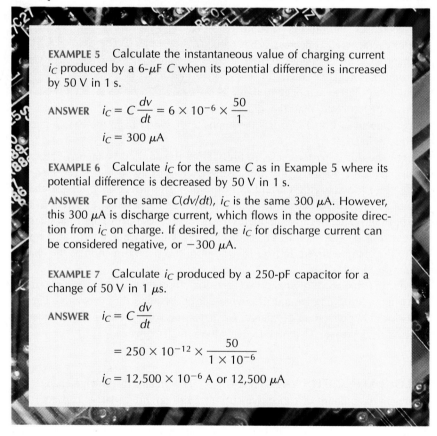

**EXAMPLE 5**   Calculate the instantaneous value of charging current $i_C$ produced by a 6-$\mu$F $C$ when its potential difference is increased by 50 V in 1 s.

**ANSWER**   $i_C = C\dfrac{dv}{dt} = 6 \times 10^{-6} \times \dfrac{50}{1}$

$i_C = 300\ \mu\text{A}$

**EXAMPLE 6**   Calculate $i_C$ for the same $C$ as in Example 5 where its potential difference is decreased by 50 V in 1 s.

**ANSWER**   For the same $C(dv/dt)$, $i_C$ is the same 300 $\mu$A. However, this 300 $\mu$A is discharge current, which flows in the opposite direction from $i_C$ on charge. If desired, the $i_C$ for discharge current can be considered negative, or $-300\ \mu$A.

**EXAMPLE 7**   Calculate $i_C$ produced by a 250-pF capacitor for a change of 50 V in 1 $\mu$s.

**ANSWER**   $i_C = C\dfrac{dv}{dt}$

$= 250 \times 10^{-12} \times \dfrac{50}{1 \times 10^{-6}}$

$i_C = 12{,}500 \times 10^{-6}\text{ A or 12,500 }\mu\text{A}$

Notice that more $i_C$ is produced in Example 7, although $C$ is smaller than in Example 6, because $dv/dt$ is a much faster voltage change.

**WAVESHAPES OF $v_C$ AND $i_C$**   More details of capacitive circuits can be analyzed by plotting the values calculated in Table 18-2. Figure 18-8 shows the waveshapes representing these values. Figure 18-8*a* shows a sine wave of volt-

## TABLE 18-2 VALUES FOR $i_C = C(dv/dt)$ CURVES IN FIG. 18-8

| TIME | | dt | | dv, V | dv/dt, V/μs | C, pF | $i_C = C(dv/dt)$, mA |
|---|---|---|---|---|---|---|---|
| θ | μs | θ | μs | | | | |
| 30° | 2 | 30° | 2 | 50 | 25 | 240 | 6 |
| 60° | 4 | 30° | 2 | 36.6 | 18.3 | 240 | 4.4 |
| 90° | 6 | 30° | 2 | 13.4 | 6.7 | 240 | 1.6 |
| 120° | 8 | 30° | 2 | −13.4 | −6.7 | 240 | −1.6 |
| 150° | 10 | 30° | 2 | −36.6 | −18.3 | 240 | −4.4 |
| 180° | 12 | 30° | 2 | −50 | −25 | 240 | −6 |
| 210° | 14 | 30° | 2 | −50 | −25 | 240 | −6 |
| 240° | 16 | 30° | 2 | −36.6 | −18.3 | 240 | −4.4 |
| 270° | 18 | 30° | 2 | −13.4 | −6.7 | 240 | −1.6 |
| 300° | 20 | 30° | 2 | 13.4 | 6.7 | 240 | 1.6 |
| 330° | 22 | 30° | 2 | 36.6 | 18.3 | 240 | 4.4 |
| 360° | 24 | 30° | 2 | 50 | 25 | 240 | 6 |

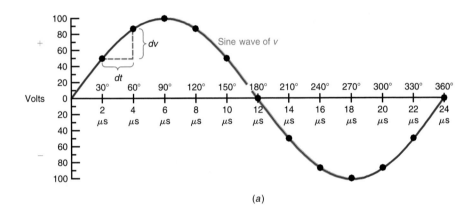

(a)

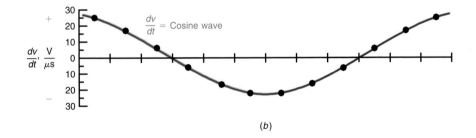

(b)

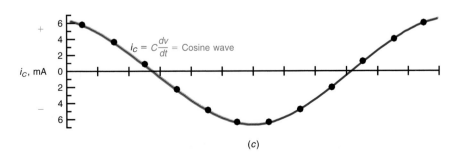

(c)

FIG. 18-8 Waveshapes of capacitive circuits. (a) Waveshape of sine-wave voltage at top. (b) Changes in voltage below causing (c) current $i_c$ charge and discharge waveshape. Values plotted are those given in Table 18-2.

age $v_C$ across a 240-pF capacitance $C$. Since the capacitive current $i_C$ depends on the rate of change of voltage, rather than the absolute value of $v$, the curve in Fig. 18-8b shows how much the voltage changes. In this curve, the $dv/dt$ values are plotted for every 30° of the cycle.

Figure 18-8c shows the actual capacitive current $i_C$. This $i_C$ curve is similar to the $dv/dt$ curve because $i_C$ equals the constant $C$ multiplied by $dv/dt$.

**90° PHASE ANGLE**  The $i_C$ curve at the bottom in Fig. 18-8 has its zero values when the $v_C$ curve at the top is at maximum. This comparison shows that the curves are 90° out of phase, as $i_C$ is a cosine wave of current for the sine wave of voltage $v_C$. The 90° phase difference results from the fact that $i_C$ depends on the $dv/dt$ rate of change, rather than on $v$ itself. More details of this 90° phase angle for capacitance are explained in the next chapter.

For each of the curves, the period $T$ is 24 $\mu$s. Therefore, the frequency is $1/T$ or $\frac{1}{24}$, which equals 41.67 kHz. Each curve has the same frequency, although there is a 90° phase difference between $i$ and $v$.

**OHMS OF $X_C$**  The ratio of $v_C/i_C$ actually specifies the capacitive reactance, in ohms. For this comparison, we use the actual value of $v_C$, which has the peak of 100 V. The rate-of-change factor is included in $i_C$. Although the peak of $i_C$ at 6 mA is 90° ahead of the peak of $v_C$ at 100 V, we can compare these two peak values. Then $v_C/i_C$ is 100/0.006, which equals 16,667 $\Omega$.

This $X_C$ is only an approximate value because $i_C$ cannot be determined exactly for the large $dt$ changes every 30°. If we used smaller intervals of time, the peak $i_C$ would be 6.28 mA with $X_C$ then 15,900 $\Omega$, the same as $1/(2\pi fC)$ with a 240-pF $C$ and a frequency of 41.67 kHz.

---

## TEST-POINT QUESTION 18-6

Answers at end of chapter.

Refer to the curves in Fig. 18-8.
**a.** At what angle does $v$ have its maximum positive value?
**b.** At what angle does $dv/dt$ have its maximum positive value?
**c.** What is the phase angle difference between $v_C$ and $i_C$?

# 18 SUMMARY AND REVIEW

- Capacitive reactance, indicated by $X_C$, is the opposition of a capacitance to the flow of sine-wave alternating current.
- Reactance $X_C$ is measured in ohms because it limits the current to the value $V/X_C$. With $V$ in volts and $X_C$ in ohms, $I$ is in amperes.
- $X_C = 1/(2\pi f C)$. With $f$ in hertz and $C$ in farads, $X_C$ is in ohms.
- For the same value of capacitance, $X_C$ decreases when the frequency increases.
- For the same frequency, $X_C$ decreases when the capacitance increases.
- With $X_C$ and $f$ known, the capacitance $C = 1/(2\pi f X_C)$.
- With $X_C$ and $C$ known, the frequency $f = 1/(2\pi C X_C)$.
- The total $X_C$ of capacitive reactances in series equals the sum of the individual values, as for series resistances. The series reactances have the same current. The voltage across each reactance is $I X_C$.
- With parallel capacitive reactances, the combined reactance is calculated by the reciprocal formula, as for parallel resistances. Each branch current is $V/X_C$. The total line current is the sum of the individual branch currents.
- Table 18-3 summarizes the differences between $C$ and $X_C$.

### TABLE 18-3 COMPARISON OF CAPACITANCE AND CAPACITIVE REACTANCE

| CAPACITANCE | CAPACITIVE REACTANCE |
| --- | --- |
| Symbol is $C$ | Symbol is $X_C$ |
| Measured in farad units | Measured in ohm units |
| Depends on construction of capacitor | Depends on frequency of sine-wave voltage |
| $C = i_C/(dv/dt)$ or $Q/V$ | $X_C = v_C/i_C$ or $1/(2\pi f C)$ |

Choose (*a*), (*b*), (*c*), or (*d*).

1. Alternating current can flow in a capacitive circuit with ac voltage applied because (*a*) of the high peak value; (*b*) varying voltage produces charge and discharge current; (*c*) charging current flows when the voltage decreases; (*d*) discharge current flows when the voltage increases.
2. With higher frequencies, the amount of capacitive reactance (*a*) increases; (*b*) stays the same; (*c*) decreases; (*d*) increases only when the voltage increases.
3. At the same frequency, larger capacitance results in (*a*) more reactance; (*b*) the same reactance; (*c*) less reactance; (*d*) less reactance if the voltage amplitude decreases.
4. The capacitive reactance of a $0.1$-$\mu$F capacitor at 1000 Hz equals (*a*) 1000 $\Omega$; (*b*) 1600 $\Omega$; (*c*) 2000 $\Omega$; (*d*) 3200 $\Omega$.
5. Two 1000-$\Omega$ $X_C$ values in series have a total reactance of (*a*) 500 $\Omega$; (*b*) 1000 $\Omega$; (*c*) 1414 $\Omega$; (*d*) 2000 $\Omega$.
6. Two 1000-$\Omega$ $X_C$ values in parallel have a combined reactance of (*a*) 500 $\Omega$; (*b*) 707 $\Omega$; (*c*) 1000 $\Omega$; (*d*) 2000 $\Omega$.
7. With 50 V rms applied across a 100-$\Omega$ $X_C$, the rms current in the circuit equals (*a*) 0.5 A; (*b*) 0.637 A; (*c*) 0.707 A; (*d*) 1.414 A.
8. With steady dc voltage from a battery applied to a capacitance, after it charges to the battery voltage, the current in the circuit (*a*) depends on the current rating of the battery; (*b*) is greater for larger values of capacitance; (*c*) is smaller for larger values of capacitance; (*d*) is zero for any capacitance value.
9. The capacitance needed for a 1000-$\Omega$ reactance at 2 MHz is (*a*) 2 pF; (*b*) 80 pF; (*c*) 1000 pF; (*d*) 2000 pF.
10. A $0.2$-$\mu$F capacitance will have a reactance of 1000 $\Omega$ at the frequency of (*a*) 800 Hz; (*b*) 1 kHz; (*c*) 1 MHz; (*d*) 8 MHz.

## QUESTIONS

1. Why is capacitive reactance measured in ohms? State two differences between capacitance and capacitive reactance.
2. Explain briefly why the bulb lights in Fig. 18-1*a* but not in Fig. 18-1*c*.
3. Explain briefly what is meant by two factors being inversely proportional. How does this apply to $X_C$ and $C$? $X_C$ and $f$?
4. In comparing $X_C$ and $R$, give two differences and one similarity.
5. Why are the waves in Fig. 18-8*a* and *b* considered to be 90° out of phase, while the waves in Fig. 18-8*b* and *c* have the same phase?
6. Referring to Fig. 18-3, how does this graph show an inverse relation between $X_C$ and $C$?
7. Referring to Fig. 18-4, how does this graph show an inverse relation between $X_C$ and $f$?

8. Referring to Fig. 18-8, draw three similar curves but for a sine wave of voltage with a period $T = 12$ $\mu$s for the full cycle. Use the same $C$ of 240 pF. Compare the value of $X_C$ obtained as $1/(2\pi fC)$ and $v_C/i_C$.

9. (a) What is the relationship between charge $q$ and current $i$? (b) How is this comparison similar to the relation between the two formulas $Q = CV$ and $i = C(dv/dt)$?

## PROBLEMS

### ANSWERS TO ODD-NUMBERED PROBLEMS AT BACK OF BOOK.

1. Referring to Fig. 18-4, give the values of $C$ needed for 2000 $\Omega$ of $X_C$ at the four frequencies listed.

2. What size capacitance is needed for 50-$\Omega$ reactance at 100 kHz?

3. A capacitor with an $X_C$ of 2000 $\Omega$ is connected across a 9-V 1000-Hz source. (a) Draw the schematic diagram. (b) How much is the current in the circuit? (c) What is the frequency of the current?

4. How much is the capacitance of a capacitor that draws 0.1 A from the 60-Hz 120-V power line?

5. A 1000-$\Omega$ $X_{C_1}$ and a 4000-$\Omega$ $X_{C_2}$ are in series across a 10-V source. (a) Draw the schematic diagram. (b) Calculate the current in the series circuit. (c) How much is the voltage across $X_{C_1}$? (d) How much is the voltage across $X_{C_2}$?

6. The 1000-$\Omega$ $X_{C_1}$ and 4000-$\Omega$ $X_{C_2}$ in Prob. 5 are in parallel across the 10-V source. (a) Draw the schematic diagram. (b) Calculate the branch current in $X_{C_1}$. (c) Calculate the branch current in $X_{C_2}$. (d) Calculate the total line current. (e) How much is the voltage across both reactances?

7. At what frequency will a 0.01-$\mu$F capacitor have a reactance of 5000 $\Omega$?

8. Four capacitive reactances of 100, 200, 300, and 400 $\Omega$ each are connected in series across a 40-V source. (a) Draw the schematic diagram. (b) How much is the total $X_{C_T}$? (c) Calculate $I$. (d) Calculate the voltages across each capacitance. (e) If the frequency of the applied voltage is 1600 kHz, calculate the required value of each capacitance.

9. Three equal capacitive reactances of 600 $\Omega$ each are in parallel. (a) How much is the equivalent combined reactance? (b) If the frequency of the applied voltage is 800 kHz, how much is the capacitance of each capacitor and what is the equivalent combined capacitance of the three in parallel?

10. A 2-$\mu$F $C$ is in series with a 4-$\mu$F $C$. The frequency is 5 kHz. (a) How much is $C_T$? (b) Calculate $X_{C_T}$. (c) Calculate $X_{C_1}$ and $X_{C_2}$ to see if their sum equals $X_{C_T}$.

11. A capacitor across the 120-V 60-Hz ac power line allows a 0.4-A current. (a) Calculate $X_C$ and $C$. (b) What size $C$ is needed to double the current?

12. A 0.01-$\mu$F capacitor is connected across a 10-V source. Tabulate the values of $X_C$ and current in the circuit at 0 Hz (for steady dc voltage) and at 20 Hz, 60 Hz, 100 Hz, 500 Hz, 5 kHz, 10 kHz, and 455 kHz.

13. Calculate $X_C$ for 470 pF at 1640 kHz.

14. What $C$ is needed for the same $X_C$ in Prob. 13 but at 500 Hz?

15. How much is $I$ with 162 mV applied for the $X_C$ in Probs. 13 and 14?
16. At what frequencies will $X_C$ be 200 Ω for the following capacitors: **(a)** 2 $\mu$F; **(b)** 0.1 $\mu$F; **(c)** 0.05 $\mu$F; **(d)** 0.002 $\mu$F; **(e)** 250 pF; **(f)** 100 pF; **(g)** 47 pF?
17. What size $C$ is needed to have $X_C$ the same as the $X_L$ of a 6-mH $L$ at 100 kHz?
18. A capacitor is in series with a 5-kΩ $R$. At what frequency will $X_C$ equal $R$ for the following values of $C$: **(a)** 47 pF; **(b)** 500 pF; **(c)** 0.1 pF; **(d)** 10 $\mu$F?
19. Find the $C$ needed for $X_C$ of 1274 Ω at the following frequencies: **(a)** 500 kHz; **(b)** 1 MHz; **(c)** 250 kHz; **(d)** 5 MHz; **(e)** 50 kHz?
20. Calculate $X_C$ for a 500 $\mu$F capacitor at the frequency of 60 Hz.
21. Calculate the frequency $f$ that will provide $X_C$ of 1274 Ω for the following values of $C$: **(a)** 250 pF; **(b)** 125 pF; **(c)** 500 pF; **(d)** 25 pF; **(e)** 2500 pF.
22. In Fig. 18-9, calculate $X_{C_1}$, $X_{C_2}$, $X_{C_3}$, $X_{C_T}$, $I$, $V_{C_1}$, $V_{C_2}$, and $V_{C_3}$.

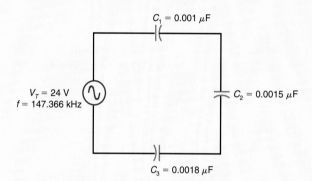

FIG. 18-9  Circuit for Probs. 22 and 23.

23. In Fig. 18-9, assume that the frequency $f$ is doubled. What happens to: **(a)** $X_{C_T}$; **(b)** $I$?
24. In Fig. 18-10, calculate $X_{C_1}$, $X_{C_2}$, $X_{C_3}$, $I_1$, $I_2$, $I_3$, $I_T$, and $X_{C_{EQ}}$?

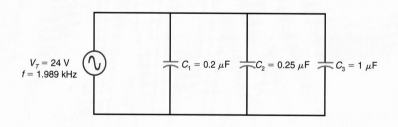

FIG. 18-10  Circuit for Probs. 24 and 25.

25. In Fig. 18-10, assume that the frequency $f$ is reduced by one-half. What happens to: **(a)** $I_T$; **(b)** $X_{C_{EQ}}$?
26. Calculate the charging current $i_c$ for a 0.33-$\mu$F capacitor if the voltage across its plates is increasing at the rate of 10 V/1 ms.
27. A capacitor has a discharge current $i_c$ of 15 mA when the voltage across its plates decreases at the rate of 150 V/1 $\mu$s. Calculate $C$.

**28.** What rate of voltage change will produce a charging current of 25 mA in a 0.01-$\mu$F capacitor? Express your answer in volts per second.

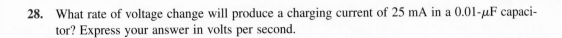

## CRITICAL THINKING

1. Explain an experimental procedure for determining the value of an unmarked capacitor. (Assume that a capacitance tester is not available.)
2. In Fig. 18-11, calculate $X_{C_T}$, $X_{C_1}$, $X_{C_2}$, $C_1$, $C_3$, $V_{C_1}$, $V_{C_2}$, $V_{C_3}$, $I_2$, and $I_3$.

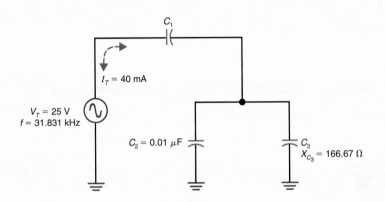

FIG. 18-11   Circuit for Critical Thinking Prob. 2.

## ANSWERS TO TEST-POINT QUESTIONS

**18-1 a.** 0.1 $\mu$F
    **b.** 0.5 $\mu$F

**18-2 a.** 200 $\Omega$
    **b.** 800 $\Omega$
    **c.** larger

**18-3 a.** 500 $\Omega$
    **b.** 120 $\Omega$

**18-4 a.** 300 $\Omega$
    **b.** 66.7 $\Omega$

**18-5 a.** 50 $\Omega$
    **b.** 1000 $\Omega$

**18-6 a.** 90°
    **b.** 0 or 360°
    **c.** 90°

# CHAPTER 19

# CAPACITIVE CIRCUITS

This chapter analyzes circuits that combine capacitive reactance $X_C$ and resistance $R$. The main questions are: how do we combine the ohms of opposition, how much current flows, and what is the phase angle? Although $X_C$ and $R$ are both measured in ohms, they have some different characteristics. Specifically, $X_C$ decreases with more $C$ and higher frequencies for sine-wave ac voltage applied, while $R$ is the same for dc and ac circuits. Furthermore, the phase angle for the voltage across $X_C$ is at $-90°$ as measured in the clockwise direction with $i_C$ as the reference at $0°$.

In addition, the practical application of a coupling capacitor shows how a low value of $X_C$ can be used to pass the desired ac signal variations, while blocking the steady dc level of a fluctuating dc voltage. In a coupling circuit with $C$ and $R$ in series, the ac component is across $R$ for the output voltage but the dc component across $C$ is not connected across the output terminals.

Finally, the general case of capacitive charge and discharge current produced when the applied voltage changes is shown with nonsinusoidal voltage variations. In this case, we compare the waveshapes of $v_C$ and $i_C$. Remember that the $-90°$ angle for an $IX_C$ voltage applies only to sine waves.

# CHAPTER OBJECTIVES

*Upon completion of this chapter, you should be able to:*

- *Explain* why the current leads the voltage by 90° for a capacitor.
- *Define* the term *impedance.*
- *Calculate* the total impedance and phase angle of a series *RC* circuit.
- *Describe* the operation and application of an *RC* phase-shifter circuit.
- *Calculate* the total current, equivalent impedance, and phase angle of a parallel *RC* circuit.
- *Understand* how a capacitor can couple some AC frequencies but not others.
- *Calculate* the individual capacitor voltage drops for capacitors in series.
- *Calculate* the capacitive current that flows with nonsinusoidal waveforms.

# IMPORTANT TERMS IN THIS CHAPTER

capacitive voltage divider
coupling capacitor
leading current

phase-shifter circuit
phasor triangle

rectangular waveform
sawtooth waveform

# TOPICS COVERED IN THIS CHAPTER

**19-1** Sine-Wave $v_C$ Lags $i_C$ by 90°
**19-2** $X_C$ and $R$ in Series
**19-3** *RC* Phase-Shifter Circuit
**19-4** $X_C$ and $R$ in Parallel

**19-5** RF and AF Coupling Capacitors
**19-6** Capacitive Voltage Dividers
**19-7** The General Case of Capacitive Current $i_C$

For a sine wave of applied voltage, the capacitor provides a cycle of alternating charge and discharge current, as shown in Fig. 19-1*a*. In Fig. 19-1*b*, the waveshape of this charge and discharge current $i_C$ is compared with the voltage $v_C$.

Note that the instantaneous value of $i_C$ is zero when $v_C$ is at its maximum value. At either its positive or negative peak, $v_C$ is not changing. For one instant at both peaks, therefore, the voltage must have a static value before changing its direction. Then $v$ is not changing and $C$ is not charging or discharging. The result is zero current at this time.

Also note that $i_C$ is maximum when $v_C$ is zero. When $v_C$ crosses the zero axis, $i_C$ has its maximum value because then the voltage is changing most rapidly.

Therefore, $i_C$ and $v_C$ are 90° out of phase, since the maximum value of one corresponds to the zero value of the other; $i_C$ leads $v_C$ because $i_C$ has its maximum value a quarter-cycle before the time that $v_C$ reaches its peak. The phasors in Fig. 19-1*c* show $i_C$ leading $v_C$ by the counterclockwise angle of 90°. Here $v_C$ is the horizontal phasor for the reference angle of 0°. In Fig. 19-1*d*, however, the current $i_C$ is the horizontal phasor for reference. Since $i_C$ must be 90° leading, $v_C$ is shown lagging by the clockwise angle of $-90°$. In series circuits, the current $i_C$ is the reference and then the voltage $v_C$ can be considered to lag $i_C$ by 90°.

The 90° phase angle results because $i_C$ depends on the rate of change of $v_C$. As shown previously in Fig. 18-8 for a sine wave of $v_C$, the capacitive charge and discharge current is a cosine wave. This 90° phase between $v_C$ and $i_C$ is true in any sine-wave ac circuit, whether $C$ is in series or parallel and whether $C$ is alone or combined with other components. We can always say that for any $X_C$ its current and voltage are 90° out of phase.

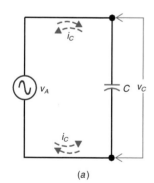

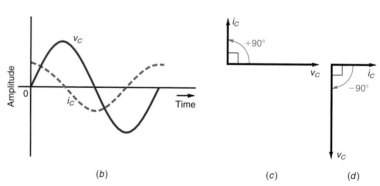

(a)    (b)    (c)    (d)

FIG. 19-1   Capacitive current $i_C$ leads $v_C$ by 90°. (*a*) Circuit with sine-wave $V_A$ across $C$. (*b*) Waveshapes of $i_C$ 90° ahead of $v_C$. (*c*) Phasor diagram of $i_C$ leading the horizontal reference $v_C$ by a counterclockwise angle of 90°. (*d*) Phasor diagram with $i_C$ as the reference phasor to show $v_C$ lagging $i_C$ by an angle of $-90°$.

**CAPACITIVE CURRENT IS THE SAME IN A SERIES CIRCUIT**   The leading phase angle of capacitive current is only with respect to the voltage across the capacitor, which does not change the fact that the current is the same in all parts of a series circuit. In Fig. 19-1*a*, for instance, the current in the generator, the connecting wires, and both plates of the capacitor must be the same because they are all in the same path.

## CAPACITIVE VOLTAGE IS THE SAME ACROSS PARALLEL BRANCHES

In Fig. 19-1$a$, the voltage is the same across the generator and $C$ because they are in parallel. There cannot be any lag or lead in time between these two parallel voltages. At any instant, whatever the voltage value is across the generator at that time, the voltage across $C$ is the same. With respect to the series current, however, both $v_A$ and $v_C$ are 90° out of phase with $i_C$.

**THE FREQUENCY IS THE SAME FOR $v_C$ AND $i_C$**   Although $v_C$ lags $i_C$ by 90°, both waves have the same frequency. For example, if the frequency of the sine wave $v_C$ in Fig. 19-1$b$ is 100 Hz, this is also the frequency of $i_C$.

---

### TEST-POINT QUESTION 19-1

Answers at end of chapter.

Refer to Fig. 19-1.
**a.** What is the phase between $v_A$ and $v_C$?
**b.** What is the phase between $v_C$ and $i_C$?
**c.** Does $v_C$ lead or lag $i_C$?

## 19-2 $X_C$ AND $R$ IN SERIES

When resistance is in series with capacitive reactance (Fig. 19-2), both determine the current. Current $I$ is the same in $X_C$ and $R$ since they are in series. Each has its own series voltage drop, equal to $IR$ for the resistance and $IX_C$ for the reactance.

If the capacitive reactance alone is considered, its voltage drop lags the series current $I$ by 90°. The $IR$ voltage has the same phase as $I$, however, because resistance provides no phase shift. Therefore, $R$ and $X_C$ combined in series must be added by phasors because of the 90° phase angle.

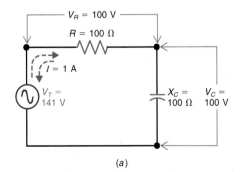

(a)

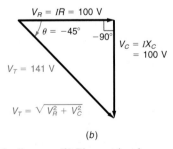

(b)

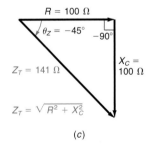

(c)

**FIG. 19-2**   Circuit with $X_C$ and $R$ in series. (*a*) Schematic diagram. (*b*) Phasor triangle of voltages with $V_C$ lagging $V_R$ by −90°. This triangle is used to find the resultant $V_T$. (*c*) Similar impedance triangle with $X_C$ lagging $R$ by −90°. This triangle is used to find the resultant $Z_T$.

**PHASOR ADDITION OF $V_C$ AND $V_R$**   In Fig. 19-2b, the current phasor is shown horizontal, as the reference phase, because $I$ is the same in a series circuit. The resistive voltage drop $IR$ has the same phase as $I$. The capacitor voltage $IX_C$ must be 90° clockwise from $I$ and $IR$, as the capacitive voltage lags.

The phasor voltages $V_R$ and $V_C$ are 90° out of phase and thus form a right triangle. Therefore

▶    $$V_T = \sqrt{V_R^2 + V_C^2} \tag{19-1}$$

This formula applies just to series circuits because then $V_C$ is 90° out of phase with $V_R$. All the voltages must be in the same units. When $V_R$ and $V_C$ are rms values, then $V_T$ is an rms value.

In calculating the value of $V_T$, first square $V_R$ and $V_C$, then add and take the square root. For the example in Fig. 19-2,

$$V_T = \sqrt{100^2 + 100^2} = \sqrt{10,000 + 10,000} = \sqrt{20,000}$$
$$V_T = 141 \text{ V}$$

The two phasor voltages total 141 V instead of 200 V because the 90° phase difference means the peak value of one occurs when the other is at zero.

**PHASOR ADDITION OF $X_C$ AND $R$**   Figure 19-2c shows a triangle for $R$ and $X_C$ in series. This corresponds to the voltage triangle in Fig. 19-2b except that the common factor $I$ cancels because the current is the same in both $R$ and $X_C$. The resultant phasor for $R$ and $X_C$ in series represents the total opposition in ohms offered by the series circuit. The phasor sum of $R$ and $X_C$ is called the *total impedance*, represented by the symbol $Z_T$. Therefore, the triangle consisting of $R$, $X_C$, and $Z_T$ is called the *impedance triangle*. Because the phasors for $R$ and $X_C$ form a right triangle, $Z_T$ is calculated as

▶    $$Z_T = \sqrt{R^2 + X_C^2} \tag{19-2}$$

With $R$ and $X_C$ in ohms, $Z_T$ is also in ohms. For the example in Fig. 19-2c, the values are

$$Z_T = \sqrt{100^2 + 100^2} = \sqrt{10,000 + 10,000} = \sqrt{20,000}$$
$$Z_T = 141 \ \Omega$$

In Fig. 19-2a, note that the total impedance of 141 Ω divided into the applied voltage of 141 V produces the current of 1 A in the series circuit. The $IR$ voltage drop is 1 × 100, or 100 V; the $IX_C$ voltage drop is also 1 × 100, or 100 V.

The phasor sum of the two series voltage drops of 100 V each equals the applied voltage of 141 V. Also, the applied voltage is equal to $I \times Z_T$, or 1 × 141, which is 141 V for $V_T$.

**PHASE ANGLE WITH SERIES $X_C$**   As shown in Fig. 19-2b and c, the phase angle $\theta$, between the generator voltage and the series current, can be calculated from the voltage or impedance triangle.

With series $X_C$, the phase angle is negative, clockwise from the zero reference angle of $I$, because the $X_C$ voltage lags its current. To indicate the negative phase angle, therefore, this 90° phasor points downward from the horizontal reference. To calculate the phase angle with series $X_C$ and $R$,

▶ $$\tan \theta_Z = -\frac{X_C}{R} \tag{19-3}$$

Using this formula for the circuit in Fig. 19-2c,

$$\tan \theta_Z = -\frac{X_C}{R} = -\frac{100}{100}$$

$$= -1$$

$$\theta_Z = \arctan(-1)$$

$$\theta_Z = -45°$$

The negative sign means the angle is clockwise from zero, to indicate that $V_T$ lags behind the leading $I$.

## Example

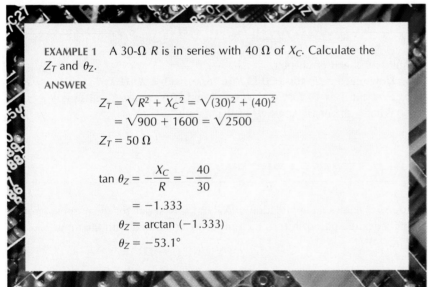

**EXAMPLE 1**    A 30-$\Omega$ $R$ is in series with 40 $\Omega$ of $X_C$. Calculate the $Z_T$ and $\theta_Z$.

**ANSWER**

$$Z_T = \sqrt{R^2 + X_C^2} = \sqrt{(30)^2 + (40)^2}$$
$$= \sqrt{900 + 1600} = \sqrt{2500}$$
$$Z_T = 50 \ \Omega$$

$$\tan \theta_Z = -\frac{X_C}{R} = -\frac{40}{30}$$
$$= -1.333$$
$$\theta_Z = \arctan(-1.333)$$
$$\theta_Z = -53.1°$$

**SERIES COMBINATIONS OF $X_C$ AND $R$**    In series, the higher the $X_C$ compared with $R$, the more capacitive the circuit. There is more voltage drop across the capacitive reactance, and the phase angle increases toward −90°. The series $X_C$ always makes the current lead the applied voltage. With all $X_C$ and no $R$, the entire applied voltage is across $X_C$, and $\theta$ equals −90°.

Several combinations of $X_C$ and $R$ in series are listed in Table 19-1, with their resultant impedance values and phase angle. Note that a ratio of 10:1, or more, for $X_C/R$ means the circuit is practically all capacitive. The phase angle of −84.3° is almost −90°, and the total impedance $Z_T$ is approximately equal to $X_C$. The voltage drop across $X_C$ in the series circuit is then practically equal to the applied voltage, with almost none across the $R$.

| R, Ω | $X_C$, Ω | $Z_T$, Ω (APPROX.) | PHASE ANGLE $\theta_Z$ |
|---|---|---|---|
| **TABLE 19-1** | **SERIES R AND $X_C$ COMBINATIONS** | | |
| 1 | 10 | $\sqrt{101} = 10$ | $-84.3°$ |
| 10 | 10 | $\sqrt{200} = 14$ | $-45°$ |
| 10 | 1 | $\sqrt{101} = 10$ | $-5.7°$ |

*Note:* $\theta_Z$ is the phase angle of $Z_T$ or $V_T$ with respect to the reference phasor $I$ in series circuits.

At the opposite extreme, when $R$ is 10 times more than $X_C$, the series circuit is mainly resistive. The phase angle of $-5.7°$ then means the current is almost in phase with the applied voltage; $Z_T$ is approximately equal to $R$, and the voltage drop across $R$ is practically equal to the applied voltage with almost none across the $X_C$.

For the case when $X_C$ and $R$ equal each other, the resultant impedance $Z_T$ is 1.41 times either one. The phase angle then is $-45°$, halfway between $0°$ for resistance alone and $-90°$ for capacitive reactance alone.

---

### TEST-POINT QUESTION 19-2

Answers at end of chapter.

**a.** How much is $Z_T$ for a 20-Ω $R$ in series with a 20-Ω $X_C$?
**b.** How much is $V_T$ for 20 V across $R$ and 20 V across $X_C$ in series?
**c.** What is the phase angle $\theta_Z$ of this circuit?

## 19-3 *RC* PHASE-SHIFTER CIRCUIT

Figure 19-3 shows an application of $X_C$ and $R$ in series for the purpose of providing a desired phase shift in the output $V_R$ compared with the input $V_T$. The

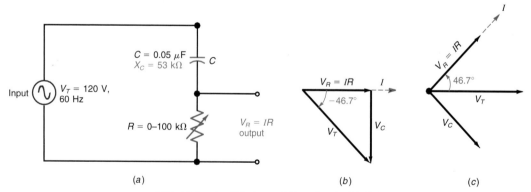

**FIG. 19-3** An *RC* phase-shifter circuit. (*a*) Schematic diagram. (*b*) Phasor triangle with *IR*, or $V_R$, as the horizontal reference. $V_R$ leads $V_T$ by 46.7° with *R* set at 50 kΩ. (*c*) Phasors shown with $V_T$ as the horizontal reference.

$R$ can be varied up to 100 kΩ to change the phase angle. The $C$ is 0.05 μF here for the 60-Hz ac power line voltage, but a smaller $C$ would be used for a higher frequency. The capacitor must have an appreciable value of reactance for the phase shift.

For the circuit in Fig. 19-3a, assume that $R$ is set for 50 kΩ, at its middle value. The reactance for the 0.05-μF capacitor at 60 Hz is approximately 53 kΩ. For these values of $X_C$ and $R$, the phase angle of the circuit is −46.7°. This angle has the tangent of −53/50 = −1.06.

The phasor triangle in Fig. 19-3b shows that $IR$ or $V_R$ is out of phase with $V_T$ by the leading angle or 46.7°. Note that $V_C$ is always 90° lagging $V_R$ in a series circuit. The angle between $V_C$ and $V_T$ then becomes 90° − 46.7° = 43.3°.

The purpose of this circuit is to provide a phase-shifted voltage $V_R$ in the output, with respect to the input. For this reason, the phasors are redrawn in Fig. 19-3c to show the voltages with the input $V_T$ as the horizontal reference. The conclusion, then, is that the output voltage across $R$ leads the input $V_T$ by 46.7°.

Now let $R$ be varied for a higher value at 90 kΩ, while $X_C$ stays the same. The phase angle becomes −30.5°. This angle has the tangent −53/90 = −0.59. As a result, $V_R$ leads $V_T$ by 30.5°.

For the opposite case, let $R$ be reduced to 10 kΩ. Then the phase angle becomes −79.3°. This angle has the tangent −53/10 = −5.3. Then $V_R$ leads $V_T$ by 79.3°. Notice that the phase angle becomes larger as the series circuit becomes more capacitive with less resistance.

A practical application for this circuit is to provide a voltage of variable phase to set the conduction time of semiconductors in power-control circuits. As $R$ is varied, the phase angle of the output $V_R$ is varied with respect to the power-line voltage $V_T$.

---

### TEST-POINT QUESTION 19-3

Answers at end of chapter.

In Fig. 19-3, give the phase angle between
**a.** $V_R$ and $V_T$.
**b.** $V_R$ and $V_C$.
**c.** $V_C$ and $V_T$.

## 19-4 $X_C$ AND $R$ IN PARALLEL

The 90° phase angle for $X_C$ in the parallel circuit must be with respect to branch currents instead of voltage drops as in a series circuit. In Fig. 19-4a, the voltage is the same across $X_C$, $R$, and the generator, since they are all in parallel. There cannot be any phase difference between the parallel voltages.

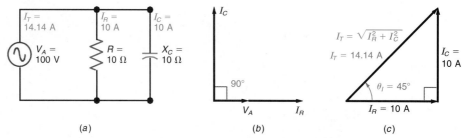

FIG. 19-4   Circuit of $X_C$ and $R$ in parallel, with branch currents $I_C$ and $I_R$. (a) Schematic diagram. (b) Current phasors showing $I_C$ leading $V_A$ by 90°. (c) Phasor triangle of branch currents $I_C$ and $I_R$ is used to calculate resultant total line current $I_T$.

Each branch, however, has its individual current. For the resistive branch, $I_R$ is $V_A/R$; in the capacitive branch, $I_C = V_A/X_C$. These current phasors are shown in Fig. 19-4b.

Note that the phasor diagram has the generator voltage $V_A$ as the reference phasor because it is the same throughout the circuit. The resistive branch current $I_R$ is in phase with $V_A$, but the capacitive branch current $I_C$ leads $V_A$ by 90°.

The phasor for $I_C$ is up, compared with down for an $X_C$ phasor, because the parallel branch current $I_C$ leads the reference $V_A$. This $I_C$ phasor for a parallel branch current is opposite from an $X_C$ phasor.

The phasor addition of the branch currents in a parallel $RC$ circuit can be calculated using the phasor triangle for currents shown in Fig. 19-4c. The phasor sum of $I_R$ and $I_C$ equals $I_T$. As a result, the formula for $I_T$ is

$$I_T = \sqrt{I_R^2 + I_C^2} \tag{19-4}$$

In Fig. 19-2c, the phasor sum of 10 A for $I_R$ and 10 A for $I_C$ equals 14.14 A. The branch currents are added by phasors since they are the factors 90° out of phase in a parallel circuit, corresponding to the voltage drops 90° out of phase in a series circuit.

**IMPEDANCE OF $X_C$ AND $R$ IN PARALLEL**   As usual, the impedance of a parallel circuit equals the applied voltage divided by the total line current: $Z_{EQ} = V_A/I_T$. In Fig. 19-4, for example,

$$Z_{EQ} = \frac{V_A}{I_T} = \frac{100}{14.14 \text{ A}} = 7.07 \text{ }\Omega$$

which is the opposition in ohms across the generator. This $Z_{EQ}$ of 7.07 $\Omega$ is equal to the resistance of 10 $\Omega$ in parallel with the reactance of 10 $\Omega$. Notice that the impedance of equal values of $R$ and $X_C$ is not one-half but equals 70.7 percent of either one.

**PHASE ANGLE IN PARALLEL CIRCUITS**   In Fig. 19-4c, the phase angle $\theta$ is 45° because $R$ and $X_C$ are equal, resulting in equal branch currents. The phase angle is between the total current $I_T$ and the generator voltage $V_A$. However, $V_A$ and $I_R$ are in phase. Therefore $\theta$ is also between $I_T$ and $I_R$.

Using the tangent formula to find $\theta$ from the current triangle in Fig. 19-4c gives

$$\blacktriangleright \quad \tan \theta_I = \frac{I_C}{I_R} \qquad\qquad (19\text{-}5)$$

The phase angle is positive because the $I_C$ phasor is upward, leading $V_A$ by 90°. This direction is opposite from the lagging phasor of series $X_C$. The effect of $X_C$ is no different, however. Only the reference is changed for the phase angle.

Note that the phasor triangle of branch currents for parallel circuits gives $\theta_I$ as the angle of $I_T$ with respect to the generator voltage $V_A$. This phase angle for $I_T$ is labeled $\theta_I$ with respect to the applied voltage. For the phasor triangle of voltages in a series circuit, the phase angle for $Z_T$ and $V_T$ is labeled $\theta_Z$ with respect to the series current.

## Example

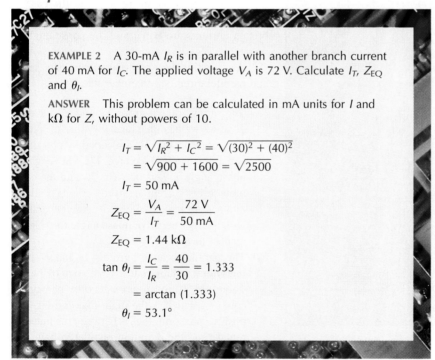

**EXAMPLE 2**   A 30-mA $I_R$ is in parallel with another branch current of 40 mA for $I_C$. The applied voltage $V_A$ is 72 V. Calculate $I_T$, $Z_{EQ}$ and $\theta_I$.

**ANSWER**   This problem can be calculated in mA units for $I$ and k$\Omega$ for $Z$, without powers of 10.

$$I_T = \sqrt{I_R^2 + I_C^2} = \sqrt{(30)^2 + (40)^2}$$
$$= \sqrt{900 + 1600} = \sqrt{2500}$$
$$I_T = 50 \text{ mA}$$
$$Z_{EQ} = \frac{V_A}{I_T} = \frac{72 \text{ V}}{50 \text{ mA}}$$
$$Z_{EQ} = 1.44 \text{ k}\Omega$$
$$\tan \theta_I = \frac{I_C}{I_R} = \frac{40}{30} = 1.333$$
$$= \arctan (1.333)$$
$$\theta_I = 53.1°$$

**PARALLEL COMBINATIONS OF $X_C$ AND $R$**   In Table 19-2, when $X_C$ is ten times $R$, the parallel circuit is practically resistive because there is little leading capacitive current in the main line. The small value of $I_C$ results from the high reactance of shunt $X_C$. Then the total impedance of the parallel circuit is approximately equal to the resistance, since the high value of $X_C$ in a parallel branch has little effect. The phase angle of 5.7° is practically 0° because almost all the line current is resistive.

## TABLE 19-2 PARALLEL RESISTANCE AND CAPACITANCE COMBINATIONS*

| $R$, $\Omega$ | $X_C$, $\Omega$ | $I_R$, A | $I_C$, A | $I_T$, A (APPROX.) | $Z_{EQ}$, $\Omega$ (APPROX.) | PHASE ANGLE $\theta_I$ |
|---|---|---|---|---|---|---|
| 1 | 10 | 10 | 1 | $\sqrt{101} = 10$ | 1 | 5.7° |
| 10 | 10 | 1 | 1 | $\sqrt{2} = 1.4$ | 7.07 | 45° |
| 10 | 1 | 1 | 10 | $\sqrt{101} = 10$ | 1 | 84.3° |

*$V_A = 10$ V. Note that $\theta_I$ is the phase angle of $I_T$ with respect to the reference $V_A$ in parallel circuits.

As $X_C$ becomes smaller, it provides more leading capacitive current in the main line. When $X_C$ is $\frac{1}{10}\,R$, practically all the line current is the $I_C$ component. Then, the parallel circuit is practically all capacitive, with a total impedance practically equal to $X_C$. The phase angle of 84.3° is almost 90° because the line current is mostly capacitive. Note that these conditions are opposite to the case of $X_C$ and $R$ in series. With $X_C$ and $R$ equal, their branch currents are equal and the phase angle is 45°.

As additional comparisons between series and parallel circuits, remember that

1. The series voltage drops $V_R$ and $V_C$ have individual values that are 90° out of phase. Therefore, $V_R$ and $V_C$ are added by phasors to equal the applied voltage $V_T$. The negative phase angle $-\theta_Z$ is between $V_T$ and the common series current $I$. More series $X_C$ allows more $V_C$ to make the circuit more capacitive, with a larger negative phase angle for $V_T$ with respect to $I$.
2. The parallel branch currents $I_R$ and $I_C$ have individual values that are 90° out of phase. Therefore, $I_R$ and $I_C$ are added by phasors to equal $I_T$, which is the main-line current. The positive phase angle $\theta_I$ is between the line current $I_T$ and the common parallel voltage $V_A$.

Less parallel $X_C$ allows more $I_C$ to make the circuit more capacitive, with a larger positive phase angle for $I_T$ with respect to $V_A$.

---

### TEST-POINT QUESTION 19-4

Answers at end of chapter.
a. How much is $I_T$ for branch currents $I_R$ of 2 A and $I_C$ of 2 A?
b. Find the phase angle $\theta_I$ between $I_T$ and $V_A$.

# 19-5 RF AND AF COUPLING CAPACITORS

In Fig. 19-5, $C_C$ is used in the application of a coupling capacitor. Its low reactance allows practically all the ac signal voltage of the generator to be developed across $R$. Very little of the ac voltage is across $C_C$.

The coupling capacitor is used for this application because at lower frequencies it provides more reactance, resulting in less ac voltage coupled across $R$ and more across $C_C$. For dc voltage, all the voltage is across $C$ with none across $R$, since the capacitor blocks direct current. As a result, the output signal voltage across $R$ includes the desired higher frequencies but not direct current or very low frequencies. This application of $C_C$, therefore, is called *ac coupling*.

The dividing line for $C_C$ to be a coupling capacitor at a specific frequency can be taken as $X_C$ one-tenth or less of the series $R$. Then the series $RC$ circuit is primarily resistive. Practically all the voltage drop of the ac generator is across $R$, with little across $C$. In addition, the phase angle is almost 0°.

Typical values of a coupling capacitor for audio or radio frequencies can be calculated if we assume a series resistance of 16,000 $\Omega$. Then $X_C$ must be 1600 $\Omega$ or less. Typical values for $C_C$ are listed in Table 19-3. At 100 Hz, a coupling capacitor must be 1 $\mu$F to provide 1600 $\Omega$ of reactance. Higher frequencies allow a smaller value of $C_C$ for a coupling capacitor having the same reactance. At 100 MHz in the VHF range the required capacitance is only 1 pF.

It should be noted that the $C_C$ values are calculated for each frequency as a lower limit. At higher frequencies, the same size $C_C$ will have less reactance than one-tenth of $R$, which improves the coupling.

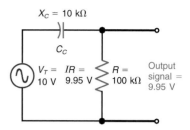

FIG. 19-5  Series circuit for $RC$ coupling. Small $X_C$ compared with $R$ allows practically all the applied voltage across $R$ for the output, with little across $C$.

## TABLE 19-3  COUPLING CAPACITORS WITH A REACTANCE OF 1600 $\Omega$*

| $f$ | $C_C$ | REMARKS |
|---|---|---|
| 100 Hz | 1 $\mu$F | Low audio frequencies |
| 1000 Hz | 0.1 $\mu$F | Audio frequencies |
| 10 kHz | 0.01 $\mu$F | Audio frequencies |
| 1000 kHz | 100 pF | Radio frequencies |
| 100 MHz | 1 pF | Very high frequencies |

*For an $X_C$ one-tenth of a series $R$ of 16,000 $\Omega$.

**CHOOSING A COUPLING CAPACITOR FOR A CIRCUIT**   As an example of using these calculations, suppose that we have the problem of determining $C_C$ for a transistorized audio amplifier. This application also illustrates the relatively large capacitance needed with low series resistance. The $C$ is to be a coupling capacitor for audio frequencies of 50 Hz and up, with a series $R$ of 4000 $\Omega$. Then the required $X_C$ is 4000/10, or 400 $\Omega$. To find $C$ at 50 Hz,

$$C = \frac{1}{2\pi f X_C} = \frac{1}{6.28 \times 50 \times 400}$$

$$= \frac{1}{125,600} = 0.0000079$$

$$C = 7.9 \times 10^{-6} \quad \text{or} \quad 7.9 \ \mu\text{F}$$

## DID YOU KNOW?

Too much current in a power line can make it heat up, enlarge, and droop into tree branches. Devices at crucial points can be on guard for gases emitted by overheated transformers. Also, thyristors can move current from a failed unit to another source of power.

A typical commercial size of low-voltage electrolytic readily available is 10 $\mu$F. The slightly higher capacitance value is better for coupling. The voltage rating can be 3 to 10 V, depending on the circuit, with a typical transistor supply voltage of 9 V. Although electrolytic capacitors have a slight leakage current, they can be used for coupling capacitors in this application because of the low series resistance.

---

### TEST-POINT QUESTION 19-5

Answers at end of chapter.
**a.** The $X_C$ of a coupling capacitor is 70 $\Omega$ at 200 Hz. How much is its $X_C$ at 400 Hz?
**b.** From Table 19-3, what $C$ would be needed for 1600 $\Omega$ of $X_C$ at 50 MHz?

## 19-6 CAPACITIVE VOLTAGE DIVIDERS

When capacitors are connected in series across a voltage source, the series capacitors serve as a voltage divider. Each capacitor has part of the applied voltage, and the sum of all the series voltage drops equals the source voltage.

The amount of voltage across each is inversely proportional to its capacitance. For instance, with 2 $\mu$F in series with 1 $\mu$F, the smaller capacitor has double the voltage of the larger capacitor. Assuming 120 V applied, one-third of this, or 40 V, is across the 2-$\mu$F capacitor, with two-thirds, or 80 V, across the 1-$\mu$F capacitor.

The two series voltage drops of 40 and 80 V add to equal the applied voltage of 120 V. The phasor addition is the same as the arithmetic sum of the two voltages because they are in phase. When voltages are out of phase with each other arithmetic addition is not possible and phasor addition becomes necessary.

**AC DIVIDER** With sine-wave alternating current, the voltage division between series capacitors can be calculated on the basis of reactance. In Fig. 19-6a, the total reactance is 120 $\Omega$ across the 120-V source. The current in the series circuit then is 1 A. This current is the same for $X_{C_1}$ and $X_{C_2}$ in series. Therefore, the $IX_C$ voltage across $C_1$ is 40 V, with 80 V across $C_2$.

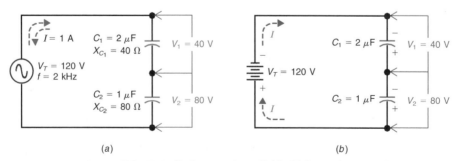

(a)                                    (b)

**FIG. 19-6** Series capacitors divide $V_T$ inversely proportional to each $C$. The smaller $C$ has more $V$. (a) An ac divider with more $X_C$ for the smaller $C$. (b) A dc divider.

The voltage division is proportional to the series reactances, as it is to series resistances. However, reactance is inversely proportional to capacitance. As a result, the smaller capacitance has more reactance and a greater part of the applied voltage.

**DC DIVIDER**   In Fig. 19-6b, both $C_1$ and $C_2$ will be charged by the battery. The voltage across the series combination of $C_1$ and $C_2$ must equal $V_T$. When charging current flows, electrons repelled from the negative battery terminal accumulate on the negative plate of $C_1$, repelling electrons from its positive plate. These electrons flow through the conductor to the negative plate of $C_2$. With the positive battery terminal attracting electrons, the charging current from the positive plate of $C_2$ returns to the positive side of the dc source. Then $C_1$ and $C_2$ become charged in the polarity shown.

Since $C_1$ and $C_2$ are in the same series path for charging current, both have the same amount of charge. However, the potential difference provided by the equal charges is inversely proportional to capacitance. The reason is that $Q = CV$, or $V = Q/C$. Therefore, the $1$-$\mu$F capacitor has double the voltage of the $2$-$\mu$F capacitor, with the same charge in both.

If you measure with a dc voltmeter across $C_1$, the meter reads 40 V. Across $C_2$ the dc voltage is 80 V. The measurement from the negative side of $C_1$ to the positive side of $C_2$ is the same as the applied battery voltage of 120 V.

If the meter is connected from the positive side of $C_1$ to the negative plate of $C_2$, however, the voltage is zero. These plates have the same potential because they are joined by a conductor of zero resistance.

The polarity marks at the junction between $C_1$ and $C_2$ indicate the voltage at this point with respect to the opposite plate of each capacitor. This junction is positive compared with the opposite plate of $C_1$ with a surplus of electrons. However, the same point is negative compared with the opposite plate of $C_2$, which has a deficiency of electrons.

In general, the following formula can be used for capacitances in series as a voltage divider:

$$\blacktriangleright \qquad V_C = \frac{C_{EQ}}{C} \times V_T \qquad\qquad\qquad \textbf{(19-6)}$$

Note that $C_{EQ}$ is in the numerator, since it must be less than the smallest individual $C$ with series capacitances. For the divider examples in Fig. 19-6a and b,

$$V_1 = \frac{C_{EQ}}{C_1} \times 120 = \frac{\frac{2}{3}}{2} \times 120 = 40 \text{ V}$$

$$V_2 = \frac{C_{EQ}}{C_2} \times 120 = \frac{\frac{2}{3}}{1} \times 120 = 80 \text{ V}$$

This method applies to series capacitances as a divider for either dc or ac voltage, as long as there is no series resistance. It should be noted that the case of capacitive dc dividers also applies to pulse circuits. Furthermore, bleeder resistors may be used across each of the capacitors to ensure more exact division.

Answers at end of chapter.

**a.** Capacitance $C_1$ of 10 pF and $C_2$ of 90 pF are across 20 kV. Calculate the amount of $V_1$ and $V_2$.

**b.** In Fig. 19-6a, how much is $X_{C_T}$?

# 19-7 THE GENERAL CASE OF CAPACITIVE CURRENT $i_C$

The capacitive charge and discharge current $i_C$ is always equal to $C(dv/dt)$. A sine wave of voltage variations for $v_C$ produces a cosine wave of current $i$. This means $v_C$ and $i_C$ have the same waveform, but they are 90° out of phase.

It is usually convenient to use $X_C$ for calculations in sine-wave circuits. Since $X_C$ is $1/(2\pi fC)$, the factors that determine the amount of charge and discharge current are included in $f$ and $C$. Then $I_C$ equals $V_C/X_C$. Or, if $I_C$ is known, $V_C$ can be calculated as $I_C \times X_C$.

With a nonsinusoidal waveform for voltage $v_C$, the concept of reactance cannot be used. Reactance $X_C$ applies only to sine waves. Then $i_C$ must be determined as $C(dv/dt)$. An example is illustrated in Fig. 19-7 to show the change of waveform here, instead of the change of phase angle in sine-wave circuits.

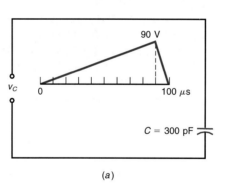

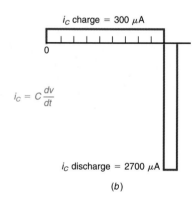

**FIG. 19-7** Waveshape of $i_C$ equal to $C(dv/dt)$. (a) Sawtooth waveform of $V_C$. (b) Rectangular current waveform of $i_C$ resulting from uniform rate of change in sawtooth waveform of voltage.

Note that the sawtooth waveform of voltage $v_C$ corresponds to a rectangular waveform of current. The linear rise of the sawtooth wave produces a constant amount of charging current $i_C$ because the rate of change is constant for the charging voltage. When the capacitor discharges, $v_C$ drops sharply. Then discharge current is in the opposite direction from charge current. Also, the discharge current has a much larger value because of the faster rate of change in $v_C$.

Answers at end of chapter.

**a.** In Fig. 19-7a, how much is $dv/dt$ in V/s for the sawtooth rise from 0 to 90 V in 90 $\mu$s?

**b.** How much is the charge current $i_C$, as $C(dv/dt)$ for this $dv/dt$?

# 19  SUMMARY AND REVIEW

- In a sine-wave ac circuit, the voltage across a capacitance lags its charge and discharge current by 90°.
- Therefore, capacitive reactance $X_C$ is a phasor quantity out of phase with its series resistance by $-90°$ because $i_C = C(dv/dt)$. This fundamental fact is the basis of all the following relations.
- The combination of $X_C$ and $R$ in series is their total impedance $Z_T$. These three types of ohms of opposition to current are compared in Table 19-4.

### TABLE 19-4   COMPARISON OF R, $X_C$, AND Z

| $R$ | $X_C = 1/(2\pi fC)$ | $Z_T = \sqrt{R^2 + X_C^2}$ |
|---|---|---|
| Ohms unit | Ohms unit | Ohms unit |
| $IR$ voltage in phase with $I$ | $IX_C$ voltage lags $I_C$ by 90° | $IZ_T$ is the applied voltage |
| Same ohm value for all $f$ | Ohms value decreases for higher $f$ | Becomes more resistive with more $f$<br>Becomes more capacitive with less $f$ |

- The opposite characteristics for series and parallel circuits with $X_C$ and $R$ are summarized in Table 19-5.

### TABLE 19-5   SERIES AND PARALLEL RC CIRCUITS

| $X_C$ AND $R$ IN SERIES | $X_C$ AND $R$ IN PARALLEL |
|---|---|
| $I$ the same in $X_C$ and $R$ | $V$ the same across $X_C$ and $R$ |
| $V_T = \sqrt{V_R^2 + V_C^2}$ | $I_T = \sqrt{I_R^2 + I_C^2}$ |
| $Z_T = \sqrt{R^2 + X_C^2}$ | $Z_{EQ} = \dfrac{V}{I_T}$ |
| $V_C$ lags $V_R$ by 90° | $I_C$ leads $I_R$ by 90° |
| $\tan \theta_Z = -\dfrac{X_C}{R}$; $\theta_Z$ increases as $X_C$ increases, resulting in more $V_C$ | $\tan \theta_I = \dfrac{I_C}{I_R}$; $\theta_I$ decreases as $X_C$ increases, resulting in less $I_C$ |

- Two or more capacitors in series across a voltage source serve as a voltage divider. The smallest $C$ has the largest part of the applied voltage.
- A coupling capacitor has $X_C$ less than its series resistance by the factor of $\frac{1}{10}$ or less, for the purpose of providing practically all the ac applied voltage across $R$ with little across $C$.
- In sine-wave circuits, $I_C = V_C/X_C$. Then $I_C$ is out of phase with $V_C$ by 90°.
- For a circuit with $X_C$ and $R$ in series, $\tan \theta_Z = -(X_C/R)$ while in parallel $\tan \theta_I = I_C/I_R$. See Table 19-5.
- When the voltage is not a sine wave, $i_C = C(dv/dt)$. Then the waveshape of $i_C$ is different from the voltage.

## SELF-TEST

### ANSWERS AT BACK OF BOOK.

Choose ($a$), ($b$), ($c$), or ($d$).

1. In a capacitive circuit ($a$) a decrease in applied voltage makes a capacitor charge; ($b$) a steady value of applied voltage causes discharge; ($c$) an increase in applied voltage makes a capacitor discharge; ($d$) an increase in applied voltage makes a capacitor charge.

2. In a sine-wave ac circuit with $X_C$ and $R$ in series, the ($a$) phase angle of the circuit is 180° with high series resistance; ($b$) voltage across the capacitance must be 90° out of phase with its charge and discharge current; ($c$) voltage across the capacitance has the same phase angle as its charge and discharge current; ($d$) charge and discharge current of the capacitor must be 90° out of phase with the applied voltage.

3. When $v_C$ across a 1-$\mu$F $C$ drops from 43 to 42 V in 1 s, the discharge current $i_C$ equals ($a$) 1 $\mu$A; ($b$) 42 $\mu$A; ($c$) 43 $\mu$A; ($d$) 43 A.

4. In a sine-wave ac circuit with $R$ and $C$ in parallel, ($a$) the voltage across $C$ lags the voltage across $R$ by 90°; ($b$) resistive $I_R$ is 90° out of phase with $I_C$; ($c$) $I_R$ and $I_C$ are in phase; ($d$) $I_R$ and $I_C$ are 180° out of phase.

5. In a sine-wave ac circuit with a 90-$\Omega$ $R$ in series with a 90-$\Omega$ $X_C$, the phase angle equals ($a$) −90°; ($b$) −45°; ($c$) 0°; ($d$) 90°.

6. The combined impedance of a 1000-$\Omega$ $R$ in parallel with a 1000-$\Omega$ $X_C$ equals ($a$) 500 $\Omega$; ($b$) 707 $\Omega$; ($c$) 1000 $\Omega$; ($d$) 2000 $\Omega$.

7. With 100 V applied across two series capacitors of 5 $\mu$F each, the voltage across each capacitor will be ($a$) 5 V; ($b$) 33$\frac{1}{3}$ V; ($c$) 50 V; ($d$) 66$\frac{2}{3}$ V.

8. In a sine-wave ac circuit with $X_C$ and $R$ in series, the ($a$) voltages across $R$ and $X_C$ are in phase; ($b$) voltages across $R$ and $X_C$ are 180° out of phase; ($c$) voltage across $R$ leads the voltage across $X_C$ by 90°; ($d$) voltage across $R$ lags the voltage across $X_C$ by 90°.

9. A 0.01-$\mu$F capacitance in series with $R$ is used as a coupling capacitor $C_C$ for 1000 Hz. At 10,000 Hz: ($a$) $C_C$ has too much reactance to be good for coupling; ($b$) $C_C$ has less reactance, which improves the coupling; ($c$) $C_C$ has the same reactance and coupling; ($d$) the voltage across $R$ is reduced by one-tenth.

10. In an $RC$ coupling circuit the phase angle is ($a$) 90°; ($b$) close to 0°; ($c$) −90°; ($d$) 180°.

1. (a) Why does a capacitor charge when the applied voltage increases? (b) Why does the capacitor discharge when the applied voltage decreases?
2. A sine wave of voltage $V$ is applied across a capacitor $C$. (a) Draw the schematic diagram. (b) Draw the sine waves of voltage and current out of phase by 90°. (c) Draw a phasor diagram showing the phase angle of $-90°$ between $V$ and $I$.
3. Why will a circuit with $R$ and $X_C$ in series be less capacitive as the frequency of the applied voltage is increased?
4. Define the following: coupling capacitor, sawtooth voltage, capacitive voltage divider.
5. Give two comparisons between $RC$ circuits with sine-wave voltage applied and nonsinusoidal voltage applied.
6. State two troubles possible in coupling capacitors and describe briefly how you would check the capacitors with an ohmmeter.
7. Explain the function of $R$ and $C$ in an $RC$ coupling circuit for an ac signal from one transistor amplifier to the next stage.
8. Explain briefly why a capacitor is able to block dc voltage.
9. What is the waveshape of $i_C$ for a sine-wave $v_C$?
10. Explain why the impedance $Z_{EQ}$ of a parallel $RC$ circuit decreases as the frequency increases.
11. In a series $RC$ circuit explain why $\theta_Z$ increases (becomes more negative) as frequency decreases.

**ANSWERS TO ODD-NUMBERED PROBLEMS AT BACK OF BOOK.**

1. A 40-$\Omega$ $R$ is in series with a 30-$\Omega$ $X_C$ across a 100-V sine-wave ac source. (a) Draw the schematic diagram. (b) Calculate $Z_T$. (c) Calculate $I$. (d) Calculate the voltages across $R$ and $C$. (e) What is the phase angle of the circuit?
2. A 40-$\Omega$ $R$ and a 30-$\Omega$ $X_C$ are in parallel across a 100-V sine-wave ac source. (a) Draw the schematic diagram. (b) Calculate each branch current. (c) How much is $I_T$? (d) Calculate $Z_{EQ}$. (e) What is the phase angle of the circuit? (f) Compare the phase angle of the voltage across $R$ and $X_C$.
3. Draw the schematic diagram of a capacitor in series with a 20-k$\Omega$ resistance across a 10-Vac source. What size $C$ is needed for equal voltages across $R$ and $X_C$ at frequencies of 100 Hz and 100 kHz?
4. Draw the schematic diagram of two capacitors $C_1$ and $C_2$ in series across 10,000 V. The $C_1$ is 900 pF and has 9000 V across it. (a) How much is the voltage across $C_2$? (b) How much is the capacitance of $C_2$?
5. In Fig. 19-2$a$, how much is $C$ for the $X_C$ value of 100 $\Omega$ at frequencies of 60 Hz, 1000 Hz, and 1 MHz?
6. A 1500-$\Omega$ $R$ is in series with a 0.01-$\mu$F $C$ across a 30-V source with a frequency of 8 kHz. Calculate $X_C$, $Z_T$, $\theta_Z$, $I$, $V_R$, and $V_C$.

7. The same $R$ and $C$ as in Prob. 6 are in parallel. Calculate $I_C$, $I_R$, $I_T$, $\theta_I$, $Z_{EQ}$, $V_R$, and $V_C$.

8. A 0.05-$\mu$F capacitor is in series with a 50,000-$\Omega$ $R$ and a 10-V source. Tabulate the values of $X_C$, $I$, $V_R$, and $V_C$ at the frequencies of 0 (for steady dc voltage), 20, 60, 100, 500, 5000, and 15,000 Hz.

9. A capacitive voltage divider has $C_1$ of 1 $\mu$F, $C_2$ of 2 $\mu$F, and $C_3$ of 4 $\mu$F in series across a 700-V source $V_T$. (a) Calculate $V_1$, $V_2$, and $V_3$ for a steady dc source. (b) Calculate $V_1$, $V_2$, and $V_3$ for an ac source with a frequency of 400 Hz.

10. (a) A 40-$\Omega$ $X_C$ and a 30-$\Omega$ $R$ are in series across a 120-V source. Calculate $Z_T$, $I$, and $\theta_Z$. (b) The same $X_C$ and $R$ are in parallel. Calculate $I_T$, $Z_{EQ}$, and $\theta_I$.

11. A 500-$\Omega$ $R$ is in series with 300-$\Omega$ $X_C$. Find $Z_T$, $I$, and $\theta_Z$. $V_T = 120$ V.

12. A 300-$\Omega$ $R$ is in series with a 500-$\Omega$ $X_C$. Find $Z_T$, $I$, and $\theta_Z$. Compare $\theta_Z$ here with Prob. 11, with the same 120 V applied.

13. A 500-$\Omega$ $R$ is parallel with a 300-$\Omega$ $X_C$. Find $I_T$, $Z_{EQ}$, and $\theta_I$. Compare $\theta_I$ here with $\theta_Z$ in Prob. 11, with the same 120 V applied.

14. For the waveshape of capacitor voltage $v_C$ in Fig. 19-8, show the corresponding charge and discharge current $i_C$, with values for a 200-pF capacitance.

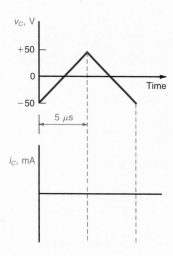

FIG. 19-8   Waveshapes for Prob. 14.

15. Calculate the values needed in Fig. 19-6a for the same voltage division but with a frequency of 60 Hz for $V_T$.

16. Find the angle $\theta_Z$ for $X_C$ and $R$ in series for the following combinations. (a) $X_C$ is 5200 $\Omega$ and $R$ is 5200 $\Omega$. (b) $X_C$ is 2600 $\Omega$ and $R$ is 5200 $\Omega$. (c) $X_C$ is 520 $\Omega$ and $R$ is 5200 $\Omega$. (d) $X_C$ is 52 $\Omega$ and $R$ is 5200 $\Omega$. (e) $X_C$ is 5200$\Omega$ and $R$ is 2600 $\Omega$.

17. Calculate the angle $\theta_Z$ for the $RC$ coupling in Fig. 19-5.

18. Find the angle $\theta_I$ for $I_C$ and $I_R$ in parallel with the same combinations as in Prob. 16. Assume $V_A$ of 10 V to determine $I_C$ and $I_R$ in mA units.

19. How much $C$ is needed for $X_C$ of 52 $\Omega$ at the frequency of 4 MHz?

20. In Fig. 19-9, calculate $X_C$, $Z_T$, $I$, $V_C$, $V_R$, and $\theta_Z$.

21. Repeat Prob. 20 if $f = 500$ Hz.

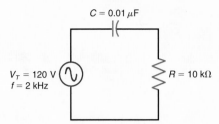

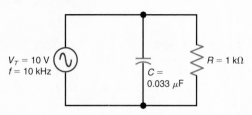

FIG. 19-9   Circuit for Probs. 20 and 21.          FIG. 19-10   Circuit for Probs. 22, 23, and 24.

22. In Fig. 19-10, calculate $X_C$, $I_C$, $I_R$, $I_T$, $Z_{EQ}$, and $\theta_I$.
23. Repeat Prob. 22 if $f = 5$ kHz.
24. In Fig. 19-10, calculate $Z_{EQ}$ if another 1-k$\Omega$ $R$ is added in parallel with the 1-k$\Omega$ $R$ shown ($f = 10$ kHz).
25. In Fig. 19-11, calculate the voltages, with respect to ground, at points A, B, and C.
26. In Fig. 19-12, show the corresponding charge and discharge current for the waveshape of capacitor voltage shown.
27. Calculate the minimum coupling capacitance $C_C$ in series with a 10-k$\Omega$ $R$ if the frequency of the applied voltage ranges from: **(a)** 100 Hz to 10 kHz; **(b)** 15 kHz to 300 kHz.

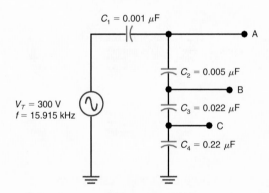

FIG. 19-11   Circuit for Prob. 25.

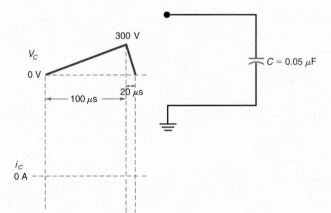

FIG. 19-12   Diagram and circuit for Prob. 26.

## CRITICAL THINKING

1. In Fig. 19-13, calculate $X_C$, $Z_T$, $I$, $f$, $V_T$, and $V_R$.
2. In Fig. 19-14, calculate $I_C$, $I_R$, $V_T$, $X_C$, $C$, and $Z_{EQ}$.
3. In Fig. 19-15, calculate $I_C$, $I_R$, $I_T$, $X_C$, $R$, and $C$.

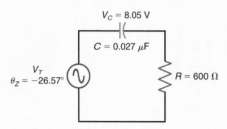

FIG. 19-13  Circuit for Critical Thinking Prob. 1.

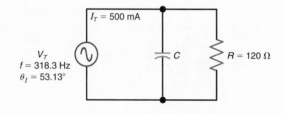

FIG. 19-14  Circuit for Critical Thinking Prob. 2.

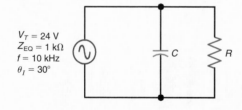

FIG. 19-15  Circuit for Critical Thinking Prob. 3.

## ANSWERS TO TEST-POINT QUESTIONS

**19-1 a.** $0°$
   **b.** $90°$
   **c.** lag

**19-2 a.** $28.28 \ \Omega$
   **b.** $28.28 \ V$
   **c.** $\theta_Z = -45°$

**19-3 a.** $46.7°$
   **b.** $90°$
   **c.** $43.3°$

**19-4 a.** $2.828 \ A$
   **b.** $\theta_I = 45°$

**19-5 a.** $35 \ \Omega$
   **b.** $2 \ pF$

**19-6 a.** $V_1 = 18 \ kV$
      $V_2 = 2 \ kV$
   **b.** $X_{C_T} = 120 \ \Omega$

**19-7 a.** $dv/dt = 1 \times 10^6 \ V/s$
   **b.** $i_C = 300 \ \mu A$

# REVIEW: CHAPTERS 17 TO 19

## SUMMARY

- A capacitor consists of two conductors separated by an insulator, which is a dielectric material. With voltage applied to the conductors, charge is stored in the dielectric. One coulomb of charge stored with one volt applied corresponds to one farad of capacitance $C$. The common units of capacitance are microfarads (1 $\mu$F = $10^{-6}$ F) or picofarads (1 pF = $10^{-12}$ F).

- Capacitance increases with plate area and larger values of dielectric constant but decreases with increased distance between the plates.

- The most common types of capacitors are air, film, paper, mica, disk ceramic, surface-mount (chip), and electrolytic. Electrolytics must be connected in the correct polarity. The capacitance coding systems for film, disk ceramic, mica, and tantalum capacitors are illustrated in Figs. 17-11, 17-13, 17-16, and 17-20, respectively. The different capacitance coding systems used with chip capacitors are illustrated in Figs. 17-17, 17-18, and 17-19.

- The total capacitance of parallel capacitors is the sum of the individual values; the combined capacitance of series capacitors is found by the reciprocal formula. These rules are opposite from the formulas used for resistors in series or parallel.

- When checking a capacitor with an ohmmeter, a good capacitor shows charging current and then the ohmmeter reads a very high value of ohms equal to the insulation resistance. A short-circuited capacitor reads zero ohms; an open capacitor does not show any charging current.

- $X_C = 1/(2\pi f C)$ $\Omega$, where $f$ is in hertz, $C$ is in farads, and $X_C$ is in ohms. The higher the frequency and the greater the capacitance, the smaller $X_C$ is.

- The total $X_C$ of capacitive reactances in series equals the sum of the individual values, just as for series resistances. The series reactances have the same current. The voltage across each $X_C$ equals $IX_C$.

- With parallel capacitive reactances the combined reactance is calculated using the reciprocal formula, as for parallel resistances. Each branch current equals $V_A/X_C$. The total current is the sum of the individual branch currents.

- A common application of $X_C$ is in AF or RF coupling capacitors, which have low reactance for higher frequencies but more reactance for lower frequencies.

- Reactance $X_C$ is a phasor quantity where the voltage across the capacitor lags 90° behind its charge and discharge current.

- In a series $RC$ circuit, $R$ and $X_C$ are added by phasors because the voltage drops are 90° out of phase. Therefore, the total impedance $Z_T$ equals $\sqrt{R^2 + X_C{}^2}$; the current $I$ equals $V_T/Z_T$.

- For parallel $RC$ circuits, the resistive and capacitive branch currents are added by phasors, $I_T = \sqrt{I_R{}^2 + I_C{}^2}$; the impedance $Z_{EQ} = V_A/I_T$.

- Capacitive charge or discharge current $i_C$ is equal to $C(dv/dt)$ for any waveshape of $v_C$.

- For series capacitors the amount of voltage drop is inversely proportional to its capacitance. That is, the smaller the capacitance, the larger is the voltage drop.

## REVIEW SELF-TEST

### ANSWERS AT BACK OF BOOK.

Answer True or False.

1. A capacitor can store charge because it has a dielectric between two conductors.
2. With 100-V applied, a 0.01-$\mu$F capacitor stores 1 $\mu$C of charge.
3. The smaller the capacitance, the higher is the potential difference across it for a given amount of charge stored in the capacitor.
4. A 250-pF capacitance equals $250 \times 10^{-12}$ F.
5. The thinner the dielectric, the greater is the capacitance and the lower is the breakdown voltage rating for a capacitor.
6. Larger plate area increases capacitance.
7. Capacitors in series provide less capacitance but a higher breakdown voltage rating for the combination.
8. Capacitors in parallel increase the total capacitance with the same voltage rating.
9. Two 0.01-$\mu$F capacitors in parallel have a total $C$ of 0.005 $\mu$F.
10. A good 0.1-$\mu$F film capacitor will show charging current and read 500 M$\Omega$ or more on an ohmmeter.
11. If the capacitance is doubled, the reactance is halved.
12. If the frequency is doubled, the capacitive reactance is doubled.
13. The reactance of a 0.1-$\mu$F capacitor at 60 Hz is approximately 60 $\Omega$.
14. In a series $RC$ circuit, the voltage across $X_C$ lags 90° behind the current.
15. The phase angle of a series $RC$ circuit can be any angle between 0° and $-90$°, depending on the ratio of $X_C$ to $R$.
16. In a parallel $RC$ circuit, the voltage across $X_C$ lags 90° behind its capacitive branch current.
17. In a parallel circuit of two resistances with 1 A in each branch, the total line current equals 1.414 A.
18. A 1000-$\Omega$ $X_C$ in parallel with a 1000-$\Omega$ $R$ has a combined $Z$ of 707 $\Omega$.
19. A 1000-$\Omega$ $X_C$ in series with a 1000-$\Omega$ $R$ has a total $Z$ of 1414 $\Omega$.
20. Neglecting its sign, the phase angle is 45° for both circuits in Probs. 18 and 19.
21. The total impedance of a 1-M$\Omega$ $R$ in series with a 5-$\Omega$ $X_C$ is approximately 1 M$\Omega$ with a phase angle of 0°.
22. The combined impedance of a 5-$\Omega$ $R$ in parallel with a 1-M$\Omega$ $X_C$ is approximately 5 $\Omega$ with a phase angle of 0°.
23. Resistance and impedance are both measured in ohms.
24. The impedance $Z$ of an $RC$ circuit can change with frequency because the circuit includes reactance.
25. Capacitors in series have the same charge and discharge current.
26. Capacitors in parallel have the same voltage.

**27.** The phasor combination of a 30-$\Omega$ $R$ in series with a 40-$\Omega$ $X_C$ equals 70 $\Omega$ impedance.

**28.** A film capacitor coded as 103 has a value of 0.001 $\mu$F.

**29.** Capacitive current can be considered leading current in a series circuit.

**30.** In a series $RC$ circuit, the higher the value of $X_C$, the greater is its voltage drop compared with the $IR$ drop.

## REFERENCES

Bogart, T.: *Electric Circuits,* Glencoe/McGraw-Hill, Columbus, Ohio.

Schuler, C., and Fowler, R.: *Electric Circuit Analysis,* Glencoe/McGraw-Hill, Columbus, Ohio.

# CHAPTER 20

# INDUCTANCE

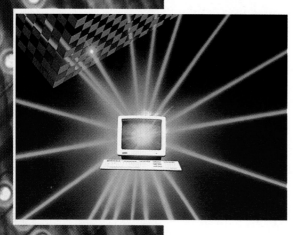

Inductance is the ability of a conductor to produce induced voltage when the current varies. A long wire has more inductance than a short wire, since more conductor length cut by magnetic flux produces more induced voltage. Similarly, a coil has more inductance than the equivalent length of straight wire because the coil concentrates magnetic flux. Components manufactured to have a definite value of inductance are just coils of wire, thus, called *inductors*. The symbol for inductance is $L$, and the unit is the henry (H).

The wire for a coil can be wound around a hollow, insulating tube. Or the coil can be just the wire itself. This type is an air-core coil, as the magnetic field of current in the coil is in air. With another basic type, the wire is wound on an iron core, in order to concentrate the magnetic flux for more inductance.

Air-core coils are used in RF circuits because higher frequencies need less $L$ for the required inductive effect. Iron-core inductors are used in the audio-frequency range, especially the ac power-line frequency of 60 Hz, and for lower frequencies in general.

# CHAPTER OBJECTIVES

*Upon completion of this chapter, you should be able to:*

- *Explain* the concept of self-inductance.
- *Define* the henry unit of inductance and *define* mutual inductance.
- *Calculate* the inductance when the induced voltage and rate of current change are known.
- *List* the physical factors affecting the inductance of an inductor.
- *Calculate* the induced voltage across an inductor given the inductance and rate of current change.
- *Explain* how induced voltage opposes a change in current.
- *Describe* how a transformer works and *list* important transformer ratings.
- *Calculate* the currents, voltages, and impedances of a transformer circuit.
- *Identify* the different types of transformer cores.
- *Calculate* the total inductance of series connected inductors.
- *Calculate* the equivalent inductance of parallel connected inductors.
- *List* some common troubles with inductors.

## IMPORTANT TERMS IN THIS CHAPTER

| | | |
|---|---|---|
| air-core | henry unit | phasing dots |
| apparent power | hysteresis | reflected impedance |
| autotransformer | impedance matching | self-inductance |
| counter emf (Cemf) | iron-core | stray inductance |
| coupling coefficient | leakage flux | transformer |
| eddy current | Lenz' law | turns ratio |
| efficiency | magnetic coupling | Variac |
| ferrite | mutual inductance | |

## TOPICS COVERED IN THIS CHAPTER

| | |
|---|---|
| **20-1** Induction by Alternating Current | **20-9** Core Losses |
| **20-2** Self-Inductance $L$ | **20-10** Types of Cores |
| **20-3** Self-Induced Voltage $v_L$ | **20-11** Variable Inductance |
| **20-4** How $v_L$ Opposes a Change in Current | **20-12** Inductances in Series or Parallel |
| **20-5** Mutual Inductance $L_M$ | **20-13** Stray Inductance |
| **20-6** Transformers | **20-14** Energy in Magnetic Field of Inductance |
| **20-7** Transformer Ratings | **20-15** Troubles in Coils |
| **20-8** Impedance Transformation | |

Induced voltage is the result of flux cutting across a conductor. This action can be produced by physical motion of either the magnetic field or the conductor. When the current in a conductor varies in amplitude, however, the variations of current and its associated magnetic field are equivalent to motion of the flux. As the current increases in value, the magnetic field expands outward from the conductor. When the current decreases, the field collapses into the conductor. As the field expands and collapses with changes of current, the flux is effectively in motion. Therefore, a varying current can produce induced voltage without the need for motion of the conductor.

Figure 20-1 illustrates the changes in the magnetic field associated with a sine wave of alternating current. Since the alternating current varies in amplitude and reverses in direction, its associated magnetic field has the same variations. At point A, the current is zero and there is no flux. At B, the positive direction of current provides some field lines taken here in the counterclockwise direction. Point C has maximum current and maximum counterclockwise flux.

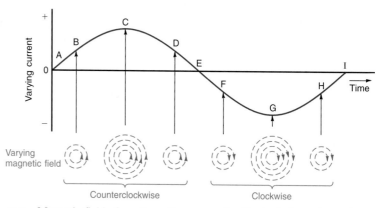

FIG. 20-1   Magnetic field of an alternating current is effectively in motion as it expands and contracts with the current variations.

At D there is less flux than at C. Now the field is collapsing because of the reduced current. At E, with zero current, there is no magnetic flux. The field can be considered as having collapsed into the wire.

The next half-cycle of current allows the field to expand and collapse again, but the directions are reversed. When the flux expands at points F and G, the field lines are clockwise, corresponding to current in the negative direction. From G to H and I, this clockwise field collapses into the wire.

The result of an expanding and collapsing field, then, is the same as that of a field in motion. This moving flux cuts across the conductor that is providing the current, producing induced voltage in the wire itself. Furthermore, any other conductor in the field, whether carrying current or not, also is cut by the varying flux and has induced voltage.

It is important to note that induction by a varying current results from the change in current, not the current value itself. The current must change to provide motion of the flux. A steady direct current of 1000 A, as an example of a large current, cannot produce any induced voltage as long as the current value is constant. A current of 1 $\mu$A changing to 2 $\mu$A, however, does induce voltage. Also, the faster the current changes, the higher the induced voltage because when the flux moves at a higher speed, it can induce more voltage.

Since inductance is a measure of induced voltage, the amount of inductance has an important effect in any circuit in which the current changes. The inductance is an additional characteristic of the circuit besides its resistance. The characteristics of inductance are important in:

1. *AC circuits.* Here the current is continuously changing and producing induced voltage. Lower frequencies of alternating current require more inductance to produce the same amount of induced voltage as a higher-frequency current. The current can have any waveform, as long as the amplitude is changing.
2. *DC circuits in which the current changes in value.* It is not necessary for the current to reverse direction. One example is a dc circuit being turned on or off. When the direct current is changing between zero and its steady value, the inductance affects the circuit at the time of switching. This effect with a sudden change is called the *transient response.* A steady direct current that does not change in value is not affected by inductance, however, because there can be no induced voltage without a change in current.

---

**TEST-POINT QUESTION 20-1**

Answers at end of chapter.
**a.** For the same number of turns and frequency, which has more inductance, a coil with an iron core or one without an iron core?
**b.** In Fig. 20-1, are the changes of current faster at time B or C?

## 20-2 SELF-INDUCTANCE *L*

The ability of a conductor to induce voltage in itself when the current changes is its *self-inductance* or simply *inductance.* The symbol for inductance is *L*, for linkages of the magnetic flux, and its unit is the *henry* (H). This unit is named after Joseph Henry (1797–1878).

**DEFINITION OF THE HENRY UNIT**   As illustrated in Fig. 20-2, one henry is the amount of inductance that allows one volt to be induced when the current changes at the rate of one ampere per second. The formula is

$$L = \frac{v_L}{di/dt} \qquad (20\text{-}1)$$

where $v_L$ is in volts and $di/dt$ is the current change in amperes per second.

Again the symbol *d* is used to indicate an infinitesimally small change in current with time. The factor $di/dt$ for the current variation with respect to time

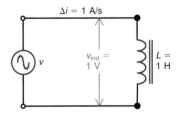

FIG. 20-2   When a current change of 1 A/s induces 1 V across *L*, its inductance equals 1 H.

really specifies how fast the current's associated magnetic flux is cutting the conductor to produce $v_L$.

## Example

**EXAMPLE 1** The current in an inductor changes from 12 to 16 A in 1 s. How much is the $di/dt$ rate of current change in amperes per second?

**ANSWER** The $di$ is the difference between 16 and 12, or 4 A in 1 s. Then

$$\frac{di}{dt} = 4 \text{ A/s}$$

**EXAMPLE 2** The current in an inductor changes by 50 mA in 2 $\mu$s. How much is the $di/dt$ rate of current change in amperes per second?

**ANSWER** $\dfrac{di}{dt} = \dfrac{50 \times 10^{-3}}{2 \times 10^{-6}} = 25 \times 10^3$

$$\frac{di}{dt} = 25{,}000 \text{ A/s}$$

**EXAMPLE 3** How much is the inductance of a coil that induces 40 V when its current changes at the rate of 4 A/s?

**ANSWER** $L = \dfrac{v_L}{di/dt} = \dfrac{40}{4}$

$$L = 10 \text{ H}$$

**EXAMPLE 4** How much is the inductance of a coil that induces 1000 V when its current changes at the rate of 50 mA in 2 $\mu$s?

**ANSWER** For this example, the $1/dt$ factor in the denominator of Formula (20-1) can be inverted to the numerator.

$$L = \frac{v_L}{di/dt} = \frac{v_L \times dt}{di}$$

$$= \frac{1 \times 10^3 \times 2 \times 10^{-6}}{50 \times 10^{-3}}$$

$$= \frac{2 \times 10^{-3}}{50 \times 10^{-3}} = \frac{2}{50}$$

$$L = 0.04 \text{ H or } 40 \text{ mH}$$

Notice that the smaller inductance in Example 4 produces much more $v_L$ than the inductance in Example 3. The very fast current change in Example 4 is equivalent to 25,000 A/s.

**INDUCTANCE OF COILS** In terms of physical construction, the inductance depends on how a coil is wound. Note the following factors.

1. A greater number of turns $N$ increases $L$ because more voltage can be induced. Actually $L$ increases in proportion to $N^2$. Double the number of turns in the same area and length increases the inductance four times.
2. More area $A$ enclosed by each turn increases $L$. This means a coil with larger turns has more inductance. The $L$ increases in direct proportion to $A$ and as the square of the diameter of each turn.
3. The $L$ increases with the permeability of the core. For an air core $\mu_r$ is 1. With a magnetic core, $L$ is increased by the $\mu_r$ factor as the magnetic flux is concentrated in the coil.
4. The $L$ decreases with more length for the same number of turns, as the magnetic field then is less concentrated.

These physical characteristics of a coil are illustrated in Fig. 20-3. For a long coil, where the length is at least ten times the diameter, the inductance can be calculated from the formula

$$ \blacktriangleright \quad L = \mu_r \times \frac{N^2 \times A}{l} \times 1.26 \times 10^{-6} \quad \text{H} \qquad \textbf{(20-2)} $$

where $L$ is in henrys, $l$ is in meters and $A$ is in square meters. The constant factor $1.26 \times 10^{-6}$ is the absolute permeability of air or vacuum, in SI units, to calculate $L$ in henrys.

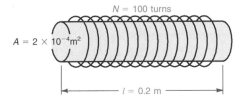

$N = 100$ turns

$A = 2 \times 10^{-4} \text{m}^2$

$l = 0.2$ m

**FIG. 20-3** Physical factors for inductance $L$ of a coil. See text for calculating $L$.

For the air-core coil in Fig. 20-3,

$$ L = 1 \times \frac{10^4 \times 2 \times 10^{-4}}{0.2} \times 1.26 \times 10^{-6} $$

$$ L = 12.6 \times 10^{-6} \text{ H} = 12.6 \ \mu\text{H} $$

This value means that the coil can produce a self-induced voltage of 12.6 $\mu$V when its current changes at the rate of 1 A/s, as $v_L = L(di/dt)$. Furthermore, if the coil has an iron core with $\mu_r = 100$, then $L$ will be 100 times greater.

**TYPICAL COIL INDUCTANCE VALUES** Air-core coils for RF applications have $L$ values in millihenrys (mH) and microhenrys ($\mu$H). A typical air-core RF inductor (called a *choke*) is shown with its schematic symbol in Fig. 20-4a. Note that

$$ 1 \text{ mH} = 1 \times 10^{-3} \text{ H} $$

$$ 1 \ \mu\text{H} = 1 \times 10^{-6} \text{ H} $$

For example, an RF coil for the radio broadcast band of 535 to 1605 kHz may have an inductance $L$ of 250 $\mu$H or 0.250 mH.

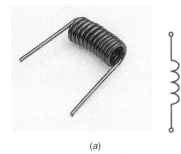

(a)

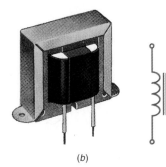

(b)

**FIG. 20-4** Typical inductors with symbols. (a) Air-core coil used as RF choke. Length is 2 in. (b) Iron-core coil used for 60 Hz. Height is 2 in.

Iron-core inductors for the 60-Hz power line and for audio frequencies have inductance values of about 1 to 25 H. An iron-core choke is shown in Fig. 20-4b.

──────── TEST-POINT QUESTION 20-2 ────────

Answers at end of chapter.
**a.** A coil induces 2 V with *di/dt* of 1 A/s. How much is *L*?
**b.** A coil has *L* of 8 mH with 125 turns. If the number of turns is doubled, how much will *L* be?

## 20-3 SELF-INDUCED VOLTAGE $v_L$

The self-induced voltage across an inductance *L* produced by a change in current *di/dt* can be stated as

▶ $$v_L = L \frac{di}{dt} \qquad\qquad (20\text{-}3)$$

where $v_L$ is in volts, *L* in henrys, and *di/dt* in amperes per second. This formula is just an inverted version of Formula (20-1) which defines inductance.

Actually both versions are based on Formula (15-1): $v = N(d\phi/dt)$ for magnetism. This gives the voltage in terms of how much magnetic flux is cut by a conductor per second. When the magnetic flux associated with the current varies the same as *i*, then Formula (20-3) gives the same results for calculating induced voltage. Remember also that the induced voltage across the coil is actually the result of inducing electrons to move in the conductor, so that there is also an induced current. In using Formula (20-3) to calculate $v_L$, just multiply *L* by the *di/dt* factor.

*Example*

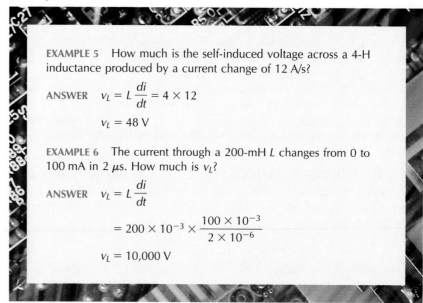

EXAMPLE 5   How much is the self-induced voltage across a 4-H inductance produced by a current change of 12 A/s?

ANSWER   $v_L = L \dfrac{di}{dt} = 4 \times 12$

$v_L = 48$ V

EXAMPLE 6   The current through a 200-mH *L* changes from 0 to 100 mA in 2 $\mu$s. How much is $v_L$?

ANSWER   $v_L = L \dfrac{di}{dt}$

$= 200 \times 10^{-3} \times \dfrac{100 \times 10^{-3}}{2 \times 10^{-6}}$

$v_L = 10{,}000$ V

Note the high voltage induced in the 200-mH inductance because of the fast change in current.

The induced voltage is an actual voltage that can be measured, although $v_L$ is produced only while the current is changing. When $di/dt$ is present for only a short time, $v_L$ is in the form of a voltage pulse. With a sine-wave current, which is always changing, $v_L$ is a sinusoidal voltage 90° out of phase with $i_L$.

---

### TEST-POINT QUESTION 20-3

Answers at end of chapter.
**a.** If $L$ is 2 H and $di/dt$ is 1 A/s, how much is $v_L$?
**b.** For the same coil, the $di/dt$ is increased to 100 A/s. How much is $v_L$?

## 20-4 HOW $v_L$ OPPOSES A CHANGE IN CURRENT

By Lenz' law, the induced voltage $v_L$ must produce current with a magnetic field that opposes the change of current that induces $v_L$. The polarity of $v_L$, therefore, depends on the direction of the current variation $di$. When $di$ increases, $v_L$ has the polarity that opposes the increase of current; when $di$ decreases, $v_L$ has the opposite polarity to oppose the decrease of current.

In both cases, the change of current is opposed by the induced voltage. Otherwise, $v_L$ could increase to an unlimited amount without the need for adding any work. *Inductance, therefore, is the characteristic that opposes any change in current.* This is the reason why an induced voltage is often called a *counter emf* or *back emf*.

More details of applying Lenz' law to determine the polarity of $v_L$ in a circuit are illustrated in Fig. 20-5. Note the directions carefully. In Fig. 20-5a, the electron flow is into the top of the coil. This current is increasing. By Lenz' law, $v_L$ must have the polarity needed to oppose the increase. The induced voltage shown with the top side negative opposes the increase in current. The reason is that this polarity of $v_L$ can produce current in the opposite direction, from minus to plus in the external circuit. Note that for this opposing current, $v_L$ is the generator. This action tends to keep the current from increasing.

In Fig. 20-5b, the source is still producing electron flow into the top of the coil, but $i$ is decreasing, because the source voltage is decreasing. By Lenz' law, $v_L$ must have the polarity needed to oppose the decrease in current. The induced voltage shown with the top side positive now opposes the decrease. The reason is that this polarity of $v_L$ can produce current in the same direction, tending to keep the current from decreasing.

In Fig. 20-5c, the voltage source reverses polarity to produce current in the opposite direction, with electron flow into the bottom of the coil. This reversed direction of current is now increasing. The polarity of $v_L$ must oppose the increase. As shown, now the bottom of the coil is made negative by $v_L$ to produce current opposing the source current. Finally, in Fig. 20-5d the reversed current is decreasing. This decrease is opposed by the polarity shown for $v_L$ to keep the current flowing in the same direction as the source current.

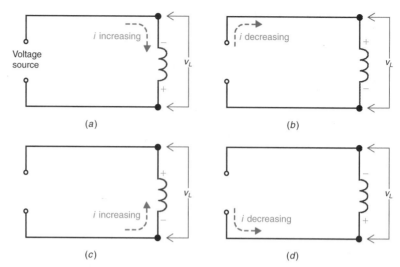

FIG. 20-5 Determining the polarity of $V_L$ that opposes the change in $i$. (*a*) The $i$ is increasing, and $V_L$ has the polarity that produces an opposing current. (*b*) The $i$ is decreasing, and $V_L$ produces an aiding current. (*c*) The $i$ is increasing but is flowing in the opposite direction. (*d*) The same direction of $i$ as in (*c*), but with decreasing values.

Notice that the polarity of $v_L$ reverses for either a reversal of direction for $i$ or a reversal of change in $di$ between increasing or decreasing values. When both the direction of the current and the direction of change are reversed, as in a comparison of Fig. 20-5*a* and *d*, the polarity of $v_L$ remains unchanged.

Sometimes the formulas for induced voltage are written with a minus sign, in order to indicate the fact that $v_L$ opposes the change, as specified by Lenz' law. However, the negative sign is omitted here so that the actual polarity of the self-induced voltage can be determined in typical circuits.

In summary, Lenz' law states that the reaction $v_L$ opposes its cause, which is the change in $i$. When $i$ is increasing, $v_L$ produces an opposing current. For the opposite case when $i$ is decreasing, $v_L$ produces an aiding current.

## TEST-POINT QUESTION 20-4

Answers at end of chapter.

Answer True or False.
**a.** In Fig. 20-5*a* and *b* the $v_L$ has opposite polarities.
**b.** In Fig. 20-5*b* and *c* the polarity of $v_L$ is the same.

## 20-5 MUTUAL INDUCTANCE $L_M$

When the current in an inductor changes, the varying flux can cut across any other inductor nearby, producing induced voltage in both inductors. In Fig. 20-6, the coil $L_1$ is connected to a generator that produces varying current in the turns. The winding $L_2$ is not connected to $L_1$, but the turns are linked by the magnetic field.

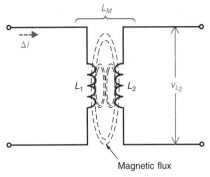

FIG. 20-6   Mutual inductance $L_M$ between $L_1$ and $L_2$ linked by magnetic flux.

A varying current in $L_1$, therefore, induces voltage across $L_1$ and across $L_2$. If all the flux of the current in $L_1$ links all the turns of the coil $L_2$, each turn in $L_2$ will have the same amount of induced voltage as each turn in $L_1$. Furthermore, the induced voltage $v_{L_2}$ can produce current in a load resistance connected across $L_2$.

When the induced voltage produces current in $L_2$, its varying magnetic field induces voltage in $L_1$. The two coils $L_1$ and $L_2$ have mutual inductance, therefore, because current in one can induce voltage in the other.

The unit of mutual inductance is the henry, and the symbol is $L_M$. *Two coils have $L_M$ of 1 H when a current change of 1 A/s in one coil induces 1 V in the other coil.*

The schematic symbol for two coils with mutual inductance is shown in Fig. 20-7a for an air core, and for an iron core in Fig. 20-7b. Iron increases the mutual inductance, since it concentrates magnetic flux. Any magnetic lines that do not link the two coils result in *leakage flux.*

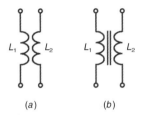

*(a)*          *(b)*

FIG. 20-7   Schematic symbols for two coils with mutual inductance. (*a*) Air core. (*b*) Iron core.

**COEFFICIENT OF COUPLING**   The fraction of total flux from one coil linking another coil is the coefficient of coupling $k$ between the two coils. As examples, if all the flux of $L_1$ in Fig. 20-6 links $L_2$, then $k$ equals 1, or unity coupling; if half the flux of one coil links the other, $k$ equals 0.5. Specifically, the coefficient of coupling is

$$\blacktriangleright \quad k = \frac{\text{flux linkages between } L_1 \text{ and } L_2}{\text{flux produced by } L_1}$$

There are no units for $k$, as it is just a ratio of two values of magnetic flux. The value of $k$ is generally stated as a decimal fraction, like 0.5, rather than as a percent.

The coefficient of coupling is increased by placing the coils close together, possibly with one wound on top of the other, by placing them parallel rather than perpendicular to each other, or by winding the coils on a common iron core. Several examples are shown in Fig. 20-8.

A high value of $k$, called *tight coupling,* allows the current in one coil to induce more voltage in the other coil. *Loose coupling,* with a low value of $k$, has the opposite effect. In the extreme case of zero coefficient of coupling, there is no mutual inductance. Two coils may be placed perpendicular to each other and far apart for essentially zero coupling when it is desired to minimize interaction between the coils.

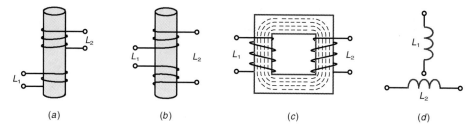

**FIG. 20-8** Examples of coupling between two coils linked by $L_M$. (a) $L_1$ or $L_2$ on paper or plastic form with air core; $k$ is 0.1. (b) $L_1$ wound over $L_2$ for tighter coupling; $k$ is 0.3. (c) $L_1$ and $L_2$ on the same iron core; $k$ is 1. (d) Zero coupling between perpendicular air-core coils.

Air-core coils wound on one form have values of $k$ equal to 0.05 to 0.3, approximately, corresponding to 5 to 30 percent linkage. Coils on a common iron core can be considered to have practically unity coupling, with $k$ equal to 1. As shown in Fig. 20-8c, for both windings $L_1$ and $L_2$ practically all the magnetic flux is in the common iron core. Mutual inductance is also called *mutual coupling*.

### Example

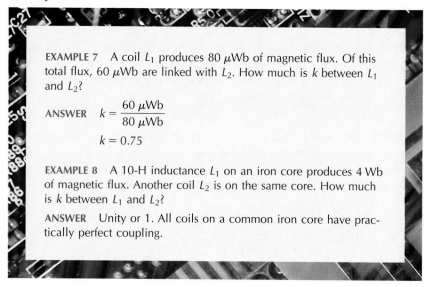

**EXAMPLE 7** A coil $L_1$ produces 80 $\mu$Wb of magnetic flux. Of this total flux, 60 $\mu$Wb are linked with $L_2$. How much is $k$ between $L_1$ and $L_2$?

**ANSWER** $k = \dfrac{60 \ \mu\text{Wb}}{80 \ \mu\text{Wb}}$

$k = 0.75$

**EXAMPLE 8** A 10-H inductance $L_1$ on an iron core produces 4 Wb of magnetic flux. Another coil $L_2$ is on the same core. How much is $k$ between $L_1$ and $L_2$?

**ANSWER** Unity or 1. All coils on a common iron core have practically perfect coupling.

**CALCULATING $L_M$** The mutual inductance increases with higher values for the primary and secondary inductances and tighter coupling:

▶ $$L_M = k \sqrt{L_1 \times L_2} \qquad \text{H} \tag{20-4}$$

where $L_1$ and $L_2$ are the self-inductance values of the two coils, $k$ is the coefficient of coupling, and $L_M$ is the mutual inductance linking $L_1$ and $L_2$, in the same units as $L_1$ and $L_2$. The $k$ factor is needed to indicate the flux linkages between the two coils.

As an example, suppose that $L_1 = 2$ H and $L_2 = 8$ H, with both coils on an iron core for unity coupling. Then the mutual inductance is

$$L_M = 1 \sqrt{2 \times 8} = \sqrt{16} = 4 \text{ H}$$

The value of 4 H for $L_M$ in this example means that when the current changes at the rate of 1 A/s in either coil, it will induce 4 V in the other coil.

## Example

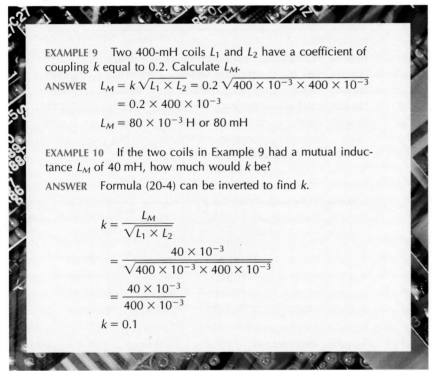

EXAMPLE 9    Two 400-mH coils $L_1$ and $L_2$ have a coefficient of coupling $k$ equal to 0.2. Calculate $L_M$.

ANSWER    $L_M = k \sqrt{L_1 \times L_2} = 0.2 \sqrt{400 \times 10^{-3} \times 400 \times 10^{-3}}$

$$= 0.2 \times 400 \times 10^{-3}$$

$$L_M = 80 \times 10^{-3} \text{ H or } 80 \text{ mH}$$

EXAMPLE 10    If the two coils in Example 9 had a mutual inductance $L_M$ of 40 mH, how much would $k$ be?

ANSWER    Formula (20-4) can be inverted to find $k$.

$$k = \frac{L_M}{\sqrt{L_1 \times L_2}}$$

$$= \frac{40 \times 10^{-3}}{\sqrt{400 \times 10^{-3} \times 400 \times 10^{-3}}}$$

$$= \frac{40 \times 10^{-3}}{400 \times 10^{-3}}$$

$$k = 0.1$$

Notice that the same two coils have one-half the mutual inductance $L_M$, because the coefficient of coupling $k$ is 0.1 instead of 0.2.

To do Example 9 on a calculator that does not have (EXP) key, multiply $L_1 \times L_2$, take the square root of the product, and multiply by $k$. Keep the powers of 10 separate. Specifically, punch in 400 for $L_1$, push the $\otimes$ key, punch in 400 for $L_2$, and push the $\ominus$ key for the product, 16,000. Press the $\sqrt{}$ key, which is sometimes the (2ndF) of the $\boxed{x^2}$ key to get 400. While it is on the display, push the $\otimes$ key, punch in 0.2, and press the $\ominus$ key for the answer of 80. For the powers of 10, $10^{-3} \times 10^{-3} = 10^{-6}$, and the square root is equal to $10^{-3}$ for the unit of mH in the answer.

For Example 10, the formula is $L_M$ divided by the reciprocal of $\sqrt{L_1 \times L_2}$. Specifically, punch in 40 for the value in the numerator, press the $\boxed{(}$ key, multiply $400 \times 400$, and press the $\boxed{)}$ key, followed by the $\sqrt{}$ and $\ominus$ keys. The display will read 0.1. The powers of 10 cancel with $10^{-3}$ in the numerator and denominator. Also, there are no units for $k$, since the units of $L$ cancel.

Answers at end of chapter.

**a.** All the flux from the current in $L_1$ links $L_2$. How much is the coefficient of coupling $k$?

**b.** Mutual inductance $L_M$ is 9 mH with $k$ of 0.2. If $k$ is doubled to 0.4, how much will $L_M$ be?

## 20-6 TRANSFORMERS

The transformer is an important application of mutual inductance. As shown in Fig. 20-9, a transformer has the primary winding inductance $L_P$ connected to a voltage source that produces alternating current, while the secondary winding inductance $L_S$ is connected across the load resistance $R_L$. The purpose of the transformer is to transfer power from the primary, where the generator is connected, to the secondary, where the induced secondary voltage can produce current in the load resistance that is connected across $L_S$.

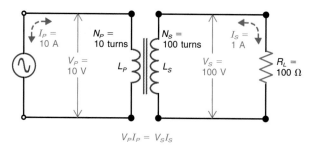

$$V_P I_P = V_S I_S$$

**FIG. 20-9** Iron-core transformer with $1:10$ turns ratio. Primary current $I_P$ induces secondary voltage $V_S$, which produces current in secondary load $R_L$.

Although the primary and secondary are not physically connected to each other, power in the primary is coupled into the secondary by the magnetic field linking the two windings. The transformer is used to provide power for the load resistance $R_L$, instead of connecting $R_L$ directly across the generator, whenever the load requires an ac voltage higher or lower than the generator voltage. By having more or fewer turns in $L_S$, compared with $L_P$, the transformer can step up or step down the generator voltage to provide the required amount of secondary voltage. Typical transformers are shown in Figs. 20-10 and 20-11. It should be noted that a steady dc voltage cannot be stepped up or down by a transformer, because a steady current cannot produce induced voltage.

**TURNS RATIO**   The ratio of the number of turns in the primary to the number in the secondary is the turns ratio of the transformer:

▶   Turns ratio $= \dfrac{N_P}{N_S}$                    **(20-5)**

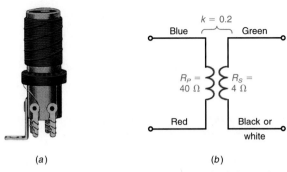

$k = 0.2$

Blue ⌒ Green

$R_P = 40 \, \Omega$   $R_S = 4 \, \Omega$

Red   Black or white

(a)   (b)

FIG. 20-10   (a) Air-core RF transformer. Height is 2 in. (b) Color code and typical dc resistance of windings.

where $N_P$ = number of turns in the primary and $N_S$ = number of turns in the secondary. For example, 500 turns in the primary and 50 turns in the secondary provide a turns ratio of 500/50, or 10:1, which is stated as "ten-to-one."

**VOLTAGE RATIO**   With unity coupling between primary and secondary, the voltage induced in each turn of the secondary is the same as the self-induced voltage of each turn in the primary. Therefore, the voltage ratio is in the same proportion as the turns ratio:

▶
$$\frac{V_P}{V_S} = \frac{N_P}{N_S}$$
**(20-6)**

When the secondary has more turns than the primary, the secondary voltage is higher than the primary voltage and the primary voltage is said to be stepped up. This principle is illustrated in Fig. 20-9 with a step-up ratio of 10/100, or 1:10. When the secondary has fewer turns, the voltage is stepped down.

In either case, the ratio is in terms of the primary voltage, which may be stepped up or down in the secondary winding.

FIG. 20-11   Iron-core power transformer.

These calculations apply only to iron-core transformers with unity coupling. Air-core transformers for RF circuits (as shown in Fig. 20-10a) are generally tuned to resonance. In this case, the resonance factor is considered instead of the turns ratio.

## Example

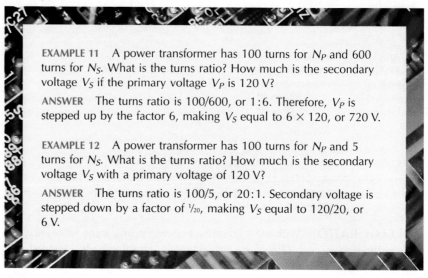

**EXAMPLE 11**   A power transformer has 100 turns for $N_P$ and 600 turns for $N_S$. What is the turns ratio? How much is the secondary voltage $V_S$ if the primary voltage $V_P$ is 120 V?

**ANSWER**   The turns ratio is 100/600, or 1:6. Therefore, $V_P$ is stepped up by the factor 6, making $V_S$ equal to $6 \times 120$, or 720 V.

**EXAMPLE 12**   A power transformer has 100 turns for $N_P$ and 5 turns for $N_S$. What is the turns ratio? How much is the secondary voltage $V_S$ with a primary voltage of 120 V?

**ANSWER**   The turns ratio is 100/5, or 20:1. Secondary voltage is stepped down by a factor of $\frac{1}{20}$, making $V_S$ equal to 120/20, or 6 V.

**SECONDARY CURRENT**   By Ohm's law, the amount of secondary current equals the secondary voltage divided by the resistance in the secondary circuit. In Fig. 20-9, with a value of 100 $\Omega$ for $R_L$ and negligible coil resistance assumed,

$$I_S = \frac{V_S}{R_L} = \frac{100 \text{ V}}{100 \text{ }\Omega} = 1 \text{ A}$$

**POWER IN THE SECONDARY**   The power dissipated by $R_L$ in the secondary is $I_S^2 \times R_L$ or $V_S \times I_S$, which equals 100 W in this example. The calculations are

$$P = I_S^2 \times R_L = 1 \times 100 = 100 \text{ W}$$
$$P = V_S \times I_S = 100 \times 1 = 100 \text{ W}$$

It is important to note that power used by the secondary load, such as $R_L$ in Fig. 20-9, is supplied by the generator in the primary. How the load in the secondary draws power from the generator in the primary can be explained as follows.

With current in the secondary winding, its magnetic field opposes the varying flux of the primary current. The generator must then produce more primary current to maintain the self-induced voltage across $L_P$ and the secondary voltage developed in $L_S$ by mutual induction. If the secondary current doubles, for instance, because the load resistance is reduced one-half, the primary current will also double in value to provide the required power for the secondary. Therefore, the effect of the secondary-load power on the generator is the same as though $R_L$ were in the primary, except that in the secondary the voltage for $R_L$ is stepped up or down by the turns ratio.

**CURRENT RATIO**   With zero losses assumed for the transformer, the power in the secondary equals the power in the primary:

▶   $V_S I_S = V_P I_P$ (20-7)

or

▶   $\dfrac{I_S}{I_P} = \dfrac{V_P}{V_S}$ (20-8)

The current ratio is the inverse of the voltage ratio; that is, voltage step-up in the secondary means current step-down, and vice versa. The secondary does not generate power but only takes it from the primary. Therefore, the current step-up or step-down is in terms of the secondary current $I_S$, which is determined by the load resistance across the secondary voltage. These points are illustrated by the following two examples.

## Example

**EXAMPLE 13**   A transformer with a 1:6 turns ratio has 720 V across 7200 Ω in the secondary. **(a)** How much is $I_S$? **(b)** Calculate the value of $I_P$.

ANSWER

**a.**   $I_S = \dfrac{V_S}{R_L} = \dfrac{720 \text{ V}}{7200 \text{ Ω}}$

$I_S = 0.1 \text{ A}$

**b.**   With a turns ratio of 1:6, the current ratio is 6:1. Therefore,

$I_P = 6 \times I_S = 6 \times 0.1$

$I_P = 0.6 \text{ A}$

**EXAMPLE 14**   A transformer with a 20:1 voltage step-down ratio has 6 V across 0.6 Ω in the secondary. **(a)** How much is $I_S$? **(b)** How much is $I_P$?

ANSWER

**a.**   $I_S = \dfrac{V_S}{R_L} = \dfrac{6 \text{ V}}{0.6 \text{ Ω}}$

$I_S = 10 \text{ A}$

**b.**   $I_P = \frac{1}{20} \times I_S = \frac{1}{20} \times 10$

$I_P = 0.5 \text{ A}$

As an aid in these calculations, remember that the side with the higher voltage has the lower current. The primary and secondary $V$ and $I$ are in the same proportion as the number of turns in the primary and secondary.

**TOTAL SECONDARY POWER EQUALS PRIMARY POWER**   Figure 20-12 illustrates a power transformer with two secondary windings $L_1$ and $L_2$. There can be one, two, or more secondary windings with unity coupling to the primary as long as all the windings are on the same iron core. Each secondary winding has induced voltage in proportion to its turns ratio with the primary winding, which is connected across the 120-V source.

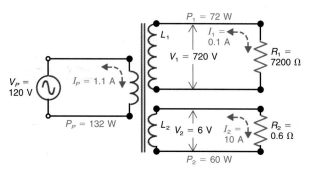

**FIG. 20-12**   Total power used by two secondary loads $R_1$ and $R_2$ is equal to the power supplied by the source in the primary.

The secondary winding $L_1$ has a voltage step-up of 6:1, providing 720 V. The 7200-$\Omega$ load resistance $R_1$, across $L_1$, allows the 720 V to produce 0.1 A for $I_1$ in this secondary circuit. The power here is 720 V $\times$ 0.1 A = 72 W.

The other secondary winding $L_2$ provides voltage step-down, with the ratio 20:1, resulting in 6 V across $R_2$. The 0.6-$\Omega$ load resistance in this circuit allows 10 A for $I_2$. Therefore, the power here is 6 V $\times$ 10 A, or 60 W. Since the windings have separate connections, each can have its individual values of voltage and current.

The total power used in the secondary circuits is supplied by the primary. In this example, the total secondary power is 132 W, equal to 72 W for $P_1$ and 60 W for $P_2$. The power supplied by the 120-V source in the primary then is 72 + 60 = 132 W.

The primary current $I_P$ equals the primary power $P_P$ divided by the primary voltage $V_P$. This is 132 W divided by 120 V, which equals 1.1 A for the primary current. The same value can be calculated as the sum of 0.6 A of primary current providing power for $L_1$ plus 0.5 A of primary current for $L_2$, resulting in the total of 1.1 A as the value of $I_P$.

This example shows how to analyze a loaded power transformer. The main idea is that the primary current depends on the secondary load. The calculations can be summarized as follows:

1.  Calculate $V_S$ from the turns ratio and $V_P$.
2.  Use $V_S$ to calculate $I_S$: $I_S = V_S/R_L$.
3.  Use $I_S$ to calculate $P_S$: $P_S = V_S \times I_S$.
4.  Use $P_S$ to find $P_P$: $P_P = P_S$.
5.  Finally, $I_P$ can be calculated: $I_P = P_P/V_P$.

With more than one secondary, calculate each $I_S$ and $P_S$. Then add all the $P_S$ for the total secondary power, which equals the primary power.

**AUTOTRANSFORMERS**    As illustrated in Fig. 20-13, an autotransformer consists of one continuous coil with a tapped connection such as terminal 2 between the ends at terminals 1 and 3. In Fig. 20-13a the autotransformer steps up the generator voltage. Voltage $V_P$ between 1 and 2 is connected across part of the total turns, while $V_S$ is induced across all the turns. With six times the turns for the secondary voltage, $V_S$ also is six times $V_P$.

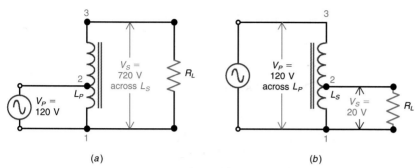

(a)           (b)

FIG. 20-13    Autotransformer with tap at terminal 2 for 10 turns of the complete 60-turn winding. (a) $V_P$ between terminals 1 and 2 stepped up across 1 and 3. (b) $V_P$ between terminals 1 and 3 stepped down across 1 and 2.

In Fig. 20-13b the autotransformer steps down the primary voltage connected across the entire coil. Then the secondary voltage is taken across less than the total turns.

The winding that connects to the voltage source to supply power is the primary, while the secondary is across the load resistance $R_L$. The turns ratio and voltage ratio apply the same way as in a conventional transformer having an isolated secondary winding.

Autotransformers are used often because they are compact, efficient, and usually cost less since they have only one winding. Note that the autotransformer in Fig. 20-13 has only three leads, compared with four leads for the transformer in Fig. 20-9 with an isolated secondary.

**ISOLATION OF THE SECONDARY**    In a transformer with a separate winding for $L_S$, as in Fig. 20-9, the secondary load is not connected directly to the ac power line in the primary. This isolation is an advantage in reducing the chance of electric shock. With an autotransformer, as in Fig. 20-13, the secondary is not isolated. Another advantage of an isolated secondary is the fact that any direct current in the primary is blocked from the secondary. Sometimes a transformer with a 1:1 turns ratio is used just for isolation from the ac power line.

**TRANSFORMER EFFICIENCY**    Efficiency is defined as the ratio of power out to power in. Stated as a formula,

▶        $\text{Efficiency} = \dfrac{P_{\text{out}}}{P_{\text{in}}} \times 100\%$                 **(20-9)**

For example, when the power out in watts equals one-half the power in, the efficiency is one-half, which equals $0.5 \times 100$ percent, or 50 percent. In a transformer, power out is secondary power, while power in is primary power.

Assuming zero losses in the transformer, power out equals power in and the efficiency is 100 percent. Actual power transformers, however, have an efficiency slightly less than 100 percent. The efficiency is approximately 80 to 90 percent for transformers that have high power ratings. Transformers for higher power are more efficient because they require heavier wire, which has less resistance. In a transformer that is less than 100 percent efficient, the primary supplies more than the secondary power. The primary power that is lost is dissipated as heat in the transformer, resulting from $I^2R$ in the conductors and certain losses in the core material. The $R$ of the primary winding is generally about 10 Ω or less, for power transformers.

**TRANSFORMER COLOR CODES**   The colors of the leads show the required connections in electronic circuits. For the RF transformer in Fig. 20-10, the leads are:

Blue—Output electrode of transistor amplifier
Red—DC supply voltage for this electrode
Green—Input electrode of next amplifier
Black or white—Return line of secondary winding

This system applies to all coupling transformers between amplifier stages, including iron-core transformers for audio circuits.
For the power transformer in Fig. 20-11, the primary is connected to the ac power line. The leads are:

Black—Primary leads without tap
Black with yellow—Tap on primary
Red—High-voltage secondary to rectifier in power supply
Red with yellow—Tap on high-voltage secondary
Green-yellow—Low-voltage secondary

---

### TEST-POINT QUESTION 20-6

Answers at end of chapter.
**a.** A transformer connected to the 120-Vac line has a turns ratio of 1 : 2. Calculate the stepped-up $V_S$.
**b.** This $V_S$ is connected across a 2400-Ω $R_L$. Calculate $I_S$.
**c.** An autotransformer has an isolated secondary. True or False?
**d.** With more $I_S$ for the secondary load, does the $I_P$ increase or decrease?

## 20-7 TRANSFORMER RATINGS

Like most other components, transformers have voltage, current, and power ratings which must not be exceeded. Exceeding any of these ratings will usually destroy the transformer. What follows is a brief description of the most important transformer ratings.

**VOLTAGE RATINGS**   Manufacturers of transformers always specify the voltage rating of the primary and secondary windings. Under no circumstances should the primary voltage rating be exceeded. In many cases the rated primary and secondary voltages are printed right on the transformer. For example, consider the transformer shown in Fig. 20-14a. Its rated primary voltage is 120 V, and its secondary voltage is specified as 12.6–0–12.6, which indicates that the secondary is center tapped. The notation 12.6–0–12.6 indicates that 12.6 V is available between the center tap connection and either outside secondary lead. The total secondary voltage available is 2 × 12.6 V or 25.2 V. In Fig. 20-14a, the black leads coming out of the top of the transformer provide connection to the primary winding. The two yellow leads coming out of the bottom of the transformer provide connection to the outer leads of the secondary winding. The bottom middle black lead connects to the center tap on the secondary winding.

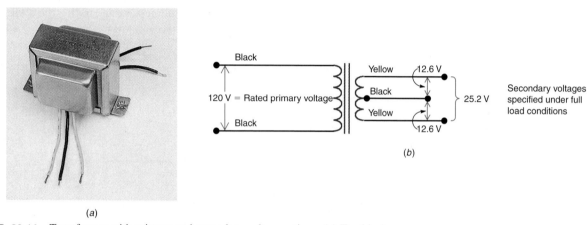

(a)

(b)

**FIG. 20-14**   Transformer with primary and secondary voltage ratings. (a) Top black leads are primary leads. Yellow and black leads on bottom are secondary leads. (b) Schematic symbol.

It should be noted that manufacturers may specify the secondary voltages of a transformer differently. For example, the secondary in Fig. 20-14a may be specified as 25.2 V CT, where CT indicates a center-tapped secondary. Another way to specify the secondary voltage in Fig. 20-14a would be: 12.6 V each side of center.

Regardless of how the secondary voltage of a transformer is specified, it should be noted that the rated value is always specified under full load conditions with the rated primary voltage applied. A transformer is considered fully loaded when the rated current is drawn from the secondary. When unloaded, the secondary voltage will measure a value which is approximately 5 to 10 percent higher than its rated value. Let's use the transformer in Fig. 20-14a as an example. It has a rated secondary current of 2 A. If 120 V is connected to the primary and no load is connected to the secondary, each half of the secondary will measure somewhere between 13.2 V and 13.9 V approximately. However, with the rated current of 2 A drawn from the secondary, each half of the secondary will measure approximately 12.6 V.

Figure 20-14b shows the schematic diagram for the transformer in Fig. 20-14a. Notice that the colors of each lead are identified for clarification.

As you already know, transformers can have more than one secondary winding. They can also have more than one primary winding. The purpose is to allow the transformer to be used with more than one value of primary voltage. Figure 20-15 shows a transformer that has two separate primaries and a single secondary. This transformer can be wired to work with a primary voltage of either 120 V or 240 V. For either value of primary voltage, the secondary voltage is 24 V. Figure 20-15a shows the individual primary windings with phasing dots to identify those leads with the same instantaneous polarity. Figure 20-15b shows how to connect the primary windings for connection to 240 V. Notice the connections of the leads with the phasing dots. With this connection, each half of the primary voltage is in the proper phase to provide a series-aiding connection of the induced voltages. Furthermore, the series connection of the primary windings provides a turns ratio $N_P/N_S$ of 10:1, thus allowing a secondary voltage of 24 V. Figure 20-15c shows how to connect the primaries for connection to 120 V. Again, notice the connection of the leads with the phasing dots. When the primary windings are in parallel, the total primary current $I_P$ is divided evenly between the windings. The parallel connection also provides a turns ratio $N_P/N_S$ of 5:1, thus allowing a secondary voltage of 24 V.

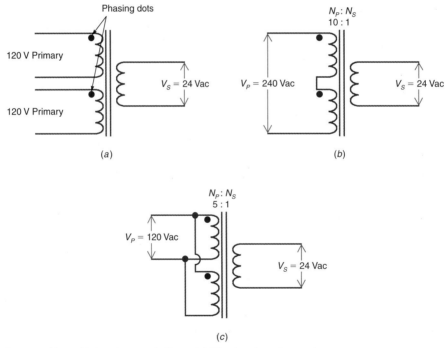

**FIG. 20-15** Transformer with multiple primary windings. (a) Phasing dots show primary leads with same instantaneous polarity. (b) Primary windings connected in series to work with a primary voltage of 240 V; $N_P/N_S = 10:1$. (c) Primary windings connected in parallel to work with a primary voltage of 120 V; $N_P/N_S = 5:1$.

Figure 20-16 shows a transformer that can operate with a primary voltage of either 120 V or 440 V. In this case, only one of the primary windings is used with a given primary voltage. For example, if 120 V is applied to the lower pri-

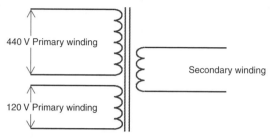

**FIG. 20-16** Transformer that has two primaries, which are used separately and never together.

mary, the upper primary winding is not used. Conversely, if 440 V is applied to the upper primary, the lower primary winding is not used.

**CURRENT RATINGS** Manufacturers of transformers usually specify the current ratings for secondary windings only. The reason is quite simple. If the secondary current is not exceeded, there is no possible way the primary current can be exceeded. If the secondary current exceeds its rated value, excessive $I^2R$ losses will result in the secondary winding. This will cause the secondary, and perhaps the primary, to overheat, thus eventually destroying the transformer. The IR voltage drop across the secondary windings is the reason why the secondary voltage decreases as the load current increases.

## *Example*

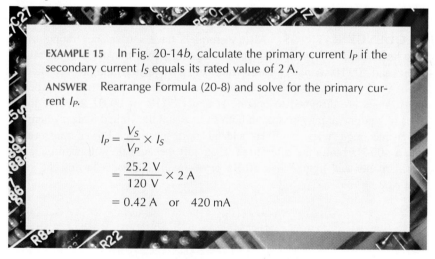

**EXAMPLE 15** In Fig. 20-14*b*, calculate the primary current $I_P$ if the secondary current $I_S$ equals its rated value of 2 A.

**ANSWER** Rearrange Formula (20-8) and solve for the primary current $I_P$.

$$I_P = \frac{V_S}{V_P} \times I_S$$

$$= \frac{25.2\ V}{120\ V} \times 2\ A$$

$$= 0.42\ A \quad \text{or} \quad 420\ mA$$

**POWER RATINGS** The power rating of a transformer refers to the amount of power the transformer can deliver to a resistive load. The power rating is specified in volt-amperes (VA) rather than watts (W), because the power is not actually dissipated by the transformer. The product VA is called *apparent power,* since it is the power which is *apparently* used by the transformer. The unit of apparent power is VA because the watt unit is reserved for the actual dissipation of power in a resistance.

Assume that a power transformer whose primary and secondary voltage ratings are 120 V and 25 V, respectively, has a power rating of 125 VA. What does this mean? It means that the product of the transformer's primary, or secondary, voltage and current must not exceed 125 VA. If it does, the transformer will overheat and be destroyed. The maximum allowable secondary current for this transformer can be calculated as

$$I_{S(\text{max})} = \frac{125 \text{ VA}}{25 \text{ V}}$$
$$= 5 \text{ A}$$

The maximum allowable primary current can be calculated as

$$I_{P(\text{max})} = \frac{125 \text{ VA}}{120 \text{ V}}$$
$$= 1.04 \text{ A}$$

With multiple secondary windings the VA rating of each individual secondary may be given without any mention of the primary's VA rating. In this case, the sum of all the secondary VA ratings must be divided by the rated primary voltage to determine the maximum allowable primary current.

In summary, you will never overload a transformer or exceed any of its maximum ratings if you obey two fundamental rules:

1. Never apply more than the rated voltage to the primary.
2. Never draw more than the rated current from the secondary.

**FREQUENCY RATINGS** All transformers have a frequency rating which must be adhered to. Typical frequency ratings for power transformers are 50 Hz, 60 Hz, and 400 Hz. A power transformer with a frequency rating of 400 Hz cannot be used at 50 Hz or 60 Hz, because it will overheat. However, many power transformers are designed to operate at either 50 Hz or 60 Hz, because many types of equipment may be sold in both Europe and the United States, where the power-line frequencies are 50 Hz and 60 Hz, respectively. Power transformers with a 400-Hz rating are often used in aircraft, because these transformers are much smaller and lighter than 50-Hz or 60-Hz transformers having the same power rating.

### TEST-POINT QUESTION 20-7

Answers at end of chapter.

Answer True or False.
**a.** The measured voltage across an unloaded secondary is usually 5 to 10 percent higher than its rated value.
**b.** The current rating of a transformer is usually specified only for the secondary windings.
**c.** A power rating of 300 VA for a transformer means that the transformer secondary must be able to dissipate this amount of power.

# 20-8 IMPEDANCE TRANSFORMATION

Transformers can be used to change or transform a secondary load impedance to a new value as seen by the primary. The secondary load impedance is said to be reflected back into the primary and is therefore called a *reflected impedance*. The reflected impedance of the secondary may be stepped up or down in accordance with the square of the transformer turns ratio.

By manipulating the relationships between the currents, voltages, and turns ratio in a transformer, an equation for the reflected impedance can be developed. This relationship is

▶ $$Z_P = \left(\frac{N_P}{N_S}\right)^2 \times Z_S \qquad\qquad\qquad \textbf{(20-10)}$$

where $Z_P$ = primary impedance and $Z_S$ = secondary impedance (see Fig. 20-17). If the turns ratio $N_P/N_S$ is greater than 1, $Z_S$ will be stepped up in value. Conversely, if the turns ratio $N_P/N_S$ is less than 1, $Z_S$ will be stepped down in value. It should be noted that the term *impedance* is used rather loosely here, since the primary and secondary impedances may be purely resistive in nature. In the discussions and examples that follow, $Z_P$ and $Z_S$ will be assumed to be purely resistive. The concept of reflected impedance has several practical applications in electronics.

To find the required turns ratio when the impedance ratio is known, rearrange Formula (20-10) as follows:

▶ $$\frac{N_P}{N_S} = \sqrt{\frac{Z_P}{Z_S}} \qquad\qquad\qquad \textbf{(20-11)}$$

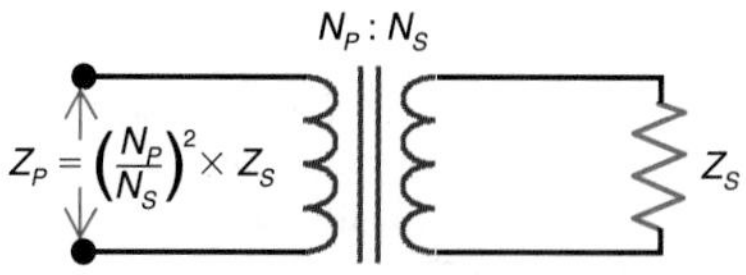

FIG. 20-17   The secondary load impedance $Z_S$ is reflected back into the primary as a new value which is proportional to the square of the turns ratio, $N_P/N_S$.

## Example

**EXAMPLE 16**   Determine the primary impedance $Z_P$ for the transformer circuit in Fig. 20-18 shown on the next page.

**ANSWER**   Use Formula (20-10). Since $Z_S = R_L$, we have

$$Z_P = \left(\frac{N_P}{N_S}\right)^2 \times R_L$$

$$= \left(\frac{4}{1}\right)^2 \times 8\ \Omega$$

$$= 16 \times 8\ \Omega$$

$$= 128\ \Omega$$

The value of 128 $\Omega$ obtained for $Z_P$ using Formula (20-10) can be verified as follows.

(*continued on next page*)

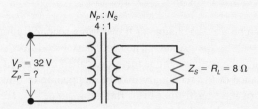

FIG. 20-18  Circuit for Example 16.

$$V_S = \frac{N_S}{N_P} \times V_P$$

$$= \frac{1}{4} \times 32 \text{ V}$$

$$= 8 \text{ V}$$

$$I_S = \frac{V_S}{R_L}$$

$$= \frac{8 \text{ V}}{8 \text{ }\Omega}$$

$$= 1 \text{ A}$$

$$I_P = \frac{V_S}{V_P} \times I_S$$

$$= \frac{8 \text{ V}}{32 \text{ V}} \times 1 \text{ A}$$

$$= 0.25 \text{ A}$$

And finally,

$$Z_P = \frac{V_P}{I_P}$$

$$= \frac{32 \text{ V}}{0.25 \text{ A}}$$

$$= 128 \text{ }\Omega$$

**EXAMPLE 17**  In Fig. 20-19, calculate the turns ratio $N_P/N_S$ which will produce a reflected primary impedance $Z_P$ of: **(a)** 75 $\Omega$; **(b)** 600 $\Omega$.

**ANSWER**  **(a)** Use Formula (20-11).

$$\frac{N_P}{N_S} = \sqrt{\frac{Z_P}{Z_S}}$$

$$= \sqrt{\frac{75 \text{ }\Omega}{300 \text{ }\Omega}}$$

$$= \sqrt{\frac{1}{4}}$$

$$= \frac{1}{2}$$

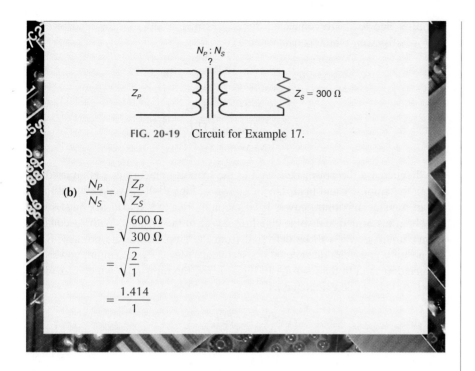

FIG. 20-19   Circuit for Example 17.

**(b)** $\dfrac{N_P}{N_S} = \sqrt{\dfrac{Z_P}{Z_S}}$

$= \sqrt{\dfrac{600\ \Omega}{300\ \Omega}}$

$= \sqrt{\dfrac{2}{1}}$

$= \dfrac{1.414}{1}$

## IMPEDANCE MATCHING FOR MAXIMUM POWER TRANSFER

Transformers are used when it is necessary to achieve maximum transfer of power from a generator to a load when the generator and load impedances are not the same. This application of a transformer is called *impedance matching*.

As an example, consider the amplifier and load in Fig. 20-20*a*. Notice that the internal resistance $r_i$ of the amplifier is 200 $\Omega$ and the load $R_L$ is 8 $\Omega$. If the

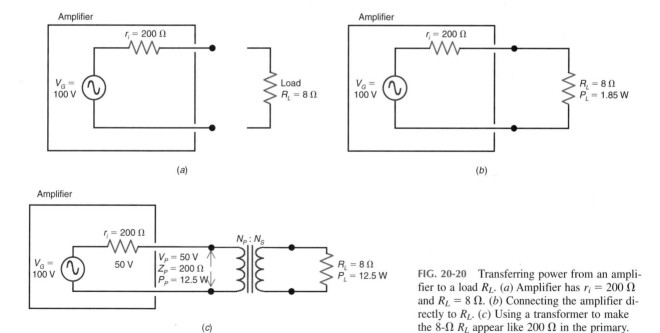

FIG. 20-20   Transferring power from an amplifier to a load $R_L$. (*a*) Amplifier has $r_i = 200\ \Omega$ and $R_L = 8\ \Omega$. (*b*) Connecting the amplifier directly to $R_L$. (*c*) Using a transformer to make the 8-$\Omega$ $R_L$ appear like 200 $\Omega$ in the primary.

amplifier and load are connected directly as in Fig. 20-20b, the load receives 1.85 W of power, which is calculated as

$$P_L = \left(\frac{V_G}{r_i + R_L}\right)^2 \times R_L$$

$$= \left(\frac{100\ \text{V}}{200\ \Omega + 8\ \Omega}\right)^2 \times 8\ \Omega$$

$$= 1.85\ \text{W}$$

To increase the power delivered to the load, a transformer can be used between the amplifier and load. This is shown in Fig. 20-20c. We know that in order to transfer maximum power from the amplifier to the load, $R_L$ must somehow be transformed to a value equaling 200 Ω in the primary. With $Z_P$ equaling $r_i$, maximum power will be delivered from the amplifier to the primary. Since the primary power $P_P$ must equal the secondary power $P_S$, maximum power will also be delivered to the load $R_L$. In Fig. 20-20c, the turns ratio which provides a $Z_P$ of 200 Ω can be calculated as

$$\frac{N_P}{N_S} = \sqrt{\frac{Z_P}{Z_S}}$$

$$= \sqrt{\frac{200\ \Omega}{8\ \Omega}}$$

$$= \frac{5}{1}$$

With $r_i$ and $Z_P$ equal, the power delivered to the primary can be calculated as

$$P_P = \left(\frac{V_G}{r_i + Z_P}\right)^2 \times Z_P$$

$$= \left(\frac{100\ \text{V}}{400\ \Omega}\right)^2 \times 200\ \Omega$$

$$= 12.5\ \text{W}$$

Since $P_P = P_S$, the load $R_L$ also receives 12.5 W of power. As proof, calculate the secondary voltage.

$$V_S = \frac{N_S}{N_P} \times V_P$$

$$= \frac{1}{5} \times 50\ \text{V}$$

$$= 10\ \text{V}$$

(Notice that $V_P$ is $\frac{1}{2}V_G$, since $r_i$ and $Z_P$ divide $V_G$ evenly.) Next, calculate the load power $P_L$.

$$P_L = \frac{V_S^2}{R_L}$$

$$= \frac{10^2\ \text{V}}{8\ \Omega}$$

$$= 12.5\ \text{W}$$

Notice how the transformer has been used as an impedance matching device to obtain the maximum transfer of power from the amplifier to the load. Compare the power dissipated by $R_L$ in Fig. 20-20b to that in Fig. 20-20c. There is a big difference between the load power of 1.85 W in Fig. 20-20b and the load power of 12.5 W in Fig. 20-20c.

### TEST-POINT QUESTION 20-8

Answers at end of chapter.

Answer True or False.
a. The turns ratio will not affect the primary impedance $Z_P$.
b. When the turns ratio $N_P/N_S$ is greater than 1, the primary impedance $Z_P$ is less than the value of $Z_S$.
c. If the turns ratio $N_P/N_S$ of a transformer is 2/1 and $Z_S = 50 \ \Omega$, the primary impedance $Z_P = 200 \ \Omega$.

# 20-9 CORE LOSSES

The fact that the magnetic core can become warm, or even hot, shows that some of the energy supplied to the coil is used up in the core as heat. The two main effects are eddy-current losses and hysteresis losses.

**EDDY CURRENTS** In any inductance with an iron core, alternating current induces voltage in the core itself. Since it is a conductor, the iron core has current produced by the induced voltage. This current is called an *eddy current* because it flows in a circular path through the cross section of the core, as illustrated in Fig. 20-21.

The eddy currents represent wasted power dissipated as heat in the core. Note in Fig. 20-21 that the eddy-current flux opposes the coil flux, so that more current is required in the coil to maintain its magnetic field. The higher the frequency of the alternating current in the inductance, the greater the eddy-current loss.

Eddy currents can be induced in any conductor near a coil with alternating current, not only in its core. For instance, a coil has eddy-current losses in a metal cover. In fact, the technique of induction heating is an application of heat resulting from induced eddy currents.

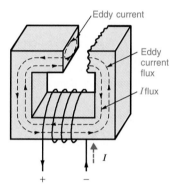

FIG. 20-21 Cross-sectional view of iron core showing eddy currents.

**RF SHIELDING** The reason why a coil may have a metal cover, usually copper or aluminum, is to provide a shield against the varying flux of RF current. In this case, the shielding effect depends on using a good conductor for the eddy currents produced by the varying flux, rather than the magnetic materials used for shielding against static magnetic flux.

The shield cover not only isolates the coil from external varying magnetic fields, but also minimizes the effect of the coil's RF current for external circuits. The reason why the shield helps both ways is the same, as the induced eddy currents have a field that opposes the field that is inducing the current. It should be

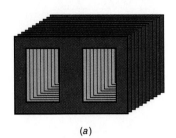

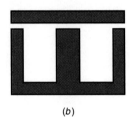

(a)

(b)

(c)

FIG. 20-22   Laminated iron core.
(*a*) Shell-type construction.
(*b*) E- and I-shaped laminations.
(*c*) Symbol for iron core.

(a)              (b)

FIG. 20-23   RF coils with ferrite
core. Width of coil is ½ in. (*a*) Variable *L* from 1 to 3 mH. (*b*) Tuning
coil for 40 MHz.

noted that the clearance between the sides of the coil and the metal should be
equal to or greater than the coil radius, to minimize the effect of the shield in reducing the inductance.

**HYSTERESIS LOSSES**   Another loss factor present in magnetic cores is hysteresis, although these are not as great as eddy-current losses. The hysteresis
losses result from the additional power needed to reverse the magnetic field in
magnetic materials in the presence of alternating current. The greater the frequency, the more hysteresis losses.

**AIR-CORE COILS**   It should be noted that air has practically no losses from
eddy currents or hysteresis. However, the inductance for small coils with an air
core is limited to low values in the microhenry or millihenry range.

## 20-10 TYPES OF CORES

In order to minimize losses while maintaining high flux density, the core can be
made of laminated steel insulated from each other. Insulated powdered-iron granules and ferrite materials can also be used. These core types are illustrated in
Figs. 20-22 and 20-23. The purpose is to reduce the amount of eddy currents.
The type of steel itself can help reduce hysteresis losses.

**LAMINATED CORE**   Figure 20-22*a* shows a shell-type core formed with a
group of individual laminations. Each laminated section is insulated by a very
thin coating of iron oxide, silicon steel, or varnish. The insulating material increases the resistance in the cross section of the core to reduce the eddy currents,
but allows a low-reluctance path for high flux density around the core. Transformers for audio frequencies and 60-Hz power are generally made with a laminated iron core.

**POWDERED-IRON CORE**   To reduce eddy currents in the iron core of an
inductance for radio frequencies, powdered iron is generally used. It consists of
individual insulated granules pressed into one solid form called a *slug*.

**FERRITE CORE**   The ferrites are synthetic ceramic materials that are ferromagnetic. They provide high values of flux density, like iron, but have the advantage of being insulators. Therefore, a ferrite core can be used for high frequencies with minimum eddy-current losses.

This core is usually a slug that can move in or out of the coil to vary $L$, as in Fig. 20-23$a$. In Fig. 20-23$b$, the core has a hole to fit a plastic alignment tool for tuning the coil. Maximum $L$ results with the slug in the coil.

**TEST-POINT QUESTION 20-10**

Answers at end of chapter.

Answer True or False.
**a.** An iron core provides a coefficient of coupling $k$ of unity or 1.
**b.** A laminated iron core reduces eddy-current losses.
**c.** The ferrites have less eddy-current losses than iron.

## 20-11 VARIABLE INDUCTANCE

The inductance of a coil can be varied by one of the methods illustrated in Fig. 20-24. In Fig. 20-24$a$, more or fewer turns can be used by connection to one of the taps on the coil. Also, in Fig. 20-24$b$, a slider contacts the coil to vary the number of turns used. These methods are for large coils.

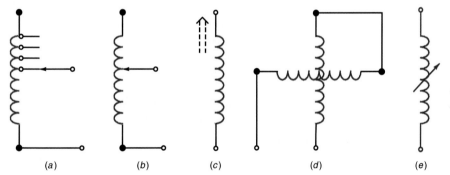

FIG. 20-24   Methods of varying inductance. ($a$) Tapped coil. ($b$) Slider contact. ($c$) Adjustable slug. ($d$) Variometer. ($e$) Symbol for variable $L$.

Figure 20-24$c$ shows the schematic symbol for a coil with a slug of powdered iron or ferrite. The dotted lines indicate that the core is not solid iron. The arrow shows that the slug is variable. Usually, an arrow at the top means the adjustment is at the top of the coil. An arrow at the bottom, pointing down, shows the adjustment is at the bottom.

The symbol in Fig. 20-24$d$ is a *variometer,* which is an arrangement for varying the position of one coil within the other. The total inductance of the series-aiding coils is minimum when they are perpendicular.

For any method of varying $L$, the coil with an arrow in Fig. 20-24$e$ can be used. However, an adjustable slug is usually shown as in Fig. 20-24$c$.

A practical application of variable inductance is the *Variac.* The Variac is an autotransformer with a variable tap to change the turns ratio. The output voltage

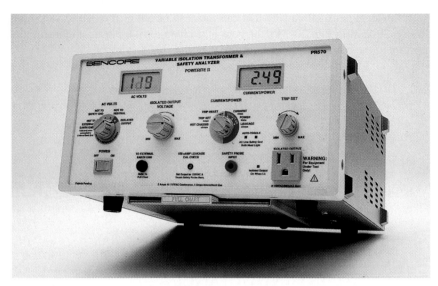

FIG. 20-25   Variac with isolated output.

in the secondary can be varied from 0 to approximately 140 V, with input from the 120-V 60-Hz power line. One use is to test equipment with voltage above or below the normal line voltage.

The Variac is plugged into the power line, and the equipment to be tested is plugged into the Variac. Note that the power rating of the Variac should be equal to or more than the power used by the equipment being tested. Figure 20-25 shows a Variac with an isolated output.

## 20-12 INDUCTANCES IN SERIES OR PARALLEL

As shown in Fig. 20-26, the total inductance of coils connected in series is the sum of the individual $L$ values, as for series $R$. Since the series coils have the same current, the total induced voltage is a result of the total number of turns. Therefore, total series inductance is,

▶    $$L_T = L_1 + L_2 + L_3 + \cdots + \text{etc.} \qquad (20\text{-}12)$$

where $L_T$ is in the same units of inductance as $L_1$, $L_2$, and $L_3$. This formula assumes no mutual induction between the coils.

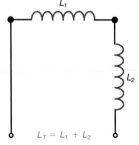

FIG. 20-26   Inductances $L_1$ and $L_2$ in series without mutual coupling.

## Example

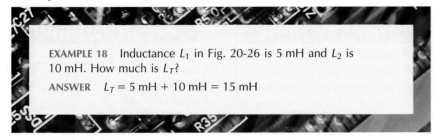

**EXAMPLE 18** Inductance $L_1$ in Fig. 20-26 is 5 mH and $L_2$ is 10 mH. How much is $L_T$?

**ANSWER** $L_T = 5\text{ mH} + 10\text{ mH} = 15\text{ mH}$

With coils connected in parallel, the equivalent inductance is calculated from the reciprocal formula

▶ $$\frac{1}{L_{EQ}} = \frac{1}{L_1} + \frac{1}{L_2} + \frac{1}{L_3} + \cdots + \text{etc.} \qquad \textbf{(20-13)}$$

Again, no mutual induction is assumed, as illustrated in Fig. 20-27.

## Example

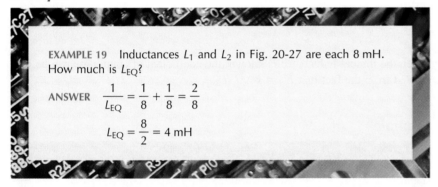

**EXAMPLE 19** Inductances $L_1$ and $L_2$ in Fig. 20-27 are each 8 mH. How much is $L_{EQ}$?

**ANSWER** $\dfrac{1}{L_{EQ}} = \dfrac{1}{8} + \dfrac{1}{8} = \dfrac{2}{8}$

$L_{EQ} = \dfrac{8}{2} = 4\text{ mH}$

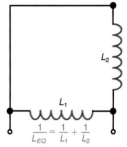

**FIG. 20-27** Inductances $L_1$ and $L_2$ in parallel without mutual coupling.

All the shortcuts for calculating parallel $R$ can be used with parallel $L$, since both are based on the reciprocal formula. In this example $L_{EQ}$ is $\frac{1}{2} \times 8 = 4$ mH.

**SERIES COILS WITH $L_M$**  This case depends on the amount of mutual coupling and on whether the coils are connected series-aiding or series-opposing. *Series-aiding* means that the common current produces the same direction of magnetic field for the two coils. The *series-opposing* connection results in opposite fields.

The coupling depends on the coil connections and direction of winding. Reversing either one reverses the field. Inductances $L_1$ and $L_2$ with the same direction of winding are connected series-aiding in Fig. 20-28*a* on the next page. However, they are series-opposing in Fig. 20-28*b* because $L_1$ is connected to the opposite end of $L_2$. To calculate the total inductance of two coils that are series-connected and have mutual inductance,

▶ $$L_T = L_1 + L_2 \pm 2L_M \qquad \textbf{(20-14)}$$

The mutual inductance $L_M$ is plus, increasing the total inductance, when the coils are series-aiding, or minus when they are series-opposing to reduce the total inductance.

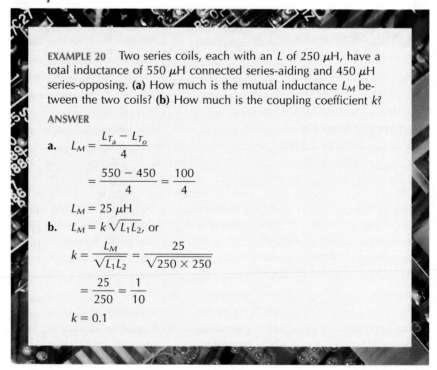

Series-aiding

$L_M$

$L_1$ $L_2$

$L_T = L_1 + L_2 + 2L_M$

(a)

Series-opposing

$L_M$

$L_1$ $L_2$

$L_T = L_1 + L_2 - 2L_M$

(b)

FIG. 20-28 Inductances $L_1$ and $L_2$ in series but with mutual coupling $L_M$. (a) Aiding magnetic fields. (b) Opposing magnetic fields.

Note the phasing dots above the coils in Fig. 20-28. Coils with phasing dots at the same end have the same direction of winding. When current enters the dotted ends for two coils, their fields are aiding and $L_M$ has the same sense as $L$.

**HOW TO MEASURE $L_M$** Formula (20-14) provides a method of determining the mutual inductance between two coils $L_1$ and $L_2$ of known inductance. First, the total inductance is measured for the series-aiding connection. Let this be $L_{T_a}$. Then the connections to one coil are reversed to measure the total inductance for the series-opposing coils. Let this be $L_{T_o}$. Then

$$L_M = \frac{L_{T_a} - L_{T_o}}{4}$$

(20-15)

When the mutual inductance is known, the coefficient of coupling $k$ can be calculated from the fact that $L_M = k\sqrt{L_1 L_2}$.

*Example*

EXAMPLE 20    Two series coils, each with an $L$ of 250 $\mu$H, have a total inductance of 550 $\mu$H connected series-aiding and 450 $\mu$H series-opposing. **(a)** How much is the mutual inductance $L_M$ between the two coils? **(b)** How much is the coupling coefficient $k$?

ANSWER

a.    $L_M = \dfrac{L_{T_a} - L_{T_o}}{4}$

$= \dfrac{550 - 450}{4} = \dfrac{100}{4}$

$L_M = 25 \ \mu$H

b.    $L_M = k\sqrt{L_1 L_2}$, or

$k = \dfrac{L_M}{\sqrt{L_1 L_2}} = \dfrac{25}{\sqrt{250 \times 250}}$

$= \dfrac{25}{250} = \dfrac{1}{10}$

$k = 0.1$

Coils may also be in parallel with mutual coupling. However, the inverse relations with parallel connections and the question of aiding or opposing fields make this case complicated. Actually, it would hardly ever be used.

───────────── **TEST-POINT QUESTION 20-12** ─────────────

Answers at end of chapter.
**a.** A 500-$\mu$H coil and a 1-mH coil are in series without $L_M$. Calculate $L_T$.
**b.** The same coils are in parallel without $L_M$. Calculate $L_{EQ}$.

## 20-13 STRAY INDUCTANCE

Although practical inductors are generally made as coils, all conductors have inductance. The amount of $L$ is $v_L/(di/dt)$, as with any inductance producing induced voltage when the current changes. The inductance of any wiring not included in the conventional inductors can be considered stray inductance. In most cases, the stray inductance is very small, typical values being less than 1 $\mu$H. For high radio frequencies, though, even a small $L$ can have an appreciable inductive effect.

One source of stray inductance is the connecting leads. A wire of 0.04-in. diameter and 4 in. long has an $L$ of approximately 0.1 $\mu$H. At low frequencies, this inductance is negligible. However, consider the case of RF current, where $i$ varies from 0 to 20-mA peak value in the short time of 0.025 $\mu$s for a quarter-cycle of a 10-MHz sine wave. Then $v_L$ equals 80 mV, which is an appreciable inductive effect. This is one reason why the connecting leads must be very short in RF circuits.

As another example, wire-wound resistors can have appreciable inductance when wound as a straight coil. This is why carbon resistors are preferred for minimum stray inductance in RF circuits. However, noninductive wire-wound resistors can also be used. These are wound in such a way that adjacent turns have current in opposite directions, so that the magnetic fields oppose each other to cancel the inductance. Another application of this technique is twisting a pair of connecting leads to reduce the inductive effect.

───────────── **TEST-POINT QUESTION 20-13** ─────────────

Answers at end of chapter.

Answer True or False.
**a.** A straight wire 1 ft long can have $L$ less than 1 $\mu$H.
**b.** Carbon resistors have less $L$ than wire-wound resistors.

## 20-14 ENERGY IN MAGNETIC FIELD OF INDUCTANCE

Magnetic flux associated with current in an inductance has electric energy supplied by the voltage source producing the current. The energy is stored in the field, since it can do the work of producing induced voltage when the flux moves. The amount of electric energy stored is

▶     $\text{Energy} = \mathscr{E} = \frac{1}{2} L I^2 \quad \text{J}$     (20-16)

The factor of ½ gives the average result of $I$ in producing energy. With $L$ in henrys and $I$ in amperes, the energy is in watt-seconds, or *joules*. For a 10-H $L$ with a 3-A $I$, the electric energy stored in the magnetic field equals

▶     $\text{Energy} = \frac{1}{2} L I^2 = \frac{10 \times 9}{2} = 45 \text{ J}$

This 45 J of energy is supplied by the voltage source that produces 3 A in the inductance. When the circuit is opened, the magnetic field collapses. The energy in the collapsing magnetic field is returned to the circuit in the form of induced voltage, which tends to keep the current flowing.

The entire 45 J is available for the work of inducing voltage, since no energy is dissipated by the magnetic field. With resistance in the circuit, however, the $I^2R$ loss with induced current dissipates all the energy after a period of time.

*Example*

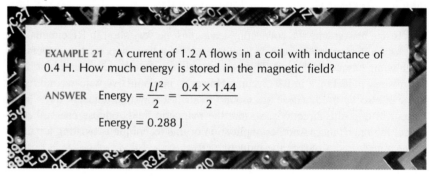

EXAMPLE 21   A current of 1.2 A flows in a coil with inductance of 0.4 H. How much energy is stored in the magnetic field?

ANSWER   $\text{Energy} = \dfrac{L I^2}{2} = \dfrac{0.4 \times 1.44}{2}$

$\text{Energy} = 0.288 \text{ J}$

To do this problem on a calculator, first square the $I$, multiply by $L$, and divide by 2. Specifically, punch in 1.2 and push the $\boxed{x^2}$ key for 1.44. While this is on the display, push the $\boxed{\times}$ key, punch in 0.4 and push the $\boxed{=}$ key for 0.576 on the display. Now push the $\boxed{\div}$ key, punch in 2, and then push the $\boxed{=}$ key to get 0.288 as the answer.

### TEST-POINT QUESTION 20-14

Answers at end of chapter.
**a.** What is the unit of electric energy stored in a magnetic field?
**b.** Does a 4-H coil store more or less energy than a 2-H coil?

# 20-15 TROUBLES IN COILS

The most common trouble in coils is an open winding. As illustrated in Fig. 20-29, an ohmmeter connected across the coil reads infinite resistance for the open circuit. It does not matter whether the coil has an air core or an iron core. Since the coil is open, it cannot conduct current and therefore has no inductance, because it cannot produce induced voltage. When the resistance is checked, the coil should be disconnected from the external circuit to eliminate any parallel paths that could affect the resistance readings.

FIG. 20-29 An open coil reads infinite ohms when its continuity is checked with an ohmmeter.

**DIRECT CURRENT RESISTANCE OF A COIL** A coil has dc resistance equal to the resistance of the wire used in the winding. The amount of resistance is less with heavier wire and fewer turns. For RF coils with inductance values up to several millihenrys, requiring 10 to 100 turns of fine wire, the dc resistance is 1 to 20 Ω, approximately. Inductors for 60 Hz and audio frequencies with several hundred turns may have resistance values of 10 to 500 Ω, depending on the wire size.

As shown in Fig. 20-30, the dc resistance and inductance of a coil are in series, since the same current that induces voltage in the turns must overcome the resistance of the wire. Although resistance has no function in producing induced voltage, it is useful to know the dc coil resistance because if it is normal, usually the inductance can also be assumed to have its normal value.

**OPEN COIL** An open winding has infinite resistance, as indicated by an ohmmeter reading. With a transformer that has four leads or more, check the resistance across the two leads for the primary, across the two leads for the secondary, and across any other pairs of leads for additional secondary windings. For an autotransformer with three leads, check the resistance from one lead to each of the other two.

When the open circuit is inside the winding, it is usually not practical to repair the coil, and the entire unit is replaced. In some cases, an open connection at the terminals can be resoldered.

**VALUE CHANGE** The value of an inductor can change over time due to core breakage, windings relaxing, or shorted turns. A coil whose inductance value has changed can be difficult to locate without the proper test equipment. It should be noted that a coil whose inductance value is changed may check okay with an ohmmeter.

**FIG. 20-30** The internal dc resistance $r_i$ of a coil is in series with its inductance $L$.

**OPEN PRIMARY WINDING**   When the primary of a transformer is open, no primary current can flow and there is no voltage induced in any of the secondary windings.

**OPEN SECONDARY WINDING**   When the secondary of a transformer is open, it cannot supply power to any load resistance across the open winding. Furthermore, with no current in the secondary, the primary current is also practically zero, as though the primary winding were open. The only primary current needed is the small magnetizing current to sustain the field producing induced voltage across the secondary without any load. If the transformer has several secondary windings, however, an open winding in one secondary does not affect transformer operation for the secondary circuits that are normal.

**SHORT ACROSS SECONDARY WINDING**   In this case excessive primary current flows, as though it were short-circuited, often burning out the primary winding. The reason is that the large secondary current has a strong field that opposes the flux of the self-induced voltage across the primary, making it draw more current from the generator.

## TEST-POINT QUESTION 20-15

Answers at end of chapter.
a. The normal $R$ of a coil is 18 $\Omega$. How much will an ohmmeter read if the coil is open?
b. The primary of a 1:3 step-up autotransformer is connected to the 120-Vac power line. How much will the secondary voltage be if the primary is open?

# 20    SUMMARY AND REVIEW

- Varying current induces voltage in a conductor, since the expanding and collapsing field of the current is equivalent to flux in motion.
- Lenz' law states that the induced voltage produces $I$ that opposes the change in current causing the induction. Inductance, therefore, tends to keep the current from changing.
- The ability of a conductor to produce induced voltage across itself when the current varies is its self-inductance, or inductance. The symbol is $L$, and the unit of inductance is the henry. One henry of inductance allows 1 V to be induced when the current changes at the rate of 1 A/s. For smaller units, 1 mH $= 1 \times 10^{-3}$ H and 1 $\mu$H $= 1 \times 10^{-6}$ H.
- To calculate the self-induced voltage, $v_L = L(di/dt)$, with $v$ in volts, $L$ in henrys, and $di/dt$ in amperes per second.
- Mutual inductance is the ability of varying current in one conductor to induce voltage in another conductor nearby. Its symbol is $L_M$, measured in henrys. $L_M = k \sqrt{L_1 L_2}$, where $k$ is the coefficient of coupling between conductors.
- A transformer consists of two or more windings with mutual inductance. The primary winding connects to the source voltage; the load resistance is connected across the secondary winding. A separate winding is an isolated secondary. The transformer is used to step up or step down ac voltage.
- An autotransformer is a tapped coil, used to step up or step down the primary voltage. There are three leads with one connection common to both the primary and secondary.
- A transformer with an iron core has essentially unity coupling. Therefore, the voltage ratio is the same as the turns ratio: $V_P/V_S = N_P/N_S$.
- Assuming 100 percent efficiency for an iron-core power transformer, the power supplied to the primary equals the power used in the secondary.
- The voltage rating of a transformer's secondary is always specified under full load conditions with the rated primary voltage applied. The measured voltage across an unloaded secondary is usually 5 to 10 percent higher than its rated value.
- The current or power rating of a transformer is usually specified only for the secondary windings.
- Transformers can be used to reflect a secondary load impedance back into the primary as a new value which is either larger or smaller than its actual value. The primary impedance $Z_P$ can be determined using Formula (20-10).
- The impedance transforming properties of a transformer make it possible to obtain maximum transfer of power from a generator to a load when the generator and load impedances are not equal. The required turns ratio can be determined using Formula (20-11).
- Eddy currents are induced in the iron core of an inductance, causing wasted power that heats the core. Eddy-current losses increase with higher frequencies of alternating current. To reduce eddy currents, the iron core is laminated. Powdered-iron and ferrite cores have minimum eddy-current losses for radio frequencies. Hysteresis also causes power loss.
- With no mutual coupling, series inductances are added like series resistances. For parallel inductances, the equivalent inductance is calculated by the reciprocal formula, as for parallel resistances.

- The magnetic field of an inductance has stored energy $\mathcal{E} = \frac{1}{2} LI^2$. With $I$ in amperes and $L$ in henrys, the energy $\mathcal{E}$ is in joules.
- In addition to its inductance, a coil has dc resistance equal to the resistance of the wire in the coil. An open coil has infinitely high resistance.
- An open primary in a transformer results in no induced voltage in any of the secondary windings.
- Figure 20-31 summarizes the main types of inductors, or coils, with their schematic symbols.
- Characteristics of inductance and capacitance are compared in Table 20-1.

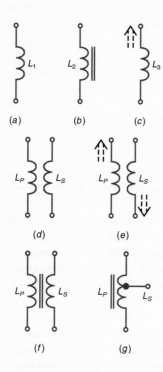

**FIG. 20-31** Summary of types of inductors. (*a*) Air-core coil. (*b*) Iron-core coil. (*c*) Adjustable ferrite core. (*d*) Air-core transformer. (*e*) Variable $L_P$ and $L_S$. (*f*) Iron-core transformer. (*g*) Auto-transformer.

**TABLE 20-1   COMPARISON OF CAPACITANCE AND INDUCTANCE**

| CAPACITANCE | INDUCTANCE |
|---|---|
| Symbol is $C$ | Symbol is $L$ |
| Unit is the farad (F) | Unit is the henry (H) |
| Needs dielectric as insulator | Needs conductor for circuit path |
| More plate area allows more $C$ | More turns allow more $L$ |
| Dielectric can concentrate electric field for more $C$ | Core can concentrate magnetic field for more $L$ |
| $\dfrac{1}{C_{EQ}} = \dfrac{1}{C_1} + \dfrac{1}{C_2}$ in series | $L_T = L_1 + L_2$ in series |
| $C_T = C_1 + C_2$ in parallel | $\dfrac{1}{L_{EQ}} = \dfrac{1}{L_1} + \dfrac{1}{L_2}$ in parallel |

Choose (*a*), (*b*), (*c*), or (*d*).

1. Alternating current can induce voltage because alternating current has a (*a*) high peak value; (*b*) varying magnetic field; (*c*) stronger magnetic field than direct current; (*d*) constant magnetic field.

2. When current in a conductor increases, Lenz' law says that the self-induced voltage will (*a*) tend to increase the amount of current; (*b*) aid the applied voltage; (*c*) produce current opposite to the increasing current; (*d*) aid the increasing current.

3. A 1:5 voltage step-up transformer has 120 V across the primary and a 600-$\Omega$ resistance across the secondary. Assuming 100 percent efficiency, the primary current equals (*a*) ⅕ A; (*b*) 600 mA; (*c*) 5 A; (*d*) 10 A.

4. An iron-core transformer with an 1:8 step-up ratio has 120 V applied across the primary. The voltage across the secondary equals (*a*) 15 V; (*b*) 120 V; (*c*) 180 V; (*d*) 960 V.

5. With double the number of turns but the same length and area, the inductance is (*a*) the same; (*b*) double; (*c*) quadruple; (*d*) one-quarter.

6. Current changing from 4 to 6 A in 1 s induces 40 V in a coil. Its inductance equals (*a*) 40 mH; (*b*) 4 H; (*c*) 6 H; (*d*) 20 H.

7. A laminated iron core has reduced eddy-current losses because (*a*) the laminations are stacked vertically; (*b*) the laminations are insulated from each other; (*c*) the magnetic flux is concentrated in the air gap of the core; (*d*) more wire can be used with less dc resistance in the coil.

8. Two 250-$\mu$H coils in series without mutual coupling have a total inductance of (*a*) 125 $\mu$H; (*b*) 250 $\mu$H; (*c*) 400 $\mu$H; (*d*) 500 $\mu$H.

9. If a transformer has a turns ratio $N_P/N_S$ of 3:1 and $Z_S = 16\ \Omega$, the primary impedance $Z_P$ equals (*a*) 48 $\Omega$; (*b*) 144 $\Omega$; (*c*) 1.78 $\Omega$; (*d*) 288 $\Omega$.

10. An open coil has (*a*) infinite resistance and zero inductance; (*b*) zero resistance and high inductance; (*c*) infinite resistance and normal inductance; (*d*) zero resistance and inductance.

## QUESTIONS

1. Define 1 H of self-inductance and 1 H of mutual inductance.

2. State Lenz' law in terms of induced voltage produced by varying current.

3. Refer to Fig. 20-5. Explain why the polarity of $v_L$ is the same for the examples in Fig. 20-5*a* and *d*.

4. Make a schematic diagram showing the primary and secondary of an iron-core transformer with a 1:6 voltage step-up ratio: (**a**) using an autotransformer; (**b**) using a transformer with isolated secondary winding. Then (**c**) with 100 turns in the primary, how many turns are in the secondary for both cases?

5. Define the following: coefficient of coupling, transformer efficiency, stray inductance, and eddy-current losses.

6. Why are eddy-current losses reduced with the following cores: (a) laminated; (b) powdered iron; (c) ferrite?

7. Why is a good conductor used for an RF shield?

8. Show two methods of providing a variable inductance.

9. (a) Why will the primary of a power transformer have excessive current if the secondary is short-circuited? (b) Why is there no voltage across the secondary if the primary is open?

10. (a) Describe briefly how to check a coil for an open winding with an ohmmeter. What ohmmeter range should be used? (b) What leads will be checked on an autotransformer with one secondary and a transformer with two isolated secondary windings?

11. Derive the formula $L_M = (L_{T_a} - L_{T_o})/4$ from the fact that $L_{T_a} = L_1 + L_2 + 2L_M$ while $L_{T_o} = L_1 + L_2 - 2L_M$.

12. Explain how a transformer with a 1:1 turns ratio and an isolated secondary can be used to reduce the chance of electric shock from the 120 Vac power line.

## PROBLEMS

ANSWERS TO ODD-NUMBERED PROBLEMS AT BACK OF BOOK.

1. Convert the following current changes to amperes per second: (a) zero to 3 A in 2 s; (b) zero to 50 mA in 5 $\mu$s; (c) 100 to 150 mA in 5 $\mu$s; (d) 150 to 100 mA in 5 $\mu$s.

2. Convert into henrys using powers of 10: (a) 250 $\mu$H; (b) 40 $\mu$H; (c) 40 mH; (d) 7 mH; (e) 0.005 H.

3. Calculate the values of $v_L$ across a 5-mH inductance for each of the current variations in Prob. 1.

4. A coil produces a self-induced voltage of 42 mV when $i$ varies at the rate of 19 mA/ms. How much is $L$?

5. A power transformer with a 1:8 turns ratio has 60 Hz 120 V across the primary. (a) What is the frequency of the secondary voltage? (b) How much is the secondary voltage? (c) With a load resistance of 10,000 $\Omega$ across the secondary, how much is the secondary current? Draw the schematic diagram showing primary and secondary circuits. (d) How much is the primary current? Assume 100 percent efficiency. (Note: The ratio of $L_P$ to $L_S$ is 1:8.)

6. How much would the primary current be in a power transformer having a primary resistance of 5 $\Omega$ if it were connected by mistake to a 120-Vdc line instead of the 120-Vac line?

7. For a 100-$\mu$H inductance $L_1$ and a 200-$\mu$H inductance $L_2$, calculate: (a) the total inductance $L_T$ of $L_1$ and $L_2$ in series without mutual coupling; (b) the combined inductance of $L_1$ and $L_2$ in parallel without mutual coupling; (c) the $L_T$ of $L_1$ and $L_2$ series-aiding, and series-opposing, with 10-$\mu$H mutual inductance; (d) the value of the coefficient of coupling $k$.

8. Calculate the inductance $L$ for the following long coils: (a) air core, 20 turns, area 3.14 cm$^2$, length 25 cm; (b) same coil as (a) with ferrite core having a $\mu_r$ of 5000; (c) air core, 200 turns, area 3.14 cm$^2$, length 25 cm; (d) air core, 20 turns, area 3.14 cm$^2$, length 50 cm; (e) air core, 20 turns, diameter 4 cm, length 50 cm. (Note: 1 cm = $10^{-2}$ m, and 1 cm$^2$ = $10^{-4}$ m$^2$.)

9. Calculate the resistance of the following coil, using Table 11-1: 400 turns, each using 3 in. of No. 30 gage wire.

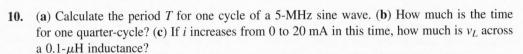

10. (a) Calculate the period $T$ for one cycle of a 5-MHz sine wave. (b) How much is the time for one quarter-cycle? (c) If $i$ increases from 0 to 20 mA in this time, how much is $v_L$ across a 0.1-$\mu$H inductance?

11. Calculate the energy in joules stored in the magnetic field of a 60-mH $L$ with a 90-mA $I$.

12. For a power transformer connected to the 120-Vac line, calculate the turns ratio needed for each of the following secondary voltages: (a) 5 V; (b) 9 V; (c) 24 V; (d) 30 V; (e) 120 V.

13. (a) A transformer delivers 400 W out with 500 W in. (a) Calculate the efficiency in percent. (b) A transformer with 80 percent efficiency delivers 400 W total secondary power. Calculate the primary power.

14. A 20-mH $L$ and a 40-mH $L$ are connected series-aiding, with $k = 0.4$. Calculate $L_T$.

15. Calculate the inductance of the coil in Fig. 20-3 with $\mu_r = 100$.

16. An autotransformer has $L_S$ with one-tenth the turns of $L_P$. When $L_P$ is connected to the 120-Vac power line, calculate: (a) secondary voltage $V_S$; (b) Secondary current $I_S$ with 500-$\Omega$ $R_L$; (c) $P_S$ in the secondary circuit; (d) $P_P$ in the primary circuit, assuming 100 percent efficiency.

17. Do the same as in Prob. 16 but with a 5-k$\Omega$ load resistance $R_L$.

18. A power transformer with a 2:1 voltage step up is connected to the 120-Vac power line. What is the lowest $R_L$ that can be connected across the secondary without exceeding the power rating of 30 VA?

19. In Fig. 20-32, calculate $V_{S_1}$, $I_{S_1}$, $P_{S_1}$, $V_{S_2}$, $I_{S_2}$, $P_{S_2}$, $P_P$, and $I_P$.

20. In Fig. 20-32, calculate the primary current $I_P$ if the load $R_{L_1}$ opens.

21. In Fig. 20-33, the rated secondary current equals 10 A as shown. Calculate: (a) the value of secondary load resistance $R_L$ which will draw 10 A of current; (b) the primary current $I_P$ when $I_S = 10$ A.

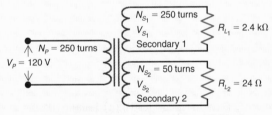

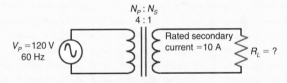

FIG. 20-32  Circuit for Probs. 19, 20, and Critical Thinking Prob. 4.

FIG. 20-33  Circuit for Prob. 21.

22. Refer to Fig. 20-34. Calculate the maximum allowable current for: (a) secondary 1; (b) secondary 2; (c) the primary.

23. In Fig. 20-35, calculate the primary impedance $Z_P$ for a turns ratio $N_P/N_S$ of: (a) 2:1; (b) 1:2; (c) 11.18:1; (d) 10:1; (e) 1:3.16.

24. In Fig. 20-36, calculate the required turns ratio $N_P/N_S$ for: (a) $Z_P = 10$ k$\Omega$, $R_L = 75$ $\Omega$; (b) $Z_P = 100$ $\Omega$, $R_L = 25$ $\Omega$; (c) $Z_P = 100$ $\Omega$, $R_L = 10$ k$\Omega$; (d) $Z_P = 1$ k$\Omega$, $R_L = 200$ $\Omega$; (e) $Z_P = 200$ $\Omega$, $R_L = 10$ $\Omega$.

25. In Fig. 20-37, what turns ratio $N_P/N_S$ will provide the maximum transfer of power from the amplifier to $R_L$?

26. Using the turns ratio from Prob. 25 in Fig. 20-37, calculate: (a) $Z_P$; (b) $P_P$; (c) $P_{RL}$.

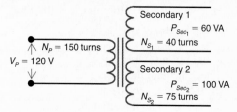

FIG. 20-34   Circuit for Prob. 22.

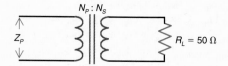

FIG. 20-35   Circuit for Prob. 23.

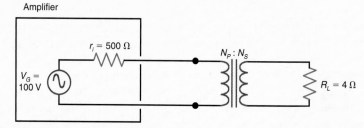

FIG. 20-37   Circuit for Probs. 25 and 26.

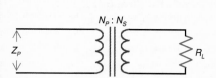

FIG. 20-36   Circuit for Prob. 24.

## CRITICAL THINKING

1. Derive the formula:

$$Z_P = \left(\frac{N_P}{N_S}\right)^2 \times Z_S$$

2. Calculate the primary impedance $Z_P$ in Fig. 20-38.
3. In Fig. 20-39, calculate the primary impedance $Z_P$ across primary leads: (**a**) 1 and 3; (**b**) 1 and 2. (Note: Terminal 2 is a center-tap connection on the transformer primary. Also, the turns ratio of $4\!:\!1$ is specified using leads 1 and 3 of the primary.)
4. Refer to Fig. 20-32. If the transformer has an efficiency of 80 percent, calculate the primary current $I_P$.

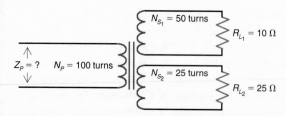

FIG. 20-38   Circuit for Critical Thinking Prob. 2.

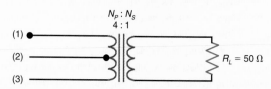

FIG. 20-39   Circuit for Critical Thinking Prob. 3.

**20-1** **a.** coil with an iron core
**b.** time B

**20-2** **a.** $L = 2$ H
**b.** $L = 32$ mH

**20-3** **a.** $v_L = 2$ V
**b.** $v_L = 200$ V

**20-4** **a.** T
**b.** T

**20-5** **a.** $k = 1$
**b.** $L_M = 18$ mH

**20-6** **a.** $V_S = 240$ V
**b.** $I_S = 0.1$ A
**c.** F
**d.** increase

**20-7** **a.** T
**b.** T
**c.** F

**20-8** **a.** F
**b.** F
**c.** T

**20-9** **a.** iron core
**b.** 60 MHz

**20-10** **a.** T
**b.** T
**c.** T

**20-11** **a.** T
**b.** T

**20-12** **a.** $L_T = 1.5$ mH
**b.** $L_{EQ} = 0.33$ mH

**20-13** **a.** T
**b.** T

**20-14** **a.** joule
**b.** more

**20-15** **a.** infinite ohms
**b.** 0 V

# CHAPTER 21

# INDUCTIVE REACTANCE

When alternating current flows in an inductance $L$, the amount of current is much less than the resistance alone would allow. The reason is that the current variations induce a voltage across $L$ that opposes the applied voltage. This additional opposition of an inductance to sine-wave alternating current is specified by the amount of its inductive reactance $X_L$. It is an opposition to current, measured in ohms. The $X_L$ is the ohms of opposition, therefore, that an inductance $L$ has for sine-wave current.

The amount of $X_L$ equals $2\pi fL$ ohms, with $f$ in hertz and $L$ in henrys. Note that the opposition in ohms of $X_L$ increases for higher frequencies and more inductance. The constant factor $2\pi$ indicates sine-wave variations.

The requirements for having $X_L$ correspond to what is needed for producing induced voltage. There must be variations in current and its associated magnetic flux. For a steady direct current without any changes in current, the $X_L$ is zero. However, with sine-wave alternating current, the $X_L$ is the best way to analyze the effect of $L$.

# CHAPTER OBJECTIVES

*Upon completion of this chapter, you should be able to:*

- *Explain* how inductive reactance reduces the amount of alternating current.
- *Calculate* the reactance of an inductor when the frequency and inductance are known.
- *Calculate* the total reactance of series connected inductors.
- *Calculate* the equivalent reactance of parallel connected inductors.
- *Understand* how Ohm's law can be applied to inductive reactance.
- *Understand* the waveshape of induced voltage produced by sine-wave alternating current.

## IMPORTANT TERMS IN THIS CHAPTER

cosine wave
inductive reactance $X_L$

90° phase angle

quadrature angle

## TOPICS COVERED IN THIS CHAPTER

**21-1** How $X_L$ Reduces the Amount of $I$
**21-2** $X_L = 2\pi fL$
**21-3** Series or Parallel Inductive Reactances
**21-4** Ohm's Law Applied to $X_L$

**21-5** Applications of $X_L$ for Different Frequencies
**21-6** Waveshape of $v_L$ Induced by Sine-Wave Current

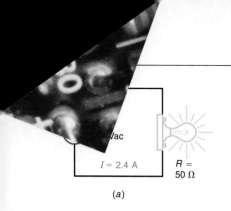

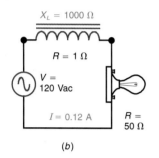

(a)

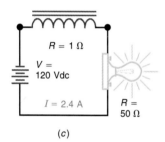

(b)

(c)

**FIG. 21-1** Illustrating the effect of inductive reactance $X_L$ in reducing the amount of sine-wave alternating current. (a) Bulb lights with 2.4 A. (b) Inserting an $X_L$ of 1000 Ω reduces $I$ to 0.12 A, and the bulb cannot light. (c) With direct current, the coil has no inductive reactance, and the bulb lights.

Figure 21-1 illustrates the effect of $X_L$ in reducing the alternating current for a light bulb. The more ohms of $X_L$, the less current flows. When $X_L$ reduces $I$ to a very small value, the bulb cannot light.

In Fig. 21-1a, there is no inductance, and the ac voltage source produces a 2.4-A current to light the bulb with full brilliance. This 2.4-A $I$ results from 120 V applied across the 50-Ω $R$ of the bulb's filament.

In Fig. 21-1b, however, a coil is connected in series with the bulb. The coil has a dc resistance of only 1 Ω, which is negligible, but the reactance of the inductance is 1000 Ω. This $X_L$ is a measure of the coil's reaction to sine-wave current in producing a self-induced voltage that opposes the applied voltage and reduces the current. Now $I$ is 120 V/1000 Ω, approximately, which equals 0.12 A. This $I$ is not enough to light the bulb.

Although the dc resistance is only 1 Ω, the $X_L$ of 1000 Ω for the coil limits the amount of alternating current to such a low value that the bulb cannot light. This $X_L$ of 1000 Ω for a 60-Hz current can be obtained with an inductance $L$ of approximately 2.65 H.

In Fig. 21-1c, the coil is also in series with the bulb, but the applied battery voltage produces a steady value of direct current. Without any current variations, the coil cannot induce any voltage and, therefore, it has no reactance. The amount of direct current, then, is practically the same as though the dc voltage source were connected directly across the bulb, and it lights with full brilliance. In this case, the coil is only a length of wire, as there is no induced voltage without current variations. The dc resistance is the resistance of the wire in the coil.

In summary, we can make the following conclusions:

1. An inductance can have appreciable $X_L$ in ac circuits, to reduce the amount of current. Furthermore, the higher the frequency of the alternating current, and the greater the inductance, the higher is the $X_L$ opposition.
2. There is no $X_L$ for steady direct current. In this case, the coil is just a resistance equal to the resistance of the wire.

These effects have almost unlimited applications in practical circuits. Consider how useful ohms of $X_L$ can be for different kinds of current, compared with resistance, which always has the same ohms of opposition. One example is to use $X_L$ where it is desired to have high ohms of opposition to alternating current but little opposition to direct current. Another example is to use $X_L$ for more opposition to a high-frequency alternating current, compared with lower frequencies.

**$X_L$ IS AN INDUCTIVE EFFECT**  An inductance can have $X_L$ to reduce the amount of alternating current because self-induced voltage is produced to oppose the applied voltage. In Fig. 21-2, $V_L$ is the voltage across $L$, induced by the variations in sine-wave current produced by the applied voltage $V_A$.

The two voltages $V_A$ and $V_L$ are the same because they are in parallel. However, the current $I_L$ is the amount that allows the self-induced voltage $V_L$ to be equal to $V_A$. In this example, $I$ is 0.12 A. This value of a 60-Hz current in the inductance produces a $V_L$ of 120 V.

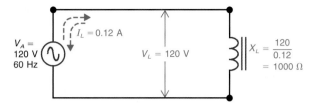

FIG. 21-2   The inductive reactance $X_L$ equals the $V_L/I_L$ ratio in ohms.

**THE REACTANCE IS A *V/I* RATIO**   When we consider the *V/I* ratio for the ohms of opposition to the sine-wave current, this value is 120/0.12, which equals 1000 Ω. This 1000 Ω is what we call $X_L$, to indicate how much current can be produced by sine-wave voltage across an inductance. The ohms of $X_L$ can be almost any amount, but the 1000 Ω here is a typical example.

**THE EFFECT OF *L* AND *f* ON $X_L$**   The $X_L$ value depends on the amount of inductance and the frequency of the alternating current. If *L* in Fig. 21-2 were increased, it could induce the same 120 V for $V_L$ with less current. Then the ratio of $V_L/I_L$ would be greater, meaning more $X_L$ for more inductance.

Also, if the frequency were increased in Fig. 21-2, the current variations would be faster with a higher frequency. Then the same *L* could produce the 120 V for $V_L$ with less current. For this condition also, the $V_L/I_L$ ratio would be greater because of the smaller current, indicating more $X_L$ for a higher frequency.

---

### TEST-POINT QUESTION 21-1

Answers at end of chapter.
**a.** For the dc circuit in Fig. 21-1*c*, how much is $X_L$?
**b.** For the ac circuit in Fig. 21-1*b*, how much is the *V/I* ratio for $X_L$?

## 21-2 $X_L = 2\pi fL$

The formula $X_L = 2\pi fL$ includes the effects of frequency and inductance for calculating the inductive reactance. The frequency is in hertz and *L* is in henrys for an $X_L$ in ohms. As an example, we can calculate $X_L$ for an inductance of 2.65 H at the frequency of 60 Hz:

▶       $X_L = 2\pi fL$                                                    **(21-1)**
        $= 6.28 \times 60 \times 2.65$
        $X_L = 1000 \ \Omega$

Note the following factors in the formula $X_L = 2\pi fL$.

1.   The constant factor $2\pi$ is always $2 \times 3.14 = 6.28$. It indicates the circular motion from which a sine wave is derived. Therefore, this formula applies

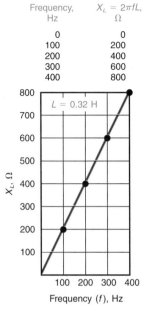

X_L increases as f increases

| Frequency, Hz | $X_L = 2\pi fL,$ $\Omega$ |
|---|---|
| 0 | 0 |
| 100 | 200 |
| 200 | 400 |
| 300 | 600 |
| 400 | 800 |

$L = 0.32$ H

FIG. 21-3 Graph of values to show linear increase of $X_L$ for higher frequencies. The $L$ is constant at 0.32 H.

X_L increases as L increases

| Inductance, H | $X_L = 2\pi fL,$ $\Omega$ |
|---|---|
| 0 | 0 |
| 0.32 | 200 |
| 0.64 | 400 |
| 0.96 | 600 |
| 1.28 | 800 |

$f = 100$ Hz

FIG. 21-4 Graph of values to show linear increase of $X_L$ for higher values of inductance $L$. The frequency is constant at 100 Hz.

only to sine-wave ac circuits. The $2\pi$ is actually $2\pi$ rad or 360° for a complete circle or cycle.

2. The frequency $f$ is a time element. Higher frequency means that the current varies at a faster rate. A faster current change can produce more self-induced voltage across a given inductance. The result is more $X_L$.

3. The inductance $L$ indicates the physical factors of the coil that determine how much voltage it can induce for a given current change.

4. Inductive reactance $X_L$ is in ohms, corresponding to a $V_L/I_L$ ratio for sine-wave ac circuits, to determine how much current $L$ allows for a given applied voltage.

Stating $X_L$ as $V_L/I_L$ and as $2\pi fL$ are two ways of specifying the same value of ohms. The $2\pi fL$ formula gives the effect of $L$ and $f$ on the $X_L$. The $V_L/I_L$ ratio gives the result of $2\pi fL$ in reducing the amount of $I$.

The formula $2\pi fL$ shows that $X_L$ is proportional to frequency. When $f$ is doubled, for instance, $X_L$ is doubled. This linear increase of inductive reactance with frequency is illustrated in Fig. 21-3.

The reactance formula also shows that $X_L$ is proportional to the inductance. When the value of henrys for $L$ is doubled, the ohms of $X_L$ is also doubled. This linear increase of inductive reactance with frequency is illustrated in Fig. 21-4.

## Example

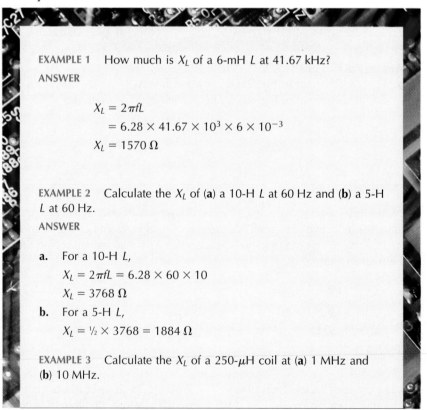

**EXAMPLE 1** How much is $X_L$ of a 6-mH $L$ at 41.67 kHz?

ANSWER

$$X_L = 2\pi fL$$
$$= 6.28 \times 41.67 \times 10^3 \times 6 \times 10^{-3}$$
$$X_L = 1570 \; \Omega$$

**EXAMPLE 2** Calculate the $X_L$ of **(a)** a 10-H $L$ at 60 Hz and **(b)** a 5-H $L$ at 60 Hz.

ANSWER

**a.** For a 10-H $L$,
$$X_L = 2\pi fL = 6.28 \times 60 \times 10$$
$$X_L = 3768 \; \Omega$$

**b.** For a 5-H $L$,
$$X_L = \frac{1}{2} \times 3768 = 1884 \; \Omega$$

**EXAMPLE 3** Calculate the $X_L$ of a 250-$\mu$H coil at **(a)** 1 MHz and **(b)** 10 MHz.

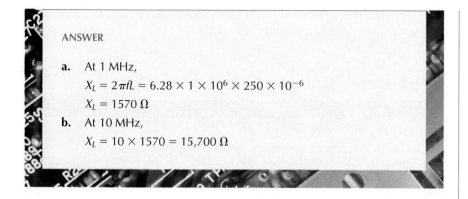

ANSWER

**a.** At 1 MHz,

$$X_L = 2\pi fL = 6.28 \times 1 \times 10^6 \times 250 \times 10^{-6}$$

$$X_L = 1570 \ \Omega$$

**b.** At 10 MHz,

$$X_L = 10 \times 1570 = 15{,}700 \ \Omega$$

The last two examples illustrate the fact that $X_L$ is proportional to frequency and inductance. In Example 2**b**, $X_L$ is one-half the value in Example 2**a** because the inductance is one-half. In Example 3**b**, the $X_L$ is ten times more than in Example 3**a** because the frequency is ten times higher.

To do a problem like Example 1 with a calculator just requires continued multiplication. Multiply all the factors and then press the $\boxed{=}$ key only at the end. If the calculator does not have an $\boxed{EXP}$ (exponential) function key, do the powers* of 10 separately without the calculator. Specifically, for this example with $2\pi \times 6 \times 10^{-3} \times 41.67 \times 10^3$, the $10^3$ and $10^{-3}$ cancel. Then calculate $2\pi \times 6 \times 41.67$ as factors. To save time in the calculation, $2\pi$ can be memorized as 6.28, since it occurs in many ac formulas. For the multiplication, punch in 6.28 for $2\pi$ then push the $\boxed{\times}$ key, punch in 6 and push the $\boxed{\times}$ key again, punch in 41.67, and push the $\boxed{=}$ key for the total product of 1570 as the final answer. It is not necessary to use the $\boxed{=}$ key until the last step for the final product. The factors can be multiplied in any order.

**FINDING $L$ FROM $X_L$**   Not only can $X_L$ be calculated from $f$ and $L$, but if any two factors are known, the third can be found. Very often $X_L$ can be determined from voltage and current measurements. With the frequency known, $L$ can be calculated as

▶   $$L = \frac{X_L}{2\pi f}$$   (21-2)

This formula just has the factors inverted from Formula (21-1). Use the basic units with ohms for $X_L$ and hertz for $f$ to calculate $L$ in henrys.

It should be noted that Formula (21-2) can also be stated as

▶   $$L = \frac{1}{2\pi f} \times X_L$$

This form is easier to use with a calculator because $1/2\pi f$ can be found as a reciprocal value and then multiplied by $X_L$.

---

*For an explanation of powers of 10 see B. Grob, *Mathematics for Basic Electronics*, Glencoe/McGraw-Hill, Columbus, Ohio, and M. Schultz, *Problems in Basic Electronics*, Glencoe/McGraw-Hill, Columbus, Ohio.

The following problems illustrate how to find $X_L$ from $V$ and $I$ measurements and using $X_L$ to determine $L$ with Formula (21-2).

## Example

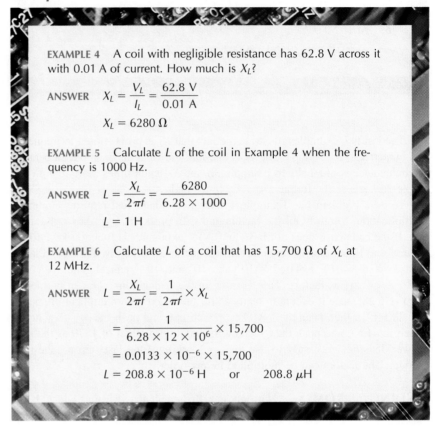

**EXAMPLE 4**    A coil with negligible resistance has 62.8 V across it with 0.01 A of current. How much is $X_L$?

ANSWER    $X_L = \dfrac{V_L}{I_L} = \dfrac{62.8 \text{ V}}{0.01 \text{ A}}$

$X_L = 6280 \ \Omega$

**EXAMPLE 5**    Calculate $L$ of the coil in Example 4 when the frequency is 1000 Hz.

ANSWER    $L = \dfrac{X_L}{2\pi f} = \dfrac{6280}{6.28 \times 1000}$

$L = 1 \text{ H}$

**EXAMPLE 6**    Calculate $L$ of a coil that has 15,700 $\Omega$ of $X_L$ at 12 MHz.

ANSWER    $L = \dfrac{X_L}{2\pi f} = \dfrac{1}{2\pi f} \times X_L$

$= \dfrac{1}{6.28 \times 12 \times 10^6} \times 15,700$

$= 0.0133 \times 10^{-6} \times 15,700$

$L = 208.8 \times 10^{-6} \text{ H}$    or    $208.8 \ \mu\text{H}$

To do Example 6 with a calculator, first find the product $2\pi f$ and then take the reciprocal to multiply by 15,700. Note that with powers of 10 a reciprocal value has the sign reversed for the exponent. Specifically, $10^6$ in the denominator here becomes $10^{-6}$ as the reciprocal. To multiply the factors, punch in 6.28 then push the $\boxed{\times}$ key, punch in 12, and push the $\boxed{=}$ key for the total product of 75.36. Take the reciprocal by using the $\boxed{1/x}$ key, while the product is still on the display. This may require pushing the $\boxed{\text{2ndF}}$ or "shift" key on the calculator. The reciprocal value is 0.0133. Now press the $\boxed{\times}$ key, punch in 15,700, and push the $\boxed{=}$ key for the answer of $208.8 \times 10^{-6}$.

**FINDING $f$ FROM $X_L$**    For a third version of the inductive reactance formula,

▶    $f = \dfrac{X_L}{2\pi L}$    **(21-3)**

Use the basic units of ohms for $X_L$ and henrys for $L$ to calculate the frequency in hertz.

Formula 21-3 can also be stated as

$$f = \frac{1}{2\pi L} \times X_L$$

This form is easier to use with a calculator. Find the reciprocal value and multiply by $X_L$, as explained before with Example 6.

## Example

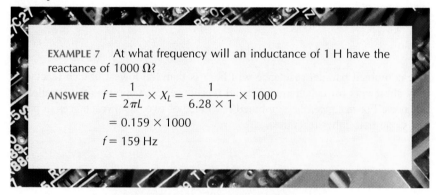

EXAMPLE 7    At what frequency will an inductance of 1 H have the reactance of 1000 Ω?

ANSWER    $f = \dfrac{1}{2\pi L} \times X_L = \dfrac{1}{6.28 \times 1} \times 1000$

$\qquad\qquad = 0.159 \times 1000$

$\qquad\quad f = 159$ Hz

---

**TEST-POINT QUESTION 21-2**

Answers at end of chapter.

Calculate $X_L$ for the following:
**a.** $L$ is 1 H and $f$ is 100 Hz.
**b.** $L$ is 0.5 H and $f$ is 100 Hz.
**c.** $L$ is 1 H and $f$ is 1000 Hz.

## 21-3 SERIES OR PARALLEL INDUCTIVE REACTANCES

Since reactance is an opposition in ohms, the values $X_L$ in series or in parallel are combined the same way as ohms of resistance. With series reactances, the total is the sum of the individual values, as shown in Fig. 21-5a. For example, the series reactances of 100 and 200 Ω add to equal 300 Ω of $X_L$ across both reactances. Therefore, in series,

$$X_{L_T} = X_{L_1} + X_{L_2} + X_{L_3} + \cdots + \text{etc.} \tag{21-4}$$

For the case of parallel reactances, the combined reactance is calculated by the reciprocal formula. As shown in Fig. 21-5b, in parallel

$$\frac{1}{X_{L_{EQ}}} = \frac{1}{X_{L_1}} + \frac{1}{X_{L_2}} + \frac{1}{X_{L_3}} + \cdots + \text{etc.} \tag{21-5}$$

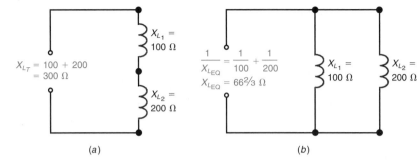

**FIG. 21-5** Combining ohms of $X_L$ for inductive reactances. (a) $X_{L_1}$ and $X_{L_2}$ in series. (b) $X_{L_1}$ and $X_{L_2}$ in parallel.

The combined parallel reactance will be less than the lowest branch reactance. Any short cuts for calculating parallel resistances also apply to the parallel reactances. For instance, the combined reactance of two equal reactances in parallel is one-half either reactance.

---

### TEST-POINT QUESTION 21-3

Answers at end of chapter.
**a.** An $X_L$ of 200 Ω is in series with a 300-Ω $X_L$. How much is the total $X_LT$?
**b.** An $X_L$ of 200 Ω is in parallel with a 300-Ω $X_L$. How much is the combined $X_{L_{EQ}}$ in this problem?

---

## 21-4 OHM'S LAW APPLIED TO $X_L$

The amount of current in an ac circuit with just inductive reactance is equal to the applied voltage divided by $X_L$. Three examples are illustrated in Fig. 21-6. No dc resistance is indicated, since it is assumed to be practically zero for the coils shown. In Fig. 21-6a, there is just one reactance of 100 Ω. Then $I$ equals $V/X_L$, or 100 V/100 Ω, which is 1 A.

In Fig. 21-6b, the total reactance is the sum of the two individual series reactances of 100 Ω each, for a total of 200 Ω. The current, calculated as $V/X_{L_T}$, then equals 100 V/200 Ω, which is ½ A or 0.5 A. This current is the same in both series reactances. Therefore, the voltage across each reactance equals its $IX_L$ product. This is 0.5 A × 100 Ω, or 50 V across each $X_L$.

In Fig. 21-6c, each parallel reactance has its individual branch current, equal to the applied voltage divided by the branch reactance. Then each branch current equals 100 V/100 Ω, which is 1 A. The voltage is the same across both reactances, equal to the generator voltage, since they are all in parallel.

The total line current of 2 A is the sum of the two individual 1-A branch currents. With the rms value for the applied voltage, all the calculated values of currents and voltage drops in Fig. 21-6 are also rms values.

Answers at end of chapter.
**a.** In Fig. 21-6*b*, how much is the *I* through both $X_{L_1}$ and $X_{L_2}$?
**b.** In Fig. 21-6*c*, how much is the *V* across both $X_{L_1}$ and $X_{L_2}$?

# 21-5 APPLICATIONS OF $X_L$ FOR DIFFERENT FREQUENCIES

The general use of inductance is to provide minimum reactance for relatively low frequencies but more for higher frequencies. In this way, the current in an ac circuit can be reduced for higher frequencies because of more $X_L$. There are many circuits in which voltages of different frequencies are applied to produce current with different frequencies. Then, the general effect of $X_L$ is to allow the most current for direct current and low frequencies, with less current for higher frequencies, as $X_L$ increases.

Compare this frequency factor for ohms of $X_L$ with ohms of resistance. The $X_L$ increases with frequency, but $R$ has the same effect in limiting direct current or alternating current of any frequency.

If 1000 $\Omega$ is taken as a suitable value of $X_L$ for many applications, typical inductances can be calculated for different frequencies. These are listed in Table 21-1.

At 60 Hz, for example, the inductance $L$ in the top row of Table 21-1 is 2.65 H for 1000 $\Omega$ of $X_L$. The calculations are

$$L = \frac{X_L}{2\pi f} = \frac{1000}{2\pi \times 60}$$

$$= \frac{1000}{377}$$

$$L = 2.65 \text{ H}$$

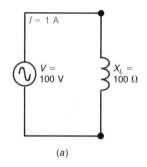

(a)

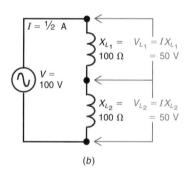

(b)

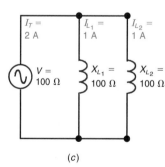

(c)

**FIG. 21-6** Circuit calculations with $V$, $I$, and ohms of reactance $X_L$. (*a*) One reactance. (*b*) Two series reactances. (*c*) Two parallel reactances.

**TABLE 21-1   VALUES OF INDUCTANCE $L$ FOR $X_L$ OF 1000 $\Omega$**

| $L$* (APPROX.) | FREQUENCY | REMARKS |
|---|---|---|
| 2.65 H | 60 Hz | Power-line frequency and low audio frequency |
| 160 mH | 1000 Hz | Medium audio frequency |
| 16 mH | 10,000 Hz | High audio frequency |
| 160 $\mu$H | 1000 kHz (RF) | In radio broadcast band |
| 16 $\mu$H | 10 MHz (HF) | In short-wave radio band |
| 1.6 $\mu$H | 100 MHz (VHF) | In FM broadcast band |

*Calculated as $L = 1000/(2\pi f)$.

For this case, the inductance has practically no reactance for direct current or for very low frequencies below 60 Hz. However, above 60 Hz, the inductive reactance increases to more than 1000 Ω.

To summarize, the effects of increasing frequencies for this 2.65-H inductance are as follows:

Inductive reactance $X_L$ is zero for 0 Hz which corresponds to a steady direct current.
Inductive reactance $X_L$ is less than 1000 Ω for frequencies below 60 Hz.
Inductive reactance $X_L$ equals 1000 Ω at 60 Hz.
Inductive reactance $X_L$ is more than 1000 Ω for frequencies above 60 Hz.

Note that the smaller inductances at the bottom of the first column still have the same $X_L$ of 1000 Ω as the frequency is increased. Typical RF coils, for instance, have an inductance value of the order of 100 to 300 $\mu$H. For the very high radio-frequency (VHF) range, only several microhenrys of inductance are needed for an $X_L$ of 1000 Ω.

It is necessary to use smaller inductance values as the frequency is increased because a coil that is too large can have excessive losses at high frequencies. With iron-core coils, particularly, the hysteresis and eddy-current losses increase with frequency.

---

### TEST-POINT QUESTION 21-5

Answers at end of chapter.

Refer to Table 21-1.
**a.** Which frequency requires the smallest $L$ for 1000 Ω of $X_L$?
**b.** How much would $X_L$ be for the 1.6-$\mu$H $L$ at 200 MHz?

## 21-6 WAVESHAPE OF $v_L$ INDUCED BY SINE-WAVE CURRENT

More details of inductive circuits can be analyzed by means of the waveshapes in Fig. 21-7, plotted for the calculated values in Table 21-2. The top curve shows a sine wave of current $i_L$ flowing through a 6-mH inductance $L$. Since induced voltage depends on rate of change of current rather than the absolute value of $i$, the curve in Fig. 21-7b shows how much the current changes. In this curve the $di/dt$ values are plotted for the current changes every 30° of the cycle. The bottom curve shows the actual induced voltage $v_L$. This $v_L$ curve is similar to the $di/dt$ curve because $v_L$ equals the constant factor $L$ multiplied by $di/dt$. It should be noted that $di/dt$ indicates infinitely small changes in $i$ and $t$.

**90° PHASE ANGLE** The $v_L$ curve at the bottom of Fig. 21-7 has its zero values when the $i_L$ curve at the top is at maximum. This comparison shows that the curves are 90° out of phase. The $v_L$ is a cosine wave of voltage for the sine wave of current $i_L$.

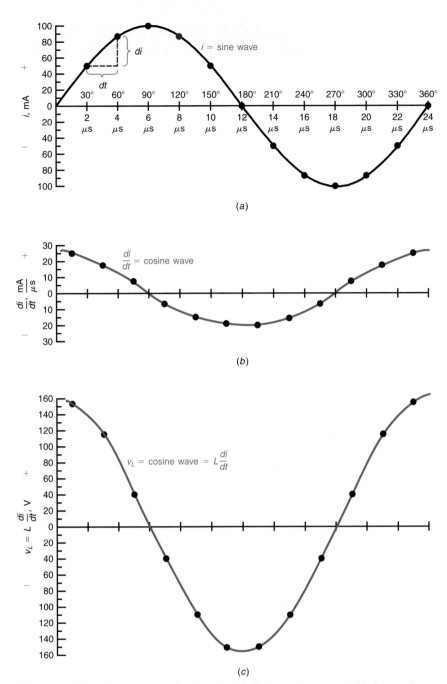

**FIG. 21-7**   Waveshapes in inductive circuits. (*a*) Sine-wave current, *i*; (*b*) changes in current with time, *di/dt*; (*c*) induced voltage, $v_L$.

    The 90° phase difference results from the fact that $v_L$ depends on the *di/dt* rate of change, rather than on *i* itself. More details of this 90° phase angle between $v_L$ and $i_L$ for inductance are explained in the next chapter.

**FREQUENCY**   For each of the curves, the period *T* is 24 $\mu$s. Therefore, the frequency is 1/*T* or $\frac{1}{24}$ $\mu$s, which equals 41.67 kHz. Each curve has the same frequency.

TABLE 21-2   VALUES FOR $v_L = L(di/dt)$ CURVES IN FIG. 21-7

| TIME | | dt | | di, mA | $di/dt$, mA/$\mu$s | L, mH | $v_L = L(di/dt)$, V |
|---|---|---|---|---|---|---|---|
| $\theta$ | $\mu s$ | $\theta$ | $\mu s$ | | | | |
| 30° | 2 | 30° | 2 | 50 | 25 | 6 | 150 |
| 60° | 4 | 30° | 2 | 36.6 | 18.3 | 6 | 109.8 |
| 90° | 6 | 30° | 2 | 13.4 | 6.7 | 6 | 40.2 |
| 120° | 8 | 30° | 2 | −13.4 | −6.7 | 6 | −40.2 |
| 150° | 10 | 30° | 2 | −36.6 | −18.3 | 6 | −109.8 |
| 180° | 12 | 30° | 2 | −50 | −25 | 6 | −150 |
| 210° | 14 | 30° | 2 | −50 | −25 | 6 | −150 |
| 240° | 16 | 30° | 2 | −36.6 | −18.3 | 6 | −109.8 |
| 270° | 18 | 30° | 2 | −13.4 | −6.7 | 6 | −40.2 |
| 300° | 20 | 30° | 2 | 13.4 | 6.7 | 6 | 40.2 |
| 330° | 22 | 30° | 2 | 36.6 | 18.3 | 6 | 109.8 |
| 360° | 24 | 30° | 2 | 50 | 25 | 6 | 150 |

**OHMS OF $X_L$**    The ratio of $v_L/i_L$ actually specifies the inductive reactance in ohms. For this comparison, we use the actual value of $i_L$, which has a peak value of 100 mA. The rate-of-change factor is included in the induced voltage $v_L$. Although the peak of $v_L$ at 150 V is 90° before the peak of $i_L$ at 100 mA, we can compare these two peak values. Then $v_L/i_L$ is 150/0.1, which equals 1500 $\Omega$.

This $X_L$ is only an approximate value because $v_L$ cannot be determined exactly for the large $dt$ changes every 30°. If we used smaller intervals of time, the peak $v_L$ would be 157 V. Then $X_L$ would be 1570 $\Omega$, the same as $2\pi fL$ $\Omega$ with a 6-mH $L$ and a frequency of 41.67 kHz. This is the same $X_L$ problem as Example 1 on page 588.

**THE TABULATED VALUES FROM 0° TO 90°**    The numerical values in Table 21-2 are calculated as follows: The $i$ curve is a sine wave. This means it rises to one-half its peak value in 30° and to 0.866 of the peak in 60°, and the peak value is at 90°.

In the $di/dt$ curve the changes in $i$ are plotted. For the first 30° the $di$ is 50 mA; the $dt$ change is 2 $\mu$s. Then $di/dt$ is 50/2 or 25 mA/$\mu$s. This point is plotted between 0° and 30° to indicate that 25 mA/$\mu$s is the rate of change of current for the 2-$\mu$s interval between 0° and 30°. If smaller intervals were used, the $di/dt$ values could be determined more accurately.

During the next 2-$\mu$s interval, from 30° to 60°, the current increases from 50 to 86.6 mA. The change of current during this time is 86.6 − 50, which equals 36.6 mA. The time is the same 2 $\mu$s for all the intervals. Then $di/dt$ for the next plotted point is 36.6/2, or 18.3.

For the final 2-$\mu$s change before $i$ reaches its peak at 100 mA, the $di$ value is 100 − 86.6, or 13.4 mA, and the $di/dt$ value is 6.7. All these values are listed in Table 21-2.

Notice that the $di/dt$ curve in Fig. 21-7b has its peak at the zero value of the $i$ curve, while the peak $i$ values correspond to zero on the $di/dt$ curves. These conditions result because the sine wave of $i$ has its sharpest slope at the zero values. The rate of change is greatest when the $i$ curve is going through the zero axis. The $i$ curve flattens near the peaks and has zero rate of change exactly at the peak. The curve must stop going up before it can come down. In summary, then, the $di/dt$ curve and the $i$ curve are 90° out of phase with each other.

The $v_L$ curve follows the $di/dt$ curve exactly, as $v_L = L(di/dt)$. The phase of the $v_L$ curve is exactly the same as that of the $di/dt$ curve, 90° out of phase with the $i$ curve. For the first plotted point,

$$v_L = L\frac{di}{dt} = 6 \times 10^{-3} \times \frac{50 \times 10^{-3}}{2 \times 10^{-6}}$$

$$v_L = 150 \text{ V}$$

The other $v_L$ values are calculated the same way, multiplying the constant factor of 6 mH by the $di/dt$ value for each 2-$\mu$s interval.

**90° TO 180°** In this quarter-cycle, the sine wave of $i$ decreases from its peak of 100 mA at 90° to zero at 180°. This decrease is considered a negative value for $di$, as the slope is negative going downward. Physically, the decrease in current means its associated magnetic flux is collapsing, compared with the expanding flux as the current increases. The opposite motion of the collapsing flux must make $v_L$ of opposite polarity, compared with the induced voltage polarity for increasing flux. This is why the $di$ values are negative from 90° to 180°. The $di/dt$ values are also negative, and the $v_L$ values are negative.

**180° TO 270°** In this quarter-cycle, the current increases in the reverse direction. If the magnetic flux is considered counterclockwise around the conductor with $+i$ values, the flux is in the reversed clockwise direction with $-i$ values. Any induced voltage produced by expanding flux in one direction will have opposite polarity from voltage induced by expanding flux in the opposite direction. This is why the $di$ values are considered negative from 180° to 270°, as in the second quarter-cycle, compared with the positive $di$ values from 0° to 90°. Actually, increasing negative values and decreasing positive values

are changing in the same direction. This is why $v_L$ is negative for both the second and third quarter-cycles.

**270° TO 360°**  In the last quarter-cycle, the negative $i$ values are decreasing. Now the effect on polarity is like two negatives making a positive. The current and its magnetic flux have the negative direction. But the flux is collapsing, which induces opposite voltage from increasing flux. Therefore, the $di$ values from 270° to 360° are positive, as are the $di/dt$ values and the induced voltages $v_L$.

The same action is repeated for each cycle of sine-wave current. Then the current $i_L$ and the induced voltage $v_L$ are 90° out of phase. The reason is that $v_L$ depends on $di/dt$, not on $i$ alone.

**APPLICATION OF THE 90° PHASE ANGLE IN A CIRCUIT**  The phase angle of 90° between $V_L$ and $I$ will always apply for any $L$ with sine-wave current. Remember, though, that the specific comparison is only between the induced voltage across any one coil and the current flowing in its turns. To emphasize this important principle, Fig. 21-8 shows an ac circuit with a few coils and resistors. The details of this complex circuit are not to be analyzed now. However, for each $L$ in the circuit, the $V_L$ is 90° out of phase with its $I$. The $I$ lags $V_L$ by 90°, or $V_L$ leads $I$. For the examples of three coils in Fig. 21-8:

Current $I_1$ lags $V_{L_1}$ by 90°.
Current $I_2$ lags $V_{L_2}$ by 90°.
Current $I_3$ lags $V_{L_3}$ by 90°.
Note that $I_3$ is also $I_T$ for the series-parallel circuit.

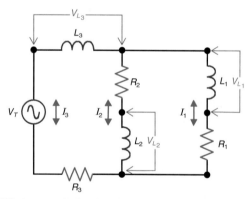

**FIG. 21-8**  How 90° phase angle for the $V_L$ applies in a complex circuit with more than one inductance. The current $I_1$ lags $V_{L_1}$ by 90°; $I_2$ lags $V_{L_2}$ by 90°; and $I_3$ lags $V_{L_3}$ by 90°.

---

**TEST-POINT QUESTION 21-6**

---

Answers at end of chapter.

Refer to Fig. 21-7.
**a.** At what angle does $i$ have its maximum positive value?
**b.** At what angle does $v_L$ have its maximum positive value?
**c.** What is the phase angle difference between the waveforms for $i$ and $v_L$?

# 21 SUMMARY AND REVIEW

- Inductive reactance is the opposition of an inductance to the flow of sine-wave alternating current. The symbol for inductive reactance is $X_L$.
- Reactance $X_L$ is measured in ohms because it limits the current to the value $I = V/X_L$. With $V$ in volts and $X_L$ in ohms, $I$ is in amperes.
- $X_L = 2\pi f L$, where $f$ is in hertz, $L$ is in henrys, and $X_L$ is in ohms.
- With a constant $L$, $X_L$ increases proportionately with higher frequencies.
- At a constant frequency, $X_L$ increases proportionately with higher inductances.
- With $X_L$ and $f$ known, the inductance $L = X_L/(2\pi f)$.
- With $X_L$ and $L$ known, the frequency $f = X_L/(2\pi L)$.
- The total $X_L$ of reactances in series is the sum of the individual values, as for series resistances. Series reactances have the same current. The voltage across each inductive reactance is $IX_L$.
- With parallel reactances, the equivalent reactance is calculated by the reciprocal formula, as for parallel resistances. Each branch current is $V/X_L$. The total line current is the sum of the individual branch currents.
- Table 21-3 summarizes the differences between $L$ and $X_L$.

### TABLE 21-3 COMPARISON OF INDUCTANCE AND INDUCTIVE REACTANCE

| INDUCTANCE | INDUCTIVE REACTANCE |
|---|---|
| Symbol is $L$ | Symbol is $X_L$ |
| Measured in henry units | Measured in ohm units |
| Depends on construction of coil | Depends on frequency and inductance |
| $L = v_L/(di/dt)$, in H units | $X_L = v_L/i_L$ or $2\pi f L$, in $\Omega$ units |

- Table 21-4 compares $X_L$ and $R$.

### TABLE 21-4 COMPARISON OF $X_L$ AND R

| $X_L$ | R |
|---|---|
| Ohm unit | Ohm unit |
| Increases for higher frequencies | Same for all frequencies |
| Current lags voltage by 90° $(\theta = 90°)$ | Current in phase with voltage $(\theta = 0°)$ |

- Table 21-5 summarizes the differences between capacitive reactance and inductive reactance.

### TABLE 21-5  COMPARISON OF CAPACITIVE AND INDUCTIVE REACTANCES

| $X_C$, $\Omega$ | $X_L$, $\Omega$ |
| --- | --- |
| Decreases with more capacitance $C$<br>Decreases with increase in frequency $f$<br>Allows less current at lower frequencies; blocks direct current. | Increases with more inductance $L$<br>Increases with increase in frequency $f$<br>Allows more current at lower frequencies; passes direct current. |

## SELF-TEST

**ANSWERS AT BACK OF BOOK.**

Choose (*a*), (*b*), (*c*), or (*d*).

1. Inductive reactance is measured in ohms because it (*a*) reduces the amplitude of alternating current; (*b*) increases the amplitude of alternating current; (*c*) increases the amplitude of direct current; (*d*) has a back emf opposing a steady direct current.

2. Inductive reactance applies only to sine waves because it (*a*) increases with lower frequencies; (*b*) increases with lower inductance; (*c*) depends on the factor $2\pi$; (*d*) decreases with higher frequencies.

3. An inductance has a reactance of 10,000 $\Omega$ at 10,000 Hz. At 20,000 Hz, its inductive reactance equals (*a*) 500 $\Omega$; (*b*) 2000 $\Omega$; (*c*) 20,000 $\Omega$; (*d*) 32,000 $\Omega$.

4. A 16-mH inductance has a reactance of 1000 $\Omega$. If two of these are connected in series without any mutual coupling, their total reactance equals (*a*) 500 $\Omega$; (*b*) 1000 $\Omega$; (*c*) 1600 $\Omega$; (*d*) 2000 $\Omega$.

5. Two 5000-$\Omega$ inductive reactances in parallel have an equivalent reactance of (*a*) 2500 $\Omega$; (*b*) 5000 $\Omega$; (*c*) 10,000 $\Omega$; (*d*) 50,000 $\Omega$.

6. With 10 V applied across an inductive reactance of 100 $\Omega$, the current equals (*a*) 10 $\mu$A; (*b*) 10 mA; (*c*) 100 mA; (*d*) 10 A.

7. A current of 100 mA through an inductive reactance of 100 $\Omega$ produces a voltage drop equal to (*a*) 1 V; (*b*) 6.28 V; (*c*) 10 V; (*d*) 100 V.

8. The inductance required for a 2000-$\Omega$ reactance at 20 MHz equals (*a*) 10 $\mu$H; (*b*) 15.9 $\mu$H; (*c*) 159 $\mu$H; (*d*) 320 $\mu$H.

9. A 160-$\mu$H inductance will have a 5000-$\Omega$ reactance at the frequency of (*a*) 5 kHz; (*b*) 200 kHz; (*c*) 1 MHz; (*d*) 5 MHz.

10. A coil has an inductive reactance of 1000 $\Omega$. If its inductance is doubled and the frequency is doubled, then the inductive reactance will be (*a*) 1000 $\Omega$; (*b*) 2000 $\Omega$; (*c*) 4000 $\Omega$; (*d*) 16,000 $\Omega$.

1. Explain briefly why $X_L$ limits the amount of alternating current.
2. Give two differences and one similarity between $X_L$ and $R$.
3. Explain why $X_L$ increases with higher frequencies and more inductance.
4. Give two differences between inductance $L$ of a coil and its reactance $X_L$.
5. Why are the waves in Fig. 21-7a and b considered to be 90° out of phase, while the waves in Fig. 21-7b and c have the same phase?
6. Referring to Fig. 21-3, how does this graph show a linear proportion between $X_L$ and frequency?
7. Referring to Fig. 21-4, how does this graph show a linear proportion between $X_L$ and $L$?
8. Referring to Fig. 21-3, tabulate the values of $L$ that would be needed for each frequency listed but for an $X_L$ of 2000 $\Omega$. (Do not include 0 Hz.)
9. (a) Draw the circuit for a 40-$\Omega$ $R$ across a 120-V 60-Hz source. (b) Draw the circuit for a 40-$\Omega$ $X_L$ across a 120-V 60-Hz source. (c) Why is $I$ equal to 3 A for both circuits? (d) Give two differences between the circuits.
10. Why are coils for RF applications generally smaller than AF coils?

**ANSWERS TO ODD-NUMBERED PROBLEMS AT BACK OF BOOK.**

1. Calculate the $X_L$ of a 0.5-H inductance at 100, 200, and 1000 Hz.
2. How much is the inductance for 628 $\Omega$ reactance at 100 Hz? 200 Hz? 1000 Hz? 500 kHz?
3. A coil with an $X_L$ of 748 $\Omega$ is connected across a 16-Vac generator. (a) Draw the schematic diagram. (b) Calculate the current. (c) How much is the voltage across the coil?
4. A 20-H coil has 10 V applied, with a frequency of 60 Hz. (a) Draw the schematic diagram. (b) How much is the inductive reactance of the coil? (c) Calculate the current. (d) What is the frequency of the current?
5. How much is the inductance of a coil with negligible resistance if the current is 0.1 A when connected across the 60-Hz 120-V power line?
6. Referring to Fig. 21-6b, how much is the inductance of $L_T$, $L_1$, and $L_2$ if the frequency of the source voltage is 400 Hz?
7. How much is the inductance of a coil that has a reactance of 1000 $\Omega$ at 1000 Hz? How much will the reactance be for the same coil at 10 kHz?
8. How much is the reactance of a 20-$\mu$H inductance at 40 MHz?
9. A 1000-$\Omega$ $X_{L_1}$ and a 4000-$\Omega$ $X_{L_2}$ are in series across a 10-V 60-Hz source. Draw the schematic diagram and calculate the following: (a) total $X_L$; (b) current in $X_{L_1}$ and in $X_{L_2}$; (c) voltage across $X_{L_1}$ and across $X_{L_2}$; (d) $L_1$ and $L_2$.
10. The same 1000-$\Omega$ $X_{L_1}$ and 4000-$\Omega$ $X_{L_2}$ are in parallel across the 10-V 60-Hz source. Draw the schematic diagram and calculate the following: branch currents in $X_{L_1}$ and in $X_{L_2}$; total current in the generator; voltage across $X_{L_1}$ and across $X_{L_2}$; inductance of $L_1$ and $L_2$.

11. At what frequencies will $X_L$ be 2000 $\Omega$ for the following inductors: (a) 2 H; (b) 250 mH; (c) 800 $\mu$H; (d) 200 $\mu$H; (e) 20 $\mu$H?

12. A 6-mH $L_1$ is in series with an 8-mH $L_2$. The frequency is 40 kHz. (a) How much is $L_T$? (b) Calculate $X_{L_T}$. (c) Calculate $X_{L_1}$ and $X_{L_2}$.

13. Calculate $X_L$ of a 2.4-mH coil at 108 kHz.

14. Calculate $X_L$ of a 40-$\mu$H coil at 3.2 MHz.

15. Calculate $X_L$ of a 2-H coil at 60 Hz.

16. How much is $I$ when the $X_L$ of Prob. 15 is connected to 120-V 60-Hz?

17. A 250-mH inductor with negligible resistance is connected across a 10-V source. Tabulate the values of $X_L$ and current in the circuit for alternating current at (a) 20 Hz; (b) 60 Hz; (c) 100 Hz; (d) 500 Hz; (e) 5000 Hz; (f) 15,000 Hz.

18. Do the same as in Prob. 17 for an 8-H inductor.

19. What inductance $L$ is needed for $X_L$ of 785 $\Omega$ at the following frequencies: (a) 500 kHz; (b) 1 MHz; (c) 250 kHz; (d) 5 MHz; (e) 50 kHz?

20. What frequency will provide $X_L$ of 785 $\Omega$ for the following values of inductance $L$? (a) 250 $\mu$H; (b) 125 $\mu$H; (c) 500 $\mu$H; (d) 25 $\mu$H; (e) 2.5 mH?

21. In Fig. 21-9, calculate $X_{L_1}$, $X_{L_2}$, $X_{L_3}$, $X_{L_T}$, $I$, $V_{L_1}$, $V_{L_2}$, and $V_{L_3}$.

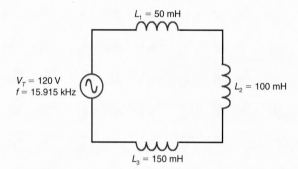

$L_1 = 50$ mH

$V_T = 120$ V
$f = 15.915$ kHz

$L_2 = 100$ mH

$L_3 = 150$ mH

**FIG. 21-9**  Circuit for Probs. 21 and 22.

22. In Fig. 21-9, what happens to $I$ if the frequency $f$ is doubled?

23. In Fig. 21-10, calculate $X_{L_1}$, $X_{L_2}$, $X_{L_3}$, $I_1$, $I_2$, $I_3$, $I_T$, and $X_{L_{EQ}}$.

24. In Fig. 21-10, what happens to $X_{L_{EQ}}$ if the frequency $f$ is doubled?

25. Two inductors connected in series have a mutual inductance $L_M$ of 1 mH. Given $L_1 = 5$ mH and $L_2 = 10$ mH, calculate $X_{L_T}$ for a frequency of 50 kHz when: (a) $L_M$ is series aiding; (b) $L_M$ is series opposing.

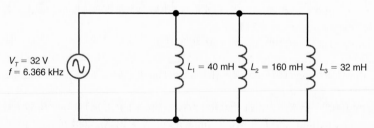

$V_T = 32$ V
$f = 6.366$ kHz

$L_1 = 40$ mH  $L_2 = 160$ mH  $L_3 = 32$ mH

**FIG. 21-10**  Circuit for Probs. 23 and 24.

1. In Fig. 21-11, calculate $L_1$, $L_2$, $L_3$, $L_T$, $X_{L_1}$, $X_{L_2}$, $X_{L_T}$, $V_{L_1}$, $V_{L_3}$, $I_{L_2}$, and $I_{L_3}$.
2. Two inductors in series without $L_M$ have a total inductance $L_T$ of 120 $\mu$H. If $L_1/L_2 = 1/20$, what are the values for $L_1$ and $L_2$?
3. Three inductors in parallel have an equivalent inductance $L_{EQ}$ of 7.5 mH. If $L_2 = 3L_3$ and $L_3 = 4L_1$, calculate $L_1$, $L_2$, and $L_3$.

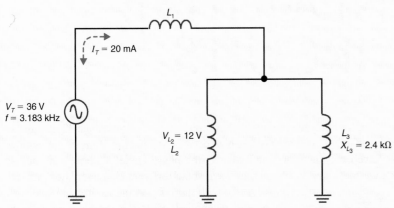

FIG. 21-11  Circuit for Critical Thinking Prob. 1.

## ANSWERS TO TEST-POINT QUESTIONS

**21-1 a.** 0 Ω
  **b.** 1000 Ω

**21-2 a.** $X_L$ = 628 Ω
  **b.** $X_L$ = 314 Ω
  **c.** $X_L$ = 6280 Ω

**21-3 a.** $X_{L_T}$ = 500 Ω
  **b.** $X_{L_T}$ = 120 Ω

**21-4 a.** 0.5 A
  **b.** 100 V

**21-5 a.** 100 MHz
  **b.** 2000 Ω

**21-6 a.** 90°
  **b.** 0° or 360°
  **c.** 90°

# CHAPTER 22

# INDUCTIVE CIRCUITS

This chapter analyzes circuits that combine inductive reactance $X_L$ and resistance $R$. The main questions are: how do we combine the ohms of opposition, how much current flows, and what is the phase angle? Although $X_L$ and $R$ both are measured in ohms, they have some different characteristics. Specifically, $X_L$ increases with more $L$ and higher frequencies, with sine-wave ac voltage applied, while $R$ is the same for dc or ac circuits. Furthermore, the phase angle for the voltage across $X_L$ is at 90° with respect to the current through $L$.

In addition, the practical application of using a coil as a choke to reduce the current for a specific frequency is explained here. For a circuit with $L$ and $R$ in series, the $X_L$ can be high for an undesired ac signal frequency, while $R$ is the same for either direct current or alternating current.

Finally, the general case of induced voltage produced across $L$ is shown with nonsinusoidal current variations. In this case, we compare the waveshapes of $i_L$ and $v_L$ instead of their phase. Remember that the 90° angle for an $IX_L$ voltage applies only to sine waves.

With nonsinusoidal waveforms, such as pulses of current or voltage, the circuit can be analyzed in terms of its $L/R$ time constant, as explained in Chap. 23.

# CHAPTER OBJECTIVES

*Upon completion of this chapter, you should be able to:*

• *Explain* why the voltage leads the current by 90° for an inductor.
• *Calculate* the total impedance and phase angle of a series *RL* circuit.
• *Calculate* the total current, equivalent impedance, and phase angle of a parallel *RL* circuit.
• *Define* what is meant by the *Q* of a coil.
• *Understand* how an inductor can be used to pass some ac frequencies but block others.
• *Calculate* the induced voltage that is produced by a nonsinusoidal current.

## IMPORTANT TERMS IN THIS CHAPTER

| | | |
|---|---|---|
| choke | lagging current | sawtooth waveform |
| impedance Z | *Q* of a coil | |

## TOPICS COVERED IN THIS CHAPTER

**22-1** Sine-Wave $i_L$ Lags $v_L$ by 90°
**22-2** $X_L$ and $R$ in Series
**22-3** Impedance $Z$ Triangle
**22-4** $X_L$ and $R$ in Parallel

**22-5** $Q$ of a Coil
**22-6** AF and RF Chokes
**22-7** The General Case of Inductive Voltage

## 22-1 SINE-WAVE $i_L$ LAGS $v_L$ BY 90°

With sine-wave variations of current producing an induced voltage, the current lags its induced voltage by exactly 90°, as shown in Fig. 22-1. The inductive circuit in Fig. 22-1$a$ has the current and voltage waveshapes shown in Fig. 22-1$b$. The phasors in Fig. 22-1$c$ show the 90° phase angle between $i_L$ and $v_L$. Therefore, we can say that $i_L$ lags $v_L$ by 90°. Or, $v_L$ leads $i_L$ by 90°.

This 90° phase relationship between $i_L$ and $v_L$ is true in any sine-wave ac circuit, whether $L$ is in series or parallel, and whether $L$ is alone or combined with other components. We can always say that the voltage across any $X_L$ is 90° out of phase with the current through it.

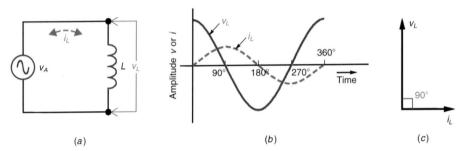

| | | |
|:---:|:---:|:---:|
| (a) | (b) | (c) |

**FIG. 22-1**   ($a$) Circuit with inductance $L$. ($b$) Sine wave of $i_L$ lags $v_L$ by 90°. ($c$) Phasor diagram.

**WHY THE PHASE ANGLE IS 90°**   This results because $v_L$ depends on the rate of change of $i_L$. As previously shown in Fig. 21-7 for a sine wave of $i_L$, the induced voltage is a cosine wave. In other words, $v_L$ has the phase of $di/dt$, not the phase of $i$.

**WHY $i_L$ LAGS $v_L$**   The 90° difference can be measured between any two points having the same value on the $i_L$ and $v_L$ waves. A convenient point is the positive peak value. Note that the $i_L$ wave does not have its positive peak until 90° after the $v_L$ wave. Therefore, $i_L$ lags $v_L$ by 90°. This 90° lag is in time. The time lag equals one quarter-cycle, which is one-quarter of the time for a complete cycle.

**INDUCTIVE CURRENT IS THE SAME IN A SERIES CIRCUIT**   The time delay and resultant phase angle for the current in an inductance apply only with respect to the voltage across the inductance. This condition does not change the fact that the current is the same in all parts of a series circuit. In Fig. 22-1$a$, the current in the generator, the connecting wires, and $L$ must be the same because they are in series. At any instant, whatever the current value is at that time, it is the same in all the series components. The time lag is between current and voltage.

**INDUCTIVE VOLTAGE IS THE SAME ACROSS PARALLEL BRANCHES**
In Fig. 22-1$a$, the voltage across the generator and the voltage across $L$ are the same because they are in parallel. There cannot be any lag or lead in time between these two parallel voltages. At any instant, whatever the voltage value is across the generator at that time, the voltage across $L$ is the same. Considering the parallel voltage $v_A$ or $v_L$, it is 90° out of phase with the current.

In this circuit the voltage across $L$ is determined by the applied voltage, since they must be the same. The inductive effect here is to make the current have the values that produce $L(di/dt)$ equal to the parallel voltage.

**THE FREQUENCY IS THE SAME FOR $i_L$ AND $v_L$**    Although $i_L$ lags $v_L$ by 90°, both waves have the same frequency. The $i_L$ wave reaches it peak values 90° later than the $v_L$ wave, but the complete cycles of variations are repeated at the same rate. As an example, if the frequency of the sine wave $v_L$ in Fig. 22-1b is 100 Hz, this is also the frequency for $i_L$.

---

### TEST-POINT QUESTION 22-1

Answers at end of chapter.

Refer to Fig. 22-1.
**a.** What is the phase angle between $v_A$ and $v_L$?
**b.** What is the phase angle between $v_L$ and $i_L$?
**c.** Does $i_L$ lead or lag $v_L$?

## 22-2 $X_L$ AND $R$ IN SERIES

When a coil has series resistance, the current is limited by both $X_L$ and $R$. This current $I$ is the same in $X_L$ and $R$, since they are in series. Each has its own series voltage drop, equal to $IR$ for the resistance and $IX_L$ for the reactance.

Note the following points about a circuit that combines series $X_L$ and $R$, as in Fig. 22-2:

1.  The current is labeled $I$, rather than $I_L$, because $I$ flows through all the series components.
2.  The voltage across $X_L$, labeled $V_L$, can be considered an $IX_L$ voltage drop, just as we use $V_R$ for an $IR$ voltage drop.
3.  The current $I$ through $X_L$ must lag $V_L$ by 90°, as this is the phase angle between current through an inductance and its self-induced voltage.
4.  The current $I$ through $R$ and its $IR$ voltage drop are in phase. There is no reactance to sine-wave current in any resistance. Therefore, $I$ and $IR$ have a phase angle of 0°.

Resistance $R$ can be either the internal resistance of the coil or an external series resistance. The $I$ and $V$ values may be rms, peak, or instantaneous, as long as the same measure is applied to all. Peak values are used here for convenience in comparing the waveforms.

**PHASE COMPARISONS**    Note the following:

1.  Voltage $V_L$ is 90° out of phase with $I$.
2.  However, $V_R$ and $I$ are in phase.
3.  If $I$ is used as the reference, $V_L$ is 90° out of phase with $V_R$.

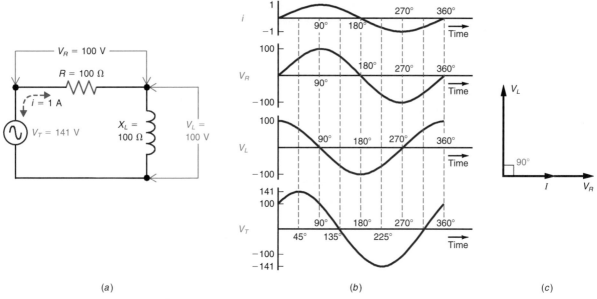

**FIG. 22-2** Inductive reactance $X_L$ and resistance $R$ in series. (*a*) Circuit. (*b*) Waveforms of current and voltages. (*c*) Phasor diagram.

Specifically, $V_R$ lags $V_L$ by 90°, just as the current $I$ lags $V_L$. These phase relations are shown by the waveforms in Fig. 22-2*b* and the phasors in Fig. 22-2*c*.

**COMBINING $V_R$ AND $V_L$**    As shown in Fig. 22-2*b*, when the $V_R$ voltage wave is combined with the $V_L$ voltage wave, the result is the voltage wave for the applied generator voltage $V_T$. The voltage drops must add to equal the applied voltage. The 100-V peak values for $V_R$ and for $V_L$ total 141 V, however, instead of 200 V, because of the 90° phase difference.

Consider some instantaneous values to see why the 100-V peak $V_R$ and 100-V peak $V_L$ cannot be added arithmetically. When $V_R$ is at its maximum of 100 V, for instance, $V_L$ is at zero. The total for $V_T$ then is 100 V. Similarly, with $V_L$ at its maximum of 100 V, then $V_R$ is zero and the total $V_T$ is also 100 V.

Actually, $V_T$ has its maximum value of 141 V at the time when $V_L$ and $V_R$ are each 70.7 V. When series voltage drops that are out of phase are combined, therefore, they cannot be added without taking the phase difference into account.

**PHASOR-VOLTAGE TRIANGLE**    Instead of combining waveforms that are out of phase, we can add them more quickly by using their equivalent phasors, as shown in Fig. 22-3. The phasors in Fig. 22-3*a* just show the 90° angle without any addition. The method in Fig. 22-3*b* is to add the tail of one phasor to the arrowhead of the other, using the angle required to show their relative phase. Voltages $V_R$ and $V_L$ are at right angles because they are 90° out of phase. The sum of the phasors is a resultant phasor from the start of one to the end of the other. Since the $V_R$ and $V_L$ phasors form a right angle, the resultant

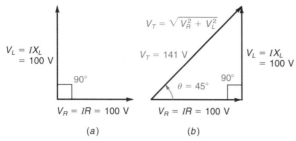

(a)                    (b)

**FIG. 22-3**  Addition of two voltages 90° out of phase. (*a*) Phasors for $V_L$ and $V_R$ are 90° out of phase. (*b*) Resultant of the two phasors is hypotenuse of right triangle for value of $V_T$.

phasor is the hypotenuse of a right triangle. The hypotenuse is the side opposite the 90° angle.

From the geometry of a right triangle, the pythagorean theorem states that the hypotenuse is equal to the square root of the sum of the squares of the sides. For the voltage triangle in Fig. 22-3*b*, therefore, the resultant is

▶  $$V_T = \sqrt{V_R^2 + V_L^2}$$   **(22-1)**

where $V_T$ is the phasor sum of the two voltages $V_R$ and $V_L$ 90° out of phase.

This formula is for $V_R$ and $V_L$ when they are in series, since then they are 90° out of phase. All the voltages must be in the same units. When $V_A$ is an rms value, $V_R$ and $V_L$ are also rms values. For the example in Fig. 22-3,

$$V_T = \sqrt{100^2 + 100^2} = \sqrt{10,000 + 10,000}$$
$$= \sqrt{20,000}$$
$$V_T = 141 \text{ V}$$

To do a problem like this on the calculator, remember that the square root sign is a sign of grouping. All terms within the group must be added before you take the square root. Also, each term must be squared individually before adding for the sum. Specifically for this problem:

1.  Punch in 100 and push the $\boxed{x^2}$ button for 10,000 as the square. Press $\boxed{+}$ and $\boxed{(}$.
2.  Next punch in 100 and $\boxed{x^2}$. Press $\boxed{)}$ and $\boxed{=}$. The display should read 20000.
3.  Press $\boxed{\sqrt{\ }}$ to read the answer 141.421.

In some calculators either the $\boxed{x^2}$ or the $\boxed{\sqrt{\ }}$ key must be preceded by the second function key $\boxed{F}$.

**TEST-POINT QUESTION 22-2**

Answers at end of chapter.
**a.** In a series circuit with $X_L$ and $R$, what is the phase angle between $I$ and $V_R$?
**b.** What is the phase angle between $V_R$ and $V_L$?

**ABOUT ELECTRONICS**

A St. Louis man, paralyzed for ten years, can now write, eat, and channel-surf by himself, having received a bionic hand wired to his shoulder and elbow muscles (which he can flex to direct his hand).

# 22-3 IMPEDANCE Z TRIANGLE

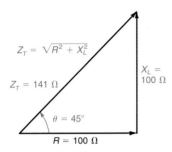

**FIG. 22-4** Addition of $R$ and $X_L$ 90° out of phase in series circuit, to find the resultant impedance $Z_T$.

A triangle of $R$ and $X_L$ in series corresponds to the voltage triangle, as shown in Fig. 22-4. It is similar to the voltage triangle in Fig. 22-3, but the common factor $I$ cancels because the current is the same in $X_L$ and $R$. The resultant of the phasor addition of $R$ and $X_L$ is their total opposition in ohms, called *impedance*, with the symbol $Z_T$.* The $Z$ takes into account the 90° phase relation between $R$ and $X_L$.

For the impedance triangle of a series circuit with reactance and resistance,

$$\blacktriangleright \qquad Z_T = \sqrt{R^2 + X_L{}^2} \qquad\qquad \textbf{(22-2)}$$

where $R$, $X_L$, and $Z_T$ are all in ohms. For the example in Fig. 22-4,

$$Z_T = \sqrt{100^2 + 100^2} = \sqrt{10{,}000 + 10{,}000}$$
$$= \sqrt{20{,}000}$$
$$Z_T = 141\ \Omega$$

Note that the total impedance of 141 Ω divided into the applied voltage of 141 V results in 1 A of current in the series circuit. The $IR$ voltage is $1 \times 100$, or 100 V; the $IX_L$ voltage is also $1 \times 100$, or 100 V. The total of the series $IR$ and $IX_L$ drops of 100 V each added by phasors equals the applied voltage of 141 V. Finally, the applied voltage equals $IZ$, or $1 \times 141$, which is 141 V.

To summarize the similar phasor triangles for volts and ohms in a series circuit:

1. The phasor for $R$, $IR$, or $V_R$ is used as a reference at 0°.
2. The phasor for $X_L$, $IX_L$, or $V_L$ is at 90°.
3. The phasor for $Z$, $IZ$, or $V_T$ has the phase angle $\theta$ of the complete circuit.

**PHASE ANGLE WITH SERIES $X_L$**   The angle between the generator voltage and its current is the phase angle of the circuit. Its symbol is $\theta$ (theta). In Fig. 22-3, the phase angle between $V_T$ and $IR$ is 45°. Since $IR$ and $I$ have the same phase, the angle is also 45° between $V_T$ and $I$.

In the corresponding impedance triangle in Fig. 22-4, the angle between $Z_T$ and $R$ is also equal to the phase angle. Therefore, the phase angle can be calculated from the impedance triangle of a series circuit by the formula

$$\blacktriangleright \qquad \tan\theta_Z = \frac{X_L}{R} \qquad\qquad \textbf{(22-3)}$$

The tangent (tan) is a trigonometric function of any angle, equal to the ratio of the opposite side to the adjacent side of a triangle. In this impedance triangle, $X_L$ is the opposite side and $R$ is the adjacent side of the angle. We use the subscript $z$ for $\theta$ to show that $\theta_Z$ is found from the impedance triangle for a series circuit. To calculate this phase angle,

$$\tan\theta_Z = \frac{X_L}{R} = \frac{100}{100} = 1$$

---

*Although the $Z_T$ is a passive component, we consider it as a phasor here because it determines the phase angle of $V$ and $I$.

The angle that has the tangent equal to 1 is 45°. Therefore, the phase angle is 45° in this example. The numerical values of the trigonometric functions can be found from a table or scientific calculator.

Note that the phase angle of 45° is halfway between 0° and 90° because $R$ and $X_L$ are equal.

## Example

EXAMPLE 1   If a 30-$\Omega$ $R$ and a 40-$\Omega$ $X_L$ are in series with 100 V applied, find the following: $Z_T$, $I$, $V_R$, $V_L$, and $\theta_Z$. What is the phase angle between $V_L$ and $V_R$ with respect to $I$? Prove that the sum of the series voltage drops equals the applied voltage $V_T$.

ANSWER   $Z_T = \sqrt{R^2 + X_L^2} = \sqrt{900 + 1600}$

$\qquad\qquad = \sqrt{2500}$

$\qquad Z_T = 50\ \Omega$

$\qquad\quad I = \dfrac{V_T}{Z_T} = \dfrac{100}{50} = 2\ \text{A}$

$\qquad\quad V_R = IR = 2 \times 30 = 60\ \text{V}$

$\qquad\quad V_L = IX_L = 2 \times 40 = 80\ \text{V}$

$\qquad \tan \theta_Z = \dfrac{X_L}{R} = \dfrac{40}{30} = \dfrac{4}{3} = 1.3333$

$\qquad\quad \theta_Z = 53.1°$

Therefore, $I$ lags $V_T$ by 53.1°. Furthermore, $I$ and $V_R$ are in phase, and $I$ lags $V_L$ by 90°. Finally.

$$V_T = \sqrt{V_R^2 + V_L^2} = \sqrt{60^2 + 80^2} = \sqrt{3600 + 6400}$$

$$= \sqrt{10,000}$$

$$V_T = 100\ \text{V}$$

Note that the phasor sum of the voltage drops equals the applied voltage.

To do the trigonometry in Example 1 with a calculator, there are several points to keep in mind:

1.  The ratio of $X_L/R$ specifies the angle's tangent function as a numerical value, but this is not the angle $\theta$ in degrees. Finding $X_L/R$ is just a division problem.
2.  The angle $\theta$ itself is an *inverse function* of tan $\theta$ that is indicated as arctan $\theta$ or $\tan^{-1} \theta$. A scientific calculator can give the trigonometric functions directly from the value of the angle, or inversely show the angle from its trig functions.
3.  As a check on your values, note that for tan $\theta = 1$, $\tan^{-1}\theta$ is 45°. Tangent values less than 1 must be for angles smaller than 45°; angles more than 45° must have tangent values higher than 1.

For the values in Example 1, specifically, punch in 40 for $X_L$, push the $\div$ key, punch in 30 for $R$, and push the $=$ key for the ratio of 1.3333 on the display. This value is tan $\theta$. While it is on the display, push the $\boxed{\text{TAN}^{-1}}$ key and the answer of 53.1° appears for angle $\theta$. Use of the tan$^{-1}$ key is usually preceded by pressing the function key $\boxed{F}$ or $\boxed{\text{2ndF}}$.

**SERIES COMBINATIONS OF $X_L$ AND $R$**  In a series circuit, the higher the value of $X_L$ compared with $R$, the more inductive the circuit is. This means there is more voltage drop across the inductive reactance and the phase angle increases toward 90°. The series current lags the applied generator voltage. With all $X_L$ and no $R$, the entire applied voltage is across $X_L$ and $\theta_Z$ equals 90°.

Several combinations of $X_L$ and $R$ in series are listed in Table 22-1 with their resultant impedance and phase angle. Note that a ratio of 10:1 or more for $X_L/R$ means that the circuit is practically all inductive. The phase angle of 84.3° is only slightly less than 90° for the ratio of 10:1, and the total impedance $Z_T$ is approximately equal to $X_L$. The voltage drop across $X_L$ in the series circuit will be practically equal to the applied voltage, with almost none across $R$.

| TABLE 22-1 SERIES R AND $X_L$ COMBINATIONS | | | |
|---|---|---|---|
| R, Ω | $X_L$, Ω | $Z_T$, Ω (APPROX.) | IMPEDANCE ANGLE $\theta_Z$ |
| 1 | 10 | $\sqrt{101} = 10$ | 84.3° |
| 10 | 10 | $\sqrt{200} = 14.1$ | 45° |
| 10 | 1 | $\sqrt{101} = 10$ | 5.7° |

Note: $\theta_Z$ is the angle of $Z_T$ with respect to the reference $I$ in a series circuit.

At the opposite extreme, when $R$ is ten times as large as $X_L$, the series circuit is mainly resistive. The phase angle of 5.7°, then, means the current is almost in phase with the applied voltage, the total impedance $Z_T$ is approximately equal to $R$, and the voltage drop across $R$ is practically equal to the applied voltage, with almost none across $X_L$.

For the case when $X_L$ and $R$ equal each other, their resultant impedance $Z_T$ is 1.41 times the value of either one. The phase angle then is 45°, halfway between 0° for resistance alone and 90° for inductive reactance alone.

**TEST-POINT QUESTION 22-3**

Answers at end of chapter.
**a.** How much is $Z_T$ for a 20-Ω $R$ in series with a 20-Ω $X_L$?
**b.** How much is $V_T$ for 20 V across $R$ and 20 V across $X_L$ in series?
**c.** What is the phase angle of the circuit in **a** and **b**?

## 22-4 $X_L$ AND $R$ IN PARALLEL

For parallel circuits with $X_L$ and $R$, the 90° phase angle must be considered for each of the branch currents, instead of voltage drops in a series circuit. Remember that any series circuit has different voltage drops but one common current. A parallel circuit has different branch currents but one common voltage.

In the parallel circuit in Fig. 22-5a, the applied voltage $V_A$ is the same across $X_L$, $R$, and the generator, since they are all in parallel. There cannot be any phase difference between these voltages. Each branch, however, has its individual current. For the resistive branch, $I_R = V_A/R$; in the inductive branch, $I_L = V_A/X_L$.

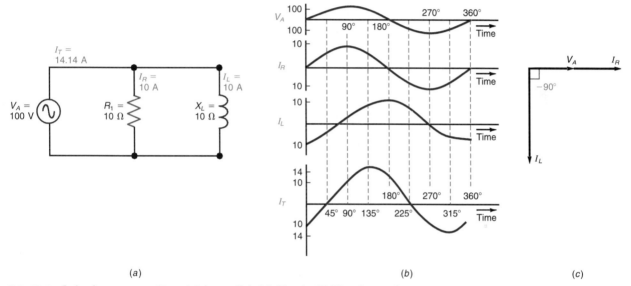

(a)                                    (b)                                    (c)

**FIG. 22-5** Inductive reactance $X_L$ and $R$ in parallel. (a) Circuit. (b) Waveforms of applied voltage and branch currents. (c) Phasor diagram.

The resistive branch current $I_R$ is in phase with the generator voltage $V_A$. The inductive branch current $I_L$ lags $V_A$, however, because the current in an inductance lags the voltage across it by 90°.

The total line current, therefore, consists of $I_R$ and $I_L$, which are 90° out of phase with each other. The phasor sum of $I_R$ and $I_L$ equals the total line current $I_T$. These phase relations are shown by the waveforms in Fig. 22-5b, with the phasors in Fig. 22-5c. Either way, the phasor sum of 10 A for $I_R$ and 10 A for $I_L$ is equal to 14.14 A for $I_T$.

Both methods illustrate the general principle that quadrature components must be combined by phasor addition. The branch currents are added by phasors here because they are the factors that are 90° out of phase in a parallel circuit. This method is similar to combining voltage drops 90° out of phase in a series circuit.

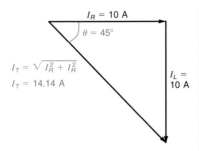

$I_R = 10$ A

$\theta = 45°$

$I_T = \sqrt{I_R^2 + I_R^2}$

$I_T = 14.14$ A

$I_L = 10$ A

**FIG. 22-6** Phasor triangle of inductive and resistive branch currents 90° out of phase in a parallel circuit to find resultant $I_T$.

**PHASOR CURRENT TRIANGLE**   Note that the phasor diagram in Fig. 22-5c has the applied voltage $V_A$ of the generator as the reference phasor. The reason is that $V_A$ is the same throughout the parallel circuit.

The phasor for $I_L$ is down, as compared with up for an $X_L$ phasor. Here the parallel branch current $I_L$ lags the parallel voltage reference $V_A$. In a series circuit the $X_L$ voltage leads the series current reference $I$. For this reason the $I_L$ phasor is shown with a negative 90° angle. The −90° means the current $I_L$ lags the reference phasor $V_A$.

The phasor addition of the branch currents in a parallel circuit can be calculated by the phasor triangle for currents shown in Fig. 22-6. Peak values are used for convenience in this example, but when the applied voltage is an rms value, the calculated currents are also in rms values. To calculate the total line current, we have

$$I_T = \sqrt{I_R^2 + I_L^2} \tag{22-4}$$

For the values in Fig. 22-6,

$$I_T = \sqrt{10^2 + 10^2} = \sqrt{100 + 100}$$
$$= \sqrt{200}$$
$$I_T = 14.14 \text{ A}$$

**IMPEDANCE OF $X_L$ AND $R$ IN PARALLEL**   A practical approach to the problem of calculating the total impedance of $X_L$ and $R$ in parallel is to calculate the total line current $I_T$ and divide this into the applied voltage:

$$Z_{EQ} = \frac{V_A}{I_T} \tag{22-5}$$

For example, in Fig. 22-5, $V_A$ is 100 V and the resultant $I_T$, obtained as the phasor sum of the resistive and reactive branch currents, is equal to 14.14 A. Therefore, we calculate the impedance as

$$Z_{EQ} = \frac{V_A}{I_T} = \frac{100 \text{ V}}{14.14 \text{ A}}$$
$$Z_{EQ} = 7.07 \ \Omega$$

This impedance is the combined opposition in ohms across the generator, equal to the resistance of 10 Ω in parallel with the reactance of 10 Ω.

Note that the impedance for equal values of $R$ and $X_L$ in parallel is not one-half but equals 70.7 percent of either one. Still, the combined value of ohms must be less than the lowest ohms value in the parallel branches.

For the general case of calculating the impedance of $X_L$ and $R$ in parallel, any number can be assumed for the applied voltage because in the calculations for $Z$ in terms of the branch currents the value of $V_A$ cancels. A good value to assume for $V_A$ is the value of either $R$ or $X_L$, whichever is the higher number. This way there are no fractions smaller than one in calculation of the branch currents.

## Example

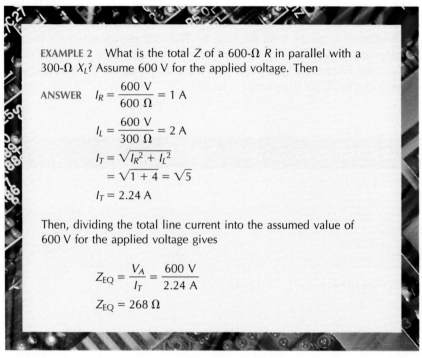

**EXAMPLE 2**  What is the total $Z$ of a 600-$\Omega$ $R$ in parallel with a 300-$\Omega$ $X_L$? Assume 600 V for the applied voltage. Then

ANSWER    $I_R = \dfrac{600 \text{ V}}{600 \text{ }\Omega} = 1 \text{ A}$

$I_L = \dfrac{600 \text{ V}}{300 \text{ }\Omega} = 2 \text{ A}$

$I_T = \sqrt{I_R^2 + I_L^2}$

$= \sqrt{1 + 4} = \sqrt{5}$

$I_T = 2.24 \text{ A}$

Then, dividing the total line current into the assumed value of 600 V for the applied voltage gives

$Z_{EQ} = \dfrac{V_A}{I_T} = \dfrac{600 \text{ V}}{2.24 \text{ A}}$

$Z_{EQ} = 268 \text{ }\Omega$

The combined impedance of a 600-$\Omega$ $R$ in parallel with a 300-$\Omega$ $X_L$ is equal to 268 $\Omega$, no matter how much the applied voltage is.

**PHASE ANGLE WITH PARALLEL $X_L$ AND $R$**   In a parallel circuit, the phase angle is between the line current $I_T$ and the common voltage $V_A$ applied across all the branches. However, the resistive branch current $I_R$ has the same phase as $V_A$. Therefore, the phase of $I_R$ can be substituted for the phase of $V_A$. This is shown in Fig. 22-5c. The triangle of currents is in Fig. 22-6. To find $\theta_I$ from the branch currents, use the tangent formula

▶     $\tan \theta_I = -\dfrac{I_L}{I_R}$     **(22-6)**

We use the subscript $I$ for $\theta$ to show that $\theta_I$ is found from the triangle of branch currents in a parallel circuit. In Fig. 22-6, $\theta_I$ is $-45°$ because $I_L$ and $I_R$ are equal. Then $\tan \theta_I = -1$.

The negative sign is used for this current ratio because $I_L$ is lagging at $-90°$, compared with $I_R$. The phase angle of $-45°$ here means that $I_T$ lags $I_R$ and $V_A$ by 45°.

Note that the phasor triangle of branch currents gives $\theta_I$ as the angle of $I_T$ with respect to the generator voltage $V_A$. This phase angle for $I_T$ is with respect to the applied voltage as the reference at 0°. For the phasor triangle of voltages in a series circuit, the phase angle $\theta_Z$ for $Z_T$ and $V_T$ is with respect to the series current as the reference phasor at 0°.

**PARALLEL COMBINATIONS OF $X_L$ AND $R$**  Several combinations of $X_L$ and $R$ in parallel are listed in Table 22-2. When $X_L$ is 10 times $R$, the parallel circuit is practically resistive because there is little inductive current in the line. The small value of $I_L$ results from the high $X_L$. The total impedance of the parallel circuit is approximately equal to the resistance, then, since the high value of $X_L$ in a parallel branch has little effect. The phase angle of $-5.7°$ is practically $0°$ because almost all the line current is resistive.

| TABLE 22-2 | PARALLEL RESISTANCE AND INDUCTANCE COMBINATIONS* | | | | | |
| --- | --- | --- | --- | --- | --- | --- |
| $R$, $\Omega$ | $X_L$, $\Omega$ | $I_R$, A | $I_L$, A | $I_T$, A (APPROX.) | $Z_{EQ} = V_A/I_T$, $\Omega$ | PHASE ANGLE $\theta_I$ |
| 1 | 10 | 10 | 1 | $\sqrt{101} = 10$ | 1 | $-5.7°$ |
| 10 | 10 | 1 | 1 | $\sqrt{2} = 1.4$ | 7.07 | $-45°$ |
| 10 | 1 | 1 | 10 | $\sqrt{101} = 10$ | 1 | $-84.3°$ |

*$V_A = 10$ V. Note that $\theta_I$ is the angle of $I_T$ with respect to the reference $V_A$ in parallel circuits.

As $X_L$ becomes smaller, it provides more inductive current in the main line. When $X_L$ is $\frac{1}{10} R$, practically all the line current is the $I_L$ component. Then the parallel circuit is practically all inductive, with a total impedance practically equal to $X_L$. The phase angle of $-84.3°$ is almost $-90°$ because the line current is mostly inductive. Note that these conditions are opposite from the case of $X_L$ and $R$ in series.

When $X_L$ and $R$ are equal, their branch currents are equal and the phase angle is $-45°$. All these phase angles are negative for parallel $I_L$ and $I_R$.

As additional comparisons between series and parallel circuits, remember that

1. The series voltage drops $V_R$ and $V_L$ have individual values that are $90°$ out of phase. Therefore, $V_R$ and $V_L$ are added by phasors to equal the applied voltage $V_T$. The phase angle $\theta_Z$ is between $V_T$ and the common series current $I$. More series $X_L$ allows more $V_L$ to make the circuit more inductive with a larger positive phase angle for $V_T$ with respect to $I$.
2. The parallel branch currents $I_R$ and $I_L$ have individual values that are $90°$ out of phase. Therefore, $I_R$ and $I_L$ are added by phasors to equal $I_T$, which is the main-line current. The negative phase angle $-\theta_I$ is between the line current $I_T$ and the common parallel voltage $V_A$. Less parallel $X_L$ allows more $I_L$ to make the circuit more inductive with a larger negative phase angle for $I_T$ with respect to $V_A$.

---

### TEST-POINT QUESTION 22-4

Answers at end of chapter.
**a.** How much is $I_T$ for a branch current $I_R$ of 2 A and $I_L$ of 2 A?
**b.** Find the phase angle $\theta_I$.

# 22-5 Q OF A COIL

The ability of a coil to produce self-induced voltage is indicated by $X_L$, since it includes the factors of frequency and inductance. However, a coil has internal resistance equal to the resistance of the wire in the coil. This internal $r_i$ of the coil reduces the current, which means less ability to produce induced voltage. Combining these two factors of $X_L$ and $r_i$, the *quality* or *merit* of a coil is indicated by

$$\blacktriangleright \qquad Q = \frac{X_L}{r_i} = \frac{2\pi f L}{r_i} \qquad\qquad (22\text{-}7)$$

As shown in Fig. 22-7, the internal $r_i$ is in series with $X_L$.

As an example, a coil with $X_L$ of 500 Ω and $r_i$ of 5 Ω has a $Q$ of 500/5 = 100. The $Q$ is a numerical value without any units, since the ohms cancel in the ratio of reactance to resistance. This $Q$ of 100 means that the $X_L$ of the coil is 100 times more than its $r_i$.

The $Q$ of coils may range in value from less than 10 for a low-$Q$ coil up to 1000 for a very high $Q$. Radio-frequency coils generally have a $Q$ of about 30 to 300.

At low frequencies, $r_i$ is just the dc resistance of the wire in the coil. However, for RF coils the losses increase with higher frequencies and the effective $r_i$ increases. The increased resistance results from eddy currents and other losses.

Because of these losses, the $Q$ of a coil does not increase without limit as $X_L$ increases for higher frequencies. Generally, the $Q$ can increase by a factor of about 2 for higher frequencies, within the range for which the coil is designed. The highest $Q$ for RF coils generally results with an inductance value that provides an $X_L$ of about 1000 Ω at the operating frequency.

More fundamentally, $Q$ can be defined as the ratio of reactive power in the inductance to the real power dissipated in the resistance. Then

$$Q = \frac{P_L}{P_{r_i}} = \frac{I^2 X_L}{I^2 r_i} = \frac{X_L}{r_i} = \frac{2\pi f L}{r_i}$$

which is the same as Formula (22-7).

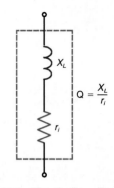

FIG. 22-7  The $Q$ of a coil depends on its inductive reactance $X_L$ and resistance $r_i$.

**SKIN EFFECT**  Radio-frequency current tends to flow at the surface of a conductor, at very high frequencies, with little current in the solid core at the center. This skin effect results from the fact that current in the center of the wire encounters slightly more inductance because of the magnetic flux concentrated in the metal, compared with the edges, where part of the flux is in air. For this reason, conductors for VHF currents are often made of hollow tubing. The skin effect increases the effective resistance, as a smaller cross-sectional area is used for the current path in the conductor.

**AC EFFECTIVE RESISTANCE**  When the power and current applied to a coil are measured for RF applied voltage, the $I^2R$ loss corresponds to a much higher resistance than the dc resistance measured with an ohmmeter. This higher resistance is the ac effective resistance $R_e$. Although a result of high-frequency

alternating current, $R_e$ is not a reactance; $R_e$ is a resistive component because it draws in-phase current from the ac voltage source.

The factors that make the $R_e$ of a coil more than its dc resistance include skin effect, eddy currents, and hysteresis losses. Air-core coils have low losses but are limited to small values of inductance.

For a magnetic core in RF coils, a powdered-iron or ferrite slug is generally used. In a powdered-iron slug, the granules of iron are insulated from each other to reduce eddy currents. Ferrite materials have small eddy-current losses, as they are insulators, although magnetic. A ferrite core is easily saturated. Therefore, its use must be limited to coils with low values of current. A common application is the ferrite-core antenna coil in Fig. 22-8.

To reduce the $R_e$ for small RF coils, stranded wire can be made with separate strands insulated from each other and braided so that each strand is as much on the outer surface as all the other strands. This is called *litzendraht* or *litz wire*.

As an example of the total effect of ac losses, assume that an air-core RF coil of 50-$\mu$H inductance has a dc resistance of 1 $\Omega$ measured with the battery in an ohmmeter. However, in an ac circuit with a 2-MHz current, the effective coil resistance $R_e$ can increase to 12 $\Omega$. The increased resistance reduces the $Q$ of the coil.

Actually, the $Q$ can be used to determine the effective ac resistance. Since $Q$ is $X_L/R_e$, then $R_e$ equals $X_L/Q$. For this 50-$\mu$H $L$ at 2 MHz, its $X_L$, equal to $2\pi fL$, is 628 $\Omega$. The $Q$ of the coil can be measured on a $Q$ meter, which operates on the principle of resonance. Let the measured $Q$ be 50. Then $R_e = 628/50$, equal to 12.6 $\Omega$.

## Example

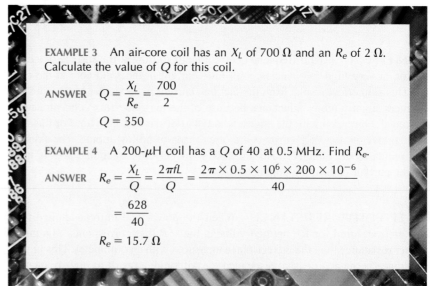

EXAMPLE 3   An air-core coil has an $X_L$ of 700 $\Omega$ and an $R_e$ of 2 $\Omega$. Calculate the value of $Q$ for this coil.

ANSWER   $Q = \dfrac{X_L}{R_e} = \dfrac{700}{2}$

$Q = 350$

EXAMPLE 4   A 200-$\mu$H coil has a $Q$ of 40 at 0.5 MHz. Find $R_e$.

ANSWER   $R_e = \dfrac{X_L}{Q} = \dfrac{2\pi fL}{Q} = \dfrac{2\pi \times 0.5 \times 10^6 \times 200 \times 10^{-6}}{40}$

$= \dfrac{628}{40}$

$R_e = 15.7\ \Omega$

FIG. 22-8   Ferrite coil antenna for a radio receiver.

In general, the lower the internal resistance for a coil, the higher is its $Q$.

## 22-6 AF AND RF CHOKES

Inductance has the useful characteristic of providing more ohms of reactance at higher frequencies. Resistance has the same opposition at all frequencies and for direct current. The skin effect for $L$ at very high frequencies is not being considered here. These characteristics of $L$ and $R$ are applied to the circuit in Fig. 22-9, where $X_L$ is much greater than $R$ for the frequency of the ac source $V_T$. The result is that $L$ has practically all the voltage drop in this series circuit with very little of the applied voltage across $R$.

**DID YOU KNOW?**

In 35 seconds on July 2d, 1996, one tree caused 2 million people to lose power in fifteen U.S. states, two Canadian provinces, and one state in Mexico. The line, carrying 345,000 volts from a Wyoming plant, short-circuited.

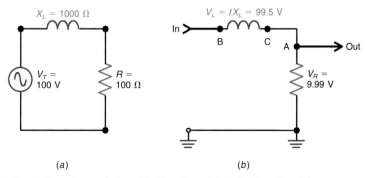

(a)                                    (b)

FIG. 22-9   Coil used as a choke with $X_L$ at least $10 \times R$. Note that $R$ is an external resistor; $V_L$ across $L$ is practically all of the applied voltage, with very little $V_R$. (a) Circuit with $X_L$ and $R$ in series. (b) Input and output voltages.

The inductance $L$ is used here as a *choke*. Therefore, a choke is an inductance in series with an external $R$ to prevent the ac signal voltage from developing any appreciable output across $R$, at the frequency of the source.

The dividing line in calculations for a choke can be taken as $X_L$ ten or more times the series $R$. Then the circuit is primarily inductive. Practically all the ac voltage drop is across $L$, with little across $R$. This case also results in $\theta$ of practically 90°, but the phase angle is not related to the action of $X_L$ as a choke.

Fig. 22-9$b$ illustrates how a choke is used to prevent ac voltage in the input from developing voltage in the output for the next circuit. Note that the output here is $V_R$ from point A to chassis ground. Practically all the ac input voltage is across $X_L$ between points B and C. However, this voltage is not coupled out because neither B nor C is grounded.

The desired output across $R$ could be direct current from the input side without any ac component. Then $X_L$ has no effect on the steady dc component. Practically all the dc voltage would be across $R$ for the output, but the ac voltage would be just across $X_L$. The same idea applies to passing an AF signal through to $R$, while blocking an RF signal as $IX_L$ across the choke because of more $X_L$ at the higher frequency.

**CALCULATIONS FOR A CHOKE**   Typical values for audio or radio frequencies can be calculated if we assume a series resistance of 100 $\Omega$, as an example. Then $X_L$ must be at least 1000 $\Omega$. As listed in Table 22-3, at 100 Hz the relatively large inductance of 1.6 H provides 1000 $\Omega$ of $X_L$. Higher frequencies allow a smaller value of $L$ for a choke with the same reactance. At 100 MHz, in the VHF range, the choke is only 1.6 $\mu$H.

(a)

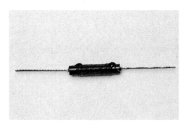

(b)

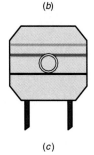

(c)

FIG. 22-10  Typical chokes. (a) Choke for 60 Hz with 8-H inductance and $r_i$ of 350 $\Omega$. Width is 2 in. (b) RF choke with 5 mH of inductance and $r_i$ of 50 $\Omega$. Height is 1 in. (c) Small RF choke encapsulated in plastic with leads for printed circuit board; $L = 42$ $\mu$H. Width is ¾ in.

| TABLE 22-3   TYPICAL CHOKES FOR A REACTANCE OF 1000 $\Omega$* | | |
|---|---|---|
| F | L | REMARKS |
| 100 Hz | 1.6 H | Low audio frequency |
| 1000 Hz | 0.16 H | Audio frequency |
| 10 kHz | 16 mH | Audio frequency |
| 1000 kHz | 0.16 mH | Radio frequency |
| 100 MHz | 1.6 $\mu$H | Very high radio frequency |

*For an $X_L$ that is 10 times a series $R$ of 100 $\Omega$.

Some typical chokes are shown in Fig. 22-10. The iron-core choke in Fig. 22-10$a$ is for audio frequencies. The air-core choke in Fig. 22-10$b$ is for radio frequencies. The RF choke in Fig. 22-10$c$ has color coding, which is often used for small coils. The color values are the same as for resistors, except that the values of $L$ are given in microhenrys. As an example, a coil with yellow, red, and black stripes or dots is 42 $\mu$H.

It should be noted that inductors are also available as surface-mount components. There are basically two body styles: completely encased and open. The encased body style looks like a thick capacitor with a black body. The open body style inductors are easy to identify because the coil is visible. The value of a surface-mount inductor, if marked, is usually represented using the same three-digit system used for resistors with the value displayed in microhenrys ($\mu$H).

**CHOOSING A CHOKE FOR A CIRCUIT**  As an example of using these calculations, suppose that we have the problem of determining what kind of a coil to use as a choke for the following application. The $L$ is to be an RF choke in series with an external $R$ of 300 $\Omega$, with a current of 90 mA and a frequency of 0.2 MHz. Then $X_L$ must be at least $10 \times 300 = 3000$ $\Omega$. At $f$ of 0.2 MHz,

$$L = \frac{X_L}{2\pi f} = \frac{3,000}{2\pi \times 0.2 \times 10^6} = \frac{3 \times 10^3}{1.256 \times 10^6}$$

$$= \frac{3}{1.256} \times 10^{-3}$$

$$L = 2.4 \text{ mH}$$

A typical commercial size easily available is 2.5 mH, with a current rating of 115 mA and an internal resistance of 20 $\Omega$, similar to the RF choke in Fig. 22-10b. Note that the higher current rating is suitable. Also, the internal resistance is negligible compared with the external $R$. An inductance a little higher than the calculated value will provide more $X_L$, which is better for a choke.

---

**TEST-POINT QUESTION 22-6**

---

Answers at end of chapter.
**a.** How much is the minimum $X_L$ for a choke in series with $R$ of 80 $\Omega$?
**b.** If $X_L$ is 800 $\Omega$ at 3 MHz, how much will $X_L$ be at 6 MHz for the same coil?

# 22-7 THE GENERAL CASE OF INDUCTIVE VOLTAGE

The voltage across any inductance in any circuit is always equal to $L(di/dt)$. This formula gives the instantaneous values of $v_L$ based on the self-induced voltage produced by a change in magnetic flux associated with a change in current.

A sine waveform of current $i$ produces a cosine waveform for the induced voltage $v_L$, equal to $L(di/dt)$. This means $v_L$ has the same waveform as $i$, but they are 90° out of phase for sine-wave variations.

The inductive voltage can be calculated as $IX_L$ in sine-wave ac circuits. Since $X_L$ is $2\pi fL$, the factors that determine the induced voltage are included in the frequency and inductance. Usually, it is more convenient to work with $IX_L$ for the inductive voltage in sine-wave ac circuits, instead of $L(di/dt)$.

However, with a nonsinusoidal current waveform, the concept of reactance cannot be used. The $X_L$ applies only to sine waves. Then $v_L$ must be calculated as $L(di/dt)$, which applies for any inductive voltage.

An example is illustrated in Fig. 22-11a for sawtooth current. This waveform is often used in the deflection circuits for the picture tube in television receivers. The sawtooth rise is a uniform or linear increase of current from zero to 90 mA in this example. The sharp drop in current is from 90 mA to zero. Note that the rise is relatively slow; it takes 90 $\mu$s. This is nine times longer than the fast drop in 10 $\mu$s.

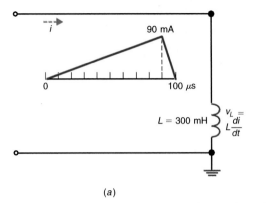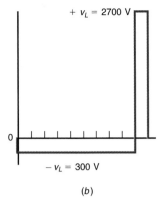

**FIG. 22-11** Rectangular waveshape of $V_L$ produced by sawtooth current through inductance $L$. (a) Waveform of current $i$. (b) Induced voltage $V_i$ equal to $L(di/dt)$.

The complete period of one cycle of this sawtooth wave is 100 $\mu$s. A cycle includes the rise of $i$ to the peak value and its drop back to the starting value.

**THE SLOPE OF *I*** The slope of any curve is a measure of how much it changes vertically for each horizontal unit. In Fig. 22-11a the increase of current has a constant slope. Here $i$ increases 90 mA in 90 $\mu$s, or 10 mA for every 10 $\mu$s of time. Then $di/dt$ is constant at 10 mA/10 $\mu$s for the entire rise time of the sawtooth waveform. Actually $di/dt$ is the slope of the $i$ curve. The constant $di/dt$ is why the $v_L$ waveform has a constant value of voltage during the linear rise of $i$. Remember that the amount of induced voltage depends on the change in current with time.

The drop in $i$ is also linear but much faster. During this time, the slope is 90 mA/10 $\mu$s for $di/dt$.

**THE POLARITY OF $v_L$** In Fig. 22-11, apply Lenz' law to indicate that $v_L$ opposes the change in current. With electron flow into the top of $L$, the $v_L$ is negative to oppose an increase of current. This polarity opposes the direction of electron flow shown for the current $i$ produced by the source. For the rise time, then, the induced voltage here is labeled $-v_L$.

During the drop of current, the induced voltage has opposite polarity, which is labeled $+v_L$. These voltage polarities are for the top of $L$ with respect to chassis ground.

**CALCULATIONS FOR $v_L$** The values of induced voltage across the 300-mH $L$ are calculated as follows.

For the sawtooth rise:

$$-v_L = L\frac{di}{dt}$$

$$= 300 \times 10^{-3} \times \frac{10 \times 10^{-3}}{10 \times 10^{-6}}$$

$$-v_L = 300 \text{ V}$$

For the sawtooth drop:

$$+v_L = L \frac{di}{dt}$$

$$= 300 \times 10^{-3} \times \frac{90 \times 10^{-3}}{10 \times 10^{-6}}$$

$$+v_L = 2700 \text{ V}$$

The decrease in current produces nine times more voltage because the sharp drop in $i$ is nine times faster than the relatively slow rise.

Remember that the $di/dt$ factor can be very large, even with small currents, when the time is short. For instance, a current change of 1 mA in 1 $\mu$s is equivalent to the very high $di/dt$ value of 1000 A/s.

An interesting feature of the inductive waveshapes in Fig. 22-11 is that they are the same as the capacitive waveshapes shown before in Fig. 19-7, but with current and voltage waveshapes interchanged. This comparison follows from the fact that both $v_L$ and $i_C$ depend on the rate of change. Then $i_C$ is $C(dv/dt)$, and the $v_L$ is $L(di/dt)$.

It is important to note that $v_L$ and $i_L$ have different waveshapes with nonsinusoidal current. In this case, we compare the waveshapes instead of the phase angle. Common examples of nonsinusoidal waveshapes for either $v$ or $i$ are the sawtooth waveform, square wave, and rectangular pulses. For a sine wave, the $L(di/dt)$ effects result in a cosine wave, as shown before, in Fig. 21-7.

---

### TEST-POINT QUESTION 22-7

Answers at end of chapter.

Refer to Fig. 22-11.
**a.** How much is $di/dt$ in amperes per second for the sawtooth rise of $i$?
**b.** How much is $di/dt$ in amperes per second for the drop in $i$?

# 22  SUMMARY AND REVIEW

- In a sine-wave ac circuit, the current through an inductance lags 90° behind the voltage across the inductance because $v_L = L(di/dt)$. This fundamental fact is the basis of all the following relations.
- Therefore, inductive reactance $X_L$ is a phasor quantity 90° out of phase with $R$. The phasor combination of $X_L$ and $R$ is their impedance $Z_T$.
- These three types of opposition to current are compared in Table 22-4.

## TABLE 22-4  COMPARISON OF R, $X_L$, AND $Z_T$

| R | $X_L = 2\pi fL$ | $Z_T = \sqrt{R^2 + X_L^2}$ |
|---|---|---|
| Ohms unit | Ohms unit | Ohms unit |
| $IR$ voltage in phase with $I$ | $IX_L$ voltage leads $I$ by 90° | $IZ$ is applied voltage; it leads line $I$ by $\theta°$ |
| Same for all frequencies | Increases as frequency increases | Increases with $X_L$ at higher frequencies |

- The phase angle $\theta$ is the angle between the applied voltage and its current.
- The opposite characteristics for series and parallel circuits with $X_L$ and $R$ are summarized in Table 22-5.

## TABLE 22-5  SERIES AND PARALLEL RL CIRCUITS

| $X_L$ AND R IN SERIES | $X_L$ AND R IN PARALLEL |
|---|---|
| $I$ the same in $X_L$ and $R$ | $V_A$ the same across $X_L$ and $R$ |
| $V_T = \sqrt{V_R^2 + V_L^2}$ | $I_T = \sqrt{I_R^2 + I_L^2}$ |
| $Z_T = \sqrt{R^2 + X_L^2}$ | $Z_{EQ} = \dfrac{V_A}{I_T}$ |
| $V_L$ leads $V_R$ by 90° | $I_L$ lags $I_R$ by 90° |
| $\tan \theta_Z = \dfrac{X_L}{R}$ | $\tan \theta_I = -\dfrac{I_L}{I_R}$ |
| The $\theta_Z$ increases with more $X_L$, which means more $V_L$, thus making the circuit more inductive | The $-\theta_I$ decreases with more $X_L$, which means less $I_L$, thus making the circuit less inductive |

- The $Q$ of a coil is $X_L/r_i$, where $r_i$ is the coil's internal resistance.
- A choke is an inductance with $X_L$ greater than the series $R$ by a factor of 10 or more.
- In sine-wave circuits, $V_L = IX_L$. Then $V_L$ is out of phase with $I$ by an angle of 90°.
- For a circuit with $X_L$ and $R$ in in series, $\tan \theta_Z = X_L/R$. When the components are in parallel, $\tan \theta_I = -(I_L/I_R)$. See Table 22-5.
- When the current is not a sine wave, $v_L = L(di/dt)$. Then the waveshape of $V_L$ is different from the waveshape of $I$.
- Inductors are available as surface-mount components. Surface-mount inductors are available in both completely encased and open body styles.

## SELF-TEST

### ANSWERS AT BACK OF BOOK.

Choose (a), (b), (c), or (d).

1. In a sine-wave ac circuit with inductive reactance, the (a) phase angle of the circuit is always 45°; (b) voltage across the inductance must be 90° out of phase with the applied voltage; (c) current through the inductance lags its induced voltage by 90°; (d) current through the inductance and voltage across it are 180° out of phase.
2. In a sine-wave ac circuit with $X_L$ and $R$ in series, the (a) voltages across $R$ and $X_L$ are in phase; (b) voltages across $R$ and $X_L$ are 180° out of phase; (c) voltage across $R$ lags the voltage across $X_L$ by 90°; (d) voltage across $R$ leads the voltage across $X_L$ by 90°.
3. In a sine-wave ac circuit with a 40-$\Omega$ $R$ in series with a 30-$\Omega$ $X_L$, the total impedance $Z_T$ equals (a) 30 $\Omega$; (b) 40 $\Omega$; (c) 50 $\Omega$; (d) 70 $\Omega$.
4. In a sine-wave ac circuit with a 90-$\Omega$ $R$ in series with a 90-$\Omega$ $X_L$, phase angle $\theta$ equals (a) 0°; (b) 30°; (c) 45°; (d) 90°.
5. A 250-$\mu$H inductance is used as a choke at 10 MHz. At 12 MHz the choke (a) does not have enough inductance; (b) has more reactance; (c) has less reactance; (d) needs more turns.
6. The combined impedance of a 1000-$\Omega$ $R$ in parallel with a 1000-$\Omega$ $X_L$ equals (a) 500 $\Omega$; (b) 707 $\Omega$; (c) 1000 $\Omega$; (d) 2000 $\Omega$.
7. A coil with a 1000-$\Omega$ $X_L$ at 3 MHz and 10 $\Omega$ internal resistance has a $Q$ of (a) 3; (b) 10; (c) 100; (d) 1000.
8. With a 2-A $I_R$ and a 2-A $I_L$ in parallel branches, $I_T$ is (a) 1 A; (b) 2 A; (c) 2.8 A; (d) 4 A.
9. In Fig. 22-11 the $di/dt$ for the drop in sawtooth current is (a) 90 mA/s; (b) 100 mA/s; (c) 100 A/s; (d) 9000 A/s.

## QUESTIONS

1. What characteristic of the current in an inductance determines the amount of induced voltage? State briefly why.
2. Draw a schematic diagram showing an inductance connected across a sine-wave voltage source and indicate the current and voltage that are 90° out of phase with one another.

3. Why is the voltage across a resistance in phase with the current through the resistance?
4. (a) Draw the sine waveforms for two voltages 90° out of phase, each with a peak value of 100 V. (b) Why does their phasor sum equal 141 V and not 200 V? (c) When will the sum of two 100-V drops in series equal 200 V?
5. (a) Define the phase angle of a sine-wave ac circuit. (b) State the formula for the phase angle in a circuit with $X_L$ and $R$ in series.
6. Define the following: (a) $Q$ of a coil; (b) ac effective resistance; (c) RF choke; (d) sawtooth current.
7. Why do the waveshapes in Fig. 22-2b all have the same frequency?
8. Describe how to check the trouble of an open choke with an ohmmeter.
9. Redraw the circuit and graph in Fig. 22-11 for a sawtooth current with a peak of 30 mA.
10. Why is the $R_e$ of a coil considered resistance rather than reactance?
11. Why are RF chokes usually smaller than AF chokes?
12. What is the waveshape of $v_L$ for a sine-wave $i_L$?

## PROBLEMS

ANSWERS TO ODD-NUMBERED PROBLEMS AT BACK OF BOOK.

1. Draw the schematic diagram of a circuit with $X_L$ and $R$ in series across a 100-V source. Calculate $Z_T$, $I$, $IR$, $IX_L$, and $\theta$ for these values: (a) 100-$\Omega$ $R$, 1-$\Omega$ $X_L$; (b) 1-$\Omega$ $R$, 100-$\Omega$ $X_L$; (c) 50-$\Omega$ $R$, 50-$\Omega$ $X_L$.
2. Draw the schematic diagram of a circuit with $X_L$ and $R$ in parallel across a 100-V source. Calculate $I_R$, $I_L$, $I_T$, and $Z_{EQ}$ for the following values: (a) 100-$\Omega$ $R$, 1-$\Omega$ $X_L$; (b) 1-$\Omega$ $R$, 100-$\Omega$ $X_L$; (c) 50-$\Omega$ $R$, 50-$\Omega$ $X_L$.
3. A coil has an inductance of 1 H and a 100-$\Omega$ internal resistance. (a) Draw the equivalent circuit of the coil showing its internal resistance in series with its inductance. (b) How much is the coil's inductive reactance at 60 Hz? (c) How much is the total impedance of the coil at 60 Hz? (d) How much current will flow when the coil is connected across a 120-V source with a frequency of 60 Hz? (e) How much is $I$ with an $f$ of 400 Hz?
4. Calculate the minimum inductance required for a choke in series with a resistance of 100 $\Omega$ when the frequency of the current is 5 kHz, 5 MHz, and 50 MHz. Do the same for the case where the series resistance is 10 $\Omega$.
5. How much is the impedance $Z$ of a coil that allows 0.3 A current when connected across a 120-V 60-Hz source? How much is the $X_L$ of the coil if its resistance is 5 $\Omega$? (Hint: $X_L^2 = Z^2 - R^2$.)
6. A 200-$\Omega$ $R$ is in series with $L$ across a 141-V 60-Hz generator $V_T$. The $V_R$ is 100 V. Find $L$. (Hint: $V_L^2 = V_T^2 - V_R^2$.)
7. A 350-$\mu$H $L$ has a $Q$ of 35 at 1.5 MHz. Calculate the effective ac resistance $R_e$ of the coil.
8. How much $L$ is required to produce $V_L$ equal to 9 kV when $i_L$ drops from 300 mA to zero in 8 $\mu$s?
9. A 400-$\Omega$ $R$ and 400-$\Omega$ $X_L$ are in series with a 100-V 400-Hz source. Find $Z_T$, $I$, $V_L$, $V_R$, and $\theta_Z$.

10. The same $R$ and $X_L$ of Prob. 9 are in parallel. Find $I_R$, $I_L$, $I_T$, $Z_{EQ}$, and $\theta_I$.

11. The frequency is raised to 800 Hz for the circuit in Prob. 10. Compare the values of $I_R$, $I_L$, and $\theta_I$ for the two frequencies of 400 and 800 Hz.

12. A 0.4-H $L$ and a 180-$\Omega$ $R$ are in series across a 120-V 60-Hz source. Find the current $I$ and $\theta_Z$.

13. An inductance $L$ has 20 V across it at 40 mA. The frequency is 5 kHz. Calculate $X_L$ in ohms and $L$ is in henrys.

14. A 500-$\Omega$ $R$ is in series with 300-$\Omega$ $X_L$. Find $Z_T$, $I$, and $\theta_Z$. $V_T = 120$ V.

15. A 300-$\Omega$ $R$ is in series with a 500-$\Omega$ $X_L$. Find $Z_T$, $I$, and $\theta_Z$. Compare $\theta_Z$ here with Prob. 14, with the same 120 V applied.

16. A 500-$\Omega$ $R$ is in parallel with a 300-$\Omega$ $X_L$. Find $I_T$, $Z_{EQ}$, and $\theta_I$. Compare $\theta_I$ here with $\theta_Z$ in Prob. 14 with the same 120 V applied.

17. The current shown in Fig. 22-12 flows through an 8-mH inductance. Show the corresponding waveform of induced voltage with values.

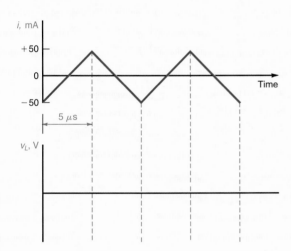

FIG. 22-12  Current waveform for Probs. 17 and 18.

18. Do the same as in Prob. 17 for a 2-mH inductance.

19. Find the angle $\theta_Z$ with the following combinations for $X_L$ and $R$ in series: (a) $X_L$ is 120 $\Omega$ and $R$ is 120 $\Omega$; (b) $X_L$ is 240 $\Omega$ and $R$ is 120 $\Omega$; (c) $X_L$ is 1200 $\Omega$ and $R$ is 120 $\Omega$; (d) $X_L$ is 120 $\Omega$ and $R$ is 60 $\Omega$.

20. What value of $L$ is needed for $X_L$ of 1200 $\Omega$ with $f$ of 4 MHz?

21. Calculate the angle $\theta_I$ for $I_L$ and $I_R$ in parallel with the same combinations as in Prob. 19. Assume $V_A$ of 1 V to determine $I_L$ and $I_R$ in mA units.

22. What is the frequency for $X_L$ of 1200 $\Omega$ with a 50-mH coil?

23. In Fig. 22-13, calculate $X_L$, $Z_T$, $I$, $V_L$, $V_R$, and $\theta_Z$.

24. Repeat Prob. 23 if $f = 1.591$ kHz.

25. In Fig. 22-14, calculate $X_L$, $I_L$, $I_R$, $I_T$, $Z_{EQ}$, and $\theta_I$.

26. Repeat Prob. 25 if $f$ is reduced to 3.183 kHz.

27. In Fig. 22-15, calculate $L$, $Z_T$, $I$, $V_L$, $V_R$, and $\theta_Z$.

28. In Fig. 22-16, calculate $X_L$, $I_L$, $I_R$, $R$, $I_T$, and $Z_{EQ}$.

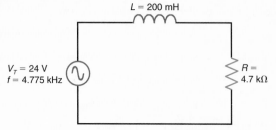

FIG. 22-13  Circuit for Probs. 23 and 24.

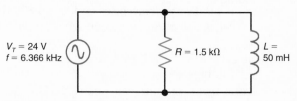

FIG. 22-14  Circuit for Probs. 25 and 26.

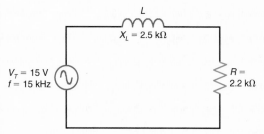

FIG. 22-15  Circuit for Prob. 27.

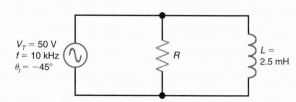

FIG. 22-16  Circuit for Prob. 28.

29. Calculate the minimum inductance $L$ for a choke in series with a resistance of 1 k$\Omega$ if the lowest frequency of the applied voltage is: **(a)** 2 kHz; **(b)** 100 kHz.

30. In Fig. 22-17, show the corresponding values of induced voltage for the waveform of current flowing through the 250-mH inductor.

## CRITICAL THINKING

1. In Fig. 22-18, calculate $X_L$, $R$, $L$, $I$, $V_L$, and $V_R$.
2. In Fig. 22-19, calculate $I_T$, $I_R$, $I_L$, $X_L$, $R$, and $L$.
3. In Fig. 22-20, calculate $V_R$, $V_{L_1}$, $X_{L_1}$, $X_{L_2}$, $I$, $Z_T$, $L_1$, $L_2$, and $\theta_Z$.

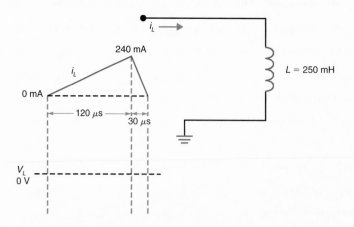

FIG. 22-17  Diagram for Prob. 30.

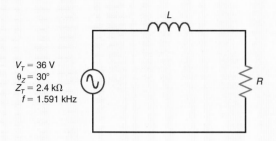

FIG. 22-18    Circuit for Critical Thinking Prob. 1.

$V_T = 36$ V
$\theta_Z = 30°$
$Z_T = 2.4$ kΩ
$f = 1.591$ kHz

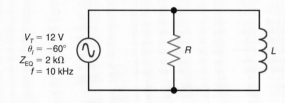

$V_T = 12$ V
$\theta_I = -60°$
$Z_{EQ} = 2$ kΩ
$f = 10$ kHz

FIG. 22-19    Circuit for Critical Thinking Prob. 2.

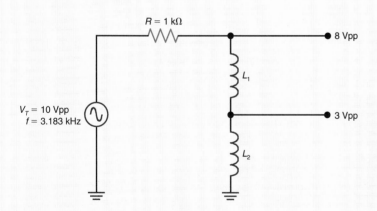

$R = 1$ kΩ

$L_1$

$L_2$

8 Vpp

3 Vpp

$V_T = 10$ Vpp
$f = 3.183$ kHz

FIG. 22-20    Circuit for Critical Thinking Prob. 3.

## ANSWERS TO TEST-POINT QUESTIONS

**22-1 a.** 0`
    **b.** 90°
    **c.** lag

**22-2 a.** 0°
    **b.** 90°

**22-3 a.** 28.28 Ω
    **b.** 28.28 V
    **c.** $\theta_Z = 45°$

**22-4 a.** $I_T = 2.828$ A
    **b.** $\theta_I = -45°$

**22-5 a.** $Q = 75$
    **b.** $R_e = 10$ Ω

**22-6 a.** $X_L = 800$ Ω
    **b.** $X_L = 1600$ Ω

**22-7 a.** $di/dt = 1000$ A/s
    **b.** $di/dt = 9000$ A/s

# CHAPTER 23

# *RC* AND *L/R* TIME CONSTANTS

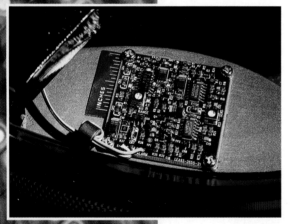

Many applications of inductance are for sine-wave ac circuits, but any time the current changes, *L* has the effect of producing induced voltage. Examples of nonsinusoidal waveshapes include dc voltages that are switched on or off, square waves, sawtooth waves, and rectangular pulses. For capacitance, also, many applications are for sine waves, but any time the voltage changes, *C* produces charge or discharge current.

Actually, *RC* circuits are more common. The reasons are that capacitors are small, economical, and do not have strong magnetic fields.

With nonsinusoidal voltage and current, the effect of *L* or *C* is to produce a change in waveshape. This effect can be analyzed by means of the time constant for capacitive and inductive circuits. The time constant is the time for a change of 63.2 percent in the current through *L* or the voltage across *C*.

# CHAPTER OBJECTIVES

*Upon completion of this chapter, you should be able to:*

- *Define* the term *transient response.*
- *Define* the term *time constant.*
- *Calculate* the time constant of a circuit containing resistance and inductance.
- *Explain* the effect of producing a high voltage when opening an *RL* circuit.
- *Calculate* the time constant of a circuit containing resistance and capacitance.
- *Explain* how capacitance opposes a change in voltage.
- *List* the criteria for proper differentiation and integration.
- *Explain* why a long time constant is required for an *RC* coupling circuit.
- *Use* the universal time constant graph.
- *Explain* the difference between time constants and reactance.

# IMPORTANT TERMS IN THIS CHAPTER

| | | |
|---|---|---|
| collapsing magnetic field | *L/R* time constant | steady-state *I* or *V* |
| decay | long time constant | transient response |
| differentiation | rate of charge or discharge | voltage pulses |
| energy stored | *RC* time constant | waveshapes |
| integration | short time constant | |

# TOPICS COVERED IN THIS CHAPTER

**23-1**   Response of Resistance Alone

**23-2**   *L/R* Time Constant

**23-3**   High Voltage Produced by Opening an *RL* Circuit

**23-4**   *RC* Time Constant

**23-5**   *RC* Charge and Discharge Curves

**23-6**   High Current Produced by Short-circuiting *RC* Circuit

**23-7**   *RC* Waveshapes

**23-8**   Long and Short Time Constants

**23-9**   Charge and Discharge with Short *RC* Time Constant

**23-10**   Long Time Constant for *RC* Coupling Circuit

**23-11**   Universal Time Constant Graph

**23-12**   Comparison of Reactance and Time Constant

# 23-1 RESPONSE OF RESISTANCE ALONE

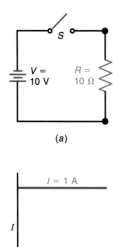

(a)

*I* = 1 A

*I*

Time

(b)

FIG. 23-1 Response of circuit with *R* alone. When switch is closed, current *I* is 10 V/10 Ω = 1 A. (a) Circuit. (b) Graph of steady *I*.

In order to emphasize the special features of *L* and *C*, the circuit in Fig. 23-1 illustrates how an ordinary resistive circuit behaves. When the switch is closed, the battery supplies 10 V across the 10-Ω *R* and the resultant *I* is 1 A. The graph in Fig. 23-1*b* shows that *I* changes from 0 to 1 A instantly when the switch is closed. If the applied voltage is changed to 5 V, the current will change instantly to 0.5 A. If the switch is opened, *I* will immediately drop to zero.

Resistance has only opposition to current; there is no reaction to a change. The reason is that *R* has no concentrated magnetic field to oppose a change in *I*, like inductance, and no electric field to store charge that opposes a change in *V*, like capacitance.

---

### TEST-POINT QUESTION 23-1

Answers at end of chapter.

Answer True or False.

**a.** Resistance *R* does not produce induced voltage for a change in *I*.

**b.** Resistance *R* does not produce charge or discharge current for a change in *V*.

## 23-2 *L/R* TIME CONSTANT

Consider the circuit in Fig. 23-2 where *L* is in series with *R*. When *S* is closed, the current changes as *I* increases from zero. Eventually, *I* will have the steady value of 1 A, equal to the battery voltage of 10 V divided by the circuit

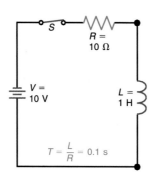

$$T = \frac{L}{R} = 0.1 \text{ s}$$

(a)

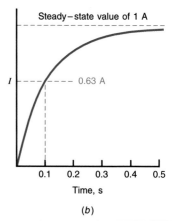

(b)

FIG. 23-2 Transient response of circuit with *R* and inductance *L*. When switch is closed, *I* rises from zero to the steady-state value of 1 A. (a) Circuit with time constant *L/R* of 1 H/10 Ω = 0.1 s. (b) Graph of *I* during five time constants. Compare with graph in Fig. 23-1*b*.

resistance of 10 Ω. While the current is building up from 0 to 1 A, however, $I$ is changing and the inductance opposes the change. The action of the $RL$ circuit during this time is its *transient response*, meaning a temporary condition existing only until the steady-state current of 1 A is reached. Similarly, when $S$ is opened, the transient response of the $RL$ circuit opposes the decay of current toward the steady-state value of zero.

The transient response is measured in terms of the ratio $L/R$, which is the time constant of an inductive circuit. To calculate the time constant

▶ $$T = \frac{L}{R} \qquad\qquad\qquad (23\text{-}1)$$

where $T$ is the time constant in seconds, $L$ is the inductance in henrys, and $R$ is the resistance in ohms. The resistance is in series with $L$, being either the coil resistance, an external resistance, or both in series. In Fig. 23-2,

$$T = \frac{L}{R} = \frac{1}{10} = 0.1 \text{ s}$$

Specifically, the time constant is a measure of how long it takes the current to change by 63.2 percent, or approximately 63 percent. In Fig. 23-2, the current increases from 0 to 0.63 A, which is 63 percent of the steady-state value, in the period of 0.1 s, which is one time constant. In the period of five time constants, the current is practically equal to its steady-state value of 1 A.

The reason why $L/R$ equals time can be illustrated as follows: Since induced voltage $V = L \, (di/dt)$, by transposing terms, $L$ has the dimensions of $V \times T/I$. Dividing $L$ by $R$ results in $V \times T/IR$. As the $IR$ and $V$ factors cancel, $T$ remains to indicate the dimension of time for the ratio $L/R$.

## *Example*

EXAMPLE 1    What is the time constant of a 20-H coil having 100 Ω of series resistance?

ANSWER    $T = \dfrac{L}{R} = \dfrac{20 \text{ H}}{100 \text{ Ω}}$

$T = 0.2 \text{ s}$

EXAMPLE 2    An applied dc voltage of 10 V will produce a steady-state current of 100 mA in the 100-Ω coil of Example 1. How much is the current after 0.2 s? After 1 s?

ANSWER    Since 0.2 s is one time constant, $I$ then is 63 percent of 100 mA, which equals 63 mA. After five time constants, or 1 s (0.2 s × 5), the current will reach its steady-state value of 100 mA and remain at this value as long as the applied voltage stays at 10 V.

*(continued on next page)*

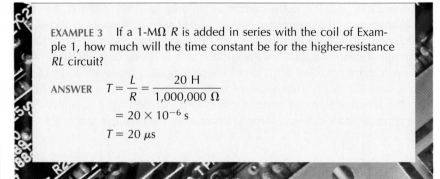

EXAMPLE 3 If a 1-M$\Omega$ $R$ is added in series with the coil of Example 1, how much will the time constant be for the higher-resistance $RL$ circuit?

ANSWER $T = \dfrac{L}{R} = \dfrac{20 \text{ H}}{1{,}000{,}000 \ \Omega}$

$= 20 \times 10^{-6} \text{ s}$

$T = 20 \ \mu s$

The $L/R$ time constant becomes longer with larger values of $L$. More series $R$, however, makes the time constant shorter. With more series resistance, the circuit is less inductive and more resistive.

---

### TEST-POINT QUESTION 23-2

Answers at end of chapter.
**a.** Calculate the time constant for 2 H in series with 100 $\Omega$.
**b.** Calculate the time constant for 2 H in series with 4000 $\Omega$.

## 23-3 HIGH VOLTAGE PRODUCED BY OPENING AN *RL* CIRCUIT

When an inductive circuit is opened, the time constant for current decay becomes very short because $L/R$ becomes smaller with the high resistance of the open circuit. Then the current drops toward zero much faster than the rise of current when the switch is closed. The result is a high value of self-induced voltage $V_L$ across a coil whenever an $RL$ circuit is opened. This high voltage can be much greater than the applied voltage.

There is no gain in energy, though, because the high-voltage peak exists only for the short time the current is decreasing at a very fast rate at the start of the decay. Then, as $I$ decays with a slower rate of change, the value of $V_L$ is reduced. After the current has dropped to zero, there is no voltage across $L$.

This effect can be demonstrated by a neon bulb connected across the coil, as shown in Fig. 23-3. The neon bulb requires 90 V for ionization, at which time it glows. The source here is only 8 V, but when the switch is opened, the self-induced voltage is high enough to light the bulb for an instant. The sharp voltage pulse or spike is more than 90 V just after the switch is opened, when $I$ drops very fast at the start of the decay in current.

Note that the 100-$\Omega$ $R_1$ is the internal resistance of the 2-H coil. This resistance is in series with $L$ whether $S$ is closed or open. The 4-k$\Omega$ $R_2$ across the switch is in the circuit only when $S$ is opened, in order to have a specific

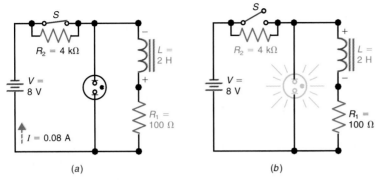

**FIG. 23-3** Demonstration of high voltage produced by opening inductive circuit. (*a*) With switch closed, 8 V applied cannot light the 90-V neon bulb. (*b*) When switch is opened, the short *L/R* time constant results in high $V_L$, which lights the bulb.

resistance across the open switch. Since $R_2$ is much more than $R_1$, the *L/R* time constant is much shorter with the switch open.

**CLOSING THE CIRCUIT**    In Fig. 23-3*a*, the switch is closed to allow current in *L* and to store energy in the magnetic field. Since $R_2$ is short-circuited by the switch, the 100-Ω $R_1$ is the only resistance. The steady-state *I* is $V/R_1 = 8/100 = 0.08$ A. This value of *I* is reached after five time constants.

One time constant is $L/R = 2/100 = 0.02$ s. Five time constants equal $5 \times 0.02 = 0.1$ s. Therefore, *I* is 0.08 A after 0.1 s, or 100 ms. The energy stored in the magnetic field is $64 \times 10^{-4}$ J, equal to $\frac{1}{2}LI^2$.

**OPENING THE CIRCUIT**    When the switch is opened in Fig. 23-3*b*, $R_2$ is in series with *L*, making the total resistance 4100 Ω, or approximately 4 kΩ. The result is a much shorter time constant for current decay. Then *L/R* is 2/4000, or 0.5 ms. The current decays practically to zero in five time constants, or 2.5 ms.

This rapid drop in current results in a magnetic field collapsing at a fast rate, inducing a high voltage across *L*. The peak $v_L$ in this example is 320 V. Then $v_L$ serves as the voltage source for the bulb connected across the coil. As a result, the neon bulb becomes ionized, and it lights for an instant. One problem produced when an inductive circuit is opened is arcing. Arcing can destroy contact points and under certain conditions cause fires or explosions.

**CALCULATING THE PEAK OF $v_L$**    The value of 320 V for the peak induced voltage when *S* is opened in Fig. 23-3 can be determined as follows: With the switch closed, *I* is 0.08 A in all parts of the series circuit. The instant *S* is opened, $R_2$ is added in series with *L* and $R_1$. The energy stored in the magnetic field maintains *I* at 0.08 A for an instant before the current decays. With 0.08 A in the 4-kΩ $R_2$ its potential difference is $0.08 \times 4000 = 320$ V. The collapsing magnetic field induces this 320-V pulse to allow an *I* of 0.08 A at the instant the switch is opened.

**THE *di/dt* FOR $v_L$**    The required rate of change in current is 160 A/s for the $v_L$ of 320 V induced by the *L* of 2 H. Since $v_L = L \, (di/dt)$, this formula can be transposed to specify $di/dt$ as equal to $v_L/L$. Then $di/dt$ corresponds to 320 V/2 H, or 160 A/s. This value is the actual $di/dt$ at the start of the decay in current when the switch is opened in Fig. 23-3b, as a result of the short time constant.*

**APPLICATIONS OF INDUCTIVE VOLTAGE PULSES**   There are many uses of the high voltage generated by opening an inductive circuit. One example is the high voltage produced for the ignition system in an automobile. Here the circuit of the battery in series with a high-inductance spark coil is opened by the breaker points of the distributor to produce the high voltage needed for each spark plug. By opening an inductive circuit very rapidly, 10,000 V can easily be produced. Another important application is the high voltage of 10 to 30 kV for the anode of the picture tube in television receivers.

---

### TEST-POINT QUESTION 23-3

Answers at end of chapter.
**a.** Is the $L/R$ time constant longer or shorter in Fig. 23-3 when $S$ is opened?
**b.** Which produces more $v_L$, a faster $di/dt$ or a slower $di/dt$?

## 23-4 *RC* TIME CONSTANT

For capacitive circuits, the transient response is measured in terms of the product $R \times C$. To calculate the time constant,

▶ $$T = R \times C \qquad\qquad (23\text{-}2)$$

where $R$ is in ohms, $C$ is in farads, and $T$ is in seconds. In Fig. 23-4, for example, with an $R$ of 3 M$\Omega$ and a $C$ of 1 $\mu$F,

$$T = 3 \times 10^6 \times 1 \times 10^{-6}$$
$$T = 3 \text{ s}$$

Note that the $10^6$ for megohms and the $10^{-6}$ for microfarads cancel. Therefore, multiplying the units of M$\Omega \times \mu$F gives the $RC$ product in seconds.

Common combinations of units for the $RC$ time constant are

$$\text{M}\Omega \times \mu\text{F} = \text{s}$$
$$\text{k}\Omega \times \mu\text{F} = \text{ms}$$
$$\text{M}\Omega \times \text{pF} = \mu\text{s}$$

The reason why the $RC$ product corresponds to time can be illustrated as follows: $C = Q/V$. The charge $Q$ is the product of $I \times T$. The factor $V$ is $IR$. Therefore, $RC$ is equivalent to $(R \times Q)/V$, or $(R \times IT)/IR$. Since $I$ and $R$ cancel, $T$ remains to indicate the dimension of time.

---

*The $di/dt$ value can be calculated from the slope at the start of decay, shown by the dashed line for curve $b$ in Fig. 23-9.

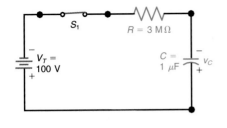
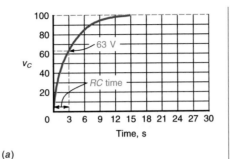

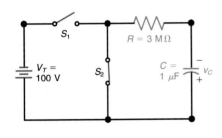
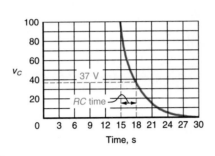

(a)

(b)

FIG. 23-4  Details of how a capacitor charges and discharges in an $RC$ circuit. (a) With $S_1$ closed, $C$ charges through $R$ to 63 percent of $V_T$ in one $RC$ time constant of 3 s and is almost completely charged in five time constants. (b) With $S_1$ opened to disconnect the battery and $S_2$ closed for $C$ to discharge through $R$, $V_C$ drops to 37 percent of its initial voltage in one time constant of 3 s and is almost completely discharged in five time constants.

## THE TIME CONSTANT INDICATES THE RATE OF CHARGE OR DISCHARGE

On charge, $RC$ specifies the time it takes $C$ to charge to 63 percent of the charging voltage. Similarly, on discharge, $RC$ specifies the time it takes $C$ to discharge 63 percent of the way down, to the value equal to 37 percent of the initial voltage across $C$ at the start of discharge.

In Fig. 23-4a, for example, the time constant on charge is 3 s. Therefore, in 3 s, $C$ charges to 63 percent of the 100 V applied, reaching 63 V in $RC$ time. After five time constants, which is 15 s here, $C$ is almost completely charged to the full 100 V applied. If $C$ discharges after being charged to 100 V, then $C$ will discharge down to 36.8 V or approximately 37 V in 3 s. After five time constants, $C$ discharges down to zero.

A shorter time constant allows the capacitor to charge or discharge faster. If the $RC$ product in Fig. 23-4 is 1 s, then $C$ will charge to 63 V in 1 s instead of 3 s. Also, $v_C$ will reach the full applied voltage of 100 V in 5 s instead of 15 s. Charging to the same voltage in less time means a faster charge.

On discharge also, the shorter time constant will allow $C$ to discharge from 100 to 37 V in 1 s instead of 3 s. Also, $v_C$ will be down to zero in the time of 5 s instead of 15 s.

For the opposite case, a longer time constant means slower charge or discharge of the capacitor. More $R$ or $C$ results in a longer time constant.

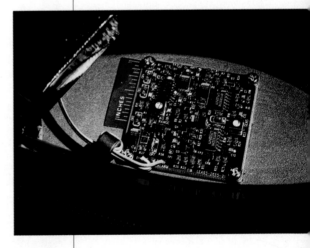

**RC APPLICATIONS** Several examples are given here to illustrate how the time constant can be applied to *RC* circuits.

## Example

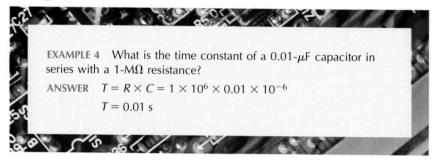

EXAMPLE 4   What is the time constant of a 0.01-$\mu$F capacitor in series with a 1-M$\Omega$ resistance?

ANSWER   $T = R \times C = 1 \times 10^6 \times 0.01 \times 10^{-6}$

$T = 0.01$ s

This is the time constant for charging or discharging, assuming the series resistance is the same for charge or discharge.

## Example

EXAMPLE 5   With a dc voltage of 300 V applied, how much is the voltage across *C* in Example 4 after 0.01 s of charging? After 0.05 s? After 2 hours? After 2 days?

ANSWER   Since 0.01 s is one time constant, the voltage across *C* then is 63 percent of 300 V, which equals 189 V. After five time constants, or 0.05 s, *C* will be charged practically to the applied voltage of 300 V. After 2 hours or 2 days *C* will still be charged to 300 V if the applied voltage is still connected.

EXAMPLE 6   If the capacitor in Example 5 is allowed to charge to 300 V and then discharged, how much is the capacitor voltage 0.01 s after the start of discharge? The series resistance is the same on discharge as on charge.

ANSWER   In one time constant *C* discharges to 37 percent of its initial voltage, or 0.37 × 300 V, which equals 111 V.

EXAMPLE 7   If the capacitor in Example 5 is made to discharge after being charged to 200 V, how much will the voltage across *C* be 0.01 s later? The series resistance is the same on discharge as on charge.

ANSWER   In one time constant *C* discharges to 37 percent of its initial voltage, or 0.37 × 200, which equals 74 V.
This example shows that the capacitor can charge or discharge from any voltage value. The rate at which it charges or discharges is determined by *RC* counting from the time the charge or discharge starts.

**EXAMPLE 8** If a 1-MΩ resistance is added in series with the capacitor and resistor in Example 4, how much will the time constant be?

**ANSWER** Now the series resistance is 2 MΩ. Therefore, $RC$ is 2 × 0.01, or 0.02 s.

The $RC$ time constant becomes longer with larger values of $R$ and $C$. More capacitance means that the capacitor can store more charge. Therefore, it takes longer to store the charge needed to provide a potential difference equal to 63 percent of the applied voltage. More resistance reduces the charging current, requiring more time for charging the capacitor.

It should be noted that the $RC$ time constant specifies just a rate. The actual amount of voltage across $C$ depends upon the applied voltage as well as upon the $RC$ time constant.

The capacitor takes on charge whenever its voltage is less than the applied voltage. The charging continues at the $RC$ rate until either the capacitor is completely charged, the applied voltage decreases, or the voltage is disconnected.

The capacitor discharges whenever its voltage is more than the applied voltage. The discharge continues at the $RC$ rate until either the capacitor is completely discharged, the applied voltage increases, or the load is disconnected.

To summarize these two important principles:

1. Capacitor $C$ charges when the net charging voltage is more than $v_C$.
2. Capacitor $C$ discharges when $v_C$ is more than the net charging voltage.

The net charging voltage equals the difference between $v_C$ and the applied voltage.

---

**TEST-POINT QUESTION 23-4**

Answers at end of chapter.
**a.** How much is the $RC$ time constant for 470 pF in series with 2 MΩ on charge?
**b.** How much is the $RC$ time constant for 470 pF in series with 1 kΩ on discharge?

## 23-5 *RC* CHARGE AND DISCHARGE CURVES

In Fig. 23-4, the $RC$ charge curve has the rise shown because the charging is fastest at the start, then tapers off as $C$ takes on additional charge at a slower rate. As $C$ charges, its potential difference increases. Then the difference in voltage between $V_T$ and $v_C$ is reduced. Less potential difference reduces the current that puts the charge in $C$. The more $C$ charges, the more slowly it takes on additional charge.

Similarly, on discharge, $C$ loses its charge at a slower rate. At the start of discharge, $v_C$ has its highest value and can produce maximum discharge current. With the discharge continuing, $v_C$ goes down and there is less discharge current. The more $C$ discharges, the more slowly it can lose the remainder of its charge.

**CHARGE AND DISCHARGE CURRENT**    There is often the question of how current can flow in a capacitive circuit with a battery as the dc source. The answer is that current flows any time there is a change in voltage. When $V_T$ is connected, the applied voltage changes from zero. Then charging current flows to charge $C$ to the applied voltage. After $v_C$ equals $V_T$, there is no net charging voltage and $I$ is zero.

Similarly, $C$ can produce discharge current any time $v_C$ is greater than $V_T$. When $V_T$ is disconnected, $v_C$ can discharge down to zero, producing discharge current in the opposite direction from the charging current. After $v_C$ equals zero, there is no current.

**CAPACITANCE OPPOSES VOLTAGE CHANGES ACROSS ITSELF**
This ability corresponds to the ability of inductance to oppose a change of current. In terms of the $RC$ circuit, when the applied voltage increases, the voltage across the capacitance cannot increase until the charging current has stored enough charge in $C$. The increase in applied voltage is present across the resistance in series with $C$ until the capacitor has charged to the higher applied voltage. When the applied voltage decreases, the voltage across the capacitor cannot go down immediately because the series resistance limits the discharge current.

The voltage across the capacitance in an $RC$ circuit, therefore, cannot follow instantaneously the changes in applied voltage. As a result, the capacitance is able to oppose changes in voltage across itself. The instantaneous variations in $V_T$ are present across the series resistance, however, since the series voltage drops must add to equal the applied voltage at all times.

---

### TEST-POINT QUESTION 23-5

Answers at end of chapter.
**a.** From the curve in Fig. 23-4a, how much is $v_C$ after 3 s of charge?
**b.** From the curve in Fig. 23-4b, how much is $v_C$ after 3 s of discharge?

## 23-6 HIGH CURRENT PRODUCED BY SHORT-CIRCUITING $RC$ CIRCUIT

Specifically, a capacitor can be charged slowly with a small charging current through a high resistance and then discharged fast through a low resistance to obtain a momentary surge, or pulse, of discharge current. This idea corresponds to the pulse of high voltage obtained by opening an inductive circuit.

The circuit in Fig. 23-5 illustrates the application of a battery-capacitor (BC) unit to fire a flash bulb for cameras. The flash bulb needs 5 A to ignite, but this

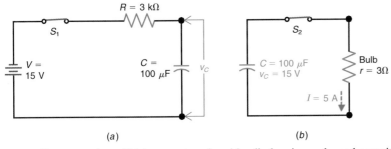

**FIG. 23-5**  Demonstration of high current produced by discharging a charged capacitor through a low resistance. (*a*) When $S_1$ is closed, $C$ charges to 15 V through 3 k$\Omega$. (*b*) Without the battery, $S_2$ is closed to allow $V_C$ to produce the peak discharge current of 5 A through the 3-$\Omega$ bulb. $V_C$ in (*b*) is across the same $C$ used in (*a*).

is too much load current for the small 15-V battery that has a rating of 30 mA for normal load current. Instead of using the bulb as a load for the battery, though, the 100-$\mu$F capacitor is charged by the battery through the 3-k$\Omega$ $R$ in Fig. 23-5*a*, and then the capacitor is discharged through the bulb in Fig. 23-5*b*.

**CHARGING THE CAPACITOR**  In Fig. 23-5*a*, $S_1$ is closed to charge $C$ through the 3-k$\Omega$ $R$ without the bulb. The time constant of the $RC$ charging circuit is 0.3 s.

After five time constants, or 1.5 s, $C$ is charged to the 15 V of the battery. The peak charging current, at the first instant of charge, is $V/R$ or 15 V/3 k$\Omega$, which equals 5 mA. This value is an easy load current for the battery.

**DISCHARGING THE CAPACITOR**  In Fig. 23-5*b*, $v_C$ is 15 V without the battery. Now $S_2$ is closed, and $C$ discharges through the 3-$\Omega$ resistance of the bulb. The time constant for discharge with the lower $r$ of the bulb is $3 \times 100 \times 10^{-6}$, which equals 300 $\mu$s. At the first instant of discharge, when $v_C$ is 15 V, the peak discharge current is 15/3, which equals 5 A. This current is enough to fire the bulb.

**ENERGY STORED IN $C$**  When the 100-$\mu$F $C$ is charged to 15 V by the battery, the energy stored in the electric field is $CV^2/2$, which equals 0.01 J, approximately. This energy is available to maintain $v_C$ at 15 V for an instant when the switch is closed. The result is the 5-A $I$ through the 3-$\Omega$ $r$ of the bulb at the start of the decay. Then $v_C$ and $i_C$ drop to zero in five time constants.

**THE $dv/dt$ FOR $i_C$**  The required rate of change in voltage is $0.05 \times 10^6$ V/s for the discharge current $i_C$ of 5 A produced by the $C$ of 100 $\mu$F. Since $i_C = C(dv/dt)$, this formula can be transposed to specify $dv/dt$ as equal to $i_C/C$. Then $dv/dt$ corresponds to 5 A/100 $\mu$F, or $0.05 \times 10^6$ V/s. This value is the actual $dv/dt$ at the start of discharge when the switch is closed in Fig. 23-5*b*. The $dv/dt$ is high because of the short $RC$ time constant.*

---

*See footnote on p. 636.

Answers at end of chapter.

**a.** Is the *RC* time constant longer or shorter in Fig. 23-5*b* compared with Fig. 23-5*a*?

**b.** Which produces more $i_C$, a faster *dv/dt* or a slower *dv/dt*?

## 23-7 *RC* WAVESHAPES

The voltage and current waveshapes in an *RC* circuit are shown in Fig. 23-6 for the case where a capacitor is allowed to charge through a resistance for *RC* time and then discharge through the same resistance for the same amount of time. It should be noted that this particular case is not typical of practical *RC* circuits, but the waveshapes show some useful details about the voltage and current for charging and discharging. The *RC* time constant here equals 0.1 s to simplify the calculations.

**SQUARE WAVE OF APPLIED VOLTAGE**   The idea of closing $S_1$ to apply 100 V and then opening it to disconnect $V_T$ at a regular rate corresponds to a square wave of applied voltage, as shown by the waveform in Fig. 23-6*a*. When $S_1$ is closed for charge, $S_2$ is open; when $S_1$ is open, $S_2$ is closed for discharge. Here the voltage is on for the *RC* time of 0.1 s and off for the same time of 0.1 s. The period of the square wave is 0.2 s, and *f* is 1/0.2 s, which equals 5 Hz for the frequency.

**CAPACITOR VOLTAGE $v_C$**   As shown in Fig. 23-6*b*, the capacitor charges to 63 V, equal to 63 percent of the charging voltage, in the *RC* time of 0.1 s. Then the capacitor discharges because the applied $V_T$ drops to zero. As a result, $v_C$ drops to 37 percent of 63 V, or 23.3 V in *RC* time.

The next charge cycle begins with $v_C$ at 23.3 V. The net charging voltage now is $100 - 23.3 = 76.7$ V. The capacitor voltage increases by 63 percent of 76.7 V, or 48.3 V. Adding 48.3 V to 23.3 V, then $v_C$ rises to 71.6 V. On discharge, after 0.3 s, $v_C$ drops to 37 percent of 71.6 V, or to 26.5 V.

**CHARGE AND DISCHARGE CURRENT**   As shown in Fig. 23-6*c*, the current *i* has its positive peak at the start of charge and its negative peak at the start of discharge. On charge, *i* is calculated as the net charging voltage, which is $(V_T - v_C)$, divided by *R*. On discharge, *i* always equals the value of $v_C/R$.

At the start of charge, *i* is maximum because the net charging voltage is maximum before *C* charges. Similarly, the peak *i* for discharge occurs at the start when $v_C$ is maximum before *C* discharges.

Note that *i* is actually an ac waveform around the zero axis, since the charge and discharge currents are in opposite directions. We are arbitrarily taking the charging current as positive values for *i*.

**DID YOU KNOW?**

Electric power is provided to homes from a group of interconnected regional plants. This makes it necessary that the 60-cycle frequency of all the generators be synchronized. Your power may arrive at your home via a loop hundreds of miles long rather than by the shortest distance.

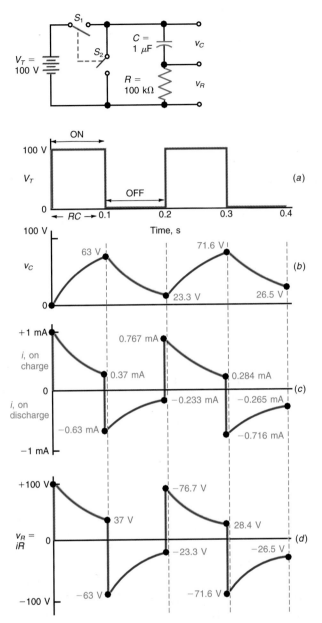

**FIG. 23-6** Waveshapes for the charge and discharge of an $RC$ circuit in $RC$ time. Circuit above with $S_1$ and $S_2$ provides the square wave of applied voltage.

**RESISTOR VOLTAGE $v_R$**  This waveshape in Fig. 23-6$d$ follows the waveshape of current, as $v_R$ is $i \times R$. Because of the opposite directions of charge and discharge current, the $iR$ waveshape is an ac voltage.

Note that on charge $v_R$ must always be equal to $V_T - v_C$ because of the series circuit.

On discharge $v_R$ has the same values as $v_C$ because they are parallel, without $V_T$. Then $S_2$ is closed to connect $R$ across $C$.

**WHY THE $i_C$ WAVESHAPE IS IMPORTANT**   The $v_C$ waveshape of capacitor voltage in Fig. 23-6 shows the charge and discharge directly, but the $i_C$ waveshape is very interesting. First, the voltage waveshape across $R$ is the same as the $i_C$ waveshape. Also, whether $C$ is charging or discharging, the $i_C$ waveshape is really the same except for the reversed polarity. We can see the $i_C$ waveshape as the voltage across $R$. It generally is better to connect an oscilloscope for voltage waveshapes across $R$, especially with one side grounded.

Finally, we can tell what $v_C$ is from the $v_R$ waveshape. The reason is that at any instant of time $V_T$ must equal the sum of $v_R$ and $v_C$. Therefore $v_C$ is equal to $V_T - v_R$, when $V_T$ is charging $C$. For the case when $C$ is discharging, there is no $V_T$. Then $v_R$ is the same as $v_C$.

---

## TEST POINT QUESTION 23-7

Answers at end of chapter.

Refer to Fig. 23-6.
**a.** When $v_C$ is 63 V, how much is $v_R$?
**b.** When $v_R$ is 76.7 V, how much is $v_C$?

# 23-8 LONG AND SHORT TIME CONSTANTS

Useful waveshapes can be obtained by using $RC$ circuits with the required time constant. In practical applications, $RC$ circuits are used more than $RL$ circuits because almost any value of an $RC$ time constant can be obtained easily. With coils, the internal series resistance cannot be short-circuited and the distributed capacitance often causes resonance effects.

**LONG $RC$ TIME**   Whether an $RC$ time constant is long or short depends on the pulse width of the applied voltage. We can arbitrarily define a long time constant as at least five times longer than the pulse width, in time, for the applied voltage. As a result, $C$ takes on very little charge. The time constant is too long for $v_C$ to rise appreciably before the applied voltage drops to zero and $C$ must discharge. On discharge also, with a long time constant, $C$ discharges very little before the applied voltage rises to make $C$ charge again.

**SHORT $RC$ TIME**   A short time constant can be defined as no more than one-fifth the pulse width, in time, for the applied voltage $V_T$. Then $V_T$ is applied for a period of at least five time constants, allowing $C$ to become completely charged. After $C$ is charged, $v_C$ remains at the value of $V_T$, while the voltage is applied. When $V_T$ drops to zero, $C$ discharges completely in five time constants and remains at zero while there is no applied voltage. On the next cycle, $C$ charges and discharges completely again.

**DIFFERENTIATION**   The voltage across $R$ in an $RC$ circuit is called a *differentiated output* because $v_R$ can change instantaneously. A short time constant is always used for differentiating circuits to provide sharp pulses of $v_R$.

**INTEGRATION** The voltage across $C$ is called an *integrated output* because it must accumulate over a period of time. A medium or long time constant is always used for integrating circuits.

# 23-9 CHARGE AND DISCHARGE WITH SHORT *RC* TIME CONSTANT

Usually, the time constant is made much shorter or longer than the factor of 5, to obtain better waveshapes. In Fig. 23-7, $RC$ is 0.1 ms. The frequency for the square wave is 25 Hz, with a period of 0.04 s, or 40 ms. One-half this period is the time $V_T$ is applied. Therefore, the applied voltage is on for 20 ms and off for 20 ms. The $RC$ time constant of 0.1 ms is shorter than the pulse width of 20 ms by a factor of $\frac{1}{200}$. Note that the time axis of all the waveshapes is calibrated in seconds for the period of $V_T$, not in $RC$ time constants.

**SQUARE WAVE OF $V_T$ IS ACROSS $C$** The waveshape of $v_C$ in Fig. 23-7$b$ is essentially the same as the square wave of applied voltage. The reason is that the short time constant allows $C$ to charge or discharge completely very soon after $V_T$ is applied or removed. The charge or discharge time of five time constants is much less than the pulse width.

**SHARP PULSES OF $i$** The waveshape of $i$ shows sharp peaks for the charge or discharge current. Each current peak is $V_T/R = 1$ mA, decaying to zero in five $RC$ time constants. These pulses coincide with the leading and trailing edges of the square wave of $V_T$.

Actually, the pulses are much sharper than shown. They are not to scale horizontally in order to indicate the charge and discharge action. Also, $v_C$ is actually a square wave like the applied voltage but with slightly rounded corners for the charge and discharge.

**SHARP PULSES OF $v_R$** The waveshape of voltage across the resistor follows the current waveshape, as $v_R = iR$. Each current pulse of 1 mA across the 100-k$\Omega$ $R$ results in a voltage pulse of 100 V.

More fundamentally, the peaks of $v_R$ equal the applied voltage $V_T$ before $C$ charges. Then $v_R$ drops to zero as $v_C$ rises to the value of $V_T$.

On discharge, $v_R = v_C$, which is 100 V at the start of discharge. Then the pulse drops to zero in five time constants. The pulses of $v_R$ in Fig. 23-7 are

**ABOUT ELECTRONICS**

In teleassistance, robots learn how to perform tasks as they "watch" and match the movements of a person wearing a virtual-reality glove.

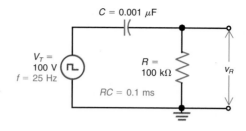

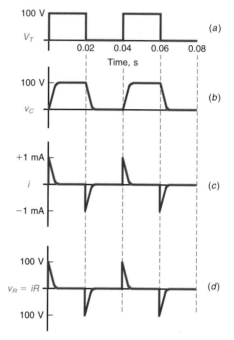

FIG. 23-7 Charge and discharge of an *RC* circuit with a short time constant. Note that the waveshape of $V_R$ in (*d*) has sharp voltage peaks for the leading and trailing edges of the square-wave applied voltage.

useful as timing pulses that match the edges of the square-wave applied voltage $V_T$. Either the positive or the negative pulses can be used.

The *RC* circuit in Fig. 23-7*a* is a good example of an *RC* differentiator. With the *RC* time constant much shorter than the pulse width of $V_T$, the voltage $V_R$ follows instantaneously the changes in the applied voltage. Keep in mind that a differentiator must have a short time constant with respect to the pulse width of $V_T$ to provide good differentiation.

## TEST-POINT QUESTION 23-9

Answers at end of chapter.

Refer to Fig. 23-7.

**a.** Is the time constant here short or long?

**b.** Is the square wave of applied voltage across *C* or *R*?

# 23-10 LONG TIME CONSTANT FOR *RC* COUPLING CIRCUIT

The *RC* circuit in Fig. 23-8 is the same as in Fig. 23-7, but now the *RC* time constant is long because of the higher frequency of the applied voltage. Specifically, the *RC* time of 0.1 ms is 200 times longer than the 0.5-$\mu$s pulse width of $V_T$ with a frequency of 1 MHz. Note that the time axis is calibrated in microseconds for the period of $V_T$, not in *RC* time constants.

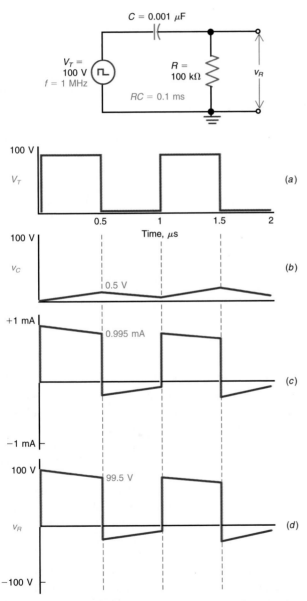

FIG. 23-8   Charge and discharge of an *RC* circuit with a long time constant. Note that the waveshape of $v_R$ in (*d*) has essentially the same waveform as the applied voltage.

**VERY LITTLE OF $V_T$ IS ACROSS $C$**    The waveshape of $v_C$ in Fig. 23-8$b$ shows very little voltage rise because of the long time constant. During the 0.5 $\mu$s that $V_T$ is applied, $C$ charges to only $\frac{1}{200}$ of the charging voltage. On discharge, also, $v_C$ drops very little.

**SQUARE WAVE OF $i$**    The waveshape of $i$ stays close to the 1-mA peak at the start of charge. The reason is that $v_C$ does not increase much, allowing $V_T$ to maintain the charging current. On discharge, the reverse $i$ for discharge current is very small because $v_C$ is low.

**SQUARE WAVE OF $V_T$ IS ACROSS $R$**    The waveshape of $v_R$ is the same square wave as $i$, as $v_R = iR$. Actually, the waveshapes of $i$ and $v_R$ are essentially the same as the square-wave $V_T$ applied. They are not shown to scale vertically in order to indicate the slight charge and discharge action.

   Eventually, $v_C$ will climb to the average dc value of 50 V, $i$ will vary $\pm0.5$ mA above and below zero, while $v_R$ will vary $\pm50$ V above and below zero. This application is an $RC$ coupling circuit to block the average value of the varying dc voltage $V_T$ as the capacitive voltage $v_C$, while $v_R$ provides an ac voltage output having the same variations as $V_T$.

   If the output is taken across $C$ rather than $R$ in Fig. 23-8$a$, the circuit is classified as an $RC$ integrator. Looking at Fig. 23-8$b$, it can be seen that $C$ combines, or integrates its original voltage with the new change in voltage. Eventually, however, the voltage across $C$ will reach a steady-state value of 50 V after the input waveform has been applied for approximately five $RC$ time constants. Keep in mind that an integrator must have a long time constant with respect to the pulse width of $V_T$ to provide good integration.

---

**TEST-POINT QUESTION 23-10**

Answers at end of chapter.

Refer to Fig. 23-8.
**a.** Is the $RC$ time constant here short or long?
**b.** Is the square wave of applied voltage across $R$ or $C$?

## 23-11 UNIVERSAL TIME CONSTANT GRAPH

We can determine transient voltage and current values for any amount of time, with the curves in Fig. 23-9. The rising curve $a$ shows how $v_C$ builds up as $C$ charges in an $RC$ circuit; the same curve applies to $i_L$, increasing in the inductance for an $RL$ circuit. The decreasing curve $b$ shows how $v_C$ drops as $C$ discharges or $i_L$ decays in an inductance.

   Note that the horizontal axis is in units of time constants rather than absolute time. Suppose that the time constant of an $RC$ circuit is 5 $\mu$s. Therefore, one $RC$ time unit = 5 $\mu$s, two $RC$ units = 10 $\mu$s, three $RC$ units = 15 $\mu$s, four $RC$ units = 20 $\mu$s, and five $RC$ units = 25 $\mu$s.

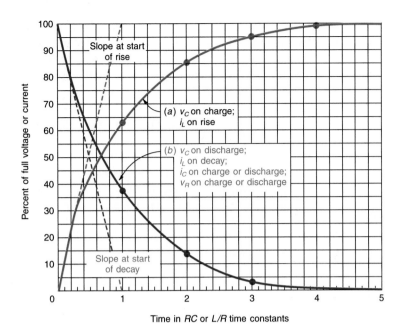

**FIG. 23-9** Universal time-constant chart for $RC$ and $RL$ circuits. The rise or fall changes by 63 percent in one time constant.

As an example, to find $v_C$ after 10 $\mu$s of charging, we can take the value of curve $a$ in Fig. 23-9 at two $RC$. This point is at 86 percent amplitude. Therefore, we can say that in this $RC$ circuit with a time constant of 5 $\mu$s, $v_C$ charges to 86 percent of the applied $V_T$, after 10 $\mu$s. Similarly, some important values that can be read from the curve are listed in Table 23-1.

If we consider curve $a$ in Fig. 23-9 as an $RC$ charge curve, $v_C$ adds 63 percent of the net charging voltage for each additional unit of one time constant, although it may not appear so. For instance, in the second interval of $RC$ time, $v_C$ adds 63 percent of the net charging voltage, which is 0.37 $V_T$. Then 0.63 $\times$ 0.37 equals 0.23, which is added to 0.63 to give 0.86, or 86 percent, as the total charge from the start.

**TABLE 23-1 TIME CONSTANT FACTORS**

| FACTOR | AMPLITUDE |
|---|---|
| 0.2 time constant | 20% |
| 0.5 time constant | 40% |
| 0.7 time constant | 50% |
| 1 time constant | 63% |
| 2 time constants | 86% |
| 3 time constants | 96% |
| 4 time constants | 98% |
| 5 time constants | 99% |

**SLOPE AT $T = 0$** The curves in Fig. 23-9 can be considered linear for the first 20 percent of change. In 0.1 time constant, for instance, the change in amplitude is 10 percent; in 0.2 time constant, the change is 20 percent. The dashed lines in Fig. 23-9 show that if this constant slope continued, the result would be 100 percent charge in one time constant. This does not happen, though, because the change is opposed by the energy stored in $L$ and $C$. However, at the first instant of rise or decay, at $t = 0$, the change in $v_C$ or $i_L$ can be calculated from the dotted slope line.

**EQUATION OF THE DECAY CURVE** The rising curve $a$ in Fig. 23-9 may seem more interesting because it describes the buildup of $v_C$ or $i_L$, but the decaying curve $b$ is more useful. For $RC$ circuits, curve $b$ can be applied to

1.  $v_C$ on discharge
2.  $i$ and $v_R$ on charge or discharge

If we use curve $b$ for the voltage in $RC$ circuits, the equation of this decay curve can be written as

▶  $$v = V \times \epsilon^{-t/RC} \tag{23-3}$$

where $V$ is the voltage at the start of decay and $v$ is the instantaneous voltage after the time $t$. Specifically, $v$ can be $v_R$ on charge and discharge, or $v_C$ only on discharge.

The constant $\epsilon$ is the base 2.718 for natural logarithms.* The negative exponent $-t/RC$ indicates a declining exponential or logarithmic curve. The value of $t/RC$ is the ratio of actual time of decline $t$ to the $RC$ time constant.

This equation can be converted to common logarithms for easier calculations. Since the natural base $\epsilon$ is 2.718, its logarithm to base 10 equals 0.434. Therefore, the equation becomes

▶  $$v = \text{antilog}\left(\log V - 0.434 \times \frac{t}{RC}\right) \tag{23-4}$$

**CALCULATIONS FOR $v_R$** As an example, let us calculate $v_R$ dropping from 100 V, after $RC$ time. Then the factor $t/RC$ is 1. Substituting these values,

$$v_R = \text{antilog} (\log 100 - 0.434 \times 1)$$
$$= \text{antilog} (2 - 0.434)$$
$$= \text{antilog } 1.566$$
$$v_R = 37 \text{ V}$$

All these logs are to base 10. Note that log 100 is taken first so that 0.434 can be subtracted from 2 before the antilog of the difference is found. The antilog of 1.566 is 37.

We can also use $V_R$ to find $V_C$, which is $V_T - V_R$. Then $100 - 37 = 63$ V for $V_C$. These answers agree with the fact that in one time constant, the $V_R$ drops 63 percent while $V_C$ rises 63 percent.

---

*For an explanation of logarithms, see Grob, B.: *Mathematics for Basic Electronics*, Glencoe/McGraw-Hill, Columbus, Ohio.

Figure 23-10 illustrates how the voltages across $R$ and $C$ in series must add to equal the applied voltage $V_T$. The four examples with 100 V applied are:

1. At time zero, at the start of charging, $V_R$ is 100 V and $V_C$ is 0 V. Then $100 + 0 = 100$ V.
2. After one time constant, $V_R$ is 37 V and $V_C$ is 63 V. Then $37 + 63 = 100$ V.
3. After two time constants, $V_R$ is 14 V and $V_C$ is 86 V. Then $14 + 86 = 100$ V.
4. After five time constants, $V_R$ is 0 V and $V_C$ is 100 V, approximately. Then $0 + 100 = 100$ V

It should be emphasized that Formulas (23-3) and (23-4) can be used to calculate any decaying value on curve $b$ in Fig. 23-9. These applications for an $RC$ circuit include $V_R$ on charge or discharge, $i$ on charge or discharge, and $V_C$ only on discharge. For an $RC$ circuit in which $C$ is charging, Formula (23-5) can be used to calculate the capacitor voltage $v_C$ at any point along curve $a$ in Fig. 23-9:

▶ $$v_C = V(1 - \epsilon^{-t/RC}) \tag{23-5}$$

In Formula (23-5), $V$ represents the maximum voltage to which $C$ can charge, whereas $v_C$ is the instantaneous capacitor voltage after the time $t$. Formula (23-5) is derived from the fact that $v_C$ must equal $V_T - V_R$ while $C$ is charging.

## Example

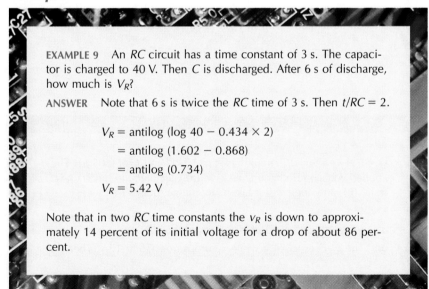

**EXAMPLE 9**  An $RC$ circuit has a time constant of 3 s. The capacitor is charged to 40 V. Then $C$ is discharged. After 6 s of discharge, how much is $V_R$?

**ANSWER**  Note that 6 s is twice the $RC$ time of 3 s. Then $t/RC = 2$.

$$V_R = \text{antilog} (\log 40 - 0.434 \times 2)$$
$$= \text{antilog} (1.602 - 0.868)$$
$$= \text{antilog} (0.734)$$
$$V_R = 5.42 \text{ V}$$

Note that in two $RC$ time constants the $v_R$ is down to approximately 14 percent of its initial voltage for a drop of about 86 percent.

To do this problem on a calculator, the steps can be as follows:

1. Find log 40. Punch in 40 on the keyboard and press the (log) key for 1.60 on the display. Be sure not to use the (ln) key for natural logs. The $\log_{10}$ key may require pushing the (2ndF) or shift key first.
2. With 1.60 on the display, push the (−) key, punch in (◯) then 0.434 (×) 2 (◯) and press the (=) key for 0.734 on the display.

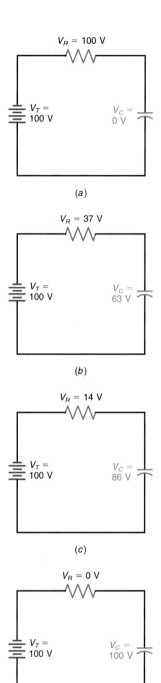

$V_R = 100$ V

$V_T = 100$ V   $V_C = 0$ V

(a)

$V_R = 37$ V

$V_T = 100$ V   $V_C = 63$ V

(b)

$V_R = 14$ V

$V_T = 100$ V   $V_C = 86$ V

(c)

$V_R = 0$ V

$V_T = 100$ V   $V_C = 100$ V

(d)

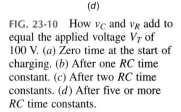

**FIG. 23-10**  How $v_C$ and $v_R$ add to equal the applied voltage $V_T$ of 100 V. (a) Zero time at the start of charging. (b) After one $RC$ time constant. (c) After two $RC$ time constants. (d) After five or more $RC$ time constants.

3. For the antilog of 0.734, use the $\boxed{10^x}$ key, which is usually a second function, for the answer of 5.42 on the display. This key is for the antilog of any logarithm to base 10.

**CALCULATIONS FOR $T$**  Furthermore, Formula (23-4) can be transposed to find the time $t$ for a specific voltage decay. Then

▶
$$t = 2.3 \, RC \log \frac{V}{v} \qquad\qquad\qquad\qquad \textbf{(23-6)}$$

where $V$ is the higher voltage at the start and $v$ is the lower voltage at the finish. The factor 2.3 is 1/0.434.

As an example, let $RC$ be 1 s. How long will it take for $v_R$ to drop from 100 to 50 V? The required time for this decay is

$$t = 2.3 \times 1 \times \log \frac{100}{50} = 2.3 \times 1 \times \log 2$$

$$= 2.3 \times 1 \times 0.3$$

$$t = 0.7 \text{ s} \qquad \text{approximately}$$

This answer agrees with the fact that the time for a drop of 50 percent takes 0.7 time constant. Formula (23-6) can also be used to calculate the time for any decay of $v_C$ or $v_R$.

Formula (23-6) cannot be used for a rise in $v_C$. However, if you convert this rise to an equivalent drop in $v_R$, the calculated time is the same for both cases.

*Example*

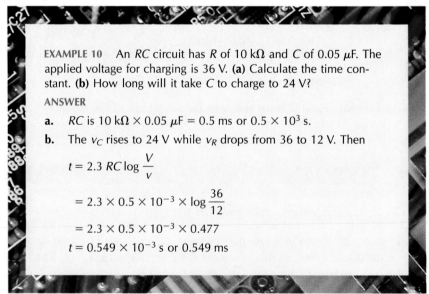

**EXAMPLE 10**  An $RC$ circuit has $R$ of 10 k$\Omega$ and $C$ of 0.05 $\mu$F. The applied voltage for charging is 36 V. **(a)** Calculate the time constant. **(b)** How long will it take $C$ to charge to 24 V?

ANSWER

a. $RC$ is 10 k$\Omega \times 0.05$ $\mu$F = 0.5 ms or $0.5 \times 10^3$ s.

b. The $v_C$ rises to 24 V while $v_R$ drops from 36 to 12 V. Then

$$t = 2.3 \, RC \log \frac{V}{v}$$

$$= 2.3 \times 0.5 \times 10^{-3} \times \log \frac{36}{12}$$

$$= 2.3 \times 0.5 \times 10^{-3} \times 0.477$$

$$t = 0.549 \times 10^{-3} \text{ s or } 0.549 \text{ ms}$$

Answers at end of chapter.

Answer True or False for the universal curves in Fig. 23-9.
**a.** Curve *a* applies to $v_C$ on charge.
**b.** Curve *b* applies to $v_C$ on discharge.
**c.** Curve *b* applies to $v_R$ when *C* charges or discharges.


# 23-12 COMPARISON OF REACTANCE AND TIME CONSTANT

The formula for capacitive reactance includes the factor of time in terms of frequency as $X_C = 1/(2\pi fC)$. Therefore, $X_C$ and the *RC* time constant are both measures of the reaction of *C* to a change in voltage. The reactance $X_C$ is a special case but a very important one that applies only to sine waves. The *RC* time constant can be applied to square waves and rectangular pulses.

**PHASE ANGLE OF REACTANCE**   The capacitive charge and discharge current $i_C$ is always equal to $C(dv/dt)$. A sine wave of voltage variations for $v_C$ produces a cosine wave of current $i_C$. This means $v_C$ and $i_C$ are both sinusoids, but 90° out of phase.

   In this case, it is usually more convenient to use $X_C$ for calculations in sine-wave ac circuits to determine *Z*, *I*, and the phase angle $\theta$. Then $I_C = V_C/X_C$. Moreover, if $I_C$ is known, $V_C = I_C \times X_C$. The phase angle of the circuit depends on the amount of $X_C$ compared with the resistance *R*.

**CHANGES IN WAVESHAPE**   With nonsinusoidal voltage applied, $X_C$ cannot be used. Then $i_C$ must be calculated as $C(dv/dt)$. In this comparison of $i_C$ and $v_C$, their waveshapes can be different, instead of the change in phase angle for sine waves. The waveshapes of $v_C$ and $i_C$ depend on the *RC* time constant.

**COUPLING CAPACITORS**   If we consider the application of a coupling capacitor, $X_C$ must be one-tenth or less of its series *R* at the desired frequency. This condition is equivalent to having an *RC* time constant that is long compared with the period of one cycle. In terms of $X_C$, the *C* has little $IX_C$ voltage, with practically all the applied voltage across the series *R*. In terms of a long *RC* time constant, *C* cannot take on much charge. Practically all the applied voltage is developed as $v_R = iR$ across the series resistance by the charge and discharge current. These comparisons are summarized in Table 23-2.

**INDUCTIVE CIRCUITS**   Similar comparisons can be made between $X_L = 2\pi fL$ for sine waves and the *L/R* time constant. The voltage across any inductance is $v_L = L(di/dt)$. Sine-wave variations for $i_L$ produce a cosine wave of voltage $v_L$, 90° out of phase.

   In this case $X_L$ can be used to determine *Z*, *I*, and the phase angle $\theta$. Then $I_L = V_L/X_L$. Furthermore, if $I_L$ is known, $V_L = I_L \times X_L$. The phase angle of the circuit depends on the amount of $X_L$ compared with *R*.

**DID YOU KNOW?**

Researchers have designed a car engine that expands to accelerate and shrinks for high-speed cruises. There are no rotating parts. The car goes from zero to 60 miles an hour in 7 seconds and gets 80 miles per gallon; its lifetime is 500,000 miles.

## TABLE 23-2 COMPARISON OF REACTANCE $X_C$ AND RC TIME CONSTANT

| SINE-WAVE VOLTAGE | NONSINUSOIDAL VOLTAGE |
|---|---|
| Examples are 60-Hz power line, AF signal voltage, RF signal voltage | Examples are dc circuit turned on and off, square waves, rectangular pulses |
| Reactance $X_C = \dfrac{1}{2\pi fC}$ | Time constant $T = RC$ |
| Larger $C$ results in smaller reactance $X_C$ | Larger $C$ results in longer time constant |
| Higher frequency results in smaller $X_C$ | Shorter pulse width corresponds to longer time constant |
| $I_C = \dfrac{V_C}{X_C}$ | $i_C = C\dfrac{dv}{dt}$ |
| $X_C$ makes $I_C$ and $V_C$ 90° out of phase | Waveshape changes between $i_C$ and $v_C$ |

With nonsinusoidal voltage, however, $X_L$ cannot be used. Then $v_L$ must be calculated as $L(di/dt)$. In this comparison, $i_L$ and $v_L$ can have different waveshapes, depending on the $L/R$ time constant.

**CHOKE COILS** For this application, the idea is to have almost all the applied ac voltage across $L$. The condition of $X_L$ being at least 10 times $R$ corresponds to having a long time constant. The high value of $X_L$ means practically all the applied ac voltage is across $X_L$ as $IX_L$, with little $IR$ voltage.

The long $L/R$ time constant means $i_L$ cannot rise appreciably, resulting in little $v_R$ voltage across the resistor. The waveform for $i_L$ and $v_R$ in an inductive circuit corresponds to $v_C$ in a capacitive circuit.

**WHEN DO WE USE THE TIME CONSTANT?** In electronic circuits, the time constant is useful in analyzing the effect of $L$ or $C$ on the waveshape of nonsinusoidal voltages, particularly rectangular pulses. Another application is the transient response when a dc voltage is turned on or off. The 63 percent change in one time constant is a natural characteristic of $v$ or $i$, where the magnitude of one is proportional to the rate of change of the other.

**WHEN DO WE USE REACTANCE?** The $X_L$ and $X_C$ are generally used for sine-wave $V$ or $I$. We can determine $Z$, $I$, voltage drops, and phase angles. The phase angle of 90° is a natural characteristic of a cosine wave where its magnitude is proportional to the rate of change in a sine wave.

──────────── **TEST-POINT QUESTION 23-12** ────────────

Answers at end of chapter.
**a.** Does an $RC$ coupling circuit have a small or large $X_C$ compared with $R$?
**b.** Does an $RC$ coupling circuit have a long or short time constant for the frequency of the applied voltage?

# 23 SUMMARY AND REVIEW

- The transient response of an inductive circuit with nonsinusoidal current is indicated by the time constant $L/R$. With $L$ in henrys and $R$ in ohms, $T$ is the time in seconds for the current $i_L$ to change by 63 percent. In five time constants, $i_L$ reaches the steady value of $V_T/R$.

- At the instant an inductive circuit is opened, high voltage is generated across $L$ because of the fast current decay with a short time constant. The induced voltage $v_L = L(di/dt)$. The $di$ is the change in $i_L$.

- The transient response of a capacitive circuit with nonsinusoidal voltage is indicated by the time constant $RC$. With $C$ in farads and $R$ in ohms, $T$ is the time in seconds for the voltage across the capacitor $v_C$ to change by 63 percent. In five time constants, $v_C$ reaches the steady value of $V_T$.

- At the instant a charged capacitor is discharged through a low resistance, a high value of discharge current can be produced. The discharge current $i_C = C(dv/dt)$ can be large because of the fast discharge with a short time constant. The $dv$ is the change in $v_C$.

- The waveshapes of $v_C$ and $i_L$ correspond, as both rise relatively slowly to the steady-state value. This is an integrated output.

- Also $i_C$ and $v_L$ correspond, as they are the waveforms that can change instantaneously. This is a differentiated output.

- For both $RC$ and $RL$ circuits the resistor voltage $v_R = iR$.

- A short time constant is one-fifth or less of the pulse width, in time, for the applied voltage.

- A long time constant is greater than the pulse width, in time, for the applied voltage by a factor of 5 or more.

- An $RC$ circuit with a short time constant produces sharp voltage spikes for $v_R$ at the leading and trailing edges of a square-wave applied voltage. The waveshape of voltage $V_T$ is across the capacitor as $v_C$. See Fig. 23-7.

- An $RC$ circuit with a long time constant allows $v_R$ to be essentially the same as the variations in applied voltage $V_T$, while the average dc value of $V_T$ is blocked as $v_C$. See Fig. 23-8.

- The universal rise and decay curves in Fig. 23-9 can be used for current or voltage in $RC$ and $RL$ circuits for any time up to five time constants.

- The concept of reactance is useful for sine-wave ac circuits with $L$ and $C$.

- The time constant method is used with $L$ or $C$ to analyze nonsinusoidal waveforms.

Choose (*a*), (*b*), (*c*), or (*d*).

1. A 250-$\mu$H $L$ is in series with a 50-$\Omega$ $R$. The time constant is (*a*) 5 $\mu$s; (*b*) 25 $\mu$s; (*c*) 50 $\mu$s; (*d*) 250 $\mu$s.
2. If $V_T$ is 500 mV in the preceding circuit, after 5 $\mu$s $I$ rises to the value of (*a*) 3.7 mA; (*b*) 5 mA; (*c*) 6.3 mA; (*d*) 10 mA.
3. In the preceding circuit, $I$ will have the steady-state value of 10 mA after (*a*) 5 $\mu$s; (*b*) 6.3 $\mu$s; (*c*) 10 $\mu$s; (*d*) 25 $\mu$s.
4. The arc across a switch when it opens an $RL$ circuit is a result of the (*a*) long time constant; (*b*) large self-induced voltage across $L$; (*c*) low resistance of the open switch; (*d*) surge of resistance.
5. A 250-pF $C$ is in series with a 1-M$\Omega$ $R$. The time constant is (*a*) 63 $\mu$s; (*b*) 100 $\mu$s; (*c*) 200 $\mu$s; (*d*) 250 $\mu$s.
6. If $V_T$ is 100 V in the preceding circuit, after 250 $\mu$s, $v_C$ rises to the value of (*a*) 37 V; (*b*) 50 V; (*c*) 63 V; (*d*) 100 V.
7. In the preceding circuit, $v_C$ will have the steady-state value of 100 V after (*a*) 250 $\mu$s; (*b*) 630 $\mu$s; (*c*) 1000 $\mu$s or 1 ms; (*d*) 1.25 ms.
8. In the preceding circuit, after 3 hours $v_C$ will be (*a*) zero; (*b*) 63 V; (*c*) 100 V; (*d*) 200 V.
9. For a square-wave applied voltage with the frequency of 500 Hz, a long time constant is (*a*) 1 ms; (*b*) 2 ms; (*c*) 3.7 ms; (*d*) 5 ms.
10. An $RC$ circuit has a 2-$\mu$F $C$ in series with a 1-M$\Omega$ $R$. The time of 6 s equals how many time constants? (*a*) one; (*b*) two; (*c*) three; (*d*) six.

## QUESTIONS

1. Give the formula, with units, for calculating the time constant of an $RL$ circuit.
2. Give the formula, with units, for calculating the time constant of an $RC$ circuit.
3. Redraw the $RL$ circuit and graph in Fig. 23-2 for a 2-H $L$ and a 100-$\Omega$ $R$.
4. Redraw the graphs in Fig. 23-4 to fit the circuit in Fig. 23-5 with a 100-$\mu$F $C$. Use a 3000-$\Omega$ $R$ for charge but a 3-$\Omega$ $R$ for discharge.
5. List two comparisons of $RC$ and $RL$ circuits for nonsinusoidal voltage.
6. List two comparisons between $RC$ circuits with nonsinusoidal voltage and sine-wave voltage applied.
7. Define the following: (**a**) a long time constant; (**b**) a short time constant; (**c**) an $RC$ differentiating circuit; (**d**) an $RC$ integrating circuit.
8. Redraw the horizontal time axis of the universal curve in Fig. 23-9, calibrated in absolute time units of milliseconds for an $RC$ circuit with a time constant equal to 2.3 ms.
9. Redraw the circuit and graphs in Fig. 23-7 with everything the same except that $R$ is 20 k$\Omega$, making the $RC$ time constant shorter.

10. Redraw the circuit and graphs in Fig. 23-8 with everything the same except that $R$ is 500 kΩ, making the $RC$ time constant longer.
11. Invert the equation $T = RC$, in two forms, to find $R$ or $C$ from the time constant.
12. Show three types of nonsinusoidal waveforms.
13. Give an application in electronic circuits for an $RC$ circuit with a long time constant and with a short time constant.
14. Why can arcing voltage be a problem with coils used in switching circuits?

**ANSWERS TO ODD-NUMBERED PROBLEMS AT BACK OF BOOK.**

1. Calculate the time constant of the following inductive circuits: (**a**) $L$ is 20 H and $R$ is 400 Ω; (**b**) $L$ is 20 μH and $R$ is 400 Ω; (**c**) $L$ is 50 mH and $R$ is 50 Ω; (**d**) $L$ is 40 μH and $R$ is 2 Ω.
2. Calculate the time constant of the following capacitive circuits: (**a**) $C$ is 0.001 μF and $R$ is 1 MΩ; (**b**) $C$ is 1 μF and $R$ is 1000 Ω; (**c**) $C$ is 0.05 μF and $R$ is 250 kΩ; (**d**) $C$ is 100 pF and $R$ is 10 kΩ.
3. A 100-V source is in series with a 2-MΩ $R$ and a 2-μF $C$. (**a**) How much time is required for $v_C$ to be 63 V? (**b**) How much is $v_C$ after 20 s?
4. The $C$ in Prob. 3 is allowed to charge for 4 s and then made to discharge for 8 s. How much is $v_C$?
5. A 100-V source is applied in series with a 1-MΩ $R$ and a 4-μF $C$ that has already been charged to 63 V. How much is $v_C$ after 4 s?
6. What value of $R$ is needed with a 0.05-μF $C$ for an $RC$ time constant of 0.02 s? For 1 ms?
7. An $RC$ circuit has a time constant of 1 ms. $V_T$ applied is 20 V. How much is $v_C$ on charge after 1.4 ms?
8. A 0.05-μF $C$ charges through a 0.5-MΩ $R$ but discharges through a 2-kΩ $R$. Calculate the time constants for charge and discharge. Why will the capacitor discharge faster than charge?
9. A 0.05-μF $C$ is charged to 264 V. It discharges through a 40-kΩ $R$. How much is the time for $v_C$ to discharge down to 132 V?
10. Referring to Fig. 23-6b, calculate the value of $v_C$ on the next charge, starting from 26.5 V.
11. Determine whether 75 μs will be a long or short time constant for applied signal voltage with the following frequencies: (**a**) 60 Hz; (**b**) 1000 Hz; (**c**) 4 MHz.
12. What $R$ is needed with $C$ of 0.001 μF for a time constant of 75 μs?
13. Calculate the $C$ needed for a time constant of 50 ms with $R$ of 5 kΩ.
14. Determine the frequency of a square-wave signal that will have voltage applied for one time constant with $RC$ of 50 ms.
15. An $RC$ circuit has a time constant of 68 μs. The capacitor is charged to 14 V. How much is $v_R$ after 136 μs of discharge?
16. For an $RC$ circuit with $R$ of 1 MΩ and $C$ of 68 pF, 9 V is applied. How long will it take $C$ to charge to 5 V?
17. Use the slope line in Fig. 23-9b to calculate $dv/dt$ at the start of the decay in $v_C$ for the circuit in Fig. 23-5b.

**18.** Use the slope line in Fig. 23-9 to calculate $di/dt$ at the start of the decay in $i_L$ for the circuit in Fig. 23-3*b*. (Hint: You can ignore the steady 8 V and 100-$\Omega$ $R_1$ because they do not change the $di/dt$ value.)

**19.** In Fig. 23-11, draw the waveform you would expect to measure across the 10-k$\Omega$ $R$. Indicate the resistor voltage $V_R$ at the beginning and end of each 1-ms pulse interval. Draw the $V_R$ waveform in the proper time relationship with respect to $V_{in}$.

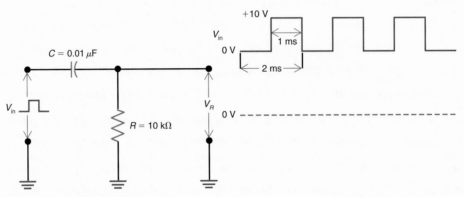

FIG. 23-11   Diagram for Prob. 19.

**20.** In Fig. 23-12, draw the waveform you would expect to measure across the 0.01-$\mu$F $C$. Indicate the capacitor voltage $V_C$ at the beginning and end of each 27.3-$\mu$s pulse interval. Draw the $V_C$ waveform in the proper time relationship with respect to $V_{in}$. ($C$ is initially uncharged.)

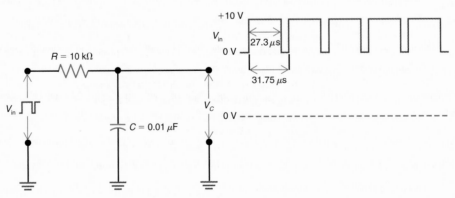

FIG. 23-12   Diagram for Prob. 20.

**21.** In Fig. 23-13, the capacitor is initially charged to 5 V. If switch $S_1$ is closed, calculate $V_C$ and $V_R$ after: **(a)** 0 s; **(b)** 0.693 s; **(c)** 1 s; **(d)** 2 s; **(e)** 3.5 s; **(f)** 5 s.

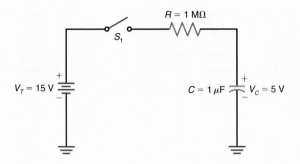

FIG. 23-13   Circuit for Prob. 21.

## CRITICAL THINKING

1.  Refer to Fig. 23-14. (a) If $S_1$ is closed long enough for the capacitor $C$ to become fully charged, what voltage is across $C$? (b) With $C$ fully charged, how long will it take $C$ to fully discharge when $S_1$ is opened?

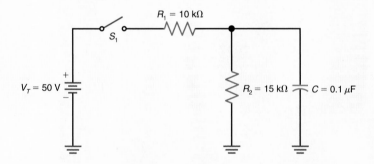

FIG. 23-14   Circuit for Critical Thinking Probs. 1 and 2.

2.  Refer to Fig. 23-14. (a) How long will it take $C$ to fully charge after $S_1$ is initially closed? (b) What is $V_C$ 1 ms after $S_1$ is initially closed? (c) What is $V_C$ 415.8 μs after $S_1$ is initially closed? (d) What is $V_C$ 1.5 ms after $S_1$ is initially closed?
3.  Refer to Fig. 23-15. Assume $C$ is allowed to charge fully and then the polarity of $V_T$ is suddenly reversed. What is the capacitor voltage $v_C$ for the following time intervals after the reversal of $V_T$: (a) 0 s; (b) 6.93 ms; (c) 10 ms; (d) 15 ms; (e) 30 ms?

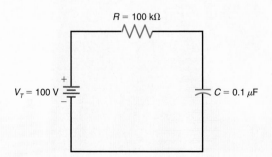

FIG. 23-15   Circuit for Critical Thinking Prob. 3.

**23-1**  **a.** T
     **b.** T

**23-2**  **a.** 0.02 s
     **b.** 0.5 ms

**23-3**  **a.** shorter
     **b.** faster

**23-4**  **a.** 940 $\mu$s
     **b.** 470 ns

**23-5**  **a.** 63.2 V
     **b.** 36.8 V

**23-6**  **a.** shorter
     **b.** faster

**23-7**  **a.** $v_R = 37$ V
     **b.** $v_C = 23.3$ V

**23-8**  **a.** short
     **b.** long

**23-9**  **a.** short
     **b.** across $C$

**23-10**  **a.** long
      **b.** across $R$

**23-11**  **a.** T
      **b.** T
      **c.** T

**23-12**  **a.** small $X_C$
      **b.** long time constant

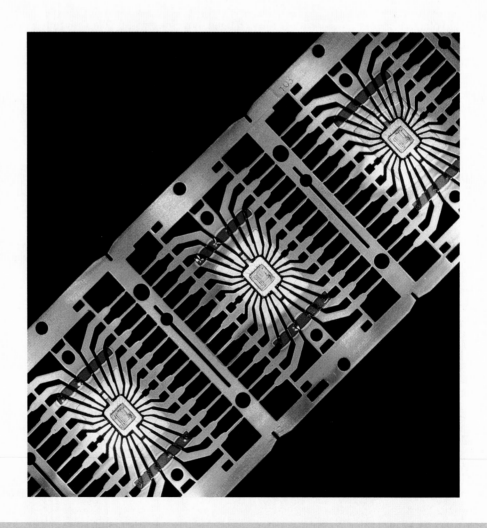

# REVIEW: CHAPTERS 20 TO 23

## SUMMARY

- The ability of a conductor to produce induced voltage across itself when the current changes is its self-inductance, or inductance. The symbol is $L$, and the unit is the henry. One henry allows 1 V to be induced when the current changes at the rate of 1 A/s.
- The polarity of the induced voltage always opposes the change in current that is causing the induced voltage. This is Lenz' law.
- Mutual inductance is the ability of varying current in one coil to induce voltage in another coil nearby, without any connection between them. Its symbol is $L_M$, and the unit is also the henry.
- A transformer consists of two or more windings with mutual inductance. The primary connects to the source voltage, the secondary to the load. With an iron core, the voltage ratio between primary and secondary equals the turns ratio.
- The efficiency of a transformer equals the ratio of power output from the secondary to power input to the primary $\times$ 100 percent.
- Eddy currents are induced in the iron core of an inductance, causing $I^2R$ losses that increase with higher frequencies. Laminated iron, powdered-iron, or ferrite cores have minimum eddy-current losses. Hysteresis also increases the losses.
- Series inductances without mutual coupling add like series resistances. With parallel inductances, the combined inductance is calculated by the reciprocal formula, as with parallel resistances.
- Inductive reactance $X_L$ equals $2\pi fL$ $\Omega$, where $f$ is in hertz and $L$ is in henrys. Reactance $X_L$ increases with more inductance and higher frequencies.
- A common application of $X_L$ is an AF or RF choke, which has high reactance for one group of frequencies but less reactance for lower frequencies.
- Reactance $X_L$ is a phasor quantity that has its current lagging 90° behind its induced voltage. In series circuits, $R$ and $X_L$ are added by phasors because their voltage drops are 90° out of phase. In parallel circuits, the resistive and inductive branch currents are 90° out of phase.
- Impedance Z, in ohms, is the total opposition of an ac circuit with resistance and reactance. For series circuits, $Z_T = \sqrt{R^2 + X_L{}^2}$ and $I = V_T/Z_T$. For parallel circuits, $I_T = \sqrt{I_R{}^2 + I_L{}^2}$ and $Z_{EQ} = V_A/I_T$.
- The $Q$ of a coil is $X_L/r_i$.
- Energy stored by an inductance is $\frac{1}{2} LI^2$, where $I$ is in amperes, $L$ in henrys, and the energy is in joules.
- The voltage across $L$ is always equal to $L(di/dt)$ for any waveshape of current.
- The transient response of a circuit refers to the temporary condition which exists until the circuit's current or voltage reaches its steady-state value. The transient response of a circuit is

measured in time constants, where one time constant is defined as the length of time over which a 63.2 percent change in current or voltage occurs.

- For an inductive circuit, one time constant is the time in seconds for the current to change by 63.2 percent. For inductive circuits, one time constant equals $L/R$; that is, $T = L/R$, where $L$ is in henries, $R$ is in ohms, and $T$ is in seconds. The current reaches its steady-state value after a time of five $L/R$ time constants has elapsed.
- For a capacitive circuit, one time constant is the time in seconds for the capacitor voltage to change by 63.2 percent. For capacitive circuits, one time constant equals $RC$; that is, $T = RC$, where $R$ is in ohms, $C$ is in farads, and $T$ is in seconds. The capacitor voltage reaches its steady-state value after a time of five $RC$ time constants has elapsed.
- When the input voltage to an inductive or capacitive circuit is nonsinusoidal in nature, time constants rather than reactances are used to determine the circuit's voltage and current values.
- Whether an $L/R$ or $RC$ time constant is considered short or long depends on its relationship to the pulse width of the applied voltage. In general, a short time constant is considered to be one which is one-fifth or less the time of the pulse width of the applied voltage. Conversely, a long time constant is generally considered to be one which is five or more times longer than the pulse width of the applied voltage.
- To calculate the voltage across a capacitor during charge, use curve $a$ in Fig. 23-9 or use Formula (23-5). To calculate the voltage across a resistor during charge, use curve $b$ in Fig. 23-9 or Formula (23-4). To calculate the voltage across a capacitor or resistor during discharge, use curve $b$ in Fig. 23-9 or Formula (23-4).

## REVIEW SELF-TEST

### ANSWERS AT BACK OF BOOK.

Choose $(a)$, $(b)$, $(c)$, or $(d)$.

1. A coil induces 200 mV when the current changes at the rate of 1 A/s. The inductance $L$ is: $(a)$ 1 mH; $(b)$ 2 mH; $(c)$ 200 mH; $(d)$ 100 mH.
2. Alternating current in an inductance produces maximum induced voltage when the current has its $(a)$ maximum value; $(b)$ maximum change in magnetic flux; $(c)$ minimum change in magnetic flux; $(d)$ rms value of 0.707 × peak.
3. An iron-core transformer connected to the 120-V 60-Hz power line has a turns ratio of 1:20. The voltage across the secondary equals $(a)$ 20 V; $(b)$ 60 V; $(c)$ 120 V; $(d)$ 2400 V.
4. Two 250-mH chokes in series have a total inductance of $(a)$ 60 mH; $(b)$ 125 mH; $(c)$ 250 mH; $(d)$ 500 mH.
5. Which of the following will have minimum eddy-current losses? $(a)$ Solid iron core; $(b)$ laminated iron core; $(c)$ powdered-iron core; $(d)$ air core.
6. Which of the following will have maximum inductive reactance? $(a)$ 2-H inductance at 60 Hz; $(b)$ 2-mH inductance at 60 kHz; $(c)$ 5-mH inductance at 60 kHz; $(d)$ 5-mH inductance at 100 kHz.
7. A 100-$\Omega$ $R$ is in series with 100 $\Omega$ of $X_L$. The total impedance $Z$ equals $(a)$ 70.7 $\Omega$; $(b)$ 100 $\Omega$; $(c)$ 141 $\Omega$; $(d)$ 200 $\Omega$.

8. A 100-$\Omega$ R is in parallel with 100 $\Omega$ of $X_L$. The total impedance Z equals (a) 70.7 $\Omega$; (b) 100 $\Omega$; (c) 141 $\Omega$; (d) 200 $\Omega$.

9. If two waves have the frequency of 1000 Hz and one is at the maximum value when the other is at zero, the phase angle between them is (a) 0°; (b) 90°; (c) 180°; (d) 360°.

10. If an ohmmeter check on a 50-$\mu$H choke reads 3 $\Omega$, the coil is probably (a) open; (b) defective; (c) normal; (d) partially open.

11. An inductive circuit with $L = 100$ mH and $R = 10$ k$\Omega$ has a time constant of: (a) 1 $\mu$s; (b) 100 $\mu$s; (c) 10 $\mu$s; (d) 1000 $\mu$s.

12. A capacitive circuit with $R = 1.5$ k$\Omega$ and $C = 0.01$ $\mu$F has a time constant of: (a) 15 $\mu$s; (b) 1.5 ms; (c) 150 $\mu$s; (d) 150 s.

13. With respect to the pulse width of the applied voltage, the time constant of an $RC$ integrator should be: (a) short; (b) the same as the pulse width of $V_T$; (c) long; (d) shorter than the pulse width of $V_T$.

14. With respect to the pulse width of the applied voltage, the time constant of an $RC$ differentiator should be: (a) long; (b) the same as the pulse width of $V_T$; (c) longer than the pulse width of $V_T$; (d) short.

15. The current rating of a transformer is usually specified for: (a) the primary windings only; (b) the secondary windings only; (c) both the primary and secondary windings; (d) the core only.

16. The secondary of a transformer is connected to a 15-$\Omega$ resistor. If the turns ratio $N_P/N_S = 3:1$, the primary impedance $Z_P$ equals: (a) 135 $\Omega$; (b) 45 $\Omega$; (c) 5 $\Omega$; (d) none of the above.

---

## REFERENCES

Bogart, Theodore F., Jr.: *Electric Circuits*, Glencoe/McGraw-Hill, Columbus, Ohio.

Lister, Eugene C.: *Electric Circuits and Machines*, Glencoe/McGraw-Hill, Columbus, Ohio.

# CHAPTER 24

# ALTERNATING CURRENT CIRCUITS

This chapter shows how to analyze sine-wave ac circuits that have $R$, $X_L$, and $X_C$. How do we combine these three types of ohms of opposition, how much current flows, and what is the phase angle? These questions are answered for both series and parallel circuits.

The problems are simplified by the fact that in series circuits $X_L$ is at 90° and $X_C$ at −90°, which are opposite phase angles. Then all of one reactance can be canceled by part of the other reactance, resulting in only a single net reactance.

Similarly, in parallel circuits, $I_L$ and $I_C$ have opposite phase angles. These phasor currents oppose each other and result in a single net reactive line current.

Finally, the idea of how ac power and dc power can differ because of ac reactance is explained. Also, types of ac current meters are described including the wattmeter.

# CHAPTER OBJECTIVES

*Upon completion of this chapter, you should be able to:*

- *Explain* why opposite reactances in series cancel.
- *Determine* the total impedance and phase angle of a series circuit containing resistance, capacitance, and inductance.
- *Determine* the total current, equivalent impedance, and phase angle of a parallel circuit containing resistance, capacitance, and inductance.
- *Define* the terms *real power, apparent power, volt-ampere reactive,* and *power factor.*
- *Calculate* the power factor of a circuit.

# IMPORTANT TERMS IN THIS CHAPTER

| | | |
|---|---|---|
| apparent power | real power | voltampere unit |
| double-subscript notation | VAR unit | wattmeter |
| power factor | | |

# TOPICS COVERED IN THIS CHAPTER

**24-1** AC Circuits with Resistance but No Reactance

**24-2** Circuits with $X_L$ Alone

**24-3** Circuits with $X_C$ Alone

**24-4** Opposite Reactances Cancel

**24-5** Series Reactance and Resistance

**24-6** Parallel Reactance and Resistance

**24-7** Series-Parallel Reactance and Resistance

**24-8** Real Power

**24-9** AC Meters

**24-10** Wattmeters

**24-11** Summary of Types of Ohms in AC Circuits

**24-12** Summary of Types of Phasors in AC Circuits

# 24-1 AC CIRCUITS WITH RESISTANCE BUT NO REACTANCE

Combinations of series and parallel resistances are shown in Fig. 24-1. In Fig. 24-1a and b, all voltages and currents throughout the resistive circuit are in phase. There is no reactance to cause a lead or lag in either current or voltage.

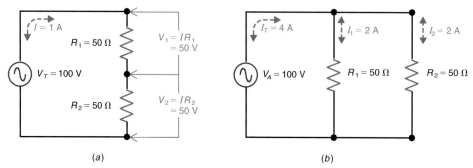

(a)                                        (b)

FIG. 24-1   Alternating-current circuits with resistance but no reactance. (a) Resistances $R_1$ and $R_2$ in series. (b) Resistances $R_1$ and $R_2$ in parallel.

**SERIES RESISTANCES**    For the circuit in Fig. 24-1a, with two 50-$\Omega$ resistances in series across the 100-V source, the calculations are as follows:

$$R_T = R_1 + R_2 = 50 + 50 = 100 \ \Omega$$
$$I = \frac{V_T}{R_T} = \frac{100}{100} = 1 \text{ A}$$
$$V_1 = IR_1 = 1 \times 50 = 50 \text{ V}$$
$$V_2 = IR_2 = 1 \times 50 = 50 \text{ V}$$

Note that the series resistances $R_1$ and $R_2$ serve as a voltage divider, as in dc circuits. Each $R$ has one-half the applied voltage for one-half the total series resistance.

The voltage drops $V_1$ and $V_2$ are both in phase with the series current $I$, which is the common reference. Also $I$ is in phase with the applied voltage $V_T$ because there is no reactance.

**PARALLEL RESISTANCES**    For the circuit in Fig. 24-1b, with two 50-$\Omega$ resistances in parallel across the 100-V source, the calculations are

$$I_1 = \frac{V_A}{R_1} = \frac{100}{50} = 2 \text{ A}$$
$$I_2 = \frac{V_A}{R_2} = \frac{100}{50} = 2 \text{ A}$$
$$I_T = I_1 + I_2 = 2 + 2 = 4 \text{ A}$$

With a total current of 4 A in the main line from the 100-V source, the combined parallel resistance is 25 $\Omega$. This $R_{EQ}$ equals 100 V/4 A for the two 50-$\Omega$ branches.

Each branch current has the same phase as the applied voltage. Voltage $V_A$ is the reference because it is common to both branches.

---

**TEST-POINT QUESTION 24-1**

---

Answers at end of chapter.

**a.** In Fig. 24-1a, what is the phase angle between $V_T$ and $I$?
**b.** In Fig. 24-1b, what is the phase angle between $I_T$ and $V_A$?

## 24-2 CIRCUITS WITH $X_L$ ALONE

The circuits with $X_L$ in Figs. 24-2 and 24-3 correspond to the series and parallel circuits in Fig. 24-1, with ohms of $X_L$ equal to the $R$ values. Since the applied voltage is the same, the values of current correspond because ohms of $X_L$ are just as effective as ohms of $R$ in limiting the current or producing a voltage drop.

Although $X_L$ is a phasor quantity with a 90° phase angle, all the ohms of opposition are the same kind of reactance in this example. Therefore, without any $R$ or $X_C$, the series ohms of $X_L$ can be combined directly. Similarly, the parallel $I_L$ currents can be added.

**DID YOU KNOW?**

Half of all available commercial energy is used by industrialized countries, which constitute only a quarter of the world's population.

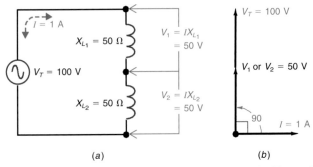

(a)  (b)

**FIG. 24-2** Series circuit with $X_L$ alone. (a) Schematic diagram. (b) Phasor diagram of voltages and line current.

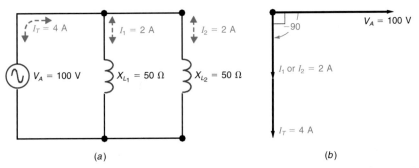

(a)  (b)

**FIG. 24-3** Parallel circuit with $X_L$ alone. (a) Schematic diagram. (b) Phasor diagram of branch and line currents and the applied voltage.

### $X_L$ VALUES IN SERIES    For Fig. 24-2a, the calculations are

$$X_{L_T} = X_{L_1} + X_{L_2} = 50 + 50 = 100 \ \Omega$$

$$I = \frac{V_T}{X_{L_T}} = \frac{100}{100} = 1 \ A$$

$$V_1 = IX_{L_1} = 1 \times 50 = 50 \ V$$

$$V_2 = IX_{L_2} = 1 \times 50 = 50 \ V$$

Note that the two series voltage drops of 50 V each add to equal the total applied voltage of 100 V.

With regard to the phase angle for the inductive reactance, the voltage across any $X_L$ always leads the current through it by 90°. In Fig. 24-2b, $I$ is the reference phasor because it is common to all the series components. Therefore, the voltage phasors for $V_1$ and $V_2$ across either reactance, or $V_T$ across both reactances, are shown leading $I$ by 90°.

### $I_L$ VALUES IN PARALLEL    For Fig. 24-3a the calculations are

$$I_1 = \frac{V_A}{X_{L_1}} = \frac{100}{50} = 2 \ A$$

$$I_2 = \frac{V_A}{X_{L_2}} = \frac{100}{50} = 2 \ A$$

$$I_T = I_1 + I_2 = 2 + 2 = 4 \ A$$

These two branch currents can be added because they both have the same phase. This angle is 90° lagging the voltage reference phasor as shown in Fig. 24-3b.

Since the voltage $V_A$ is common to the branches, this voltage is across $X_{L_1}$ and $X_{L_2}$. Therefore $V_A$ is the reference phasor for parallel circuits.

Note that there is no fundamental change between Fig. 24-2b, which shows each $X_L$ voltage leading its current by 90°, and Fig. 24-3b, showing each $X_L$ current lagging its voltage by −90°. The phase angle between the inductive current and voltage is still the same 90°.

---

### TEST-POINT QUESTION 24-2

Answers at end of chapter.
**a.** In Fig. 24-2, what is the phase angle of $V_T$ with respect to $I$?
**b.** In Fig. 24-3, what is the phase angle of $I_T$ with respect to $V_A$?

## 24-3 CIRCUITS WITH $X_C$ ALONE

Again, reactances are shown in Figs. 24-4 and 24-5 but with $X_C$ values of 50 $\Omega$. Since there is no R or $X_L$, the series ohms of $X_C$ can be combined directly. Also the parallel $I_C$ currents can be added.

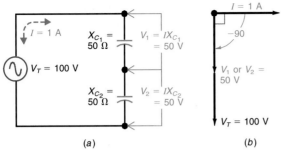

(a)                (b)

**FIG. 24-4** Series circuit with $X_C$ alone. (*a*) Schematic diagram. (*b*) Phasor diagram of voltages and line current.

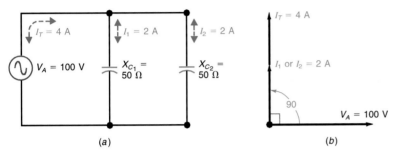

(a)                (b)

**FIG. 24-5** Parallel circuit with $X_C$ alone. (*a*) Schematic diagram. (*b*) Phasor diagram of branch and line currents and the applied voltage.

$X_C$ **VALUES IN SERIES** For Fig. 24-4*a*, the calculations for $V_1$ and $V_2$ are the same as before. These two series voltage drops of 50 V each add to equal the total applied voltage.

With regard to the phase angle for the capacitive reactance, the voltage across any $X_C$ always lags its capacitive charge and discharge current $I$ by 90°. For the series circuit in Fig. 24-4, $I$ is the reference phasor. The capacitive current leads by 90°. Or, we can say that each voltage lags $I$ by −90°.

$I_C$ **VALUES IN PARALLEL** For Fig. 24-5, $V_A$ is the reference phasor. The calculations for $I_1$ and $I_2$ are the same as before. However, now each of the capacitive branch currents or the $I_T$ leads $V_A$ by 90°.

---

**TEST-POINT QUESTION 24-3**

Answers at end of chapter.
**a.** In Fig. 24-4, what is the phase angle of $V_T$ with respect to $I$?
**b.** In Fig. 24-5, what is the phase angle of $I_T$ with respect to $V_A$?

## 24-4 OPPOSITE REACTANCES CANCEL

In a circuit with both $X_L$ and $X_C$, the opposite phase angles enable one to offset the effect of the other. For $X_L$ and $X_C$ in series, the net reactance is the difference between the two series reactances, resulting in less reactance than either one. In parallel circuits, the net reactive current is the difference between the $I_L$ and $I_C$ branch currents resulting in less total line current than either branch current.

### $X_L$ AND $X_C$ IN SERIES

For the example in Fig. 24-6, the series combination of a 60-$\Omega$ $X_L$ and a 40-$\Omega$ $X_C$ in Fig. 24-6a and b is equivalent to the net reactance of the 20-$\Omega$ $X_L$ shown in Fig. 24-6c. Then, with 20 $\Omega$ as the net reactance across the 120-V source, the current is 6 A. This current lags the applied voltage $V_T$ by 90° because the net reactance is inductive.

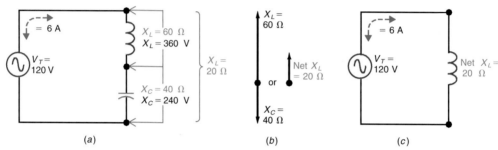

FIG. 24-6   When $X_L$ and $X_C$ are in series, their ohms of reactance subtract. (a) Series circuit with 60-$\Omega$ $X_L$ and 40-$\Omega$ $X_C$. (b) Phasor diagram. (c) Equivalent circuit with net value of 20 $\Omega$ of $X_L$ for the total reactance.

For the two series reactances in Fig. 24-6a, the current is the same through both $X_L$ and $X_C$. Therefore, the voltage drops can be calculated as

$$V_L \text{ or } IX_L = 6 \text{ A} \times 60 \ \Omega = 360 \text{ V}$$
$$V_C \text{ or } IX_C = 6 \text{ A} \times 40 \ \Omega = 240 \text{ V}$$

Note that each individual reactive voltage drop can be more than the applied voltage. The phasor sum of the series voltage drops still is 120 V, however, equal to the applied voltage. This results because the $IX_L$ and $IX_C$ voltages are opposite. The $IX_L$ voltage leads the series current by 90°; the $IX_C$ voltage lags the same current by 90°. Therefore, $IX_L$ and $IX_C$ are 180° out of phase with each other, which means they are of opposite polarity and offset one another. Then the total voltage across the two in series is 360 V minus 240 V, which equals the applied voltage of 120 V.

If the values in Fig. 24-6 were reversed, with an $X_C$ of 60 $\Omega$ and an $X_L$ of 40 $\Omega$, the net reactance would be a 20-$\Omega$ $X_C$. The current would be 6 A again, but with a lagging phase angle of −90° for the capacitive voltage. The $IX_C$ voltage would then be greater at 360 V, than an $IX_L$ value of 240 V, but the difference still equals the applied voltage of 120 V.

### $X_L$ AND $X_C$ IN PARALLEL

In Fig. 24-7, the 60-$\Omega$ $X_L$ and 40-$\Omega$ $X_C$ are in parallel across the 120-V source. Then the 60-$\Omega$ $X_L$ branch current $I_L$ is 2 A, and the 40-$\Omega$ $X_C$ branch current $I_C$ is 3 A. The $X_C$ branch has more current because its reactance is less than $X_L$.

In terms of phase angle, $I_L$ lags the parallel voltage $V_A$ by 90°, while $I_C$ leads the same voltage by 90°. Therefore, the opposite reactive branch currents are 180°

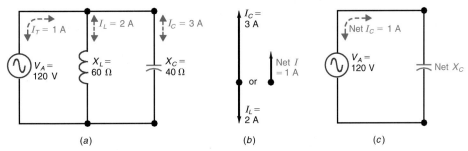

FIG. 24-7   When $X_L$ and $X_C$ are in parallel, their branch currents subtract. (*a*) Parallel circuit with 3-A $I_C$ and 2-A $I_L$. (*b*) Phasor diagram. (*c*) Equivalent circuit with net value of 1 A of $I_C$ for the total line current.

out of phase with each other. The net line current then is the difference between 3 A for $I_C$ and 2 A for $I_L$, which equals the net value of 1 A. This resultant current leads $V_A$ by 90° because it is capacitive current.

If the values in Fig. 24-7 were reversed, with an $X_C$ of 60 Ω and an $X_L$ of 40 Ω, $I_L$ would be larger. The $I_L$ then equals 3 A, with an $I_C$ of 2 A. The net line current is 1 A again but inductive, with a net $I_L$.

### TEST-POINT QUESTION 24-4

Answers at end of chapter.
**a.** In Fig. 24-6, how much is the net $X_L$?
**b.** In Fig. 24-7, how much is the net $I_C$?

## 24-5 SERIES REACTANCE AND RESISTANCE

In the case of series reactance and resistance, the resistive and reactive effects must be combined by phasors. For series circuits, the ohms of opposition are added to find $Z_T$. First add all the series resistances for one total $R$. Also combine all the series reactances, adding all the $X_L$s and all the $X_C$s and finding the net $X$ by subtraction. The result is one net reactance. It may be either capacitive or inductive, depending on which kind of reactance is larger. Then the total $R$ and net $X$ can be added by phasors to find the total ohms of opposition for the entire series circuit.

**MAGNITUDE OF $Z_T$**   After the total $R$ and net reactance $X$ are found, they can be combined by the formula

$$\blacktriangleright \qquad Z_T = \sqrt{R^2 + X^2} \qquad\qquad\qquad \textbf{(24-1)}$$

The circuit's total impedance $Z_T$ is the phasor sum of the series resistance and reactance. Whether the net $X$ is at +90° for $X_L$ or −90° for $X_C$ does not matter in calculating the magnitude of $Z_T$.

An example is illustrated in Fig. 24-8. Here the net series reactance in Fig. 24-8*b* is a 30-Ω $X_C$. This value is equal to a 60-Ω $X_L$ subtracted from a

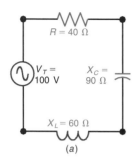

(a)

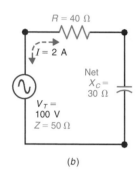

(b)

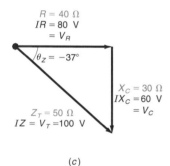

(c)

**FIG. 24-8** Impedance $Z_T$ of series circuit with resistance and reactance. (*a*) Circuit with $R$, $X_L$, and $X_C$ in series. (*b*) Equivalent circuit with one net reactance. (*c*) Phasor diagram. The voltage triangle of phasors is equivalent to an impedance triangle for series circuits.

90-$\Omega$ $X_C$ as shown in Fig. 24-8*a*. The net 30-$\Omega$ $X_C$ in Fig. 24-8*b* is in series with a 40-$\Omega$ $R$. Therefore

$$Z_T = \sqrt{R^2 + X^2} = \sqrt{(40)^2 + (30)^2} = \sqrt{1600 + 900}$$
$$= \sqrt{2500}$$
$$Z_T = 50\ \Omega$$

$I = V/Z_T$    The current is 100 V/50 $\Omega$ in this example, or 2 A. This value is the magnitude, without considering the phase angle.

**SERIES VOLTAGE DROPS**    All the series components have the same 2-A current. Therefore, the individual drops in Fig. 24-8*a* are

$$V_R = IR = 2 \times 40 = 80\ \text{V}$$
$$V_C = IX_C = 2 \times 90 = 180\ \text{V}$$
$$V_L = IX_L = 2 \times 60 = 120\ \text{V}$$

Since $IX_C$ and $IX_L$ are voltages of opposite polarity, the net reactive voltage is 180 V minus 120 V, which equals 60 V. The phasor sum of $IR$ at 80 V and the net reactive voltage $IX$ of 60 V equals the applied voltage $V_T$ of 100 V.

**ANGLE OF $Z_T$**    The impedance angle of the series circuit is the angle whose tangent equals $X/R$. This angle is negative for $X_C$ but positive for $X_L$.

In this example, $X$ is the net reactance of 30 $\Omega$ for $X_C$ and $R$ is 40 $\Omega$. Then $\tan \theta_Z = -0.75$ and $\theta_Z$ is $-37°$, approximately.

The negative angle for $Z$ indicates a net capacitive reactance for the series circuit. If the values of $X_L$ and $X_C$ were reversed, the $\theta_Z$ would be $+37°$, instead of $-37°$, because of the net $X_L$. However, the magnitude of $Z$ would still be the same.

## Example

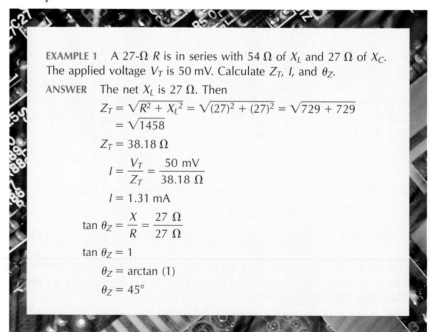

**EXAMPLE 1**    A 27-$\Omega$ $R$ is in series with 54 $\Omega$ of $X_L$ and 27 $\Omega$ of $X_C$. The applied voltage $V_T$ is 50 mV. Calculate $Z_T$, $I$, and $\theta_Z$.

**ANSWER**    The net $X_L$ is 27 $\Omega$. Then
$$Z_T = \sqrt{R^2 + X_L^2} = \sqrt{(27)^2 + (27)^2} = \sqrt{729 + 729}$$
$$= \sqrt{1458}$$
$$Z_T = 38.18\ \Omega$$
$$I = \frac{V_T}{Z_T} = \frac{50\ \text{mV}}{38.18\ \Omega}$$
$$I = 1.31\ \text{mA}$$
$$\tan \theta_Z = \frac{X}{R} = \frac{27\ \Omega}{27\ \Omega}$$
$$\tan \theta_Z = 1$$
$$\theta_Z = \arctan(1)$$
$$\theta_Z = 45°$$

In general, when the series resistance and reactance are equal, $Z_T$ is 1.414 times either value. Here, $Z_T$ is $1.414 \times 27 = 38.18\ \Omega$. Also, $\tan \theta$ must be 1 and the angle is 45° for equal sides in a right triangle. To find $Z_T$ on a calculator, see the procedure described on page 609 for the square root of the sum of two squares.

**MORE SERIES COMPONENTS**  How to combine any number of series resistances and reactances is illustrated by Fig. 24-9. Here the total series $R$ of 40 Ω is the sum of 30 Ω for $R_1$ and 10 Ω for $R_2$. Note that the order of connection does not matter, since the current is the same in all series components.

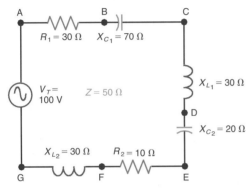

**FIG. 24-9**  Series circuit with more components than Fig. 24-8 but the same $Z_T$, $I$, and $\theta_Z$.

The total series $X_C$ is 90 Ω, equal to the sum of 70 Ω for $X_{C_1}$ and 20 Ω for $X_{C_2}$. Similarly, the total series $X_L$ is 60 Ω. This value is equal to the sum of 30 Ω for $X_{L_1}$ and 30 Ω for $X_{L_2}$.

The net reactance $X$ equals 30 Ω, which is 90 Ω of $X_C$ minus 60 Ω of $X_L$. Since $X_C$ is larger than $X_L$, the net reactance is capacitive. The circuit in Fig. 24-9 is equivalent to Fig. 24-8, therefore, since a 40-Ω $R$ is in series with a net $X_C$ of 30 Ω.

**DOUBLE-SUBSCRIPT NOTATION**  This method for specifying ac and dc voltages is useful to indicate the polarity or phase. For instance, in Fig. 24-9 the voltage across $R_2$ can be taken as either $V_{EF}$ or $V_{FE}$. With opposite subscripts, these two voltages are 180° out of phase. In using double subscripts, note that the first letter in the subscript is the point of measurement with respect to the second letter.

**TEST-POINT QUESTION 24-5**

Answers at end of chapter.
**a.** In Fig. 24-8, how much is the net reactance?
**b.** In Fig. 24-9, how much is the net reactance?
**c.** In Fig. 24-9, give the phase difference between $V_{CD}$ and $V_{DC}$.

With parallel circuits, the branch currents for resistance and reactance are added by phasors. Then the total line current is found by the formula

▶ $$I_T = \sqrt{I_R^2 + I_X^2}$$ (24-2)

**CALCULATING $I_T$**   As an example, Fig. 24-10a shows a circuit with three branches. Since the voltage across all the parallel branches is the applied 100 V, the individual branch currents are

$$I_R = \frac{V_A}{R} = \frac{100 \text{ V}}{25 \text{ }\Omega} = 4 \text{ A}$$

$$I_L = \frac{V_A}{X_L} = \frac{100 \text{ V}}{25 \text{ }\Omega} = 4 \text{ A}$$

$$I_C = \frac{V_A}{X_C} = \frac{100 \text{ V}}{100 \text{ }\Omega} = 1 \text{ A}$$

The net reactive branch current $I_X$ is 3 A, then, equal to the difference between the 4-A $I_L$ and the 1-A $I_C$, as shown in Fig. 24-10b.

The next step is to calculate $I_T$ as the phasor sum of $I_R$ and $I_X$. Then

$$I_T = \sqrt{I_R^2 + I_X^2} = \sqrt{4^2 + 3^2} = \sqrt{16 + 9} = \sqrt{25}$$
$$I_T = 5 \text{ A}$$

The phasor diagram for $I_T$ is shown in Fig. 24-10c.

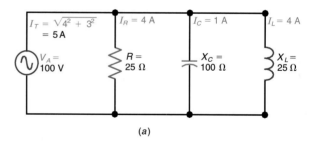

(a)

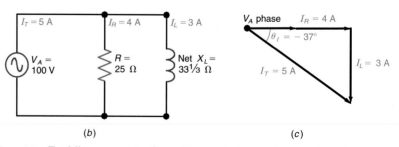

(b)                                              (c)

**FIG. 24-10**   Total line current $I_T$ of parallel circuit with resistance and reactance. (a) Parallel branches with $I_R$, $I_C$, and $I_L$. (b) Equivalent circuit with net $I_X$. (c) Phasor diagram.

$Z_{EQ} = V_A/I_T$   This gives the total impedance of a parallel circuit. In this example, $Z_{EQ}$ is 100 V/5 A, which equals 20 Ω. This value is the equivalent impedance of all three branches in parallel across the source.

**PHASE ANGLE**   The phase angle of the parallel circuit is found from the branch currents. Now $\theta$ is the angle whose tangent equals $I_X/I_R$.

For this example, $I_X$ is the net inductive current of the 3-A $I_L$. Also, $I_R$ is 4 A. These phasors are shown in Fig. 24-10c. Then $\theta$ is a negative angle with the tangent of $-\frac{3}{4}$ or $-0.75$. This phase angle is $-37°$, approximately.

The negative angle for $I_T$ indicates lagging inductive current. The value of $-37°$ is the phase angle of $I_T$ with respect to the voltage reference $V_A$.

When $Z_{EQ}$ is calculated as $V_A/I_T$ for a parallel circuit, the phase angle is the same value as for $I_T$ but with opposite sign. In this example, $Z_{EQ}$ is 20 Ω with a phase angle of $+37°$, for an $I_T$ of 5 A with an angle of $-37°$. We can consider that $Z_{EQ}$ has the phase angle of the voltage source with respect to $I_T$.

## *Example*

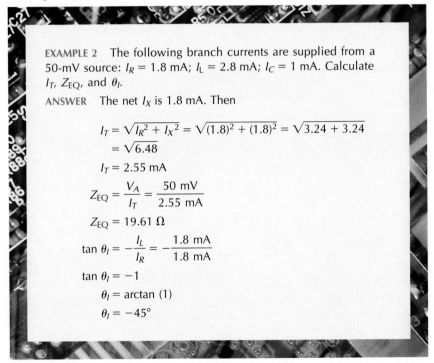

EXAMPLE 2   The following branch currents are supplied from a 50-mV source: $I_R = 1.8$ mA; $I_L = 2.8$ mA; $I_C = 1$ mA. Calculate $I_T$, $Z_{EQ}$, and $\theta_I$.

ANSWER   The net $I_X$ is 1.8 mA. Then

$$I_T = \sqrt{I_R^2 + I_X^2} = \sqrt{(1.8)^2 + (1.8)^2} = \sqrt{3.24 + 3.24}$$
$$= \sqrt{6.48}$$
$$I_T = 2.55 \text{ mA}$$
$$Z_{EQ} = \frac{V_A}{I_T} = \frac{50 \text{ mV}}{2.55 \text{ mA}}$$
$$Z_{EQ} = 19.61 \text{ Ω}$$
$$\tan \theta_I = -\frac{I_L}{I_R} = -\frac{1.8 \text{ mA}}{1.8 \text{ mA}}$$
$$\tan \theta_I = -1$$
$$\theta_I = \arctan (1)$$
$$\theta_I = -45°$$

Note that with equal branch currents, $I_T$ is $1.414 \times 1.8 = 2.55$ mA. Also, the phase angle $\theta_I$ is negative for inductive branch current.

**MORE PARALLEL BRANCHES**   Figure 24-11 shows how any number of parallel resistances and reactances can be combined. The total resistive branch current $I_R$ of 4 A is the sum of 2 A each for the $R_1$ branch and the $R_2$ branch. Note that the order of connection does not matter, since the parallel branch currents

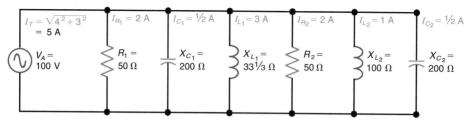

**FIG. 24-11** Parallel ac circuit with more components than Fig. 24-10 but the same values of $I_T$, $Z_{EQ}$, and $\theta$.

add in the main line. Effectively, two 50-$\Omega$ resistances in parallel are equivalent to one 25-$\Omega$ resistance.

Similarly, the total inductive branch current $I_L$ is 4 A, equal to 3 A for $I_{L_1}$ and 1 A for $I_{L_2}$. Also, the total capacitive branch current $I_C$ is 1 A, equal to ½ A each for $I_{C_1}$ and $I_{C_2}$.

The net reactive branch current $I_X$ is 3 A, then, equal to a 4-A $I_L$ minus a 1-A $I_C$. Since $I_L$ is larger, the net current is inductive.

The circuit in Fig. 24-11 is equivalent to the circuit in Fig. 24-10, therefore. Both have a 4-A resistive current $I_R$ and a 3-A net reactive current $I_X$. These values added by phasors make a total of 5 A for $I_T$ in the main line.

---

### TEST-POINT QUESTION 24-6

Answers at end of chapter.
**a.** In Fig. 24-10, what is the net reactive branch current?
**b.** In Fig. 24-11, what is the net reactive branch current?

## 24-7 SERIES-PARALLEL REACTANCE AND RESISTANCE

Figure 24-12 shows how a series-parallel circuit can be reduced to a series circuit with just one reactance and one resistance. The method is straightforward as long as resistance and reactance are not combined in one parallel bank or series string.

Working backward toward the generator from the outside branch in Fig. 24-12a, we have an $X_{L_1}$ and an $X_{L_2}$ of 100 $\Omega$ each in series, which total 200 $\Omega$. This string in Fig. 24-12a is equivalent to $X_{L_5}$ in Fig. 24-12b.

In the other branch, the net reactance of $X_{L_3}$ and $X_C$ is equal to 600 $\Omega$ minus 400 $\Omega$. This is equivalent to the 200 $\Omega$ of $X_{L_4}$ in Fig. 24-12b. The $X_{L_4}$ and $X_{L_5}$ of 200 $\Omega$ each in parallel are combined for an $X_L$ of 100 $\Omega$.

In Fig. 24-12c, the 100-$\Omega$ $X_L$ is in series with the 100-$\Omega$ $R_{1\text{-}2}$. This value is for $R_1$ and $R_2$ in parallel.

The triangle diagram for the equivalent circuit in Fig. 24-12d shows the total impedance $Z$ of 141 $\Omega$ for a 100-$\Omega$ $R$ in series with a 100-$\Omega$ $X_L$.

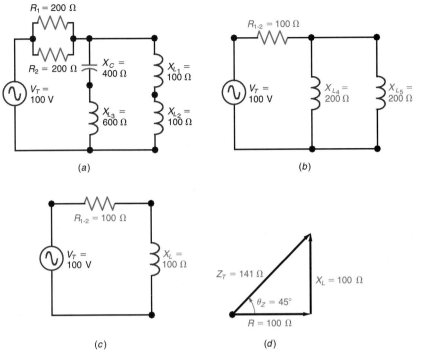

**FIG. 24-12** Reducing an ac series-parallel circuit with $R$, $X_L$, and $X_C$ to a series circuit with one net resistance and one net reactance. (*a*) Actual circuit. (*b*) Simplified arrangement. (*c*) Equivalent series circuit. (*d*) Impedance triangle with phase angle.

With a 141-$\Omega$ impedance across the applied $V_T$ of 100 V, the current in the generator is 0.7 A. The phase angle $\theta$ is 45° for this circuit.*

---

### TEST-POINT QUESTION 24-7

Answers at end of chapter.

Refer to Fig. 24-12.
**a.** How much is $X_{L_1} + X_{L_2}$?
**b.** How much is $X_{L_3} - X_C$?
**c.** How much is $X_{L_4}$ in parallel with $X_{L_5}$?

## 24-8 REAL POWER

In an ac circuit with reactance, the current $I$ supplied by the generator either leads or lags the generator voltage $V$. Then the product $VI$ is not the real power pro-

---

*More complicated ac circuits with series-parallel impedances are analyzed with complex numbers, as explained in Chap. 25.

duced by the generator, since the instantaneous voltage may have a high value while at the same time the current is near zero, or vice versa. The real power, in watts however, can always be calculated as $I^2R$, where $R$ is the total resistive component of the circuit, because current and voltage are in phase in a resistance. To find the corresponding value of power as $VI$, this product must be multiplied by the cosine of the phase angle $\theta$. Then

▶ Real power = $P = I^2R$                          (24-3)

or

▶ Real power = $P = VI \cos \theta$                  (24-4)

where $V$ and $I$ are in rms values, and $P$, the real power, is in watts. Multiplying $VI$ by the cosine of the phase angle provides the resistive component for real power equal to $I^2R$.

For example, the ac circuit in Fig. 24-13 has 2 A through a 100-$\Omega$ $R$ in series with the $X_L$ of 173 $\Omega$. Therefore

$$P = I^2R = 4 \times 100 = 400 \text{ W}$$

Furthermore, in this circuit the phase angle is 60° with a cosine of 0.5. The applied voltage is 400 V. Therefore

$$P = VI \cos \theta = 400 \times 2 \times 0.5 = 400 \text{ W}$$

In both examples, the real power is the same 400 W, because this is the amount of power supplied by the generator and dissipated in the resistance. Either formula can be used for calculating the real power, depending on which is more convenient.

Real power can be considered as resistive power, which is dissipated as heat. A reactance does not dissipate power but stores energy in the electric or magnetic field.

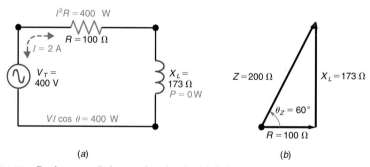

FIG. 24-13   Real power, $P$, in a series circuit. (*a*) Schematic diagram. (*b*) Impedance triangle with phase angle.

**POWER FACTOR**    Because it indicates the resistive component, $\cos \theta$ is the power factor of the circuit, converting the $VI$ product to real power. The power factor formulas are

*For series circuits:*

► Power factor $= PF = \cos\theta = \dfrac{R}{Z}$         **(24-5)**

*For parallel circuits:*

► Power factor $= \cos\theta = \dfrac{I_R}{I_T}$         **(24-6)**

In Fig. 24-13, as an example of a series circuit, we use $R$ and $Z$ for the calculations:

$$PF = \cos\theta = \frac{R}{Z} = \frac{100\ \Omega}{200\ \Omega} = 0.5$$

For the parallel circuit in Fig. 24-10, we use the resistive current $I_R$ and the $I_T$:

$$PF = \cos\theta = \frac{I_R}{I_T} = \frac{4\ \text{A}}{5\ \text{A}} = 0.8$$

The power factor is not an angular measure but a numerical ratio, with a value between 0 and 1, equal to the cosine of the phase angle.

With all resistance and zero reactance, $R$ and $Z$ are the same for a series circuit, or $I_R$ and $I_T$ are the same for a parallel circuit, and the ratio is 1. Therefore, unity power factor means a resistive circuit. At the opposite extreme, all reactance with zero resistance makes the power factor zero, meaning that the circuit is all reactive. Power factor is frequently given in percent so that unity power factor is 100 percent. To convert from decimal $PF$ to percent $PF$, merely multiply by 100 percent.

**APPARENT POWER**    When $V$ and $I$ are out of phase because of reactance, the product of $V \times I$ is called *apparent power.* The unit is *voltamperes* (VA) instead of watts, since the watt is reserved for real power.

For the example in Fig. 24-13, with 400 V and the 2-A $I$, 60° out of phase, the apparent power is $VI$, or $400 \times 2 = 800$ VA. Note that apparent power is the $VI$ product alone, without considering the power factor cos $\theta$.

The power factor can be calculated as the ratio of real power to apparent power, as this ratio equals cos $\theta$. As an example, in Fig. 24-13, the real power is 400 W, and the apparent power is 800 VA. The ratio of 400/800 then is 0.5 for the power factor, the same as cos 60°.

**THE VAR**    This is an abbreviation for voltampere reactive. Specifically, VARs are voltamperes at the angle of 90°.

In general, for any phase angle $\theta$ between $V$ and $I$, multiplying $VI$ by sin $\theta$ gives the vertical component at 90° for the value of the VARs. In Fig. 24-13, the value of $VI$ sin 60° is $800 \times 0.866 = 692.8$ VAR.

Note that the factor sin $\theta$ for the VARs gives the vertical or reactive component of the apparent power $VI$. However, multiplying $VI$ by cos $\theta$ as the power factor gives the horizontal or resistive component for the real power.

**CORRECTING THE POWER FACTOR**    In commercial use, the power factor should be close to unity for efficient distribution of electric power. However, the inductive load of motors may result in a power factor of 0.7, as an example, for the phase angle of 45°. To correct for this lagging inductive component of the current in the main line, a capacitor can be connected across the line to draw leading current from the source. To bring the power factor up to 1.0, that is, unity PF, the value of capacitance is calculated to take the same amount of voltamperes as the VARs of the load.

---

**TEST-POINT QUESTION 24-8**

Answers at end of chapter.
**a.** What is the unit for real power?
**b.** What is the unit for apparent power?
**c.** Is $I^2R$ real or apparent power?

## 24-9 AC METERS

The D'Arsonval moving-coil type of meter movement will not read if it is used in an ac circuit because the ac wave is changing polarity too rapidly. Since the two opposite polarities cancel, an alternating current cannot deflect the meter movement either up-scale or down-scale. An ac meter must produce deflection of the meter pointer up-scale regardless of polarity. This deflection is accomplished by one of the following three methods for nonelectronic ac meters.

1. *Thermal type.* In this method, the heating effect of the current, which is independent of polarity, is used to provide meter deflection. Two examples are the thermocouple type and hot-wire meter.

2. *Electromagnetic type.* In this method, the relative magnetic polarity is maintained constant although the current reverses. Examples are the iron-vane meter, dynamometer, and wattmeter.
3. *Rectifier type.* The rectifier changes the ac input to dc output for the meter, which is usually a D'Arsonval movement. This type is the most common for ac voltmeters generally used for audio and radio frequencies.

All analog ac meters (meters with scales and pointers) have scales calibrated in rms values, unless noted otherwise on the meter.

A thermocouple consists of two dissimilar metals joined together at one end but open at the opposite side. Heat at the short-circuited junction produces a small dc voltage across the open ends, which are connected to a dc meter movement. In the hot-wire meter, current heats a wire to make it expand, and this motion is converted into meter deflection. Both types are used as ac meters for radio frequencies.

The iron-vane meter and dynamometer have very low sensitivity, compared with a D'Arsonval movement. They are used in power circuits, for either direct current or 60-Hz alternating current.

---

## TEST-POINT QUESTION 24-9

Answers at end of chapter.

Answer True or False.
**a.** The iron-vane meter can read alternating current.
**b.** The D'Arsonval meter movement is for direct current only.

# 24-10 WATTMETERS

The wattmeter uses fixed coils to measure current in the circuit, while the movable coil measures voltage (Fig. 24-14). The deflection then is proportional to power. Either dc power or real ac power can be read directly by the wattmeter.

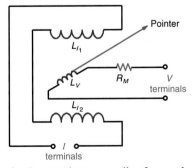

FIG. 24-14 Schematic of voltage and current coils of an analog wattmeter.

In Fig. 24-14, the coils $L_{I_1}$ and $L_{I_2}$ in series are the heavy stationary coils serving as an ammeter to measure current. The two $I$ terminals are connected in one side of the line in series with the load. The movable coil $L_V$ and its multiplier resistance $R_M$ are used as a voltmeter, with the $V$ terminals connected across the line in parallel with the load. Then the current in the fixed coils is proportional to $I$, while the current in the movable coil is proportional to $V$. As a result, the deflection is proportional to $V$ and $I$.

Furthermore, it is the $VI$ product for each instant of time that produces deflection. For instance, if the $V$ value is high when the $I$ value is low, for a phase angle close to 90°, there will be little deflection. The meter deflection is proportional to the watts of real power, therefore, regardless of the power factor in ac circuits. The wattmeter is commonly used to measure power from the 60-Hz power line. For radio frequencies, however, power is generally measured in terms of heat transfer.

---

### TEST-POINT QUESTION 24-10

Answers at end of chapter.
**a.** Does a wattmeter measure real or apparent power?
**b.** In Fig. 24-14, does the movable coil of the wattmeter measure $V$ or $I$?

## 24-11 SUMMARY OF TYPES OF OHMS IN AC CIRCUITS

The differences in $R$, $X_L$, $X_C$, and $Z_T$ are listed in Table 24-1, but the following general features should also be noted. Ohms of opposition limit the amount of current in dc circuits or ac circuits. Resistance $R$ is the same for either case. However, ac circuits can have ohms of reactance because of the variations in alternating current or voltage. Reactance $X_L$ is the reactance of an inductance with sine-wave changes in current. Reactance $X_C$ is the reactance of a capacitor with sine-wave changes in voltage.

### TABLE 24-1 TYPES OF OHMS IN AC CIRCUITS

| | RESISTANCE R, $\Omega$ | INDUCTIVE REACTANCE $X_L$, $\Omega$ | CAPACITIVE REACTANCE $X_C$, $\Omega$ | IMPEDANCE $Z_T$, $\Omega$ |
|---|---|---|---|---|
| Definition | In-phase opposition to alternating or direct current | 90° leading opposition to alternating current | 90° lagging opposition to alternating current | Combination of resistance and reactance $Z_T = \sqrt{R^2 + X^2}$ |
| Effect of frequency | Same for all frequencies | Increases with higher frequencies | Decreases with higher frequencies | $X_L$ component increases, but $X_C$ decreases with higher frequencies |
| Phase angle | 0° | $I_L$ lags $V_L$ by 90° | $I_C$ leads $V_C$ by 90° | $\tan \theta_Z = \pm\dfrac{X}{R}$ in series, $\tan \theta_I = \pm\dfrac{I_X}{I_R}$ in parallel |

Both $X_L$ and $X_C$ are measured in ohms, like $R$, but reactance has a 90° phase angle, while the phase angle for resistance is 0°. A circuit with steady direct current cannot have any reactance.

Ohms of $X_L$ or $X_C$ are opposite, as $X_L$ has a phase angle of $+90°$, while $X_C$ has the angle of $-90°$. Any individual $X_L$ or $X_C$ always has a phase angle that is exactly 90°.

Ohms of impedance $Z$ result from the phasor combination of resistance and reactance. In fact, $Z$ can be considered the general form of any ohms of opposition in ac circuits.

Impedance can have any phase angle, depending on the relative amounts of $R$ and $X$. When $Z$ consists mostly of $R$ with little reactance, the phase angle of $Z$ is close to 0°. With $R$ and $X$ equal, the phase angle of $Z$ is 45°. Whether the angle is positive or negative depends on whether the net reactance is inductive or capacitive. When $Z$ consists mainly of $X$ with little $R$, the phase angle of $Z$ is close to 90°.

The phase angle is $\theta_Z$ for $Z$ or $V_T$ with respect to the common $I$ in a series circuit. With parallel branch currents, $\theta_I$ is for $I_T$ in the main line with respect to the common voltage.

---

### TEST-POINT QUESTION 24-11

Answers at end of chapter.
- **a.** Which of the following does not change with frequency: $Z$, $X_L$, $X_C$, or $R$?
- **b.** Which has lagging current: $R$, $X_L$, or $X_C$?
- **c.** Which has leading current: $R$, $X_L$, or $X_C$?

---

## 24-12 SUMMARY OF TYPES OF PHASORS IN AC CIRCUITS

The phasors for ohms, volts, and amperes are shown in Fig. 24-15. Note the similarities and differences.

**SERIES COMPONENTS**    In series circuits, ohms and voltage drops have similar phasors. The reason is the common $I$ for all the series components. Therefore:

$V_R$ or $IR$ has the same phase as $R$.
$V_L$ or $IX_L$ has the same phase as $X_L$.
$V_C$ or $IX_C$ has the same phase as $X_C$.

**RESISTANCE**    The $R$, $V_R$, and $I_R$ always have the same phase angle because there is no phase shift in a resistance. This applies to $R$ in either a series or a parallel circuit.

**REACTANCE**    Reactances $X_L$ and $X_C$ are 90° phasors in opposite directions. The $X_L$ or $V_L$ has the angle of $+90°$ with an upward phasor, while the $X_C$ or $V_C$ has the angle of $-90°$ with a downward phasor.

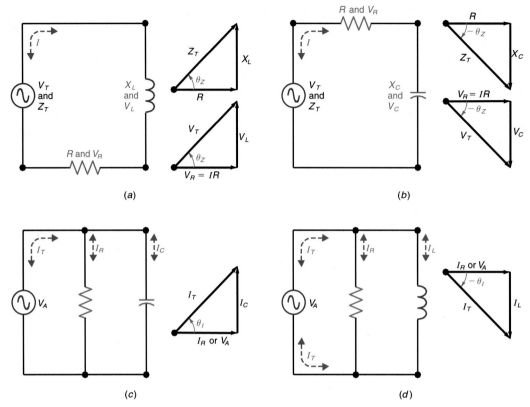

FIG. 24-15   Summary of phasor relations in ac circuits. (a) Series $R$ and $X_L$. (b) Series $R$ and $X_C$. (c) Parallel branches with $I_R$ and $I_C$. (d) Parallel branches with $I_R$ and $I_L$.

**REACTIVE BRANCH CURRENTS**   The phasor of a parallel branch current is opposite from its reactance. Therefore, $I_C$ is upward at $+90°$, opposite from $X_C$ downward at $-90°$. Also, $I_L$ is downward at $-90°$, opposite from $X_L$ upward at $+90°$.

In short, $I_C$ and $I_L$ are opposite from each other, and both are opposite from their corresponding reactances.

**ANGLE $\theta_Z$**   The phasor resultant for ohms of reactance and resistance is $Z$. The phase angle $\theta$ for $Z$ can be any angle between $0°$ and $90°$. In a series circuit $\theta_Z$ for $Z$ is the same as $\theta$ for $V_T$ with respect to the common current $I$.

**ANGLE $\theta_I$**   The phasor resultant of branch currents is the total line current $I_T$. The phase angle of $I_T$ can be any angle between 0 and $90°$. In a parallel circuit, $\theta_I$ is the angle of $I_T$ with respect to the applied voltage $V_A$.

Such phasor combinations are necessary in sine-wave ac circuits in order to take into account the effect of reactance. The phasors can be analyzed either graphically, as in Fig. 24-15, or by the shorter technique of complex numbers, with a $j$ operator that corresponds to the $90°$ phasor. Complex numbers are explained in the next chapter.

**CIRCUIT PHASE ANGLE θ**   For all types of sine-wave ac circuits, the phase angle is usually considered as the angle between the current $I$ from the source and its applied voltage as the reference. This angle can be labeled $\theta$, without any subscript. No special identification is necessary because $\theta$ is the phase angle of the circuit. Then there are only the two possibilities shown in Fig. 24-16. In Fig. 24-16a, the $\theta$ is a counterclockwise angle for a positive value, which means that $I$ leads $V$. The leading $I$ is in a circuit with series $X_C$ or with $I_C$ in a parallel branch. In Fig. 24-16b, the phase angle is clockwise for $-\theta$, meaning that $I$ lags $V$. The lagging $I$ is produced in a circuit with series $X_L$ or with $I_L$ in a parallel branch.

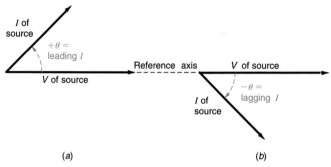

**FIG. 24-16**   Positive and negative values of $\theta$ as the phase angle for an ac circuit. (a) Positive $\theta$ with $I$ leading $V$. (b) Negative $\theta$ with $I$ lagging $V$.

It should be noted that, in general, $\theta$ is the same as $\theta_I$ in parallel branch currents. However, $\theta$ has the opposite sign from $\theta_Z$ with series reactances.

---

### TEST-POINT QUESTION 24-12

Answers at end of chapter.
**a.** Of the following phasors, which two are 180° apart: $V_L$, $V_C$, or $V_R$?
**b.** Of the following phasors, which two are out of phase by 90°: $I_R$, $I_T$, or $I_L$?

# 24 SUMMARY AND REVIEW

- In ac circuits with resistance alone, the circuit is analyzed the same way as for dc circuits, generally with rms ac values. Without any reactance, the phase angle between $V$ and $I$ is zero.
- When capacitive reactances alone are combined, the $X_C$ values are added in series and combined by the reciprocal formula in parallel, just like ohms of resistance. Similarly, ohms of $X_L$ alone can be added in series or combined by the reciprocal formula in parallel, just like ohms of resistance.
- Since $X_C$ and $X_L$ are opposite reactances, they offset each other. In series, the ohms of $X_C$ and $X_L$ can be subtracted. In parallel, the capacitive and inductive branch currents $I_C$ and $I_L$ can be subtracted.
- In ac circuits, $R$, $X_L$, and $X_C$ can be reduced to one equivalent resistance and one net reactance.
- In series, the total $R$ and net $X$ at 90° are combined as $Z_T = \sqrt{R^2 + X^2}$. The phase angle of the series $R$ and $X$ is the angle with tangent $\pm X/R$. To find $I$, first we calculate $Z_T$ and then divide into $V_T$.
- For parallel branches, the total $I_R$ and net reactive $I_X$ at 90° are combined as $I_T = \sqrt{I_R^2 + I_X^2}$. The phase angle of the parallel $R$ and $X$ is the angle with tangent $\pm I_X/I_R$. To find $Z_T$, first we calculate $I_T$ and then divide into $V_A$.
- The quantities $R$, $X_L$, $X_C$, and $Z$ in ac circuits all are ohms of opposition. The differences with respect to frequency and phase angle are summarized in Table 24-1.
- The phase relations for resistance and reactance are summarized in Fig. 24-15.
- In ac circuits with reactance, the real power, $P$, in watts equals $I^2R$, or $VI \cos \theta$, where $\theta$ is the phase angle. The real power is the power dissipated as heat in resistance. $\cos \theta$ is the power factor of the circuit.
- The wattmeter measures real ac power or dc power.

---

## SELF-TEST

**ANSWERS AT BACK OF BOOK.**

Choose (a), (b), (c), or (d).

1. In an ac circuit with resistance but no reactance, (a) two 1000-$\Omega$ resistances in series total 1414 $\Omega$; (b) two 1000-$\Omega$ resistances in series total 2000 $\Omega$; (c) two 1000-$\Omega$ resistances in parallel total 707 $\Omega$; (d) a 1000-$\Omega$ $R$ in series with a 400-$\Omega$ $R$ totals 600 $\Omega$.
2. An ac circuit has a 100-$\Omega$ $X_{C_1}$, a 50-$\Omega$ $X_{C_2}$, a 40-$\Omega$ $X_{L_1}$, and a 30-$\Omega$ $X_{L_2}$, all in series. The net reactance is equal to (a) an 80-$\Omega$ $X_L$; (b) a 200-$\Omega$ $X_L$; (c) an 80-$\Omega$ $X_C$; (d) a 220-$\Omega$ $X_C$.

3. An ac circuit has a 40-$\Omega$ $R$, a 90-$\Omega$ $X_L$, and a 60-$\Omega$ $X_C$, all in series. The impedance $Z$ equals (a) 50 $\Omega$; (b) 70.7 $\Omega$; (c) 110 $\Omega$; (d) 190 $\Omega$.

4. An ac circuit has a 100-$\Omega$ $R$, a 100-$\Omega$ $X_L$, and a 100-$\Omega$ $X_C$, all in series. The impedance $Z$ of the series combination is equal to (a) 33⅓ $\Omega$; (b) 70.7 $\Omega$; (c) 100 $\Omega$; (d) 300 $\Omega$.

5. An ac circuit has a 100-$\Omega$ $R$, a 300-$\Omega$ $X_L$, and a 200-$\Omega$ $X_C$, all in series. The phase angle $\theta$ of the circuit equals (a) 0°; (b) 37°; (c) 45°; (d) 90°.

6. The power factor of an ac circuit equals (a) the cosine of the phase angle; (b) the tangent of the phase angle; (c) zero for a resistive circuit; (d) unity for a reactive circuit.

7. Which phasors in the following combinations are *not* in opposite directions? (a) $X_L$ and $X_C$; (b) $X_L$ and $I_C$; (c) $I_L$ and $I_C$; (d) $X_C$ and $I_C$.

8. In Fig. 24-8a, the voltage drop across $X_L$ equals (a) 60 V; (b) 66⅔ V; (c) 120 V; (d) 200 V.

9. In Fig. 24-10a, the combined impedance of the parallel circuit equals (a) 5 $\Omega$; (b) 12.5 $\Omega$; (c) 20 $\Omega$; (d) 100 $\Omega$.

10. The wattmeter (a) has voltage and current coils to measure real power; (b) has three connections, two of which are used at a time; (c) measures apparent power because the current is the same in the voltage and current coils; (d) can measure dc power but not 60-Hz ac power.

## QUESTIONS

1. Why can series or parallel resistances be combined in ac circuits the same way as in dc circuits?

2. **(a)** Why do $X_L$ and $X_C$ reactances in series offset each other? **(b)** With $X_L$ and $X_C$ reactances in parallel, why can their branch currents be subtracted?

3. Give one difference in electrical characteristics comparing $R$ and $X_C$, $R$ and $Z$, $X_C$ and $C$, $X_L$ and $L$.

4. Name three types of ac meters.

5. Make a diagram showing a resistance $R_1$ in series with the load resistance $R_L$, with a wattmeter connected to measure the power in $R_L$.

6. Make a phasor diagram for the circuit in Fig. 24-8a showing the phase of the voltage drops $IR$, $IX_C$, and $IX_L$ with respect to the reference phase of the common current $I$.

7. Explain briefly why the two opposite phasors at +90° for $X_L$ and −90° for $I_L$ both follow the principle that any self-induced voltage leads the current through the coil by 90°.

8. Why is it that a reactance phasor is always at exactly 90° but an impedance phasor can be less than 90°?

9. Why must the impedance of a series circuit be more than either its $X$ or $R$?

10. Why must $I_T$ in a parallel circuit be more than either $I_R$ or $I_X$?

11. Compare real power and apparent power.

12. Define power factor.

13. Make a phasor diagram showing the opposite direction of positive and negative angles.

14. In Fig. 24-15, which circuit has leading current with a positive phase angle $\theta$ where $I$ from the source leads the $V$ applied by the source?

**ANSWERS TO ODD-NUMBERED PROBLEMS AT BACK OF BOOK.**

1. For Fig. 24-1$a$, (**a**) What is the total real power supplied by the source? (**b**) Why is the phase angle zero? (**c**) What is the power factor of the circuit?

2. In a series ac circuit, 2 A flows through a 20-$\Omega$ $R$, a 40-$\Omega$ $X_L$, and a 60-$\Omega$ $X_C$. (**a**) Make a schematic diagram of the series circuit. (**b**) Calculate the voltage drop across each series component. (**c**) How much is the applied voltage? (**d**) Calculate the power factor of the circuit. (**e**) What is the phase angle $\theta_Z$?

3. A parallel circuit has the following five branches: three resistances of 30 $\Omega$ each; an $X_L$ of 600 $\Omega$; an $X_C$ of 400 $\Omega$. (**a**) Make a schematic diagram of the circuit. (**b**) If 100 V is applied, how much is $I_T$? (**c**) What is $Z_{EQ}$ for the circuit? (**d**) What is the phase angle $\theta_I$?

4. Referring to Fig. 24-8, assume that the frequency is doubled from 500 to 1000 Hz. Find $X_L$, $X_C$, $Z$, $I$, and $\theta_I$ for 1000 Hz. Find $L$ and $C$.

5. A series circuit has a 300-$\Omega$ $R$, a 500-$\Omega$ $X_{C_1}$, a 300-$\Omega$ $X_{C_2}$, an 800-$\Omega$ $X_{L_1}$, and 400-$\Omega$ $X_{L_2}$, all in series with an applied voltage $V$ of 400 V. (**a**) Draw the schematic diagram with all components. (**b**) Draw the equivalent circuit reduced to one resistance and one reactance. (**c**) Calculate $Z_T$, $I$, and $\theta_Z$.

6. Repeat Prob. 5 for a circuit with the same components in parallel across the voltage source.

7. A series circuit has a 600-$\Omega$ $R$, a 10-$\mu$H inductance $L$, and a 4-$\mu$F capacitance $C$, all in series with the 60-Hz 120-V power line as applied voltage. (**a**) Find the reactance of $L$ and of $C$. (**b**) Calculate $Z_T$, $I$, and $\theta_Z$.

8. Repeat Prob. 7 for the same circuit, but the 120-V source has $f = 10$ MHz.

9. (**a**) Referring to the series circuit Fig. 24-6, what is the phase angle between the $IX_L$ voltage of 360 V and the $IX_C$ voltage of 240 V? (**b**) Draw the two sine waves for these voltages, showing their relative amplitudes and phase corresponding to the phasor diagram in Fig. 24-6$b$. Also show the resultant sine wave of voltage across the net $X$.

10. What resistance dissipates 600 W ac power, with 4.3-A rms current?

11. How much resistance must be inserted in series with a 0.95-H inductance to limit the current to 0.25 A from the 120-V 60-Hz power line?

12. How much resistance is needed in series with a 10-$\mu$F capacitance to provide the angle of $-45°$ for $\theta_Z$? The source is the 120-V 60-Hz power line.

13. With the same $R$ as in Prob. 12, what value of $C$ is necessary for $\theta_Z$ angle of $-45°$ at the frequency of 2 MHz?

14. A parallel ac circuit has the following branch currents: $I_{R_1} = 4.2$ mA; $I_{R_2} = 2.4$ mA; $I_{L_1} = 7$ mA; $I_{L_2} = 1$ mA; $I_C = 6$ mA. Calculate $I_T$.

15. What $R$ is needed in series with a 0.01-$\mu$F capacitor for $\theta_Z$ of $-64°$, with $f$ of 800 Hz?

16. What $C$ is needed with a 5-k$\Omega$ $R$ for a phase angle of 45° if $f = 2.5$ MHz?

17. Refer to the series-parallel ac circuit in Fig. 24-17. Calculate $Z_T$, $I$, $\theta_Z$, and $\theta$.

18. Calculate the values of $L$ and $C$ for the reactances in Fig. 24-17 with frequency of 8 kHz.

19. (**a**) Double the value of $f$ in Fig. 24-17 to 16 kHz and calculate the values of $L$ and $C$ needed for the reactances given. (**b**) Why are $Z_T$, $I$, and $\theta$ the same as in Prob. 19?

20. In Fig. 24-18, calculate $Z_T$, $I$, $V_L$, $V_C$, $V_R$, $\theta_Z$, real power, apparent power, and power factor (PF).

21. In Fig. 24-19, calculate $I_L$, $I_C$, $I_R$, $I_T$, $Z_{EQ}$, $\theta_I$, real power, apparent power, and power factor (PF).

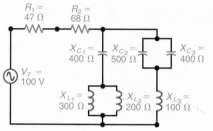

FIG. 24-17    Circuit for Probs. 17, 18, and 19.

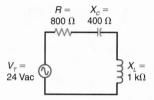

FIG. 24-18    Circuit for Prob. 20.

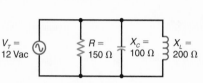

FIG. 24-19    Circuit for Prob. 21.

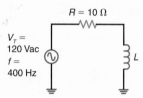

FIG. 24-20    Circuit for Critical Thinking Prob. 1.

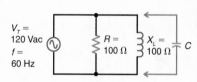

FIG. 24-21    Circuit for Critical Thinking Prob. 2.

## CRITICAL THINKING

1.  In Fig. 24-20, what value of $L$ will produce a circuit power factor of 0.8?
2.  In Fig. 24-21, what value of $C$ in parallel with $R$ and $L$ will produce a power factor of 0.9?

## ANSWERS TO TEST-POINT QUESTIONS

24-1  a. 0°
      b. 0°

24-2  a. 90°
      b. −90°

24-3  a. −90°
      b. 90°

24-4  a. 20 Ω
      b. 1 A

24-5  a. $X_C = 30$ Ω
      b. $X_C = 30$ Ω
      c. 180°

24-6  a. $I_L = 3$ A
      b. $I_L = 3$ A

24-7  a. 200 Ω
      b. 200 Ω
      c. 100 Ω

24-8  a. watt
      b. voltampere
      c. real

24-9  a. T
      b. T

24-10 a. real power
      b. V

24-11 a. $R$
      b. $X_L$
      c. $X_C$

24-12 a. $V_L$ and $V_C$
      b. $I_R$ and $I_L$

# CHAPTER 25

# COMPLEX NUMBERS FOR AC CIRCUITS

Complex numbers refer to a numerical system that includes the phase angle of a quantity, with its magnitude. Therefore, complex numbers are useful in ac circuits when the reactance of $X_L$ or $X_C$ makes it necessary to consider the phase angle. For instance, the complex notation really explains why $\theta_Z$ is negative with $X_C$ and $\theta_I$ is negative with $I_L$.

Any type of ac circuit can be analyzed with complex numbers. They are especially convenient for solving series-parallel circuits that have both resistance and reactance in one or more branches. Although graphical analysis with phasor arrows can be used, the method of complex numbers is probably the best way to analyze ac circuits with series-parallel impedances.

# CHAPTER OBJECTIVES

*Upon completion of this chapter, you should be able to:*

- *Explain* the *j* operator.
- *Describe* the makeup of a complex number.
- *Understand* how to add, subtract, multiply, and divide complex numbers.
- *Explain* the difference between the rectangular and polar forms of a complex number.
- *Convert* a complex number from polar to rectangular form and vice versa.
- *Explain* how to use complex numbers to solve series and parallel ac circuits containing resistance, capacitance, and inductance.

# IMPORTANT TERMS IN THIS CHAPTER

| | | |
|---|---|---|
| admittance | *j* operator | rectangular form |
| complex numbers | polar form | susceptance |
| imaginary numbers | real numbers | |

# TOPICS COVERED IN THIS CHAPTER

25-1   Positive and Negative Numbers
25-2   The *j* Operator
25-3   Definition of a Complex Number
25-4   How Complex Numbers Are Applied to AC Circuits
25-5   Impedance in Complex Form
25-6   Operations with Complex Numbers
25-7   Magnitude and Angle of a Complex Number
25-8   Polar Form of Complex Numbers
25-9   Converting Polar to Rectangular Form
25-10  Complex Numbers in Series AC Circuits
25-11  Complex Numbers in Parallel AC Circuits
25-12  Combining Two Complex Branch Impedances
25-13  Combining Complex Branch Currents
25-14  Parallel Circuit with Three Complex Branches

# 25-1 POSITIVE AND NEGATIVE NUMBERS

Our common use of numbers as either positive or negative represents only two special cases. In their more general form, numbers have both quantity and phase angle. In Fig. 25-1, positive and negative numbers are shown as corresponding to the phase angles of 0° and 180°, respectively.

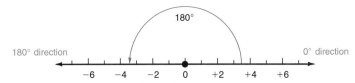

FIG. 25-1 Positive and negative numbers.

For example, the numbers 2, 4, and 6 represent units along the horizontal or *x* axis, extending toward the right along the line of zero phase angle. Therefore, positive numbers really represent units having the phase angle of 0°. Or this phase angle corresponds to the factor of +1. To indicate 6 units with zero phase angle, then, 6 is multiplied by +1 as a factor for the positive number 6. The + sign is often omitted, as it is assumed unless indicated otherwise.

In the opposite direction, negative numbers correspond to 180°. Or, this phase angle corresponds to the factor of −1. Actually, −6 represents the same quantity as 6 but rotated through the phase angle of 180°. The angle of rotation is the *operator* for the number. The operator for −1 is 180°; the operator for +1 is 0°.

---

**TEST-POINT QUESTION 25-1**

Answers at end of chapter.
**a.** What is the angle for the number +5?
**b.** What is the angle for the number −5?

# 25-2 THE *j* OPERATOR

The operator for a number can be any angle between 0° and 360°. Since the angle of 90° is important in ac circuits, the factor *j* is used to indicate 90°. See Fig. 25-2. Here, the number 5 means 5 units at 0°, the number −5 is at 180°, while *j*5 indicates the number 5 at the 90° angle.

The *j* is usually written before the number. The reason is that the *j* sign is a 90° operator, just as the + sign is a 0° operator and the − sign is a 180° operator. Any quantity at right angles to the zero axis, or 90° counterclockwise, is on the +*j* axis.

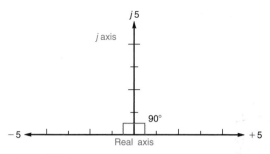

FIG. 25-2   The *j* axis at 90° from the horizontal real axis.

In mathematics, numbers on the horizontal axis are real numbers, including positive and negative values. Numbers on the *j* axis are called *imaginary numbers,* only because they are not on the real axis. In mathematics the abbreviation *i* is used to indicate imaginary numbers. In electricity, however, *j* is used to avoid confusion with *i* as the symbol for current. Furthermore, there is nothing imaginary about electrical quantities on the *j* axis. An electric shock from *j*500 V is just as dangerous as 500 V positive or negative.

More features of the *j* operator are shown in Fig. 25-3. The angle of 180° corresponds to the *j* operation of 90° repeated twice. This angular rotation is indicated by the factor $j^2$. Note that the *j* operation multiplies itself, instead of adding.

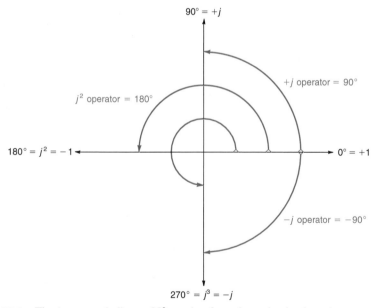

FIG. 25-3   The *j* operator indicates 90° rotation from the real axis; the −*j* operator is −90°; $j^2$ operation is 180° rotation back to the real axis in a negative direction.

Since $j^2$ means 180°, which corresponds to the factor of −1, we can say that $j^2$ is the same as −1. In short, the operator $j^2$ for a number means multiply by −1. For instance, $j^2 8$ is −8.

Furthermore, the angle of 270° is the same as −90°, which corresponds to the operator −$j$. These characteristics of the $j$ operator are summarized as follows:

▶
$$0° = 1$$
$$90° = j$$
$$180° = j^2 = -1$$
$$270° = j^3 = j^2 \times j = -1 \times j = -j$$
$$360° = \text{same as } 0°$$

As examples, the number 4 or −4 represents 4 units on the real horizontal axis; $j4$ means 4 units with a leading phase angle of 90°; −$j4$ means 4 units with a lagging phase angle of −90°.

---

### TEST-POINT QUESTION 25-2

Answers at end of chapter.
**a.** What is the angle for the operator $j$?
**b.** What is the angle for the operator −$j$?

## 25-3 DEFINITION OF A COMPLEX NUMBER

The combination of a real and an imaginary term is called a *complex number*. Usually, the real number is written first. As an example, $3 + j4$ is a complex number including 3 units on the real axis added to 4 units 90° out of phase on the $j$ axis. Complex numbers must be added as phasors.

Phasors for complex numbers are shown in Fig. 25-4 as typical examples. The +$j$ phasor is up for 90°; the −$j$ phasor is down for −90°. The phasors are shown with the end of one joined to the start of the next, to indicate addition. Graphically, the sum is the hypotenuse of the right triangle formed by the two phasors. Since a number like $3 + j4$ specifies the phasors in rectangular coordinates, this system is the *rectangular form* of complex numbers.

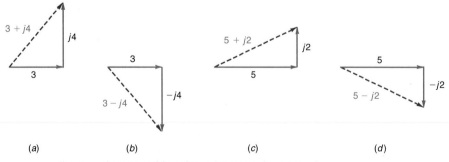

|     |     |     |     |
| --- | --- | --- | --- |
| (a) | (b) | (c) | (d) |

**FIG. 25-4** Phasors corresponding to real terms and imaginary ($j$) terms, in rectangular coordinates.

Be careful to distinguish a number like $j2$, where 2 is a coefficient, from $j^2$, where 2 is the exponent. The number $j2$ means 2 units up on the $j$ axis of 90°. However, $j^2$ is the operator of $-1$, which is on the real axis in the negative direction.

Another comparison to note is between $j3$ and $j^3$. The number $j3$ is 3 units up on the $j$ axis, while $j^3$ is the same as the $-j$ operator, which is down on the $-90°$ axis.

Also note that either the real term or $j$ term can be the larger of the two. When the $j$ term is larger, the angle is more than 45°; when the $j$ term is smaller, the angle is less than 45°. If the $j$ term and the real term are equal, the angle is 45°.

---

### TEST-POINT QUESTION 25-3

Answers at end of chapter.

Answer True or False.
**a.** For $7 + j6$, the 6 is at 90° leading the 7.
**b.** For $7 - j6$, the 6 is at 90° lagging the 7.

## 25-4 HOW COMPLEX NUMBERS ARE APPLIED TO AC CIRCUITS

Applications of complex numbers are just a question of using a real term for 0°, $+j$ for 90°, and $-j$ for $-90°$, to denote the phase angles. Figure 25-5 illustrates the following rules:

An *angle of 0°* or a real number without any $j$ operator is used for resistance $R$. For instance, 3 Ω of $R$ is stated just as 3 Ω.

An *angle of 90° or $+j$* is used for inductive reactance $X_L$. For instance, a 4-Ω $X_L$ is $j4$ Ω. This rule always applies to $X_L$, whether it is in series or parallel with $R$. The reason is the fact that $IX_L$ represents voltage across an inductance, which always leads the current in the inductance by 90°. The $+j$ is also used for $V_L$.

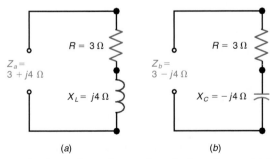

(a)                     (b)

**FIG. 25-5** Rectangular form of complex numbers for impedances. (*a*) Reactance $X_L$ is $+j$. (*b*) Reactance $X_C$ is $-j$.

An *angle of* −90° *or* −*j* is used for $X_C$. For instance, a 4-Ω $X_C$ is −*j*4 Ω. This rule always applies to $X_C$, whether it is in series or parallel with $R$. The reason is that $IX_C$ is the voltage across a capacitor, which always lags the capacitor's charge and discharge current by −90°. The −*j* is also used for $V_C$.

With reactive branch currents, the sign for *j* is reversed, compared with reactive ohms, because of the opposite phase angle. In Fig. 25-6*a* and *b* on the next page, −*j* is used for inductive branch current $I_L$ and +*j* for capacitive branch current $I_C$.

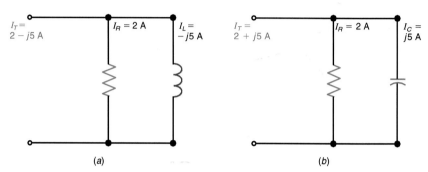

**FIG. 25-6** Rectangular form of complex numbers for branch currents. (*a*) Current $I_L$ is −*j*. (*b*) Current $I_C$ is +*j*.

---

**TEST-POINT QUESTION 25-4**

Answers at end of chapter.
**a.** Write 3 kΩ of $X_L$ using the *j* operator.
**b.** Write 5 mA of $I_L$ using the *j* operator.

## 25-5 IMPEDANCE IN COMPLEX FORM

The rectangular form of complex numbers is a convenient way to state the impedance of series resistance and reactance. In Fig. 25-5*a*, the impedance is 3 + *j*4, as $Z_a$ is the phasor sum of a 3-Ω $R$ in series with *j*4 Ω for $X_L$. Similarly, $Z_b$ is 3 − *j*4 for a 3-Ω $R$ in series with −*j*4 Ω for $X_C$. The minus sign in $Z_b$ results from adding the negative term for −*j*. That is, 3 + (−*j*4) = 3 − *j*4.

For a 4-kΩ $R$ and a 2-kΩ $X_L$ in series: $Z_T = 4000 + j2000$ Ω
For a 3-kΩ $R$ and a 9-kΩ $X_C$ in series: $Z_T = 3000 − j9000$ Ω
For $R = 0$ and a 7-Ω $X_L$ in series: $Z_T = 0 + j7$ Ω
For a 12-Ω $R$ and $X = 0$ in series: $Z_T = 12 + j0$

Note the general form of stating $Z = R \pm jX$. If one term is zero, substitute 0 for this term, in order to keep $Z$ in its general form. This procedure is not required, but there is usually less confusion when the same form is used for all types of $Z$.

The advantage of this method is that multiple impedances written as complex numbers can then be calculated as follows:

*For series impedances:*

▶ $Z_T = Z_1 + Z_2 + Z_3 + \cdots + \text{etc.}$

*For parallel impedances:*

▶ $\dfrac{1}{Z_T} = \dfrac{1}{Z_1} + \dfrac{1}{Z_2} + \dfrac{1}{Z_3} + \cdots + \text{etc.}$

*For two parallel impedances:*

▶ $Z_T = \dfrac{Z_1 \times Z_2}{Z_1 + Z_2}$

Examples are shown in Fig. 25-7. The circuit in Fig. 25-7a is just a series combination of resistances and reactances. Combining the real terms and $j$ terms separately, $Z_T = 12 + j4$. The calculations are $3 + 9 = 12\ \Omega$ for $R$ and $j6$ added to $-j2$ equals $j4$ for the net $X$.

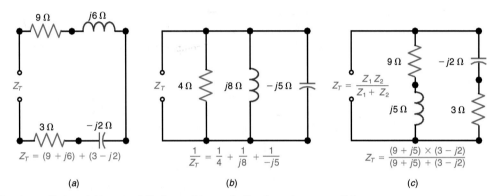

(a)  (b)  (c)

FIG. 25-7   Reactance $X_L$ is a $+j$ term and $X_C$ is a $-j$ term whether in series or parallel. (a) Series circuit. (b) Parallel branches. (c) Complex branch impedances $Z_1$ and $Z_2$ in parallel.

The parallel circuit in Fig. 25-7b shows that $X_L$ is $+j$ and $X_C$ is $-j$ even though they are in parallel branches, as they are reactances, not currents.

So far, these types of circuits can be analyzed with or without complex numbers. For the series-parallel circuit in Fig. 25-7c, however, the notation of complex numbers is necessary to state the complex impedance $Z_T$, consisting of branches with reactance and resistance in one or more of the branches. Impedance $Z_T$ is just stated here in its form as a complex impedance. In order to calculate $Z_T$, some of the rules described in the next section must be used for combining complex numbers.

___

### TEST-POINT QUESTION 25-5

Answers at end of chapter.

Write the following impedances in complex form.
**a.** $X_L$ of 7 $\Omega$ in series with $R$ of 4 $\Omega$.
**b.** $X_C$ of 7 $\Omega$ in series with zero $R$.

Real numbers and $j$ terms cannot be combined directly because they are 90° out of phase. The following rules apply:

**FOR ADDITION OR SUBTRACTION**   Add or subtract the real and $j$ terms separately:

$$(9 + j5) + (3 + j2) = 9 + 3 + j5 + j2$$
$$= 12 + j7$$
$$(9 + j5) + (3 - j2) = 9 + 3 + j5 - j2$$
$$= 12 + j3$$
$$(9 + j5) + (3 - j8) = 9 + 3 + j5 - j8$$
$$= 12 - j3$$

The answer should be in the form of $R \pm jX$, where $R$ is the algebraic sum of all the real or resistive terms and $X$ is the algebraic sum of all the imaginary or reactive terms.

**TO MULTIPLY OR DIVIDE A $j$ TERM BY A REAL NUMBER**   Just multiply or divide the numbers. The answer is still a $j$ term. Note the algebraic signs in the following examples. If both factors have the same sign, either $+$ or $-$, the answer is $+$; if one factor is negative, the answer is negative.

$$4 \times j3 = j12 \qquad\qquad j12 \div 4 = j3$$
$$j5 \times 6 = j30 \qquad\qquad j30 \div 6 = j5$$
$$j5 \times (-6) = -j30 \qquad\quad -j30 \div (-6) = j5$$
$$-j5 \times 6 = -j30 \qquad\quad -j30 \div 6 = -j5$$
$$-j5 \times (-6) = j30 \qquad\quad j30 \div (-6) = -j5$$

**TO MULTIPLY OR DIVIDE A REAL NUMBER BY A REAL NUMBER** Just multiply or divide the real numbers, as in arithmetic. There is no $j$ operation. The answer is still a real number.

**TO MULTIPLY A $j$ TERM BY A $j$ TERM**   Multiply the numbers and the $j$ coefficients to produce a $j^2$ term. The answer is a real term because $j^2$ is $-1$, which is on the real axis. Multiplying two $j$ terms shifts the number 90° from the $j$ axis to the real axis of 180°. As examples:

$$j4 \times j3 = j^2 12 = (-1)(12)$$
$$= -12$$
$$j4 \times (-j3) = -j^2 12 = -(-1)(12)$$
$$= 12$$

**TO DIVIDE A $j$ TERM BY A $j$ TERM**    Divide the $j$ coefficients to produce a real number; the $j$ factors cancel. For instance:

$$j12 \div j4 = 3 \qquad -j12 \div j4 = -3$$
$$j30 \div j5 = 6 \qquad j30 \div (-j6) = -5$$
$$j15 \div j3 = 5 \qquad -j15 \div (-j3) = 5$$

**TO MULTIPLY COMPLEX NUMBERS**    Follow the rules of algebra for multiplying two factors, each having two terms:

$$(9 + j5) \times (3 - j2) = 27 - j18 + j15 - j^2 10$$
$$= 27 - j3 - (-1)10$$
$$= 27 - j3 + 10$$
$$= 37 - j3$$

Note that $-j^2 10$ equals $+10$ because the operator $j^2$ is $-1$ and $-(-1)10$ becomes $+10$.

**TO DIVIDE COMPLEX NUMBERS**    This process becomes more involved because division of a real number by an imaginary number is not possible. Therefore, the denominator must first be converted to a real number without any $j$ term.

Converting the denominator to a real number without any $j$ term is called *rationalization* of the fraction. To do this, multiply both numerator and denominator by the *conjugate* of the denominator. Conjugate complex numbers have equal terms but opposite signs for the $j$ term. For instance, $(1 + j2)$ has the conjugate $(1 - j2)$.

Rationalization is permissible because the value of a fraction is not changed when both numerator and denominator are multiplied by the same factor. This procedure is the same as multiplying by 1. In the following example of division with rationalization the denominator $(1 + j2)$ has the conjugate $(1 - j2)$:

$$\frac{4 - j1}{1 + j2} = \frac{4 - j1}{1 + j2} \times \frac{(1 - j2)}{(1 - j2)} = \frac{4 - j8 - j1 + j^2 2}{1 - j^2 + j^2 - j^2 4}$$
$$= \frac{4 - j9 - 2}{1 + 4}$$
$$= \frac{2 - j9}{5}$$
$$= 0.4 - j1.8$$

As a result of the rationalization, $4 - j1$ has been divided by $1 + j2$ to find the quotient that is equal to $0.4 - j1.8$.

Note that the product of a complex number and its conjugate always equals the sum of the squares of the numbers in each term. As another example, the product of $(2 + j3)$ and its conjugate $(2 - j3)$ must be $4 + 9$, which equals 13. Simple numerical examples of division and multiplication are given here because when the required calculations become too long, it is easier to divide and multiply complex numbers in polar form, as explained in Sec. 25-8.

Answers at end of chapter.
**a.** $(2 + j3) + (3 + j4) = ?$
**b.** $(2 + j3) \times 2 = ?$

## 25-7 MAGNITUDE AND ANGLE OF A COMPLEX NUMBER

In electrical terms a complex impedance $(4 + j3)$ means 4 Ω of resistance and 3 Ω of inductive reactance with a leading phase angle of 90°. See Fig. 25-8*a*. The magnitude of Z is the resultant, equal to $\sqrt{16 + 9} = \sqrt{25} = 5$ Ω. Finding the square root of the sum of the squares is vector or phasor addition of two terms in quadrature, 90° out of phase.

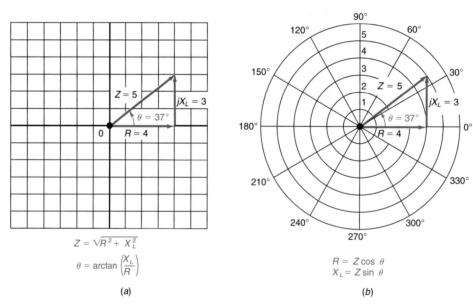

$$Z = \sqrt{R^2 + X_L^2}$$
$$\theta = \arctan\left(\frac{X_L}{R}\right)$$

(a)

$$R = Z \cos \theta$$
$$X_L = Z \sin \theta$$

(b)

**FIG. 25-8** Magnitude and angle of a complex number. (*a*) Rectangular form. (*b*) Polar form.

The phase angle of the resultant is the angle whose tangent is ¾ or 0.75. This angle equals 37°. Therefore, $4 + j3 = 5 \angle 37°$.

When calculating the tangent ratio, note that the *j* term is the numerator and the real term is the denominator because the tangent of an angle is the ratio of the opposite side to the adjacent side. With a negative *j* term, the tangent is negative, which means a negative angle.

Note the following definitions: $(4 + j3)$ is the complex number in rectangular coordinates. The real term is 4. The imaginary term is $j3$. The resultant 5 is the magnitude, absolute value, or modulus of the complex number. Its phase angle or argument is 37°. The resultant value by itself can be written as $|5|$, with vertical lines to indicate it is the magnitude without the phase angle. The magnitude is the value a meter would read. For instance, with a current of $5\angle 37°$ A in a circuit, an ammeter reads 5 A. As additional examples:

$$2 + j4 = \sqrt{4 + 16} \angle \text{arctan } 2 = 4.47 \angle 63°$$
$$4 + j2 = \sqrt{16 + 4} \angle \text{arctan } 0.5 = 4.47 \angle 26.5°$$
$$8 + j6 = \sqrt{64 + 36} \angle \text{arctan } 0.75 = 10 \angle 37°$$
$$8 - j6 = \sqrt{64 + 36} \angle \text{arctan } -0.75 = 10 \angle -37°$$
$$4 + j4 = \sqrt{16 + 16} \angle \text{arctan } 1 = 5.66 \angle 45°$$
$$4 - j4 = \sqrt{16 + 16} \angle \text{arctan } -1 = 5.66 \angle -45°$$

Note that arctan 0.75 in the third example means the angle with a tangent equal to 0.75. This value is ⅚ or ¾ for the ratio of the opposite side to the adjacent side. The arctan can also be indicated as $\tan^{-1} 0.75$. In either case, this angle is specified as having 0.75 for its tangent, which makes the angle 36.87°.

Many scientific calculators have keys that can convert from rectangular coordinates to the magnitude-phase angle form (called polar coordinates) directly. See your calculator manual for the particular steps used. If your calculator does not have these keys, the problem can be done in two separate parts: (1) the magnitude as the square root of the sum of two squares, and (2) the angle as the arctan equal to the $j$ term divided by the real term.

Using the calculator for the magnitude in the first example, punch in 2 and then press the $\boxed{x^2}$ key for the square, equal to 4. Press $\boxed{+}$ then $\boxed{(}$ and 4; press $\boxed{x^2}$, $\boxed{)}$, $\boxed{=}$, and $\boxed{\sqrt{}}$ in sequence. The display will show 4.47 which is the magnitude.

To find the angle from its tangent value, after the display is cleared, punch in 4 for the opposite side. Then press the $\boxed{\div}$ key, punch in 2 for the adjacent side, and push the $\boxed{=}$ key for the ratio of 2 as the tangent. With 2 as tan $\theta$ on the display, press the $\boxed{\text{TAN}^{-1}}$ key, which is usually the second function of the $\boxed{\text{TAN}}$ key. Then 63.4 appears on the display as the angle. Be sure the calculator is set for degrees in the answer, not rad or grad units.

---

### TEST-POINT QUESTION 25-7

Answers at end of chapter.

For the complex impedance $10 + j10$ Ω,
**a.** Calculate the magnitude.
**b.** Calculate the phase angle.

## 25-8 POLAR FORM OF COMPLEX NUMBERS

Calculating the magnitude and phase angle of a complex number is actually converting to an angular form in polar coordinates. As shown in Fig. 25-8, the rectangular form $4 + j3$ is equal to $5\angle 37°$ in polar form. In polar coordinates, the distance out from the center is the magnitude of the phasor Z. Its phase angle $\theta$ is counterclockwise from the 0° axis.

To convert any complex number to polar form:

1. Find the magnitude by phasor addition of the $j$ term and real term.
2. Find the angle whose tangent is the $j$ term divided by the real term. As examples:

$$2 + j4 = 4.47 \underline{/63°}$$
$$4 + j2 = 4.47 \underline{/26.5°}$$
$$8 + j6 = 10 \underline{/37°}$$
$$8 - j6 = 10 \underline{/-37°}$$
$$4 + j4 = 5.66 \underline{/45°}$$
$$4 - j4 = 5.66 \underline{/-45°}$$

These examples are the same as those given before for finding the magnitude and phase angle of a complex number.

The magnitude in polar form must be more than either term in rectangular form, but less than their arithmetic sum. For instance, in $8 + j6 = 10 \underline{/37°}$ the magnitude of 10 is more than 8 or 6 but less than their sum of 14.

Applied to ac circuits with resistance for the real term and reactance for the $j$ term, then, the polar form of a complex number states the resultant impedance and its phase angle. Note the following cases for an impedance where either the resistance or reactance is zero.

$$0 + j5 = 5 \underline{/90°}$$
$$0 - j5 = 5 \underline{/-90°}$$
$$5 + j0 = 5 \underline{/0°}$$

The polar form is much more convenient for multiplying or dividing complex numbers. The reason is that multiplication in polar form merely involves multiplying the magnitudes and adding the angles. Division involves dividing the magnitudes and subtracting the angles. The following rules apply.

**FOR MULTIPLICATION**   Multiply the magnitudes but add the angles algebraically:

$$24 \underline{/40°} \times 2 \underline{/30°} = 24 \times 2 \underline{/40° + 30°} = 48 \underline{/+70°}$$
$$24 \underline{/40°} \times (-2 \underline{/30°}) = -48 \underline{/+70°}$$
$$12 \underline{/-20°} \times 3 \underline{/-50°} = 36 \underline{/-70°}$$
$$12 \underline{/-20°} \, 4 \underline{/5°} = 48 \underline{/-15°}$$

When you multiply by a real number, just multiply the magnitudes:

$$4 \times 2 \underline{/30°} = 8 \underline{/30°}$$
$$4 \times 2 \underline{/-30°} = 8 \underline{/-30°}$$
$$-4 \times 2 \underline{/30°} = -8 \underline{/30°}$$
$$-4 \times (-2 \underline{/30°}) = 8 \underline{/30°}$$

This rule follows from the fact that a real number has an angle of 0°. When you add 0° to any angle, the sum equals the same angle.

**DID YOU KNOW?**

Even an activity as close to nature as sailing can make use of electronics. *Microship,* an electronic sailboat made by Steven Roberts, uses 12 Motorola processors to control all the ship's functions such as bilge pumps and security sensors. Onboard are also electronic communication devices such as a cellular phone and notebook computer.

**FOR DIVISION**   Divide the magnitudes and subtract the angles algebraically:

$$24\underline{/40°} \div 2\underline{/30°} = 24 \div 2\underline{/40° - 30°} = 12\underline{/10°}$$
$$12\underline{/20°} \div 3\underline{/50°} = 4\underline{/-30°}$$
$$12\underline{/-20°} \div 4\underline{/50°} = 3\underline{/-70°}$$

To divide by a real number, just divide the magnitudes:

$$12\underline{/30°} \div 2 = 6\underline{/30°}$$
$$12\underline{/-30°} \div 2 = 6\underline{/-30°}$$

This rule is also a special case that follows from the fact that a real number has a phase angle of 0°. When you subtract 0° from any angle, the remainder equals the same angle.

For the opposite case, however, when you divide a real number by a complex number, the angle of the denominator changes its sign in the answer in the numerator. This rule still follows the procedure of subtracting angles for division, since a real number has a phase angle of 0°. As examples,

$$\frac{10}{5\underline{/30°}} = \frac{10\underline{/0°}}{5\underline{/30°}} = 2\underline{/0° - 30°}$$
$$= 2\underline{/-30°}$$
$$\frac{10}{5\underline{/-30°}} = \frac{10\underline{/0°}}{5\underline{/-30°}} = 2\underline{/0° - (-30°)}$$
$$= 2\underline{/+30°}$$

Stated another way, we can say that the reciprocal of an angle is the same angle but with opposite sign. Note that this operation is similar to working with powers of 10. Angles and powers of 10 follow the general rules of exponents.

---

**TEST-POINT QUESTION 25-8**

Answers at end of chapter.
**a.** $6\underline{/20°} \times 2\underline{/30°} = ?$
**b.** $6\underline{/20°} \div 2\underline{/30°} = ?$

# 25-9 CONVERTING POLAR TO RECTANGULAR FORM

Complex numbers in polar form are convenient for multiplication and division, but they cannot be added or subtracted if their angles are different. The reason is the real and imaginary parts that make up the magnitude are different. When complex numbers in polar form are to be added or subtracted, therefore, they must be converted back into rectangular form.

Consider the impedance $Z\underline{/\theta}$ in polar form. Its value is the hypotenuse of a right triangle with sides formed by the real term and $j$ term in rectangular coordinates. See Fig. 25-9. Therefore, the polar form can be converted to rectangular form by finding the horizontal and vertical sides of the right triangle. Specifically:

▶ Real term for $R = Z \cos \theta$

  $j$ term for $X = Z \sin \theta$

In Fig. 25-9a, assume that $Z\underline{/\theta}$ in polar form is $5\underline{/37°}$. The sine of 37° is 0.6 and its cosine is 0.8.

To convert to rectangular form:

$$R = Z \cos \theta = 5 \times 0.8 = 4$$
$$X = Z \sin \theta = 5 \times 0.6 = 3$$

Therefore,

$$5\underline{/37°} = 4 + j3$$

This example is the same as the illustration in Fig. 25-8. The $+$ sign for the $j$ term means it is $X_L$, not $X_C$.

In Fig. 25-9b, the values are the same, but the $j$ term is negative when $\theta$ is negative. The negative angle has a negative $j$ term because the opposite side is in the fourth quadrant, where the sine is negative. However, the real term is still positive because the cosine is positive.

Note that $R$ for $\cos \theta$ is the horizontal component, which is an adjacent side of the angle. The $X$ for $\sin \theta$ is the vertical component, which is opposite the angle. The $+X$ is $X_L$; the $-X$ is $X_C$.

These rules apply for angles in the first or fourth quadrant, from 0 to 90° or from 0 to $-90°$. As examples:

$$14.14\underline{/45°} = 14.14 \cos 45° + 14.14 \sin 45° = 10 + j10$$
$$14.14\underline{/-45°} = 14.14 \cos (-45°) + 14.14 \sin (-45°) = 10 + j(-10) = 10 - j10$$
$$10\underline{/90°} = 0 + j10$$
$$10\underline{/-90°} = 0 - j10$$
$$100\underline{/30°} = 86.6 + j50$$
$$100\underline{/-30°} = 86.6 - j50$$
$$100\underline{/60°} = 50 + j86.6$$
$$100\underline{/-60°} = 50 - j86.6$$

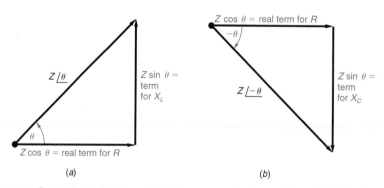

(a)                                        (b)

**FIG. 25-9** Converting polar form of $Z\underline{/\theta}$ to rectangular form of $R \pm jX$. (a) Positive angle $\theta$ in first quadrant has $+j$ term. (b) Negative angle $-\theta$ in fourth quadrant has $-j$ term.

When going from one form to the other, keep in mind whether the angle is smaller or greater than 45° and if the $j$ term is smaller or larger than the real term. For angles between 0 and 45°, the opposite side, which is the $j$ term, must be smaller than the real term. For angles between 45 and 90°, the $j$ term must be larger than the real term.

Conversion to rectangular form can be done fast with a calculator. Again, some scientific calculators contain conversion keys that make going from polar coordinates to rectangular coordinates a simple four-key procedure. Check your calculator manual for the exact procedure. If your calculator does not have this capability, use the following routine. Punch in the value of the angle $\theta$ in degrees. Make sure the correct sign is used and the calculator is set to handle angles in degrees. Find $\cos\theta$ or $\sin\theta$ and multiply by the magnitude for each term. Remember to use $\cos\theta$ for the real term and $\sin\theta$ for the $j$ term. For the example of $100\angle30°$, punch in the number 30 and press the (COS) key for 0.866 as $\cos\theta$. While it is on the display, press the (×) key, punch in 100, and press the (=) key or the answer of 86.6 as the real term. Clear the display for the next operation with $\sin\theta$. Punch in 30, push the (SIN) key for 0.5 as $\sin\theta$, press the (×) key, punch in 100, and push the (=) key for the answer of 50 as the $j$ term.

To summarize how complex numbers are used in ac circuits in rectangular and polar form:

1. For addition or subtraction, complex numbers must be in rectangular form. This procedure applies to the addition of impedances in a series circuit. If the series impedances are in rectangular form, just combine all the real terms and the $j$ terms separately. If the series impedances are in polar form, they must be converted to rectangular form to be added.
2. For multiplication and division, complex numbers are generally used in polar form because the calculations are faster. If the complex number is in rectangular form, convert to polar form. With the complex number available in both forms, then you can quickly add or subtract in rectangular form and multiply or divide in polar form. Sample problems showing how to apply these methods in ac circuits are illustrated in the following sections.

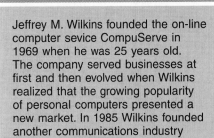

---

**TEST-POINT QUESTION 25-9**

Answers at end of chapter.

Convert to rectangular form.
**a.** $14.14\angle45°$.
**b.** $14.14\angle-45°$.

## 25-10 COMPLEX NUMBERS IN SERIES AC CIRCUITS

Refer to Fig. 25-10. Although a circuit like this with only series resistances and reactances can be solved graphically with phasor arrows, the complex numbers show more details of the phase angles.

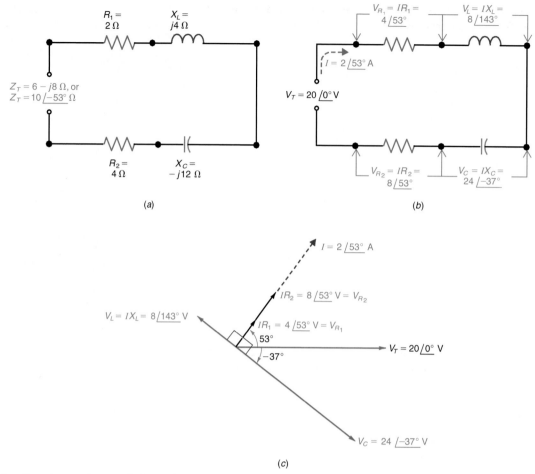

**FIG. 25-10** Complex numbers applied to series ac circuits. See text for analysis. (*a*) Circuit with series impedances. (*b*) Current and voltages in the circuit. (*c*) Phasor diagram of current and voltages.

**$Z_T$ IN RECTANGULAR FORM** The total $Z_T$ in Fig. 25-10*a* is the sum of the impedances:

$$Z_T = 2 + j4 + 4 - j12$$
$$= 6 - j8$$

The total series impedance then is $6 - j8$. Actually, this amounts to adding all of the series resistances for the real term and finding the algebraic sum of all the series reactances for the $j$ term.

**$Z_T$ IN POLAR FORM** We can convert $Z_T$ from rectangular to polar form as follows:

$$Z_T = 6 - j8$$
$$= \sqrt{36 + 64} \; \underline{/\arctan -8/6}$$
$$= \sqrt{100} \; \underline{/\arctan -1.33}$$
$$Z_T = 10 \underline{/-53°} \; \Omega$$

The angle of $-53°$ for $Z_T$ means the applied voltage and the current are $53°$ out of phase. Specifically, this angle is $\theta_Z$.

**CALCULATING $I$**  The reason for the polar form is to divide $Z_T$ into the applied voltage $V_T$ to calculate the current $I$. See Fig. 25-10*b*. Note that the $V_T$ of 20 V is a real number without any $j$ term. Therefore, the applied voltage is $20 \angle 0°$. This angle of $0°$ for $V_T$ makes it the reference phase for the following calculations. We can find the current as

$$I = \frac{V_T}{Z_T} = \frac{20 \angle 0°}{10 \angle -53°} = 2 \angle 0° - (-53°)$$
$$I = 2 \angle 53° \text{ A}$$

Note that $Z_T$ has the negative angle of $-53°$ but the sign changes to $+53°$ for $I$ because of the division into a quantity with the angle of $0°$. In general, the reciprocal of an angle in polar form is the same angle with opposite sign.

**PHASE ANGLE OF THE CIRCUIT**  The fact that $I$ has the angle of $+53°$ means it leads $V_T$. The positive angle for $I$ shows the series circuit is capacitive, with leading current. This angle is more than $45°$ because the net reactance is more than the total resistance, resulting in a tangent function greater than 1.

**FINDING EACH $IR$ DROP**  To calculate the voltage drops around the circuit, each resistance or reactance can be multiplied by $I$:

$$V_{R_1} = IR_1 = 2 \angle 53° \times 2 \angle 0° = 4 \angle 53° \text{ V}$$
$$V_L = IX_L = 2 \angle 53° \times 4 \angle 90° = 8 \angle 143° \text{ V}$$
$$V_C = IX_C = 2 \angle 53° \times 12 \angle -90° = 24 \angle -37° \text{ V}$$
$$V_{R_2} = IR_2 = 2 \angle 53° \times 4 \angle 0° = 8 \angle 53° \text{ V}$$

**PHASE ANGLE OF EACH VOLTAGE**  The phasors for these voltages are in Fig. 25-10*c*. They show the phase angles using the applied voltage $V_T$ as the zero reference phase.

The angle of $53°$ for $V_{R_1}$ and $V_{R_2}$ shows that the voltage across a resistance has the same phase as $I$. These voltages lead $V_T$ by $53°$ because of the leading current.

For $V_C$, its angle of $-37°$ means it lags the generator voltage $V_T$ by this much. However, this voltage across $X_C$ still lags the current by $90°$, which is the difference between $53°$ and $-37°$.

The angle of $143°$ for $V_L$ in the second quadrant is still $90°$ leading the current at $53°$, as $143° - 53° = 90°$. With respect to the generator voltage $V_T$, though, the phase angle of $V_L$ is $143°$.

**TOTAL VOLTAGE $V_T$ EQUALS THE PHASOR SUM OF THE SERIES VOLTAGE DROPS**  If we want to add the voltage drops around the circuit to see if they equal the applied voltage, each $V$ must be converted to rectangular form. Then these values can be added. In rectangular form then the individual voltages are

$$V_{R_1} = 4\angle 53° = \quad 2.408 + \quad j3.196 \text{ V}$$
$$V_L = 8\angle 143° = -6.392 + \quad j4.816 \text{ V}$$
$$V_C = 24\angle -37° = 19.176 - j14.448 \text{ V}$$
$$V_{R_2} = 8\angle 53° = \quad 4.816 + \quad j6.392 \text{ V}$$
$$\text{Total } V = \quad 20.008 - \quad j0.044 \text{ V}$$

or converting to polar form,

$$V_T = 20\angle 0° \text{ V} \qquad \text{approximately}$$

Note that for $8\angle 143°$ in the second quadrant, the cosine is negative for a negative real term but the sine is positive for a positive $j$ term.*

---

### TEST-POINT QUESTION 25-10

Answers at end of chapter.

Refer to Fig. 25-10.
**a.** What is the phase angle of $I$ with reference to $V_T$?
**b.** What is the phase angle of $V_L$ with reference to $V_T$?
**c.** What is the phase angle of $V_L$ with reference to $V_R$?

## 25-11 COMPLEX NUMBERS IN PARALLEL AC CIRCUITS

A useful application is converting a parallel circuit to an equivalent series circuit. See Fig. 25-11, with a 10-$\Omega$ $X_L$ in parallel with a 10-$\Omega$ $R$. In complex notation, $R$ is $10 + j0$ while $X_L$ is $0 + j10$. Their combined parallel impedance $Z_T$ equals the product over the sum. For Fig. 25-11$a$, then:

$$Z_T = \frac{(10 + j0) \times (0 + j10)}{(10 + j0) + (0 + j10)} = \frac{10 \times j10}{10 + j10} = \frac{j100}{10 + j10}$$

$$Z_T = \frac{j10}{1 + j1}$$

Converting to polar form for division,

$$Z_T = \frac{j100}{10 + j10} = \frac{100\angle 90°}{} = 7.07\angle 45°$$

---

*For an explanation of quadrants, see B. Grob, *Mathematics for Basic Electronics*, Glencoe/McGraw-Hill, Columbus, Ohio.

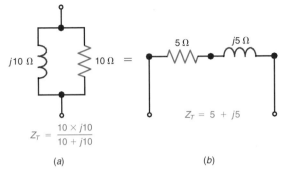

$$Z_T = \frac{10 \times j10}{10 + j10}$$

(a)

$$Z_T = 5 + j5$$

(b)

FIG. 25-11  Complex numbers used for parallel ac circuit to convert a parallel bank to an equivalent series impedance.

Converting the $Z_T$ of $7.07 \underline{/45°}$ into rectangular form to see its resistive and reactive components,

$$\text{Real term} = 7.07 \cos 45°$$
$$= 7.07 \times 0.707 = 5$$
$$j \text{ term} = 7.07 \sin 45°$$
$$= 7.07 \times 0.707 = 5$$

Therefore,

$$Z_T = 7.07 \underline{/45°} \qquad \text{in polar form}$$
$$Z_T = 5 + j5 \qquad \text{in rectangular form}$$

The rectangular form of $Z_T$ means that 5-$\Omega$ $R$ in series with 5-$\Omega$ $X_L$ is the equivalent of 10-$\Omega$ $R$ in parallel with 10-$\Omega$ $X_L$, as shown in Fig. 25-11b.

**ADMITTANCE Y AND SUSCEPTANCE B**  In parallel circuits, it is usually easier to add branch currents than to combine reciprocal impedances. For this reason, branch conductance $G$ is often used instead of branch resistance, where $G = 1/R$. Similarly, reciprocal terms can be defined for complex impedances. The two main types are *admittance Y,* which is the reciprocal of impedance, and *susceptance B,* which is the reciprocal of reactance. These reciprocals can be summarized as follows:

▶  $\qquad$ Conductance $= G = \dfrac{1}{R} \quad$ S

$\qquad$ Susceptance $= B = \dfrac{1}{\pm X} \quad$ S

$\qquad$ Admittance $= Y = \dfrac{1}{Z} \quad$ S

With $R$, $X$, and $Z$ in units of ohms, the reciprocals $G$, $B$, and $Y$ are in siemens (S) units.

The phase angle for $B$ or $Y$ is the same as current. Therefore, the sign is opposite from the angle of $X$ or $Z$ because of the reciprocal relation. An inductive

**ABOUT ELECTRONICS**

Half of the American population doesn't get a good fit with retail clothing. An electronic body scan can fix this by cloning your form for the tailor. In the future, your body "grid" may be modemed to the factory, which will then be able to provide custom-made clothes or shoes.

branch has susceptance $-jB$, while a capacitive branch has susceptance $+jB$, with the same angle as branch current.

With parallel branches of conductance and susceptance the total admittance $Y_T = G \pm jB$. For the two branches in Fig. 25-11$a$, as an example, $G$ is $\frac{1}{10}$ or 0.1 and $B$ is also 0.1.

*In rectangular form:*

$$Y_T = 0.1 - j0.1 \text{ S}$$

*In polar form:*

$$Y_T = 0.14 \underline{/-45°} \text{ S}$$

This value for $Y_T$ is the same as $I_T$ with 1 V applied across $Z_T$ of $7.07 \underline{/45°} \ \Omega$.

As another example, suppose that a parallel circuit has 4 $\Omega$ for $R$ in one branch and $-j4 \ \Omega$ for $X_C$ in the other branch. In rectangular form, then, $Y_T$ is $0.25 + j0.25$ S. Also, the polar form is $Y_T = 0.35 \underline{/45°}$ S.

---

### TEST-POINT QUESTION 25-11

Answers at end of chapter.
**a.** A $Z$ of $3 + j4 \ \Omega$ is in parallel with an $R$ of 2 $\Omega$. State $Z_T$ in rectangular form.
**b.** Do the same as in Part **a** for $X_C$ instead of $X_L$.

## 25-12 COMBINING TWO COMPLEX BRANCH IMPEDANCES

A common application is a circuit with two branches $Z_1$ and $Z_2$, where each is a complex impedance with both reactance and resistance. A circuit, such as the one in Fig. 25-12, can be solved only graphically or by complex numbers. Actually, using complex numbers is the shortest method.

The procedure here is to find $Z_T$ as the product divided by the sum for $Z_1$ and $Z_2$. A good way to start is to state each branch impedance in both rectangular and polar forms. Then $Z_1$ and $Z_2$ are ready for addition, multiplication, and division. The solution of this circuit is as shown on the next page.

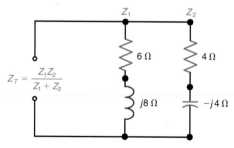

**FIG. 25-12** Finding $Z_T$ for any two complex impedances $Z_1$ and $Z_2$ in parallel. See text for solution.

$$Z_1 = 6 + j8 = 10\angle 53°$$
$$Z_2 = 4 - j4 = 5.66\angle -45°$$

The combined impedance is

▶ $$Z_T = \frac{Z_1 \times Z_2}{Z_1 + Z_2}$$

Use the polar form of $Z_1$ and $Z_2$ to multiply, but add in rectangular form:

$$Z_T = \frac{10\angle 53° \times 5.66\angle -45°}{}$$

$$= \frac{56.6\angle 8°}{}$$

Converting the denominator to polar form for easier division,

$$10 + j4 = 10.8\angle 22°$$

Then

$$Z_T = \frac{56.6\angle 8°}{} = 5.24\angle -14° \ \Omega$$

We can convert $Z_T$ into rectangular form. The $R$ component is $5.24 \times \cos(-14°)$ or $5.24 \times 0.97 = 5.08$. Note that $\cos\theta$ is positive in the first and fourth quadrants. The $j$ component equals $5.24 \times \sin(-14°)$ or $5.24 \times (-0.242) = -1.127$. In rectangular form, then,

$$Z_T = 5.08 - j1.27$$

Therefore, this series-parallel circuit combination is equivalent to $5.08\ \Omega$ of $R$ in series with $1.27\ \Omega$ of $X$. Notice that the minus $j$ term means the circuit is capacitive. This problem can also be done in rectangular form by rationalizing the fraction for $Z_T$.

## TEST-POINT QUESTION 25-12

Answers at end of chapter.

Refer to Fig. 25-12.
**a.** Add $(6 + j8) + (4 - j4)$ for the sum of $Z_1$ and $Z_2$.
**b.** Multiply $10\angle 53° \times 5.66\angle -45°$ for the product of $Z_1$ and $Z_2$.

# 25-13 COMBINING COMPLEX BRANCH CURRENTS

An example with two branches is shown in Fig. 25-13, to find $I_T$. The branch currents can just be added in rectangular form for the total $I_T$ of parallel branches.

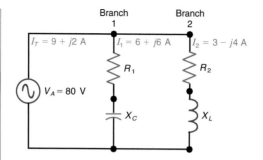

FIG. 25-13  Finding $I_T$ for two branch currents in parallel.

This method corresponds to adding series impedances in rectangular form to find $Z_T$. The rectangular form is necessary for the addition of phasors.

Adding the branch currents in Fig. 25-13,

$$I_T = I_1 + I_2$$
$$= (6 + j6) + (3 - j4)$$
$$I_T = 9 + j2 \text{ A}$$

Note that $I_1$ has $+j$ for the $+90°$ of capacitive current, while $I_2$ has $-j$ for inductive current. These current phasors have the opposite signs from their reactance phasors.

In polar form the $I_T$ of $9 + j2$ A is calculated as the phasor sum of the branch currents.

$$I_T = \sqrt{9^2 + 2^2} = \sqrt{85}$$
$$I_T = 9.22 \text{ A}$$

$$\tan \theta = \frac{2}{9} = 0.222$$

$$\theta_I = \arctan (0.22)$$
$$\theta_I = 12.53°$$

Therefore, $I_T$ is $9 + j2$ A in rectangular form or $9.22 \angle 12.53°$ A in polar form. The complex currents for any number of branches can be added in rectangular form.

---

### TEST-POINT QUESTION 25-13

Answers at end of chapter.
**a.** Find $I_T$ in rectangular form for $I_1$ of $0 + j2$ A and $I_2$ of $4 + j3$ A.
**b.** Find $I_T$ in rectangular form for $I_1$ of $6 + j7$ A and $I_2$ of $3 - j9$ A.

## 25-14 PARALLEL CIRCUIT WITH THREE COMPLEX BRANCHES

Because the circuit in Fig. 25-14 has more than two complex impedances in parallel, the method of branch currents is used. There will be several conver-

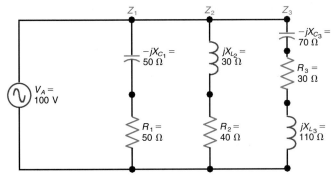

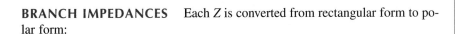

FIG. 25-14 Finding $Z_T$ for any three complex impedances in parallel. See text for solution by means of branch currents.

sions between rectangular and polar form, since addition must be in rectangular form, but division is easier in polar form. The sequence of calculations is:

1. Convert each branch impedance to polar form. This is necessary for dividing into the applied voltage $V_A$ to calculate the individual branch currents. If $V_A$ is not given, any convenient value can be assumed. Note that $V_A$ has a phase angle of $0°$ because it is the reference.

2. Convert the individual branch currents from polar to rectangular form so that they can be added for the total line current. This step is necessary because the resistive and reactive components must be added separately.

3. Convert the total line current from rectangular to polar form for dividing into the applied voltage to calculate $Z_T$.

4. The total impedance can remain in polar form with its magnitude and phase angle, or can be converted to rectangular form for its resistive and reactive components.

These steps are used in the following calculations to solve the circuit in Fig. 25-14. All the values are in A, V, or $\Omega$ units.

**BRANCH IMPEDANCES**    Each $Z$ is converted from rectangular form to polar form:

$$Z_1 = 50 - j50 = 70.7 \angle{-45°}$$
$$Z_2 = 40 + j30 = 50 \angle{+37°}$$
$$Z_3 = 30 + j40 = 50 \angle{+53°}$$

**BRANCH CURRENTS**     Each $I$ is calculated as $V_A$ divided by $Z$ in polar form:

$$I_1 = \frac{V_A}{Z_1} = \frac{100\angle 0°}{} = 1.414\angle +45° = 1 + j1$$

$$I_2 = \frac{V_A}{Z_2} = \frac{100\angle 0°}{} = 2.00\angle -37° = 1.6 - j1.2$$

$$I_3 = \frac{V_A}{Z_3} = \frac{100\angle 0°}{} = 2.00\angle -53° = 1.2 - j1.6$$

The polar form of each $I$ is converted to rectangular form, for addition of the branch currents.

**TOTAL LINE CURRENT**     In rectangular form,

$$
\begin{aligned}
I_T &= I_1 + I_2 + I_3 \\
&= (1 + j1) + (1.6 - j1.2) + (1.2 - j1.6) \\
&= 1 + 1.6 + 1.2 + j1 - j1.2 - j1.6 \\
I_T &= 3.8 - j1.8
\end{aligned}
$$

Converting $3.8 - j1.8$ into polar form,

$$I_T = 4.2\angle -25.4°$$

**TOTAL IMPEDANCE**     In polar form,

$$Z_T = \frac{V_A}{I_T} = \frac{100\angle 0°}{}$$

$$Z_T = 23.8\angle +25.4° \ \Omega$$

Converting $23.8\angle +25.4°$ into rectangular form,

$$Z_T = 21.5 + j10.2 \ \Omega$$

Therefore, the complex ac circuit in Fig. 25-14 is equivalent to the combination of 21.5 $\Omega$ of $R$ in series with 10.2 $\Omega$ of $X_L$. The circuit is inductive.

This problem can also be done by combining $Z_1$ and $Z_2$ in parallel as $Z_1 Z_2 / (Z_1 + Z_2)$. Then combine this value with $Z_3$ in parallel to find the total $Z_T$ of the three branches.

---

### TEST-POINT QUESTION 25-14

Answers at end of chapter.

Refer to Fig. 25-14.
**a.** State $Z_2$ in rectangular form for branch 2.
**b.** State $Z_2$ in polar form.
**c.** Find $I_2$.

# 25 SUMMARY AND REVIEW

- In complex numbers, resistance $R$ is a real term and reactance is a $j$ term. Thus, an 8-$\Omega$ $R$ is 8; an 8-$\Omega$ $X_L$ is $j8$; an 8-$\Omega$ $X_C$ is $-j8$. The general form of a complex impedance with series resistance and reactance then is $Z_T = R \pm jX$, in rectangular form.
- The same notation can be used for series voltages where $V = V_R \pm jV_X$.
- For branch currents $I_T = I_R \pm jI_X$, but the reactive branch currents have signs opposite from impedances. Capacitive branch current is $jI_C$, while inductive branch current is $-jI_L$.
- The complex branch currents are added in rectangular form for any number of branches to find $I_T$.
- To convert from rectangular to polar form: $R \pm jX = Z_T \angle \theta$. The angle is $\theta_Z$. The magnitude of $Z_T$ is $\sqrt{R^2 + X^2}$. Also, $\theta_Z$ is the angle with $\tan = X/R$.
- To convert from polar to rectangular form, $Z_T \angle \theta_Z = R \pm jX$, where $R$ is $Z_T \cos \theta_Z$ and the $j$ term is $Z_T \sin \theta_Z$. A positive angle has a positive $j$ term; a negative angle has a negative $j$ term. Also, the angle is more than 45° for a $j$ term larger than the real term; the angle is less than 45° for a $j$ term smaller than the real term.
- The rectangular form must be used for addition or subtraction of complex numbers.
- The polar form is usually more convenient in multiplying and dividing complex numbers. For multiplication, multiply the magnitudes and add the angles; for division, divide the magnitudes and subtract the angles.
- To find the total impedance $Z_T$ of a series circuit, add all the resistances for the real term and find the algebraic sum of the reactances for the $j$ term. The result is $Z_T = R \pm jX$. Then convert $Z_T$ to polar form for dividing into the applied voltage to calculate the current.
- To find the total impedance $Z_T$ of two complex branch impedances $Z_1$ and $Z_2$ in parallel, $Z_T$ can be calculated as $Z_1Z_2/(Z_1 + Z_2)$.

## SELF-TEST

**ANSWERS AT BACK OF BOOK.**

Match the values in the column at the left with those at the right (*list continues on p. 716*).

1. $24 + j5 + 16 + j10$
2. $24 - j5 + 16 - j10$
3. $j12 \times 4$
4. $j12 \times j4$
5. $j12 \div j3$
6. $(4 + j2) \times (4 - j2)$

a. $14 \angle 50°$
b. $7 \angle 6°$
c. $1200 - j800 \ \Omega$
d. $40 + j15$
e. $90 + j60 \ V$
f. $45 \angle 42°$

7. $1200\ \Omega$ of $R + 800\ \Omega$ of $X_C$
8. 5 A of $I_R + 7$ A of $I_C$
9. 90 V of $V_R + 60$ V of $V_L$
10. $14\underline{/28°} \times \underline{/22°}$
11. $14\underline{/28°} \div 2\underline{/22°}$
12. $15\underline{/42°} \times 3\underline{/0°}$
13. $6\underline{/-75°} \times 4\underline{/30°}$

g. $24\underline{/-45°}$
h. 4
i. $j48$
j. $-48$
k. $5 + j7$ A
l. 20
m. $40 - j15$

---

## QUESTIONS

1. Give the mathematical operator for the angles of 0°, 90°, 180°, 270°, and 360°.
2. Define the sine, cosine, and tangent functions of an angle.
3. How are mathematical operators similar for logarithms, exponents, and angles?
4. Compare the following combinations: resistance $R$ and conductance $G$; reactance $X$ and susceptance $B$; impedance $Z$ and admittance $Y$.
5. What are the units for admittance $Y$ and susceptance $B$?
6. Why do $Z_T$ and $I_T$ for a circuit have angles with opposite signs?

---

## PROBLEMS

**ANSWERS TO ODD-NUMBERED PROBLEMS AT BACK OF BOOK.**

1. State $Z_T$ in rectangular form for the following series circuits: **(a)** 4-$\Omega$ $R$ and 3-$\Omega$ $X_C$; **(b)** 4-$\Omega$ $R$ and 3-$\Omega$ $X_L$; **(c)** 3-$\Omega$ $R$ and 6-$\Omega$ $X_L$; **(d)** 3-$\Omega$ $R$ and 3-$\Omega$ $X_C$.
2. Draw the schematic diagrams for the impedances in Prob. 1.
3. Convert the following impedances to polar form: **(a)** $4 - j3$; **(b)** $4 + j3$; **(c)** $3 + j$; **(d)** $3 - j3$.
4. Convert the following impedances to rectangular form: **(a)** $5\underline{/-27°}$; **(b)** $5\underline{/27°}$; **(c)** $6.71\underline{/63.4°}$; **(d)** $4.24\underline{/-45°}$.
5. Find the total $Z_T$ in rectangular form for the following three series impedances: **(a)** $12\underline{/10°}$; **(b)** $25\underline{/15°}$; **(c)** $34\underline{/26°}$.
6. Multiply the following, in polar form: **(a)** $45\underline{/24°} \times 10\underline{/54°}$; **(b)** $45\underline{/-24°} \times 10\underline{/54°}$; **(c)** $18\underline{/-64°} \times 4\underline{/14°}$; **(d)** $18\underline{/-64°} \times 4\underline{/-14°}$.
7. Divide the following, in polar form: **(a)** $45\underline{/24°} \div 10\underline{/10°}$; **(b)** $45\underline{/24°} \div 10\underline{/-10°}$; **(c)** $500\underline{/-72°} \div 5\underline{/12°}$; **(d)** $500\underline{/-72°} \div 5\underline{/-12°}$.
8. Match the four phasor diagrams in Fig. 25-4a, b, c, and d with the four circuits in Figs. 25-5 and 25-6.
9. Find $Z_T$ in polar form for the series circuit in Fig. 25-7a.
10. Find $Z_T$ in polar form for the series-parallel circuit in Fig. 25-7c.
11. In Fig. 25-12, find $Z_T$ in rectangular form by rationalization.
12. Solve the circuit in Fig. 25-12 to find $Z_T$ in polar form, using the method of branch currents. Assume an applied voltage of 56.6 V.

13. Show the equivalent series circuit of Fig. 25-12.
14. Solve the circuit in Fig. 25-14 to find $Z_T$ in polar form, without using branch currents. (Find the $Z$ of two branches in parallel; then combine this $Z$ with the third branch $Z$.)
15. Show the equivalent series circuit of Fig. 25-14.
16. Refer to Fig. 25-13. (a) Find $Z_1$ and $Z_2$ for the two branch currents given. (b) Calculate the values needed for $R_1$, $R_2$, $X_C$, and $X_L$ for these impedances. (c) What are the $L$ and $C$ values for a frequency of 60 Hz?
17. Solve the series ac circuit in Fig. 24-8 in the previous chapter by the use of complex numbers. Find $Z\angle\theta$, $I\angle\theta$, and each $V\angle\theta$. Prove that the sum of the complex voltage drops around the circuit equals the applied voltage $V_T$. Make a phasor diagram showing all phase angles with respect to $V_T$.
18. The following components are in series: $L = 100\ \mu\text{H}$, $C = 20\ \text{pF}$, $R = 2000\ \Omega$. At the frequency of 2 MHz calculate $X_L$, $X_C$, $Z_T$, $I$, $\theta_Z$, $V_R$, $V_L$, and $V_C$. The applied $V_T = 8$ V.
19. Solve the same circuit as in Prob. 18 for the frequency of 4 MHz. Give three effects of the higher frequency.
20. In Fig. 25-15, show that $Z_T = 4.8\ \Omega$ and $\theta_Z = 36.9°$ by (a) the method of branch currents; (b) calculating $Z_T$ as $Z_1 Z_2/(Z_1 + Z_2)$.
21. In Fig. 25-16, find $Z_T\angle\theta$ by calculating $Z_{bc}$ of the parallel bank and combining with the series $Z_{ab}$.

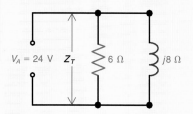

FIG. 25-15   Circuit for Prob. 20.

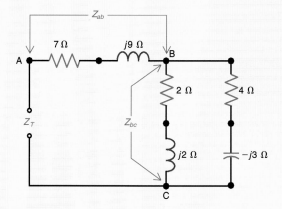

FIG. 25-16   Circuit for Prob. 21.

22. Find $Z_T$, in polar form, for the series-parallel circuit in Fig. 25-17.
23. Find $Z_T$ and $I_T$, in polar form, for the series-parallel circuit in Fig. 25-18. Also, find $V_{R_1}$, $V_{C_1}$, $V_{L_1}$, and $V_{R_2}$. State each voltage drop in polar form.
24. In Fig. 25-19, calculate the output voltage $V_{\text{out}}$, in polar form.

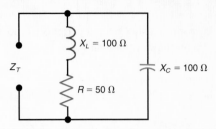

FIG. 25-17   Circuit for Prob. 22.

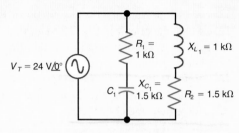

FIG. 25-18   Circuit for Prob. 23.

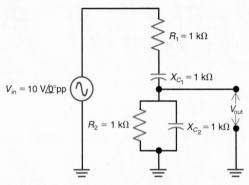

FIG. 25-19   Circuit for Prob. 24.

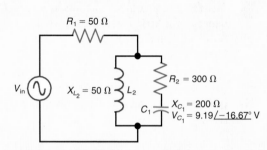

FIG. 25-20   Circuit for Critical Thinking Prob. 1.

## CRITICAL THINKING

1.   In Fig. 25-20, calculate the input voltage $V_{in}$, in polar form.

## ANSWERS TO TEST-POINT QUESTIONS

**25-1**   **a.** $0°$
  **b.** $180°$

**25-2**   **a.** $90°$
  **b.** $-90$ or $270°$

**25-3**   **a.** T
  **b.** T

**25-4**   **a.** $j3\ k\Omega$
  **b.** $-j5\ mA$

**25-5**   **a.** $4 + j7$
  **b.** $0 - j7$

**25-6**   **a.** $5 + j7$
  **b.** $4 + j6$

**25-7**   **a.** $14.14\ \Omega$
  **b.** $45°$

**25-8**   **a.** $12\underline{/50°}$
  **b.** $3\underline{/-10°}$

**25-9**   **a.** $10 + j10$
  **b.** $10 - j10$

**25-10**   **a.** $53°$
  **b.** $143°$
  **c.** $90°$

**25-11**   **a.** $(6 + j8)/(5 + j4)$
  **b.** $(6 - j8)/(5 - j4)$

**25-12**   **a.** $10 + j4$
  **b.** $56.6\underline{/8°}$

**25-13**   **a.** $4 + j5\ A$
  **b.** $9 - j2\ A$

**25-14**   **a.** $40 + j30$
  **b.** $50\underline{/37°}\ \Omega$
  **c.** $2\underline{/-37°}\ A$

A photographic history of the computer. One of the first computers was the Eniac (*upper left*), developed in the 1940s. The 1970s marked the expanded use of the computer by businesses. The mainframe computer (*upper right*) was the tool of the time. In the 1980s personal computers such as the Apple IIe (*lower left*) brought computers into our homes and schools. Today, personal computers can go anywhere, as laptop computers (*lower right*) increase in popularity.

# REVIEW: CHAPTERS 24 AND 25

## SUMMARY

- Reactances $X_C$ and $X_L$ are opposite. In series, the ohms of $X_C$ and $X_L$ cancel. In parallel, the branch currents $I_C$ and $I_L$ cancel.
- As a result, circuits with $R$, $X_C$, and $X_L$ can be reduced to one net reactance $X$ and one equivalent $R$.
- In series circuits, the net $X$ is added with the total $R$ by phasors for the impedance: $Z_T = \sqrt{R^2 + X^2}$. Then $I = V_T/Z_T$.
- For the branch currents in parallel circuits, the net $I_X$ is added with $I_R$ by phasors for the total line current: $I_T = \sqrt{I_R^2 + I_X^2}$. Then $Z_{EQ} = V/I_T$.
- The characteristics for ohms of $R$, $X_C$, $X_L$, and $Z$ in ac circuits are compared in Table 24-1.
- In ac circuits with reactance, the real power in watts equals $I^2 R$. This value equals $VI \cos\theta$, where $\theta$ is the phase angle of the circuit and $\cos\theta$ is the power factor.
- The wattmeter uses an ac meter movement to read $V$ and $I$ at the same time, measuring watts of real power.
- In complex numbers, $R$ is a real term at $0°$ and reactance is a $\pm j$ term at $\pm 90°$. In rectangular form, $Z_T = R \pm jX$. For example, $10\ \Omega$ of $R$ in series with $10\ \Omega$ of $X_L$ is $10 + j10\ \Omega$.
- The polar form of $10 + j10\ \Omega$ is $14\ \angle 45°\ \Omega$. The angle of $45°$ is arctan $X/R$. The magnitude of 14 is $\sqrt{R^2 + X^2}$.
- The rectangular form of complex numbers must be used for addition and subtraction. Add or subtract the real terms and the $j$ terms separately.
- The polar form of complex numbers is easier for multiplication and division. For multiplication, multiply the magnitudes and add the angles. For division, divide the magnitudes and subtract the angle of the divisor.
- In double-subscript notation for a voltage, such as $V_{BE}$, the first letter in the subscript is the point of measurement with respect to the second letter. So $V_{BE}$ is the base voltage with respect to the emitter, in a transistor.

## ANSWERS AT BACK OF BOOK.

Fill in the numerical answer.

**1.** An ac circuit with 100 Ω $R_1$ in series with 200 Ω $R_2$ has $R_T$ of _____ Ω.

**2.** With 100 Ω $X_{L_1}$ in series with 200 Ω $X_{L_2}$, the total $X_L$ is _____ Ω.

**3.** For 200 Ω $X_{C_1}$ in series with 100 Ω $X_{C_2}$, the total $X_C$ is _____ Ω.

**4.** Two $X_C$ branches of 500 Ω each in parallel have combined $X_C$ of _____ Ω.

**5.** Two $X_L$ branches of 500 Ω each in parallel have combined $X_L$ of _____ Ω.

**6.** A 500-Ω $X_L$ is in series with a 300-Ω $X_C$. The net $X_L$ is _____ Ω.

**7.** For 500 Ω $X_C$ in series with 300 Ω $X_{L_1}$, the net $X_C$ is _____ Ω.

**8.** A 10-Ω $X_L$ is in series with a 10-Ω $R$. The total $Z_T$ is _____ Ω.

**9.** With a 10-Ω $X_C$ in series with a 10-Ω $R$, the total $Z_T$ is _____ Ω.

**10.** With 14 V applied across 14 Ω $Z_T$, the $I$ is _____ A.

**11.** For 10 Ω $X_L$ and 10 Ω $R$ in series, the phase angle $\theta$ is _____ degrees.

**12.** For 10 Ω $X_C$ and 10 Ω $R$ in series, the phase angle $\theta$ is _____ degrees.

**13.** A 10-Ω $X_L$ and a 10-Ω $R$ are in parallel across 10 V. The amount of each branch $I$ is _____ A.

**14.** In question 13, the total line current $I_T$ equals _____ A.

**15.** In questions 13 and 14, $Z_T$ of the parallel branches equals _____ Ω.

**16.** With 120 V, an $I$ of 10 A, and $\theta$ of 60°, a wattmeter reads _____ W.

**17.** The $Z$ of $4 + j4$ Ω converted to polar form is _____ Ω.

**18.** The impedance value of $8\ \angle 40°/2\ \angle 30°$ is equal to _____ Ω.

Answer True or False.

**19.** In an ac circuit with $X_C$ and $R$ in series, if the frequency is raised, the current will increase.

**20.** In an ac circuit with $X_L$ and $R$ in series, if the frequency is increased, the current will be reduced.

**21.** The voltampere is a unit of apparent power.

**22.** The polar form of complex numbers is best for adding impedance values.

## REFERENCES

Bogart, T.: *Electric Circuits,* Glencoe/McgrawHill, Columbus, Ohio.

Schuler, C., and R. Fowler: *Electric Circuit Analysis,* Glencoe/McGraw-Hill, Columbus, Ohio.

# CHAPTER 26

# RESONANCE

This chapter explains how $X_L$ and $X_C$ can be combined to favor one particular frequency, the resonant frequency to which the *LC* circuit is tuned. The resonance effect occurs when the inductive and capacitive reactances are equal. The main application of resonance is in RF circuits for tuning to an ac signal of the desired frequency. Tuning in radio and television receivers, transmitters, and electronics equipment in general are applications of resonance.

Tuning by means of the resonant effect provides the practical application of selectivity. The resonant circuit can select a particular frequency for the output, with many different frequencies at the input.

# CHAPTER OBJECTIVES

*Upon completion of this chapter, you should be able to:*

- *Define* the term *resonance.*
- *List* four circuit characteristics of a series resonant circuit.
- *List* four circuit characteristics of a parallel resonant circuit.
- *Understand* how the resonant frequency formula is derived.
- *Calculate* the $Q$ of a series and parallel resonant circuit.
- *Calculate* the equivalent impedance of a parallel resonant circuit.
- *Explain* what is meant by the *bandwidth of a resonant circuit.*
- *Calculate* the bandwidth of a series or parallel resonant circuit.
- *Explain* the effect of varying $L$ or $C$ in tuning an $LC$ circuit.
- *Choose* $L$ or $C$ for a resonant circuit.

## IMPORTANT TERMS IN THIS CHAPTER

| | | |
|---|---|---|
| antiresonance | half-power frequencies | series resonance |
| bandwidth | parallel resonance | tank circuit |
| damping | $Q$ of resonant circuit | tuning |
| flywheel effect | ringing | |

## TOPICS COVERED IN THIS CHAPTER

**26-1** The Resonance Effect

**26-2** Series Resonance

**26-3** Parallel Resonance

**26-4** Resonant Frequency $f_r = 1/(2\pi\sqrt{LC})$

**26-5** $Q$ Magnification Factor of Resonant Circuit

**26-6** Bandwidth of Resonant Circuit

**26-7** Tuning

**26-8** Mistuning

**26-9** Analysis of Parallel Resonant Circuits

**26-10** Damping of Parallel Resonant Circuits

**26-11** Choosing $L$ and $C$ for a Resonant Circuit

Inductive reactance increases as the frequency is increased, but capacitive reactance decreases with higher frequencies. Because of these opposite characteristics, for any $LC$ combination there must be a frequency at which the $X_L$ equals the $X_C$, as one increases while the other decreases. This case of equal and opposite reactances is called *resonance,* and the ac circuit is then a *resonant circuit.*

Any $LC$ circuit can be resonant. It all depends on the frequency. At the resonant frequency, an $LC$ combination provides the resonance effect. Off the resonant frequency, either below or above, the $LC$ combination is just another ac circuit.

The frequency at which the opposite reactances are equal is the *resonant frequency.* This frequency can be calculated as $f_r = 1/(2\pi\sqrt{LC})$ where $L$ is the inductance in henrys, $C$ is the capacitance in farads, and $f_r$ is the resonant frequency in hertz that makes $X_L = X_C$.

In general, we can say that large values of $L$ and $C$ provide a relatively low resonant frequency. Smaller values of $L$ and $C$ allow higher values for $f_r$. The resonance effect is most useful for radio frequencies, where the required values of microhenrys for $L$ and picofarads for $C$ are easily obtained.

The most common application of resonance in RF circuits is called <u>tuning</u>. In this use, the $LC$ circuit provides maximum voltage output at the resonant frequency, compared with the amount of output at any other frequency either below or above resonance. This idea is illustrated in Fig. 26-1, where the $LC$ circuit resonant at 1000 kHz magnifies the effect of this particular frequency. The result is maximum output at 1000 kHz, compared with lower or higher frequencies.

Tuning in radio and television are applications of resonance. When you tune a radio to one station, the $LC$ circuits are tuned to resonance for that particular carrier frequency. Also, when you tune a television receiver to a particular channel, the $LC$ circuits are tuned to resonance for that station. There are almost unlimited uses for resonance in ac circuits.

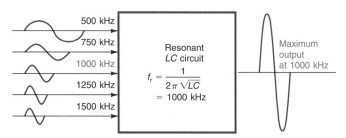

**FIG. 26-1** $LC$ circuit resonant at $f_r$ of 1000 kHz to provide maximum output at this frequency.

## TEST-POINT QUESTION 26-1

Answers at end of chapter.

Refer to Fig. 26-1.
**a.** Give the resonant frequency.
**b.** Give the frequency that has maximum output.

# 26-2 SERIES RESONANCE

In the series ac circuit in Fig. 26-2*a*, when the frequency of the applied voltage is 1000 kHz, the reactance of the 239-$\mu$H inductance equals 1500 $\Omega$. At the same frequency, the reactance of the 106-pF capacitance also is 1500 $\Omega$. Therefore, this *LC* combination is resonant at 1000 kHz. This is $f_r$, because the inductive reactance and capacitive reactance are equal at this frequency.

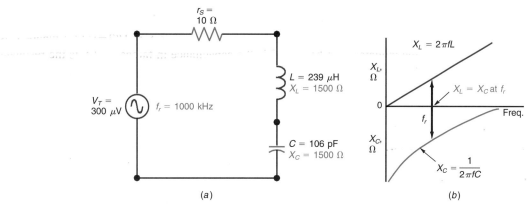

**FIG. 26-2** Series resonance. (*a*) Schematic diagram of series $r_S$, *L*, and *C*. (*b*) Graph to show reactances $X_C$ and $X_L$ are equal and opposite at the resonant frequency $f_r$. Inductive reactance is shown up for $jX_L$ and capacitive reactance is down for $-jX_C$.

In a series ac circuit, inductive reactance leads by 90°, compared with the zero reference angle of the resistance, while capacitive reactance lags by 90°. Therefore, $X_L$ and $X_C$ are 180° out of phase. The opposite reactances cancel each other completely when they are equal.

Figure 26-2*b* shows $X_L$ and $X_C$ equal, resulting in a net reactance of zero ohms. The only opposition to current then is the coil resistance $r_S$, which is the limit on how low the series resistance in the circuit can be. With zero reactance and just the low value of series resistance, the generator voltage produces the greatest amount of current in the series *LC* circuit at the resonant frequency. The series resistance should be as small as possible for a sharp increase in current at resonance.

**MAXIMUM CURRENT AT SERIES RESONANCE**    The main characteristic of series resonance is the resonant rise of current to its maximum value of $V_T/r_S$ at the resonant frequency. For the circuit in Fig. 26-2*a*, the maximum current at series resonance is 30 $\mu$A, equal to 300 $\mu$V/10 $\Omega$. At any other frequency either below or above the resonant frequency, there is less current in the circuit.

This resonant rise of current to 30 $\mu$A at 1000 kHz is illustrated in Fig. 26-3. In Fig. 26-3*a*, the amount of current is shown as the amplitude of individual cycles of the alternating current produced in the circuit by the ac generator voltage. Whether the amplitude of one ac cycle is considered in terms of peak, rms, or average value, the amount of current is greatest at the resonant frequency. In Fig. 26-3*b*, the current amplitudes are plotted on a graph for frequencies at and near the resonant frequency, producing a typical *response*

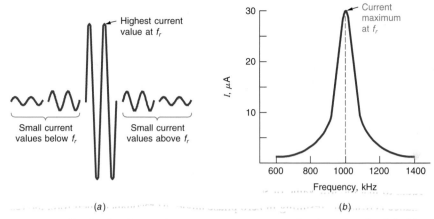

**FIG. 26-3** Graphs showing maximum current at resonance for the series circuit in Fig. 26-2. (*a*) Amplitudes of individual cycles. (*b*) Response curve to show amount of *I* below and above resonance. Values of *I* are in Table 26-1.

*curve* for a series resonant circuit. The response curve in Fig. 26-3*b* can be considered as an outline of the increasing and decreasing amplitudes for the individual cycles shown in Fig. 26-3*a*.

The response curve of the series resonant circuit shows that the current is small below resonance, rises to its maximum value at the resonant frequency, and then drops off to small values above resonance. To prove this fact, Table 26-1 lists the calculated values of impedance and current in the circuit of Fig. 26-2 at the resonant frequency of 1000 kHz and at two frequencies below and two frequencies above resonance.

Below resonance, at 600 kHz, $X_C$ is more than $X_L$ and there is appreciable net reactance, which limits the current to a relatively low value. At the higher frequency of 800 kHz, $X_C$ decreases and $X_L$ increases, making the two reactances closer to the same value. The net reactance is then smaller, allowing more current.

At the resonant frequency, $X_L$ and $X_C$ are equal, the net reactance is zero, and the current has its maximum value equal to $V_T/r_S$.

Above resonance at 1200 and 1400 kHz, $X_L$ is greater than $X_C$, providing net reactance that limits the current to much smaller values than at resonance.

**TABLE 26-1   SERIES-RESONANCE CALCULATIONS FOR THE CIRCUIT IN FIG. 26-2***

| FREQUENCY, kHz | $X_L = 2\pi f L, \Omega$ | $X_C = 1/(2\pi f C), \Omega$ | NET REACTANCE, $\Omega$ | | $Z_T, \Omega$† | $I = V_T/Z_T,$ $\mu A$† | $V_L = IX_L,$ $\mu V$ | $V_C = IX_C,$ $\mu V$ |
| --- | --- | --- | --- | --- | --- | --- | --- | --- |
| | | | $X_C - X_L$ | $X_L - X_C$ | | | | |
| 600 | 900 | 2500 | 1600 | | 1600 | 0.19 | 171 | 475 |
| 800 | 1200 | 1875 | 675 | | 675 | 0.44 | 528 | 825 |
| $f_r \rightarrow$ 1000 | 1500 | 1500 | 0 | 0 | 10 | 30 | 45,000 | 45,000 |
| 1200 | 1800 | 1250 | | 550 | 550 | 0.55 | 990 | 688 |
| 1400 | 2100 | 1070 | | 1030 | 1030 | 0.29 | 609 | 310 |

*$L = 239\ \mu H$, $C = 106$ pF, $V_T = 300\ \mu V$, $r_S = 10\ \Omega$.
†$Z_T$ and $I$ calculated without $r_S$ when its resistance is very small compared with the net $X_L$ or $X_C$. $Z_T$ and $I$ are resistive at $f_r$.

In summary:

1. Below the resonant frequency, $X_L$ is small, but $X_C$ has high values that limit the amount of current.
2. Above the resonant frequency, $X_C$ is small, but $X_L$ has high values that limit the amount of current.
3. At the resonant frequency, $X_L$ equals $X_C$, and they cancel to allow maximum current.

**MINIMUM IMPEDANCE AT SERIES RESONANCE** Since the reactances cancel at the resonant frequency, the impedance of the series circuit is minimum, equal to just the low value of series resistance. This minimum impedance at resonance is resistive, resulting in zero phase angle. At resonance, therefore, the resonant current is in phase with the generator voltage.

**RESONANT RISE IN VOLTAGE ACROSS SERIES $L$ OR $C$** The maximum current in a series $LC$ circuit at resonance is useful because it produces maximum voltage across either $X_L$ or $X_C$ at the resonant frequency. As a result, the series resonant circuit can select one frequency by providing much more voltage output at the resonant frequency, compared with frequencies above and below resonance. Figure 26-4 illustrates the resonant rise in voltage across the capacitance in a series ac circuit. At the resonant frequency of 1000 kHz, the voltage across $C$ rises to the value of 45,000 $\mu$V, while the input voltage is only 300 $\mu$V.

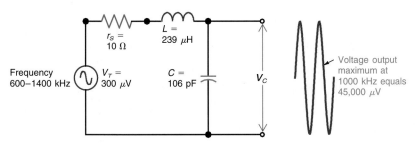

**FIG. 26-4** Series circuit selects frequency by producing maximum $IX_C$ voltage output across $C$ at resonance.

In Table 26-1, the voltage across $C$ is calculated as $IX_C$ and across $L$ as $IX_L$. Below the resonant frequency, $X_C$ has a higher value than at resonance, but the current is small. Similarly, above the resonant frequency, $X_L$ is higher than at resonance, but the current has a low value because of the inductive reactance. At resonance, although $X_L$ and $X_C$ cancel each other to allow maximum current, each reactance by itself has an appreciable value. Since the current is the same in all parts of a series circuit, the maximum current at resonance produces maximum voltage $IX_C$ across $C$ and an equal $IX_L$ voltage across $L$ for the resonant frequency.

Although the voltage across $X_C$ and $X_L$ is reactive, it is an actual voltage that can be measured. In Fig. 26-5, the voltage drops around the series resonant circuit are 45,000 $\mu$V across $C$ and 45,000 $\mu$V across $L$, with 300 $\mu$V across $r_S$. The voltage across the resistance is equal to and in phase with the generator voltage.

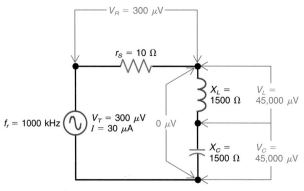

FIG. 26-5    Voltage drops around series resonant circuit.

Across the series combination of both $L$ and $C$, the voltage is zero because the two series voltage drops are equal and opposite. In order to use the resonant rise of voltage, therefore, the output must be connected across either $L$ or $C$ alone. We can consider the $V_L$ and $V_C$ voltages as similar to the idea of two batteries connected in series opposition. Together, the resultant is zero for the equal and opposite voltages, but each battery still has its own potential difference.

In summary, for a series resonant circuit the main characteristics are:

1.  The current $I$ is maximum at the resonant frequency $f_r$.
2.  The current $I$ is in phase with the generator voltage, or the phase angle of the circuit is 0°.
3.  The voltage is maximum across either $L$ or $C$ alone.
4.  The impedance is minimum at $f_r$, equal only to the low $r_S$.

**TEST-POINT QUESTION 26-2**

Answers at end of chapter.

Answer True or False, for series resonance.
**a.** Impedances $X_L$ and $X_C$ are maximum.
**b.** Impedances $X_L$ and $X_C$ are equal.
**c.** Current $I$ is maximum.

## 26-3 PARALLEL RESONANCE

With $L$ and $C$ in parallel as shown in Fig. 26-6, when $X_L$ equals $X_C$, the reactive branch currents are equal and opposite at resonance. Then they cancel each other to produce minimum current in the main line. Since the line current is minimum, the impedance is maximum. These relations are based on $r_S$ being very small compared with $X_L$ at resonance. In this case, the branch currents are practically equal when $X_L$ and $X_C$ are equal.

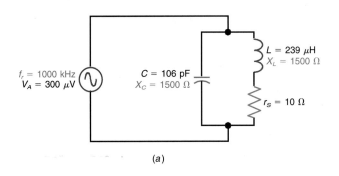

(a)

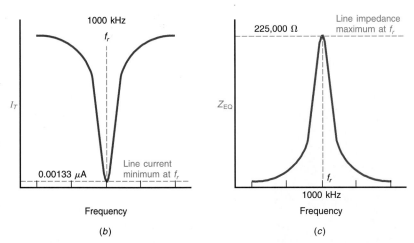

(b)                                    (c)

**FIG. 26-6** Parallel resonant circuit. (*a*) Schematic diagram of *L* and *C* in parallel branches. (*b*) Response curve of $I_T$ shows that the line current dips to minimum at $f_r$. (*c*) Response curve of $Z_{EQ}$ shows that it rises to maximum at $f_r$.

## MINIMUM LINE CURRENT AT PARALLEL RESONANCE

To show how the current in the main line dips to its minimum value when the parallel *LC* circuit is resonant, Table 26-2 lists the values of branch currents and the total line current for the circuit in Fig. 26-6.

### TABLE 26-2  PARALLEL-RESONANCE CALCULATIONS FOR THE CIRCUIT IN FIG. 26-6*

| FREQUENCY, kHz | $X_C = 1/(2\pi fC),$ $\Omega$ | $X_L = 2\pi fL,$ $\Omega$ | $I_C = V/X_C,$ $\mu A$ | $I_L = V/X_L,$ $\mu A\dagger$ | NET REACTIVE LINE CURRENT, $\mu A$ | | $I_T,$ $\mu A\dagger$ | $Z_{EQ} = V_A/I_T,$ $\Omega\dagger$ |
|---|---|---|---|---|---|---|---|---|
| | | | | | $I_L - I_C$ | $I_C - I_L$ | | |
| 600 | 2500 | 900 | 0.12 | 0.33 | 0.21 | | 0.21 | 1400 |
| 800 | 1875 | 1200 | 0.16 | 0.25 | 0.09 | | 0.09 | 3333 |
| $f_r \rightarrow$ 1000 | 1500 | 1500 | 0.20 | 0.20 | 0 | 0 | 0.001 33 | 225,000‡ |
| 1200 | 1250 | 1800 | 0.24 | 0.17 | | 0.07 | 0.07 | 3800 |
| 1400 | 1070 | 2100 | 0.28 | 0.14 | | 0.14 | 0.14 | 2143 |

*$L = 239\ \mu H$, $C = 106\ pF$, $V_T = 300\ \mu V$, $r_S = 10\ \Omega$.
†$Z_{EQ}$ and $I$ calculated without $r_S$ when its resistance is very small compared with the net $X_L$ or $X_C$. $Z_{EQ}$ and $I$ are resistive at $f_r$.
‡At resonance $Z_{EQ}$ calculated by formula (26-7). $Z_{EQ}$ and $I_T$ are resistive at $f_r$.

With $L$ and $C$ the same as in the series circuit of Fig. 26-2, $X_L$ and $X_C$ have the same values at the same frequencies. Since $L$, $C$, and the generator are in parallel, the voltage applied across the branches equals the generator voltage of 300 $\mu$V. Therefore, each reactive branch current is calculated as 300 $\mu$V divided by the reactance of the branch.

The values in the top row of Table 26-2 are obtained as follows: At 600 kHz the capacitive branch current equals 300 $\mu$V/2500 $\Omega$, or 0.12 $\mu$A. The inductive branch current at this frequency is 300 $\mu$V/900 $\Omega$, or 0.33 $\mu$A. Since this is a parallel ac circuit, the capacitive current leads by 90° while the inductive current lags by 90°, compared with the reference angle of the generator voltage, which is applied across the parallel branches. Therefore, the opposite currents are 180° out of phase. The net current in the line, then, is the difference between 0.33 and 0.12, which equals 0.21 $\mu$A.

Following this procedure, the calculations show that as the frequency is increased toward resonance, the capacitive branch current increases because of the lower value of $X_C$, while the inductive branch current decreases with higher values of $X_L$. As a result, there is less net line current as the two branch currents become more nearly equal.

At the resonant frequency of 1000 kHz, both reactances are 1500 $\Omega$, and the reactive branch currents are both 0.20 $\mu$A, canceling each other completely.

Above the resonant frequency, there is more current in the capacitive branch than in the inductive branch, and the net line current increases above its minimum value at resonance.

The dip in $I_T$ to its minimum value at $f_r$ is shown by the graph in Fig. 26-6b. At parallel resonance, $I_T$ is minimum and $Z_{EQ}$ is maximum.

The in-phase current due to $r_S$ in the inductive branch can be ignored off resonance because it is so small compared with the reactive line current. At the resonant frequency when the reactive currents cancel, however, the resistive component is the entire line current. Its value at resonance equals 0.00133 $\mu$A in this example. This small resistive current is the minimum value of the line current at parallel resonance.

**MAXIMUM LINE IMPEDANCE AT PARALLEL RESONANCE**   The minimum line current resulting from parallel resonance is useful because it corresponds to maximum impedance in the line across the generator. Therefore, an impedance that has a high value for just one frequency but a low impedance for other frequencies, either below or above resonance, can be obtained by using a parallel $LC$ circuit resonant at the desired frequency. This is another method of selecting one frequency by resonance. The response curve in Fig. 26-6c shows how the impedance rises to maximum for parallel resonance.

The main application of parallel resonance is the use of an $LC$ tuned circuit as the load impedance $Z_L$ in the output circuit of RF amplifiers. Because of the high impedance, then, the gain of the amplifier is maximum at $f_r$. The voltage gain of an amplifier is directly proportional to $Z_L$. The advantage of a resonant $LC$ circuit is that $Z$ is maximum only for an ac signal at the resonant frequency. Also, $L$ has practically no dc resistance, which means practically no dc voltage drop.

Referring to Table 26-2, the total impedance of the parallel ac circuit is calculated as the generator voltage divided by the total line current. At 600 kHz, for example, $Z_{EQ}$ equals 300 $\mu$V/0.21 $\mu$A, or 1400 $\Omega$. At 800 kHz, the impedance is higher because there is less line current.

At the resonant frequency of 1000 kHz, the line current is at its minimum value of 0.00133 $\mu$A. Then the impedance is maximum and is equal to 300 $\mu$V/0.00133 $\mu$A, or 225,000 $\Omega$.

Above 1000 kHz, the line current increases, and the impedance decreases from its maximum value.

The idea of how the line current can have a very low value even though the reactive branch currents are appreciable is illustrated in Fig. 26-7. In Fig. 26-7a, the resistive component of the total line current is shown as though it were a separate branch drawing an amount of resistive current from the generator in the main line equal to the current resulting from the coil resistance. Each reactive branch current has its value equal to the generator voltage divided by the reactance. Since they are equal and of opposite phase, however, in any part of the circuit where both reactive currents are present, the net amount of electron flow in one direction at any instant of time corresponds to zero current. The graph in Fig. 26-7b shows how equal and opposite currents for $I_L$ and $I_C$ cancel.

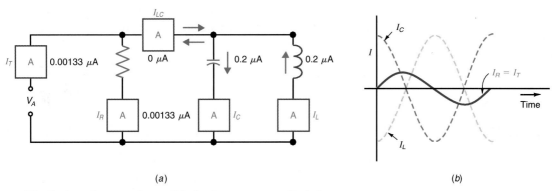

(a)                                                                 (b)

FIG. 26-7 Distribution of currents in parallel circuit at resonance. Resistive current shown as an equivalent branch for $I_R$. (a) Circuit with branch currents for $R$, $L$, and $C$. (b) Graph of equal and opposite reactive currents $I_L$ and $I_C$.

If a meter is inserted in series with the main line to indicate total line current $I_T$, it dips sharply to the minimum value of line current at the resonant frequency. With minimum current in the line, the impedance across the line is maximum at the resonant frequency. The maximum impedance at parallel resonance corresponds to a high value of resistance, without reactance, since the line current is then resistive with zero phase angle.

In summary, for a parallel resonant circuit, the main characteristics are

1. The line current $I_T$ is minimum at the resonant frequency.
2. The current $I_T$ is in phase with the generator voltage $V_A$, or the phase angle of the circuit is 0°.
3. The impedance $Z_{EQ}$, equal to $V_A/I_T$, is maximum at $f_r$ because of the minimum $I_T$.

**THE *LC* TANK CIRCUIT** It should be noted that the individual branch currents are appreciable at resonance, although $I_T$ is minimum. For the example in Table 26-2, at $f_r$ either the $I_L$ or $I_C$ equals 0.2 $\mu$A. This current is greater than the $I_C$ values below $f_r$ or the $I_L$ values above $f_r$.

The branch currents cancel in the main line because $I_C$ is at 90° with respect to the source $V_A$ while $I_L$ is at $-90°$, making them opposite with respect to each other.

However, inside the *LC* circuit, $I_L$ and $I_C$ do not cancel because they are in separate branches. Then $I_L$ and $I_C$ provide a circulating current in the *LC* circuit, which equals 0.2 $\mu$A in this example. For this reason, a parallel resonant *LC* circuit is often called a *tank circuit*.

Because of the energy stored by $L$ and $C$, the circulating tank current can provide full sine waves of current and voltage output when the input is only a pulse. The sine-wave output is always at the natural resonant frequency of the *LC* tank circuit. This ability of the *LC* circuit to supply complete sine waves is called the *flywheel effect*. Also, the process of producing sine waves after a pulse of energy has been applied is called *ringing* of the *LC* circuit.

---

### TEST-POINT QUESTION 26-3

Answers at end of chapter.

Answer True or False, for parallel resonance.
**a.** Currents $I_L$ and $I_C$ are maximum.
**b.** Currents $I_L$ and $I_C$ are equal.
**c.** Current $I_T$ is minimum.

---

## 26-4 RESONANT FREQUENCY $f_r = 1/(2\pi\sqrt{LC})$

The formula for the resonant frequency is derived from $X_L = X_C$. Using $f_r$ to indicate the resonant frequency in the formulas for $X_L$ and $X_C$, we have

▶ $$2\pi f_r L = \frac{1}{2\pi f_r C}$$

Inverting the factor $f_r$ gives

$$2\pi L(f_r)^2 = \frac{1}{2\pi C}$$

Inverting the factor $2\pi L$ gives

$$(f_r)^2 = \frac{1}{(2\pi)^2 LC}$$

The square root of both sides is then

▶ $$f_r = \frac{1}{2\pi\sqrt{LC}} \qquad\qquad\text{(26-1)}$$

where $L$ is in henrys, $C$ is in farads, and the resonant frequency $f_r$ is in hertz (Hz) units. For example, to find the resonant frequency of the $LC$ combination in Fig. 26-2, the values of $239 \times 10^{-6}$ and $106 \times 10^{-12}$ are substituted for $L$ and $C$. Then:

$$f_r = \frac{1}{2\pi\sqrt{LC}} = \frac{1}{2\pi\sqrt{239 \times 10^{-6} \times 106 \times 10^{-12}}}$$

$$= \frac{1}{6.28\sqrt{25,334 \times 10^{-18}}} = \frac{1}{6.28 \times 159.2 \times 10^{-9}} = \frac{1}{1000 \times 10^{-9}}$$

$$f_r = 1 \times 10^6 \text{ Hz} = 1 \text{ MHz} = 1000 \text{ kHz}$$

For any $LC$ circuit, series or parallel, the $f_r$ equal to $1/(2\pi\sqrt{LC})$ is the resonant frequency that makes the inductive and capacitive reactances equal.

To do this problem on a calculator, keep in mind the following points:

1. If your calculator does not have an exponential (EXP) key, work with the powers* of 10 separately, without the calculator. For multiplication, add the exponents. The square root has one-half the exponent, but be sure the exponent is an even number before dividing by 2. The reciprocal has the same exponent but with opposite sign.
2. Multiply the $L$ and $C$ first, take the square root of the product, and multiply by $2\pi$ or 6.28. The $(\sqrt{\phantom{x}})$ key is usually a second function of the $(x^2)$ key.
3. After all the multiplications are complete, take the reciprocal of the final product by using the $(1/x)$ key. This operation may require using the $(2ndF)$ key.

For the example just solved with 239 $\mu$H for $L$ and 106 pF for $C$, first punch in 239, push the $(\times)$ key, punch in 106 and then press the $(=)$ key for the product of 25,334. While this number is on the display, push the $(\sqrt{\phantom{x}})$ key for 159.2. Keep this display, press the $(\times)$ key, punch in 6.28 for $2\pi$ and push the $(=)$ key for the total product of approximately 1000 in the denominator.

The powers of 10 in the denominator are $10^{-6} \times 10^{-12} = 10^{-18}$. Its square root is $10^{-9}$.

For the reciprocal, while 1000 for the denominator is on the display, press the $(1/x)$ key for the reciprocal, equal to 0.001. The reciprocal of $10^{-9}$ is $10^9$. The answer for $f_r$ then is $0.001 \times 10^9$, which equals $1 \times 10^6$.

**HOW THE $f_r$ VARIES WITH $L$ AND $C$**  It is important to note that higher values of $L$ and $C$ result in lower values of $f_r$. Either $L$ or $C$, or both, can be varied. An $LC$ circuit can be resonant at any frequency, from a few hertz to many megahertz.

As examples, an $LC$ combination with the relatively large values of an 8-H inductance and a 20-$\mu$F capacitance is resonant at the low audio frequency of 12.6 Hz. For a much higher frequency in the RF range, a small inductance of 2 $\mu$H will resonate with the small capacitance of 3 pF for an $f_r$ of 64.9 MHz. These examples are solved in the next two problems for more practice with the resonant frequency formula. Such calculations are often used in practical

**DID YOU KNOW?**

Nuclear plants in the United States number 110 and meet 20 percent of the country's power needs. Since 1986, no new reactors have been authorized.

---

*For an explanation of powers of 10 see Grob, B.: *Mathematics for Basic Electronics*, Glencoe/McGraw-Hill, Columbus, Ohio.

applications of tuned circuits. Probably the most important feature of any *LC* combination is its resonant frequency, especially in RF circuits. The applications of resonance are mainly for radio frequencies.

## Example

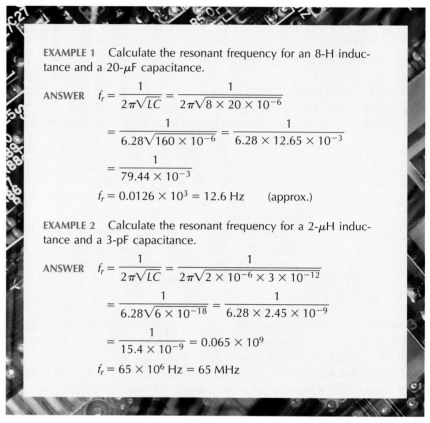

EXAMPLE 1    Calculate the resonant frequency for an 8-H inductance and a 20-$\mu$F capacitance.

ANSWER    $f_r = \dfrac{1}{2\pi\sqrt{LC}} = \dfrac{1}{2\pi\sqrt{8 \times 20 \times 10^{-6}}}$

$= \dfrac{1}{6.28\sqrt{160 \times 10^{-6}}} = \dfrac{1}{6.28 \times 12.65 \times 10^{-3}}$

$= \dfrac{1}{79.44 \times 10^{-3}}$

$f_r = 0.0126 \times 10^3 = 12.6$ Hz    (approx.)

EXAMPLE 2    Calculate the resonant frequency for a 2-$\mu$H inductance and a 3-pF capacitance.

ANSWER    $f_r = \dfrac{1}{2\pi\sqrt{LC}} = \dfrac{1}{2\pi\sqrt{2 \times 10^{-6} \times 3 \times 10^{-12}}}$

$= \dfrac{1}{6.28\sqrt{6 \times 10^{-18}}} = \dfrac{1}{6.28 \times 2.45 \times 10^{-9}}$

$= \dfrac{1}{15.4 \times 10^{-9}} = 0.065 \times 10^9$

$f_r = 65 \times 10^6$ Hz $= 65$ MHz

Specifically, because of the square root in the denominator of Formula (26-1), the $f_r$ decreases inversely as the square root of *L* or *C*. For instance, if *L* or *C* is quadrupled, the $f_r$ is reduced one half. The ½ is equal to the square root of ¼.

As a numerical example, suppose $f_r$ is 6 MHz with particular values of *L* and *C*. If either *L* or *C* is made four times larger, then $f_r$ will be reduced to 3 MHz.

Or, to take the opposite case of doubling the frequency from 6 MHz to 12 MHz, the following can be done:

1.   Use one-fourth the *L* with the same *C*.
2.   Use one-fourth the *C* with the same *L*.
3.   Reduced both *L* and *C* by one-half.
4.   Use any new combination of *L* and *C* whose product will be one-fourth the original product of *L* and *C*.

*LC* **PRODUCT DETERMINES** $f_r$    There are any number of *LC* combinations that can be resonant at one frequency. With more *L*, then less *C* can be used for the same $f_r$. Or less *L* can be used with more *C*. Table 26-3 lists five

TABLE 26-3    LC COMBINATIONS RESONANT AT 1000 kHz

| L, $\mu$H | C, pF | L × C LC PRODUCT | $X_L$, $\Omega$ AT 1000 kHz | $X_C$, $\Omega$ AT 1000 kHz |
|---|---|---|---|---|
| 23.9 | 1060 | 25,334 | 150 | 150 |
| 119.5 | 212 | 25,334 | 750 | 750 |
| 239 | 106 | 25,334 | 1,500 | 1,500 |
| 478 | 53 | 25,334 | 3,000 | 3,000 |
| 2390 | 10.6 | 25,334 | 15,000 | 15,000 |

possible combinations of $L$ and $C$ resonant at 1000 kHz, just as an example of one $f_r$. The resonant frequency is the same 1000 kHz here for all five combinations. When either $L$ or $C$ is increased by a factor of 10 or 2, the other is decreased by the same factor, resulting in a constant value for the $LC$ product.

The reactance at resonance changes with different combinations of $L$ and $C$, but in all five cases $X_L$ and $X_C$ are equal to each other at 1000 kHz. This is the resonant frequency determined by the value of the $LC$ product in $f_r = 1/(2\pi\sqrt{LC})$.

**MEASURING $L$ OR $C$ BY RESONANCE**    Of the three factors $L$, $C$, and $f_r$ in the resonant-frequency formula, any one can be calculated when the other two are known. The resonant frequency of the $LC$ combination can be found experimentally by determining the frequency that produces the resonant response in an $LC$ combination. With a known value of either $L$ or $C$, and the resonant frequency determined, the third factor can be calculated. This method is commonly used for measuring inductance or capacitance. A test instrument for this purpose is the $Q$ meter, which also measures the $Q$ of a coil.

**CALCULATING $C$ FROM $f_r$**    The $C$ can be taken out of the square root sign or radical in the resonance formula, as follows:

$$f_r = \frac{1}{2\pi\sqrt{LC}}$$

Squaring both sides to eliminate the radical gives

$$f_r^2 = \frac{1}{(2\pi)^2 LC}$$

Inverting $C$ and $f_r^2$ gives

$$\blacktriangleright \qquad C = \frac{1}{4\pi^2 f_r^2 L} \qquad\qquad\qquad (26\text{-}2)$$

where $f_r$ is in hertz, $C$ is in farads, and $L$ is in henrys.

**CALCULATING $L$ FROM $f_r$**    Similarly, the resonance formula can be transposed to find $L$. Then

$$\blacktriangleright \qquad L = \frac{1}{4\pi^2 f_r^2 C} \qquad\qquad\qquad (26\text{-}3)$$

With Formula (26-3), $L$ is determined by its $f_r$ with a known value of $C$. Similarly, $C$ is determined from Formula (26-2) by its $f_r$ with a known value of $L$.

## Example

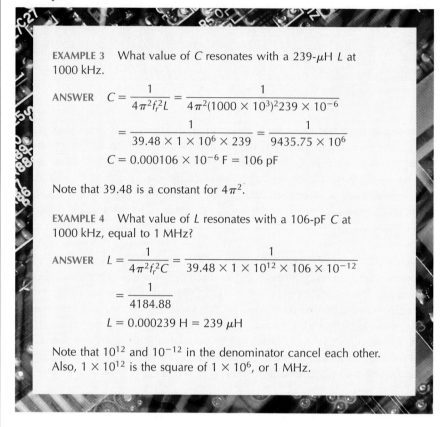

**EXAMPLE 3** What value of $C$ resonates with a 239-$\mu$H $L$ at 1000 kHz.

**ANSWER** $C = \dfrac{1}{4\pi^2 f_r^2 L} = \dfrac{1}{4\pi^2(1000 \times 10^3)^2 239 \times 10^{-6}}$

$= \dfrac{1}{39.48 \times 1 \times 10^6 \times 239} = \dfrac{1}{9435.75 \times 10^6}$

$C = 0.000106 \times 10^{-6}\text{ F} = 106\text{ pF}$

Note that 39.48 is a constant for $4\pi^2$.

**EXAMPLE 4** What value of $L$ resonates with a 106-pF $C$ at 1000 kHz, equal to 1 MHz?

**ANSWER** $L = \dfrac{1}{4\pi^2 f_r^2 C} = \dfrac{1}{39.48 \times 1 \times 10^{12} \times 106 \times 10^{-12}}$

$= \dfrac{1}{4184.88}$

$L = 0.000239\text{ H} = 239\ \mu\text{H}$

Note that $10^{12}$ and $10^{-12}$ in the denominator cancel each other. Also, $1 \times 10^{12}$ is the square of $1 \times 10^6$, or 1 MHz.

The values in Examples 3 and 4 are from the $LC$ circuit illustrated in Fig. 26-2 for series resonance and Fig. 26-6 for parallel resonance.

**TEST-POINT QUESTION 26-4**

Answers at end of chapter.
**a.** To increase $f_r$, must the $C$ be increased or decreased?
**b.** If $C$ is increased from 100 to 400 pF, $L$ must be decreased from 800 $\mu$H to what value for the same $f_r$?
**c.** Give the constant value for $4\pi^2$.

## 26-5 $Q$ MAGNIFICATION FACTOR OF RESONANT CIRCUIT

The quality, or *figure of merit,* of the resonant circuit, in sharpness of resonance, is indicated by the factor $Q$. In general, the higher the ratio of the reactance at resonance to the series resistance, the higher is the $Q$ and the sharper the resonance effect.

**$Q$ OF SERIES CIRCUIT**    In a series resonant circuit we can calculate $Q$ from the following formula:

▶     $$Q = \frac{X_L}{r_S}$$     **(26-4)**

where $Q$ is the figure of merit, $X_L$ is the inductive reactance in ohms at the resonant frequency, and $r_S$ is the resistance in ohms in series with $X_L$. For the series resonant circuit in Fig. 26-2,

$$Q = \frac{1500\ \Omega}{10\ \Omega} = 150$$

The $Q$ is a numerical factor without any units, because it is a ratio of reactance to resistance and the ohms cancel. Since the series resistance limits the amount of current at resonance, the lower the resistance, the sharper the increase to maximum current at the resonant frequency, and the higher the $Q$. Also, a higher value of reactance at resonance allows the maximum current to produce a higher value of voltage for the output.

The $Q$ has the same value if it is calculated with $X_C$ instead of $X_L$, since they are equal at resonance. However, the $Q$ of the circuit is generally considered in terms of $X_L$, because usually the coil has the series resistance of the circuit. In this case, the $Q$ of the coil and the $Q$ of the series resonant circuit are the same. If extra resistance is added, the $Q$ of the circuit will be less than the $Q$ of the coil. The highest possible $Q$ for the circuit is the $Q$ of the coil.

The value of 150 can be considered as a high $Q$. Typical values are 50 to 250, approximately. Less than 10 is a low $Q$; more than 300 is a very high $Q$.

**HIGHER $L/C$ RATIO CAN PROVIDE HIGHER $Q$**    As shown before in Table 26-3, different combinations of $L$ and $C$ can be resonant at the same frequency. However, the amount of reactance at resonance is different. More $X_L$ can be obtained with a higher $L$ and lower $C$ for resonance, although $X_L$ and $X_C$ must be equal at the resonant frequency. Therefore, both $X_L$ and $X_C$ are higher with a higher $L/C$ ratio for resonance.

More $X_L$ can allow a higher $Q$ if the ac resistance does not increase as much as the reactance. With typical RF coils, an approximate rule is that maximum $Q$ can be obtained when $X_L$ is about 1000 $\Omega$. In many cases, though, the minimum $C$ is limited by the stray capacitance in the circuit.

**$Q$ RISE IN VOLTAGE ACROSS SERIES $L$ OR $C$**    The $Q$ of the resonant circuit can be considered a magnification factor that determines how much the voltage across $L$ or $C$ is increased by the resonant rise of current in a series circuit. Specifically, the voltage output at series resonance is $Q$ times the generator voltage:

▶     $$V_L = V_C = Q \times V_{\text{gen}}$$     **(26-5)**

In Fig. 26-4, for example, the generator voltage is 300 $\mu$V and $Q$ is 150. The resonant rise of voltage across either $L$ or $C$ then equals 300 $\mu$V $\times$ 150, or 45,000 $\mu$V. Note that this is the same value calculated in Table 26-1 for $V_C$ or $V_L$ at resonance.

## HOW TO MEASURE Q IN A SERIES RESONANT CIRCUIT   The fundamental nature of $Q$ for a series resonant circuit is seen from the fact that the $Q$ can be determined experimentally by measuring the $Q$ rise in voltage across either $L$ or $C$ and comparing this voltage with the generator voltage. As a formula,

$$Q = \frac{V_{out}}{V_{in}} \qquad\qquad\qquad \textbf{(26-6)}$$

where $V_{out}$ is the ac voltage measured across the coil or capacitor and $V_{in}$ is the generator voltage.

Referring to Fig. 26-5, suppose that you measure with an ac voltmeter across $L$ or $C$ and this voltage equals 45,000 $\mu$V at the resonant frequency. Also, measure the generator input of 300 $\mu$V. Then

$$Q = \frac{V_{out}}{V_{in}}$$

$$= \frac{45{,}000 \ \mu V}{300 \ \mu V}$$

$$Q = 150$$

This method is better than the $X_L/r_S$ formula for determining $Q$ because $r_S$ is the ac resistance of the coil, which is not so easily measured. Remember that the coil's ac resistance can be more than double the dc resistance measured with an ohmmeter. In fact, measuring $Q$ with Formula (26-6) makes it possible to calculate the ac resistance. These points are illustrated in the following examples.

## *Example*

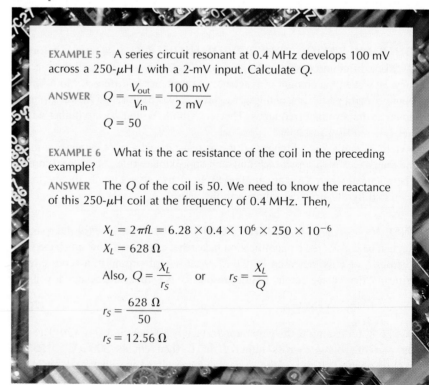

EXAMPLE 5   A series circuit resonant at 0.4 MHz develops 100 mV across a 250-$\mu$H $L$ with a 2-mV input. Calculate $Q$.

ANSWER   $Q = \dfrac{V_{out}}{V_{in}} = \dfrac{100 \text{ mV}}{2 \text{ mV}}$

$Q = 50$

EXAMPLE 6   What is the ac resistance of the coil in the preceding example?

ANSWER   The $Q$ of the coil is 50. We need to know the reactance of this 250-$\mu$H coil at the frequency of 0.4 MHz. Then,

$$X_L = 2\pi f L = 6.28 \times 0.4 \times 10^6 \times 250 \times 10^{-6}$$

$$X_L = 628 \ \Omega$$

$$\text{Also, } Q = \frac{X_L}{r_S} \quad \text{or} \quad r_S = \frac{X_L}{Q}$$

$$r_S = \frac{628 \ \Omega}{50}$$

$$r_S = 12.56 \ \Omega$$

**Q OF PARALLEL CIRCUIT** In a parallel resonant circuit, where $r_S$ is very small compared with $X_L$, the $Q$ also equals $X_L/r_S$. Note that $r_S$ is still the resistance of the coil in series with $X_L$ (see Fig. 26-8). The $Q$ of the coil determines the $Q$ of the parallel circuit here because it is less than the $Q$ of the capacitive branch. Capacitors used in tuned circuits generally have a very high $Q$ because of their low losses. In Fig. 26-8, the $Q$ is 1500 $\Omega$/10 $\Omega$, or 150, the same as the series resonant circuit with the same values.

This example assumes that the generator resistance is very high and that there is no other resistance branch shunting the tuned circuit. Then the $Q$ of the parallel resonant circuit is the same as the $Q$ of the coil. Actually, shunt resistance can lower the $Q$ of a parallel resonant circuit, as analyzed in Sec. 26-10.

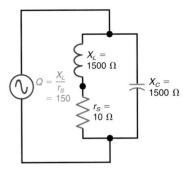

### Q RISE IN IMPEDANCE ACROSS PARALLEL RESONANT CIRCUIT

For parallel resonance, the $Q$ magnification factor determines by how much the impedance across the parallel $LC$ circuit is increased because of the minimum line current. Specifically, the impedance across the parallel resonant circuit is $Q$ times the inductive reactance at the resonant frequency:

$$Z_{EQ} = Q \times X_L \qquad \text{(26-7)}$$

Referring back to the parallel resonant circuit in Fig. 26-6, as an example, $X_L$ is 1500 $\Omega$ and $Q$ is 150. The result is a rise of impedance to the maximum value of 150 $\times$ 1500 $\Omega$, or 225,000 $\Omega$, at the resonant frequency.

Since the line current equals $V_A/Z_{EQ}$, the minimum value of line current is 300 $\mu$V/225,000 $\Omega$, which equals 0.00133 $\mu$A.

At $f_r$ the minimum line current is $1/Q$ of either branch current. In Fig. 26-7, $I_L$ or $I_C$ is 0.2 $\mu$A and $Q$ is 150. Therefore, $I_T$ is 0.2/150, or 0.00133 $\mu$A, which is the same answer as $V_A/Z_{EQ}$. Or, stated another way, the circulating tank current is $Q$ times the minimum $I_T$.

### HOW TO MEASURE $Z_{EQ}$ OF A PARALLEL RESONANT CIRCUIT

Formula (26-7) for $Z_{EQ}$ is also useful in its inverted form as $Q = Z_{EQ}/X_L$. We can measure $Z_{EQ}$ by the method illustrated in Fig. 26-9. Then $Q$ can be calculated from the value of $Z_{EQ}$ and the inductive reactance of the coil.

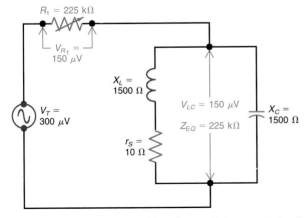

FIG. 26-9 How to measure $Z_{EQ}$ of a parallel resonant circuit. Adjust $R_1$ to make its $V_R$ equal to $V_{LC}$. Then $Z_{EQ} = R_1$.

To measure $Z_{EQ}$, first tune the $LC$ circuit to resonance. Then adjust $R_1$ in Fig. 26-9 to the resistance that makes its ac voltage equal to the ac voltage across the tuned circuit. With equal voltages, the $Z_{EQ}$ must be the same value as $R_1$.

For the example here, which corresponds to the parallel resonance shown in Figs. 26-6 and 26-8, the $Z_{EQ}$ is equal to 225,000 $\Omega$. This high value is a result of parallel resonance. The $X_L$ is 1500 $\Omega$. Therefore, to determine $Q$, the calculations are

$$Q = \frac{Z_{EQ}}{X_L} = \frac{225,000}{1500} = 150$$

*Example*

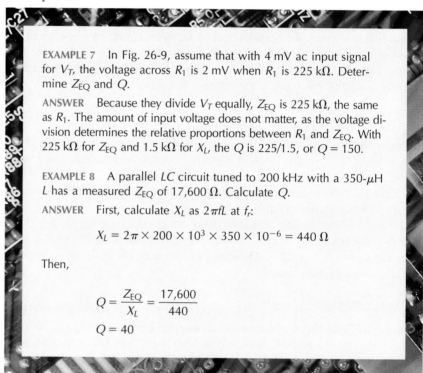

EXAMPLE 7    In Fig. 26-9, assume that with 4 mV ac input signal for $V_T$, the voltage across $R_1$ is 2 mV when $R_1$ is 225 k$\Omega$. Determine $Z_{EQ}$ and $Q$.

ANSWER    Because they divide $V_T$ equally, $Z_{EQ}$ is 225 k$\Omega$, the same as $R_1$. The amount of input voltage does not matter, as the voltage division determines the relative proportions between $R_1$ and $Z_{EQ}$. With 225 k$\Omega$ for $Z_{EQ}$ and 1.5 k$\Omega$ for $X_L$, the $Q$ is 225/1.5, or $Q = 150$.

EXAMPLE 8    A parallel $LC$ circuit tuned to 200 kHz with a 350-$\mu$H $L$ has a measured $Z_{EQ}$ of 17,600 $\Omega$. Calculate $Q$.

ANSWER    First, calculate $X_L$ as $2\pi f L$ at $f_r$:

$$X_L = 2\pi \times 200 \times 10^3 \times 350 \times 10^{-6} = 440 \ \Omega$$

Then,

$$Q = \frac{Z_{EQ}}{X_L} = \frac{17,600}{440}$$

$$Q = 40$$

---

### TEST-POINT QUESTION 26-5

Answers at end of chapter.
**a.** In a series resonant circuit, $V_L$ is 300 mV with input of 3 mV. Calculate $Q$.
**b.** In a parallel resonant circuit, $X_L$ is 500 $\Omega$. With a $Q$ of 50, calculate $Z_{EQ}$.

## 26-6 BANDWIDTH OF RESONANT CIRCUIT

When we say an $LC$ circuit is resonant at one frequency, this is true for the maximum resonance effect. However, other frequencies close to $f_r$ also are effective.

For series resonance, frequencies just below and above $f_r$ produce increased current, but a little less than the value at resonance. Similarly, for parallel resonance, frequencies close to $f_r$ can provide a high impedance, although a little less than the maximum $Z_{EQ}$.

Therefore, any resonant frequency has an associated band of frequencies that provide resonance effects. How wide the band is depends on the $Q$ of the resonant circuit. Actually, it is practically impossible to have an $LC$ circuit with a resonant effect at only one frequency. The width of the resonant band of frequencies centered around $f_r$ is called the *bandwidth* of the tuned circuit.

**MEASUREMENT OF BANDWIDTH**  The group of frequencies with a response 70.7 percent of maximum, or more, is generally considered the bandwidth of the tuned circuit, as shown in Fig. 26-10b. The resonant response here is increasing current for the series circuit in Fig. 26-10a. Therefore, the bandwidth is measured between the two frequencies, $f_1$ and $f_2$, producing 70.7 percent of the maximum current at $f_r$.

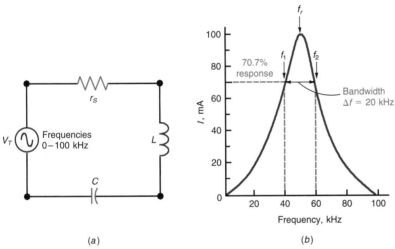

FIG. 26-10  Bandwidth of a tuned $LC$ circuit. (a) Series circuit with input of 0 to 100 kHz. (b) Response curve with bandwidth $\Delta f$ equal to 20 kHz between $f_1$ and $f_2$.

For a parallel circuit, the resonant response is increasing impedance $Z_{EQ}$. Then the bandwidth is measured between the two frequencies allowing 70.7 percent of the maximum $Z_{EQ}$ at $f_r$.

The bandwidth indicated on the response curve in Fig. 26-10b equals 20 kHz. This value is the difference between $f_2$ at 60 kHz and $f_1$ at 40 kHz, both with 70.7 percent response.

Compared with the maximum current of 100 mA for $f_r$ at 50 kHz, $f_1$ below resonance and $f_2$ above resonance each allow a rise to 70.7 mA. All frequencies in this band 20 kHz wide allow 70.7 mA, or more, as the resonant response in this example.

**BANDWIDTH EQUALS $f_r/Q$**  Sharp resonance with high $Q$ means narrow bandwidth. The lower the $Q$, the broader the resonant response and the greater the bandwidth.

Also, the higher the resonant frequency, the greater is the range of frequency values included in the bandwidth for a given sharpness of resonance. Therefore, the bandwidth of a resonant circuit depends on the factors $f_r$ and $Q$. The formula is

$$\blacktriangleright \qquad f_2 - f_1 = \Delta f = \frac{f_r}{Q} \qquad \qquad \text{(26-8)}$$

where $\Delta f$ is the total bandwidth in the same units as the resonant frequency $f_r$. The bandwidth $\Delta f$ can also be abbreviated BW.

For example, a series circuit resonant at 800 kHz with a $Q$ of 100 has a bandwidth of 800/100, or 8 kHz. Then the $I$ is 70.7 percent of maximum, or more, for all frequencies for a band 8 kHz wide. This frequency band is centered around 800 kHz, from 796 to 804 kHz.

With a parallel resonant circuit having a $Q$ higher than 10, Formula (26-8) also can be used for calculating the bandwidth of frequencies which provide 70.7 percent or more of the maximum $Z_{EQ}$. However, the formula cannot be used for parallel resonant circuits with low $Q$, as the resonance curve then becomes unsymmetrical.

**HIGH $Q$ MEANS NARROW BANDWIDTH**   The effect for different values of $Q$ is illustrated in Fig. 26-11. Note that a higher $Q$ for the same resonant frequency results in less bandwidth. The slope is sharper for the sides or *skirts* of the response curve, in addition to its greater amplitude.

High $Q$ is generally desirable for more output from the resonant circuit. However, it must have enough bandwidth to include the desired range of signal frequencies.

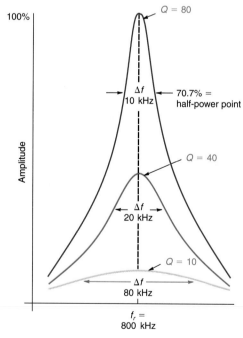

**FIG. 26-11**   Higher $Q$ provides a sharper resonant response. Amplitude is $I$ for series resonance or $Z_{EQ}$ for parallel resonance. Bandwidth at half-power frequencies is $\Delta f$.

**THE EDGE FREQUENCIES**   Both $f_1$ and $f_2$ are separated from $f_r$ by one-half of the total bandwidth. For the top curve in Fig. 26-11, as an example, with a $Q$ of 80, $\Delta f$ is ±5 kHz centered around 800 kHz for $f_r$. To determine the edge frequencies:

$$f_1 = f_r - \frac{\Delta f}{2} = 800 - 5 = 795 \text{ kHz}$$

$$f_2 = f_r + \frac{\Delta f}{2} = 800 + 5 = 805 \text{ kHz}$$

These examples assume the resonance curve is symmetrical. This is true for a high-$Q$ parallel resonant circuit and a series resonant circuit with any $Q$.

## Example

**EXAMPLE 9**   An $LC$ circuit resonant at 2000 kHz has a $Q$ of 100. Find the total bandwidth $\Delta f$ and the edge frequencies $f_1$ and $f_2$.

**ANSWER**   $\Delta f = \dfrac{f_r}{Q} = \dfrac{2000 \text{ kHz}}{100} = 20 \text{ kHz}$

$$f_1 = f_r - \frac{\Delta f}{2} = 2000 - 10 = 1990 \text{ kHz}$$

$$f_2 = f_r + \frac{\Delta f}{2} = 2000 + 10 = 2010 \text{ kHz}$$

**EXAMPLE 10**   Repeat Example 9 for an $f_r$ equal to 6000 kHz and the same $Q$ of 100.

**ANSWER**   $f = \dfrac{f_r}{Q} = \dfrac{6000 \text{ kHz}}{100} = 60 \text{ kHz}$

$$f_1 = 6000 - 30 = 5970 \text{ kHz}$$

$$f_2 = 6000 + 30 = 6030 \text{ kHz}$$

Notice that $\Delta f$ is three times as wide as $\Delta f$ in Example 9 for the same $Q$ because $f_r$ is three times higher.

**HALF-POWER POINTS**   It is simply for convenience in calculations that the bandwidth is defined between the two frequencies having 70.7 percent response. At each of these frequencies, the net capacitive or inductive reactance equals the resistance. Then the total impedance of the series reactance and resistance is 1.4 times greater than $R$. With this much more impedance, the current is reduced to 1/1.414, or 0.707, of its maximum value.

Furthermore, the relative current or voltage value of 70.7 percent corresponds to 50 percent in power, since power is $I^2R$ or $V^2/R$ and the square of 0.707 equals 0.50. Therefore, the bandwidth between frequencies having 70.7 percent response in current or voltage is also the bandwidth in terms of half-power points. Formula (26-8) is derived for $\Delta f$ between the points with 70.7 percent response on the resonance curve.

**MEASURING BANDWIDTH TO CALCULATE $Q$**   The half-power frequencies $f_1$ and $f_2$ can be determined experimentally. For series resonance, find the two frequencies at which the current is 70.7 percent of maximum $I$. Or, for parallel resonance, find the two frequencies that make the impedance 70.7 percent of the maximum $Z_{EQ}$. The following method uses the circuit in Fig. 26-9 for measuring $Z_{EQ}$, but with different values to determine its bandwidth and $Q$.

1.  Tune the circuit to resonance and determine its maximum $Z_{EQ}$ at $f_r$. In this example, assume that $Z_{EQ}$ is 10,000 $\Omega$ at the resonant frequency of 200 kHz.
2.  Keep the same amount of input voltage, but change its frequency slightly below $f_r$ to determine the frequency $f_1$ which results in a $Z_1$ equal to 70.7 percent of $Z_{EQ}$. The required value here is $0.707 \times 10{,}000$, or 7070 $\Omega$, for $Z_1$ at $f_1$. Assume this frequency $f_1$ is determined to be 195 kHz.
3.  Similarly, find the frequency $f_2$ above $f_r$ that results in the impedance $Z_2$ of 7070 $\Omega$. Assume $f_2$ is 205 kHz.
4.  The total bandwidth between the half-power frequencies equals $f_2 - f_1$ or $205 - 195$. Then the value of $\Delta f = 10$ kHz.
5.  Then $Q = f_r/\Delta f$ or 200 kHz/10 kHz = 20 for the calculated value of $Q$.

In this way, measuring the bandwidth makes it possible to determine the $Q$. With $\Delta f$ and $f_r$, the $Q$ can be determined for either parallel or series resonance.

---

### TEST-POINT QUESTION 26-6

Answers at end of chapter.
**a.** An $LC$ circuit with $f_r$ of 10 MHz has a $Q$ of 40. Calculate the half-power bandwidth.
**b.** For an $f_r$ of 500 kHz and bandwidth $\Delta f$ of 10 kHz, calculate $Q$.

## 26-7 TUNING

Tuning means obtaining resonance at different frequencies by varying either $L$ or $C$. As illustrated in Fig. 26-12, the variable capacitance $C$ can be adjusted to tune the series $LC$ circuit to resonance at any one of the five different frequencies. Each of the voltages $V_1$ to $V_5$ indicates an ac input with a specific frequency. Which one is selected for maximum output is determined by the resonant frequency of the $LC$ circuit.

When $C$ is set to 424 pF, for example, the resonant frequency of the $LC$ circuit is 500 kHz for $f_{r_1}$. The input voltage that has the frequency of 500 kHz then produces a resonant rise of current which results in maximum output voltage across $C$. At other frequencies, such as 707 kHz, the voltage output is less than the input. With $C$ at 424 pF, therefore, the $LC$ circuit tuned to 500 kHz selects this frequency by providing much more voltage output than other frequencies.

Suppose that we want maximum output for the ac input voltage that has the frequency of 707 kHz. Then $C$ is set at 212 pF to make the $LC$ circuit resonant at 707 kHz for $f_{r_2}$. Similarly, the tuned circuit can resonate at a different frequency for each input voltage. In this way, the $LC$ circuit is tuned to select the desired frequency.

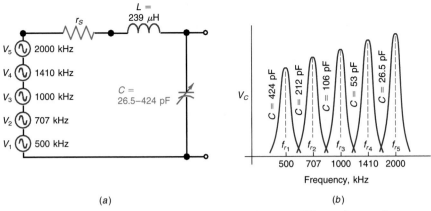

FIG. 26-12  Tuning a series *LC* circuit. (*a*) Input voltages at different frequencies. (*b*) Relative response for each frequency when *C* is varied. (Not to scale.)

The variable capacitance *C* can be set at the values listed in Table 26-4 to tune the *LC* circuit to different frequencies. Only five frequencies are listed here, but any one capacitance value between 26.5 and 424 pF can tune the 239-$\mu$H coil to resonance at any frequency in the range of 500 to 2000 kHz. It should be noted that a parallel resonant circuit also can be tuned by varying *C* or *L*.

| TABLE 26-4  TUNING LC CIRCUIT BY VARYING C | | |
|---|---|---|
| L, $\mu$H | C, pF | $f_r$, kHz |
| 239 | 424 | 500 |
| 239 | 212 | 707 |
| 239 | 106 | 1000 |
| 239 | 53 | 1410 |
| 239 | 26.5 | 2000 |

**TUNING RATIO**  When an *LC* circuit is tuned, the change in resonant frequency is inversely proportional to the square root of the change in *L* or *C*. Referring to Table 26-4, notice that when *C* is decreased to one-fourth, from 424 to 106 pF, the resonant frequency doubles from 500 to 1000 kHz. Or the frequency is increased by the factor $1/\sqrt{\frac{1}{4}}$, which equals 2.

Suppose that we want to tune through the whole frequency range of 500 to 2000 kHz. This is a tuning ratio of 4:1 for the highest frequency to the lowest frequency. Then the capacitance must be varied from 424 to 26.5 pF, which is a 16:1 capacitance ratio.

**RADIO TUNING DIAL**  Figure 26-13 illustrates a typical application of resonant circuits in tuning a receiver to the carrier frequency of a desired station in the band. The tuning is done by the air capacitor *C*, which can be varied from 360 pF with the plates completely in mesh to 40 pF out of mesh. The fixed plates form the *stator*, while the *rotor* has the plates that move in and out.

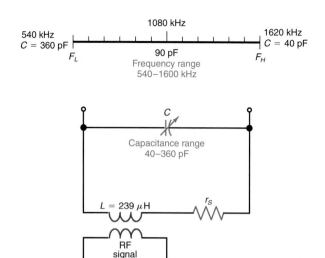

FIG. 26-13   Application of tuning an *LC* circuit through the AM radio band.

Note that the lowest frequency $F_L$ at 540 kHz is tuned in with the highest $C$ at 360 pF. Resonance at the highest frequency $F_H$ at 1620 kHz results with the lowest $C$ at 40 pF.

The capacitance range of 40 to 360 pF tunes through the frequency range from 1620 kHz down to 540 kHz. Frequency $F_L$ is one-third $F_H$ because the maximum $C$ is nine times the minimum $C$. The tuning dial, in kHz, usually omits the last zero to save space.

The same idea applies to tuning through the commercial FM broadcast band of 88 to 108 MHz, with smaller values of $L$ and $C$. Also, television receivers are tuned to a specific broadcast channel by resonance at the desired frequencies.

For electronic tuning, the $C$ is varied by a *varactor*. This is a semiconductor diode that varies in capacitance when its voltage is changed. See Chapter 28, "Electronic Devices."

---

### TEST-POINT QUESTION 26-7

Answers at end of chapter.
**a.** When a tuning capacitor is completely in mesh, is the station tuned in the highest or lowest frequency in the band?
**b.** A tuning ratio of 2 : 1 in frequency requires what ratio of variable $L$ or $C$?

## 26-8 MISTUNING

Suppose that a series *LC* circuit is tuned to 1000 kHz but the frequency of the input voltage is 17 kHz, completely off resonance. The circuit could provide a $Q$ rise in output voltage for current having the frequency of 1000 kHz, but there is no input voltage and therefore no current at this frequency.

The input voltage produces current that has the frequency of 17 kHz. This frequency cannot produce a resonant rise in current, however, because the current is limited by the net reactance. When the frequency of the input voltage and the resonant frequency of the *LC* circuit are not the same, therefore, the mistuned circuit has very little output compared with the *Q* rise in voltage at resonance.

Similarly, when a parallel circuit is mistuned, it does not have a high value of impedance. Furthermore, the net reactance off resonance makes the *LC* circuit either inductive or capacitive.

**SERIES CIRCUIT OFF RESONANCE**    When the frequency of the input voltage is lower than the resonant frequency of a series *LC* circuit, the capacitive reactance is greater than the inductive reactance. As a result, there is more voltage across the capacitive reactance than across the inductive reactance. The series *LC* circuit is capacitive below resonance, therefore, with capacitive current leading the generator voltage.

Above the resonant frequency, the inductive reactance is greater than the capacitive reactance. As a result, the circuit is inductive above resonance, with inductive current that lags the generator voltage. In both cases, there is much less output voltage than at resonance.

**PARALLEL CIRCUIT OFF RESONANCE**    With a parallel *LC* circuit, the smaller amount of inductive reactance below resonance results in more inductive branch current than capacitive branch current. The net line current is inductive, therefore, making the parallel *LC* circuit inductive below resonance, as the line current lags the generator voltage.

Above the resonant frequency, the net line current is capacitive because of the higher value of capacitive branch current. Then the parallel *LC* circuit is capacitive, with line current leading the generator voltage. In both cases the total impedance of the parallel circuit is much less than the maximum impedance at resonance. Note that the capacitive and inductive effects off resonance are opposite for series and parallel *LC* circuits.

---

### TEST-POINT QUESTION 26-8

Answers at end of chapter.
   **a.** Is a series resonant circuit inductive or capacitive below resonance?
   **b.** Is a parallel resonant circuit inductive or capacitive below resonance?

## 26-9 ANALYSIS OF PARALLEL RESONANT CIRCUITS

Parallel resonance is more complex than series resonance because the reactive branch currents are not exactly equal when $X_L$ equals $X_C$. The reason is that the coil has its series resistance $r_S$ in the $X_L$ branch, while the capacitor has only $X_C$ in its branch.

For high-*Q* circuits, we consider $r_S$ to be negligible. In low-*Q* circuits, however, the inductive branch must be analyzed as a complex impedance with $X_L$ and $r_S$ in series. This impedance is in parallel with $X_C$, as shown in Fig. 26-14. The

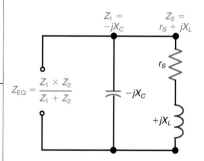

**FIG. 26-14**   General method of calculating $Z_{EQ}$ for a parallel resonant circuit as $(Z_1 \times Z_2)/(Z_1 + Z_2)$ with complex numbers.

total impedance $Z_{EQ}$ can then be calculated by using complex numbers, as explained in Chap. 25.

**HIGH-$Q$ CIRCUIT**   We can apply the general method in Fig. 26-14 to the parallel resonant circuit shown before in Fig. 26-6 to see if $Z_{EQ}$ is 225,000 Ω. In this example, $X_L$ and $X_C$ are 1500 Ω and $r_S$ is 10 Ω. The calculations are

$$\blacktriangleright \quad Z_{EQ} = \frac{Z_1 \times Z_2}{Z_1 + Z_2} = \frac{-j1500 \times (j1500 + 10)}{-j1500 + j1500 + 10}$$

$$= \frac{-j^2 2.25 \times 10^6 - j15,000}{10} = -j^2 2.25 \times 10^5 - j1500$$

$$Z_{EQ} = 225,000 - j1500 = 225,000 \underline{/0°}\ \Omega$$

Note that $-j^2$ is $+1$. Also, the reactive $j1500$ Ω is negligible compared with the resistive 225,000 Ω. This answer for $Z_{EQ}$ is the same as $Q \times X_L$, or $150 \times 1,500$, because of the high $Q$ with negligibly small $r_S$.

**LOW-$Q$ CIRCUIT**   We can consider a $Q$ less than 10 as low. For the same circuit in Fig. 26-6, if $r_S$ is 300 Ω with an $X_L$ of 1500 Ω, the $Q$ will be 1500/300, which equals 5. For this case of appreciable $r_S$, the branch currents cannot be equal when $X_L$ and $X_C$ are equal because then the inductive branch will have more impedance and less current.

With a low-$Q$ circuit $Z_{EQ}$ must be calculated in terms of the branch impedances. For this example, the calculations are simpler with all impedances stated in kilohms:

$$Z_{EQ} = \frac{Z_1 \times Z_2}{Z_1 + Z_2} = \frac{-j1.5 \times (j1.5 + 0.3)}{-j1.5 + j1.5 + 0.3} = \frac{-j^2 2.25 - j0.45}{0.3}$$

$$Z_{EQ} = 7.5 - j1.5\ \Omega = 7.65\ \underline{/-11.3°}\ k\Omega = 7650\ \underline{/-11.3°}\ \Omega$$

The phase angle $\theta$ is not zero because the reactive branch currents are unequal, even though $X_L$ and $X_C$ are equal. The appreciable value of $r_S$ in the $X_L$ branch makes this branch current smaller than $I_C$ in the $X_C$ branch.

**CRITERIA FOR PARALLEL RESONANCE**   The frequency $f_r$ that makes $X_L = X_C$ is always $1/(2\pi\sqrt{LC})$. However, for low-$Q$ circuits $f_r$ does not necessarily provide the desired resonance effect. The three main criteria for parallel resonance are

1. Zero phase angle and unity power factor.
2. Maximum impedance and minimum line current.
3. $X_L = X_C$. This is the resonance at $f_r = 1/(2\pi\sqrt{LC})$.

These three effects do not occur at the same frequency in parallel circuits that have a low $Q$. The condition for unity power factor is often called *antiresonance* in a parallel $LC$ circuit to distinguish it from the case of equal $X_L$ and $X_C$.

It should be noted that when $Q$ is 10 or higher, though, the parallel branch currents are practically equal when $X_L = X_C$. Then at $f_r = 1/(2\pi\sqrt{LC})$, the line current is minimum with zero phase angle, and the impedance is maximum.

For a series resonant circuit there are no parallel branches to consider. Therefore, the current is maximum at exactly $f_r$, whether the $Q$ is high or low.

**a.** Is the $Q$ of 8 a high or low value?

**b.** With this $Q$, will the $I_L$ be more or less than $I_C$ in the parallel branches when $X_L = X_C$?

# 26-10 DAMPING OF PARALLEL RESONANT CIRCUITS

In Fig. 26-15$a$, the shunt $R_P$ across $L$ and $C$ is a damping resistance because it lowers the $Q$ of the tuned circuit. The $R_P$ may represent the resistance of the external source driving the parallel resonant circuit, or $R_P$ can be an actual resistor added for lower $Q$ and greater bandwidth. Using the parallel $R_P$ to reduce $Q$ is better than increasing the series resistance $r_S$ because the resonant response is more symmetrical with shunt damping.

The effect of varying the parallel $R_P$ is opposite from the series $r_S$. A lower value of $R_P$ lowers the $Q$ and reduces the sharpness of resonance. Remember that less resistance in a parallel branch allows more current. This resistive branch current cannot be canceled at resonance by the reactive currents. Therefore, the resonant dip to minimum line current is less sharp with more resistive line current. Specifically, when $Q$ is determined by parallel resistance

▶ $$Q = \frac{R_P}{X_L} \qquad\qquad\qquad \textbf{(26-9)}$$

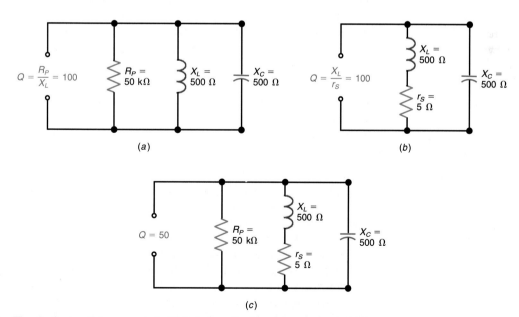

(a)

(b)

(c)

**FIG. 26-15** The $Q$ of a parallel resonant circuit in terms of coil resistance $r_S$ and parallel damping resistor $R_P$. See Formula (26-10) for calculating $Q$. ($a$) Parallel $R_P$ but negligible $r_S$. ($b$) Series $r_S$ but no $R_P$ branch. ($c$) Both $R_P$ and $r_S$.

This relationship with shunt $R_P$ is the reciprocal of the $Q$ formula with series $r_S$. Reducing $R_P$ decreases $Q$, but reducing $r_S$ increases $Q$. The damping can be done by series $r_S$, parallel $R_P$, or both.

**PARALLEL $R_P$ WITHOUT $r_S$** In Fig. 26-15a, $Q$ is determined only by the $R_P$, as no series $r_S$ is shown. We can consider that $r_S$ is zero or very small. Then the $Q$ of the coil is infinite or high enough to be greater than the damped $Q$ of the tuned circuit, by a factor of 10 or more. The $Q$ of the damped resonant circuit here is $R_P/X_L = 50,000/500 = 100$.

**SERIES $r_S$ WITHOUT $R_P$** In Fig. 26-15b, $Q$ is determined only by the coil resistance $r_S$, as no shunt damping resistance is used. Then $Q = X_L/r_S = 500/5 = 100$. This value is the $Q$ of the coil, which is also the $Q$ of the parallel resonant circuit without shunt damping.

**CONVERSION OF $r_S$ OR $R_P$** For the circuits in both Fig. 26-15a and b, $Q$ is 100 because the 50,000-$\Omega$ $R_P$ is equivalent to the 5-$\Omega$ $r_S$ as a damping resistance. One value can be converted to the other. Specifically,

▶
$$r_S = \frac{X_L^2}{R_P} \quad \text{or} \quad R_P = \frac{X_L^2}{r_S}$$

In this example, $r_S$ equals $250,000/50,000 = 5\ \Omega$, or $R_P$ is $250,000/5 = 50,000\ \Omega$.

**DAMPING WITH BOTH $r_S$ AND $R_P$** Figure 26-15c shows the general case of damping where both $r_S$ and $R_P$ must be considered. Then the $Q$ of the circuit can be calculated as

▶
$$Q = \frac{X_L}{r_S + X_L^2/R_P} \qquad (26\text{-}10)$$

For the values in Fig. 26-15c,

$$Q = \frac{500}{5 + 250,000/50,000} = \frac{500}{5 + 5} = \frac{500}{10}$$
$$Q = 50$$

The $Q$ is lower here compared with Fig. 26-15a or b because this circuit has both series and shunt damping.

It should be noted that for an $r_S$ of zero, Formula (26-10) can be inverted and simplified to $Q = R_P/X_L$. This is the same as Formula (26-9) for shunt damping alone.

For the opposite case of $R_P$ being infinite, that is, an open circuit, Formula (26-10) reduces to $X_L/r_S$. This is the same as Formula (26-4) without shunt damping.

Answers at end of chapter.

**a.** A parallel resonant circuit has an $X_L$ of 1000 $\Omega$ and an $r_S$ of 20 $\Omega$, without any shunt damping. Calculate $Q$.

**b.** A parallel resonant circuit has an $X_L$ of 1000 $\Omega$, negligible $r_S$, and shunt $R_P$ of 50 k$\Omega$. Calculate $Q$.

**c.** How much is $Z_{EQ}$ at $f_r$ for the circuits in (**a**) and (**b**)?

# 26-11 CHOOSING *L* AND *C* FOR A RESONANT CIRCUIT

The following example illustrates how resonance is really just an application of $X_L$ and $X_C$. Suppose that we have the problem of determining the inductance and capacitance for a circuit to be resonant at 159 kHz. First, we need a known value for either $L$ or $C$, in order to calculate the other. Which one to choose depends on the application. In some cases, particularly at very high frequencies, $C$ must be the minimum possible value, which might be about 10 pF. At medium frequencies, though, we can choose $L$ for the general case where an $X_L$ of 1000 $\Omega$ is desirable and can be obtained. Then the inductance of the required $L$, equal to $X_L/2\pi f$, is 0.001 H or 1 mH, for the inductive reactance of 1000 $\Omega$.

For resonance at 159 kHz with a 1-mH $L$, the required $C$ is 0.001 $\mu$F or 1000 pF. This value of $C$ can be calculated for an $X_C$ of 1000 $\Omega$, equal to $X_L$ at the $f_r$ of 159 kHz, or from Formula (26-2). In either case, if you substitute $1 \times 10^{-9}$ F for $C$ and $1 \times 10^{-3}$ H for $L$ in the resonant frequency formula, $f_r$ will be 159 kHz.

This combination is resonant at 159 kHz whether $L$ and $C$ are in series or parallel. In series, the resonant effect is to produce maximum current and maximum voltage across $L$ or $C$ at 159 kHz. The effect is desirable for the input circuit of an RF amplifier tuned to $f_r$ because of the maximum signal. In parallel, the resonant effect at 159 kHz is minimum line current and maximum impedance across the generator. This effect is desirable for the output circuit of an RF amplifier, as the gain is maximum at $f_r$ because of the high $Z$.

If we assume the 1-mH coil used for $L$ has an internal resistance of 20 $\Omega$, the $Q$ of the coil is 1000 $\Omega$/20 $\Omega$, which equals 50. This value is also the $Q$ of the series resonant circuit. If there is no shunt damping resistance across the parallel $LC$ circuit, its $Q$ is also 50. With a $Q$ of 50 the bandwidth of the resonant circuit is 159 kHz/50, which equals 3.18 kHz for $\Delta f$.

Answers at end of chapter.

**a.** What is $f_r$ for 1000 pF of $C$ and 1 mH of $L$?

**b.** What is $f_r$ for 250 pF of $C$ and 1 mH of $L$?

# 26  SUMMARY AND REVIEW

Series and parallel resonance are compared in Table 26-5. The main difference is that series resonance produces maximum current and very low impedance at $f_r$, but with parallel resonance the line current is minimum to provide a very high impedance. Remember that these formulas for parallel resonance are very close approximations that can be used for circuits with a $Q$ higher than 10. For series resonance, the formulas apply whether the $Q$ is high or low.

### TABLE 26-5  COMPARISON OF SERIES AND PARALLEL RESONANCE

| SERIES RESONANCE | PARALLEL RESONANCE (HIGH Q) |
|---|---|
| $f_r = \dfrac{1}{2\pi\sqrt{LC}}$ | $f_r = \dfrac{1}{2\pi\sqrt{LC}}$ |
| $I$ maximum at $f_r$ with $\theta$ of $0°$ | $I_T$ minimum at $f_r$ with $\theta$ of $0°$ |
| Impedance $Z$ minimum at $f_r$ | Impedance $Z$ maximum at $f_r$ |
| $Q = X_L/r_S$, or | $Q = X_L/r_s$, or |
| $Q = V_{out}/V_{in}$ | $Q = Z_{max}/X_L$ |
| $Q$ rise in voltage $= Q \times V_{gen}$ | $Q$ rise in impedance $= Q \times X_L$ |
| Bandwidth $\Delta f = f_r/Q$ | Bandwidth $\Delta f = f_r/Q$ |
| Circuit capacitive below $f_r$, but inductive above $f_r$ | Circuit inductive below $f_r$, but capacitive above $f_r$ |
| Needs low-resistance source for low $r_S$, high $Q$, and sharp tuning | Needs high-resistance source for high $R_P$, high $Q$, and sharp tuning |
| Source is inside $LC$ circuit | Source is outside $LC$ circuit |

## SELF-TEST

**ANSWERS AT BACK OF BOOK.**

Choose $(a)$, $(b)$, $(c)$, or $(d)$.

1. For a series or parallel $LC$ circuit, resonance occurs when $(a)$ $X_L$ is 10 times $X_C$ or more; $(b)$ $X_C$ is 10 times $X_L$ or more; $(c)$ $X_L = X_C$; $(d)$ the phase angle of the circuit is $90°$.
2. When either $L$ or $C$ is increased, the resonant frequency of the $LC$ circuit $(a)$ increases; $(b)$ decreases; $(c)$ remains the same; $(d)$ is determined by the shunt resistance.

3. The resonant frequency of an $LC$ circuit is 1000 kHz. If $L$ is doubled but $C$ is reduced to one-eighth of its original value, the resonant frequency then is (*a*) 250 kHz; (*b*) 500 kHz; (*c*) 1000 kHz; (*d*) 2000 kHz.

4. A coil has a 1000-$\Omega$ $X_L$ and a 5-$\Omega$ internal resistance. Its $Q$ equals (*a*) 0.005; (*b*) 5; (*c*) 200; (*d*) 1000.

5. In a parallel $LC$ circuit, at the resonant frequency, the (*a*) line current is maximum; (*b*) inductive branch current is minimum; (*c*) total impedance is minimum; (*d*) total impedance is maximum.

6. At resonance, the phase angle equals (*a*) 0°; (*b*) 90°; (*c*) 180°; (*d*) 270°.

7. In a series $LC$ circuit, at the resonant frequency, the (*a*) current is minimum; (*b*) voltage across $C$ is minimum; (*c*) impedance is maximum; (*d*) current is maximum.

8. A series $LC$ circuit has a $Q$ of 100 at resonance. When 5 mV is applied at the resonant frequency, the voltage across $C$ equals (*a*) 5 mV; (*b*) 20 mV; (*c*) 100 mV; (*d*) 500 mV.

9. An $LC$ circuit resonant at 1000 kHz has a $Q$ of 100. The bandwidth between half-power points equals (*a*) 10 kHz between 995 and 1005 kHz; (*b*) 10 kHz between 1000 and 1010 kHz; (*c*) 5 kHz between 995 and 1000 kHz; (*d*) 200 kHz between 900 and 1100 kHz.

10. In a low-$Q$ parallel resonant circuit, when $X_L = X_C$, (*a*) $I_L$ equals $I_C$; (*b*) $I_L$ is less than $I_C$; (*c*) $I_L$ is more than $I_C$; (*d*) the phase angle is 0°.

## QUESTIONS

1. **(a)** State two characteristics of series resonance. **(b)** With a microammeter measuring current in the series $LC$ circuit of Fig. 26-2, describe the meter readings for the different frequencies from 600 to 1400 kHz.

2. **(a)** State two characteristics of parallel resonance. **(b)** With a microammeter measuring current in the main line for the parallel $LC$ circuit in Fig. 26-6*a*, describe the meter readings for frequencies from 600 to 1400 kHz.

3. State the $Q$ formula for the following $LC$ circuits: **(a)** series resonant; **(b)** parallel resonant, with series resistance $r_S$ in the inductive branch; **(c)** parallel resonant, with zero series resistance but shunt $R_P$.

4. Explain briefly why a parallel $LC$ circuit is inductive but a series $LC$ circuit is capacitive below $f_r$.

5. What is the effect on $Q$ and bandwidth of a parallel resonant circuit if its shunt damping resistance is decreased from 50,000 to 10,000 $\Omega$?

6. Describe briefly how you would use an ac meter to measure the bandwidth of a series resonant circuit in order to calculate the circuits $Q$.

7. Why is a low-resistance generator good for a high $Q$ in series resonance, while a high-resistance generator is needed for a high $Q$ in parallel resonance?

8. Referring to Fig. 26-13, why is it that the middle frequency of 1080 kHz does not correspond to the middle capacitance value of 200 pF?

9. **(a)** Give three criteria for parallel resonance. **(b)** Why is the antiresonant frequency $f_a$ different from $f_r$ with a low-$Q$ circuit? **(c)** Why are they the same for a high-$Q$ circuit?

10. Show how Formula (26-10) reduces to $R_P/X_L$ when $r_S$ is zero.
11. (a) Specify the edge frequencies $f_1$ and $f_2$ for each of the three response curves in Fig. 26-11. (b) Why does lower $Q$ allow more bandwidth?
12. (a) Why does maximum $Z$ for a parallel resonant circuit correspond to minimum line current? (b) Why does zero phase angle for a resonant circuit correspond to unity power factor?
13. Explain how manual tuning of an $LC$ circuit can be done with a capacitor or a coil.
14. What is meant by electronic tuning?
15. Suppose it is desired to tune an $LC$ circuit from 540 to 1600 kHz by varying either $L$ or $C$. Explain how the bandwidth $\Delta f$ is affected by: (a) varying $L$ to tune the $LC$ circuit; (b) varying $C$ to tune the $LC$ circuit.

## PROBLEMS

**ANSWERS TO ODD-NUMBERED PROBLEMS AT BACK OF BOOK.**

1. Calculate $f_r$ for a series $LC$ circuit with $L = 5\ \mu\text{H}$ and $C = 202.64$ pF.
2. Calculate $f_r$ for a series $LC$ circuit with $L = 33\ \mu\text{H}$ and $C = 7.67$ pF.
3. Calculate $f_r$ for a parallel $LC$ circuit with $L = 25.48\ \mu\text{H}$ and $C = 500$ pF.
4. Calculate $f_r$ for a parallel $LC$ circuit with $L = 2.2\ \mu\text{H}$ and $C = 58.74$ pF.
5. What value of inductance $L$ must be connected in series with a 50-pF capacitance for an $f_r$ of 3.8 MHz?
6. What value of capacitance $C$ must be connected in parallel with a 100-$\mu$H inductance for an $f_r$ of 1.9 MHz?
7. Calculate $f_r$ in Fig. 26-16.

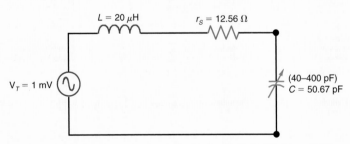

**FIG. 26-16** Series resonant circuit for Probs. 7, 8, 9, 10, 11, and 19.

8. In Fig. 26-16, calculate the following values at $f_r$: $X_L$, $X_C$, $Z_T$, $I$, $V_L$, $V_C$, and $\theta_Z$.
9. In Fig. 26-16, calculate $Q$, $\Delta f$, and the edge frequencies $f_1$ and $f_2$.
10. In Fig. 26-16, calculate $Z_T$, $I$, and $\theta_Z$ at: (a) $f_1$; (b) $f_2$.
11. Refer to Fig. 26-16. (a) To what value must the capacitance, $C$ be adjusted to provide an $f_r$ of 2.5 MHz? (b) What are the values for $X_L$, $X_C$, $Q$, and $\Delta f$ for an $f_r$ of 2.5 MHz?
12. Calculate $f_r$ in Fig. 26-17.

**13.** In Fig. 26-17, calculate the following values at $f_r$: $X_L$, $X_C$, $I_L$, $I_C$, $Q$, $Z_{EQ}$, and $I_T$.

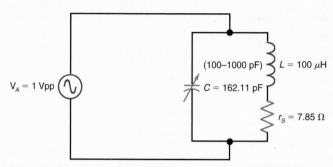

**FIG. 26-17** Parallel resonant circuit for Probs. 12, 13, 14, 15, 16, and 17.

**14.** In Fig. 26-17, calculate $\Delta f$, $f_1$, and $f_2$.

**15.** In Fig. 26-17, determine $Z_{EQ}$, $I_T$, and $\theta_I$ at: (**a**) $f_1$; (**b**) $f_2$.

**16.** In Fig. 26-17, calculate $Q$ and $\Delta f$ if a 100-k$\Omega$ resistance $R_P$ is placed across the tank circuit.

**17.** Refer to Fig. 26-17. (**a**) To what value must the capacitance $C$ be adjusted to provide an $f_r$ of 1 MHz? (**b**) What are the values for $X_L$, $X_C$, $Q$, $\Delta f$, $Z_{EQ}$, and $I_T$ at 1 MHz?

**18.** Calculate the lowest and highest values of capacitance $C$ needed to tune an $LC$ circuit from 3.5 MHz to 4 MHz if a 25-$\mu$H inductor is used.

**19.** Using the original values in Fig. 26-16, calculate the power factor (PF), real power, and apparent power at: (**a**) $f_r$; (**b**) $f_1$; (**c**) $f_2$.

**20.** A series resonant circuit whose $f_r$ is 10 MHz has a bandwidth $\Delta f$ of 100 kHz. If the circuit's $L/C$ ratio is doubled, calculate the edge frequencies $f_1$ and $f_2$.

**21.** Calculate $f_r$ in Fig. 26-18.

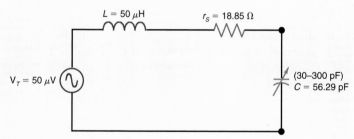

**FIG. 26-18** Series resonant circuit for Probs. 21, 22, 23, 24, 25, and 26.

**22.** In Fig. 26-18, calculate the following values at $f_r$: $X_L$, $X_C$, $Z_T$, $I$, $Q$, $V_L$, $V_C$, and $\theta_Z$.

**23.** In Fig. 26-18, calculate $\Delta f$, $f_1$, and $f_2$.

**24.** In Fig. 26-18, calculate $Z_T$, $I$, and $\theta_Z$ at $f_1$ and $f_2$.

**25.** In Fig. 26-18, what value of series resistance $R_S$ must be added to double the bandwidth $\Delta f$ when $C = 56.29$ pF?

26. Refer to Fig. 26-18. (a) To what value must the capacitance $C$ be adjusted to provide an $f_r$ of 1.5 MHz? (b) What are the values for $X_L$, $X_C$, $Q$, and $\Delta f$ at 1.5 MHz?
27. Calculate $f_r$ in Fig. 26-19.
28. In Fig. 26-19, calculate the following values at $f_r$: $X_L$, $X_C$, $I_L$, $I_C$, $Q$, $Z_{EQ}$, and $\theta_I$.
29. In Fig. 26-19, calculate $\Delta f$, $f_1$, and $f_2$.
30. In Fig. 26-19, calculate $Q$ and $\Delta f$ if a 1-M$\Omega$ $R_P$ is placed across the tank.

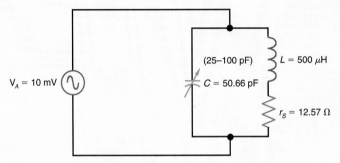

FIG. 26-19   Parallel resonant circuit for Probs. 27, 28, 29, and 30.

---

## CRITICAL THINKING

1. Prove that

$$X_L = \sqrt{\frac{L}{C}}$$

for an $LC$ circuit at $f_r$.

2. Suppose you are an engineer designing a coil to be used in a resonant $LC$ circuit. Besides obtaining the required inductance $L$, your main concern is in reducing skin effect so as to obtain as high a $Q$ as possible for the $LC$ circuit. List three design techniques which would reduce or minimize skin effect in the coil windings.

**26-1** **a.** 1000 kHz
     **b.** 1000 kHz

**26-2** **a.** F
     **b.** T
     **c.** T

**26-3** **a.** F
     **b.** T
     **c.** T

**26-4** **a.** decreased
     **b.** 200 $\mu$H
     **c.** 39.48

**26-5** **a.** $Q = 100$
     **b.** $Z_{EQ} = 25$ k$\Omega$

**26-6** **a.** $\Delta f = 0.25$ MHz
     **b.** $Q = 50$

**26-7** **a.** lowest
     **b.** 1:4

**26-8** **a.** capacitive
     **b.** inductive

**26-9** **a.** low
     **b.** less

**26-10** **a.** $Q = 50$
     **b.** $Q = 50$
     **c.** $Z_{EQ} = 50$ k$\Omega$

**26-11** **a.** $f_r = 159$ kHz
     **b.** $f_r = 318$ kHz

# CHAPTER 27

# FILTERS

A filter separates different components that are mixed together. For instance, a mechanical filter can separate particles from liquid, or small particles from large particles. An electrical filter can separate different frequency components.

Generally, inductors and capacitors are used for filtering because of their opposite frequency characteristics. Inductive reactance $X_L$ increases but capacitive reactance $X_C$ decreases with higher frequencies. In addition, their filtering action depends on whether $L$ and $C$ are in series or parallel with the load.

The amount of attenuation offered by a filter is usually specified in decibels (dB). The decibel is a logarithmic expression which compares two power levels. The frequency response of a filter is usually drawn as a graph of frequency versus decibel attenuation.

The most common filtering applications are separating audio from radio frequencies, or vice versa, and separating ac variations from the average dc level. There are many of these applications in electronic circuits.

# CHAPTER OBJECTIVES

*Upon completion of this chapter, you should be able to:*

- *State* the difference between a low-pass and a high-pass filter.
- *Explain* what is meant by *pulsating direct current*.
- *Understand* how a transformer acts as a high-pass filter.
- *Understand* how an *RC* coupling circuit couples ac but blocks dc.
- *Understand* the function of a bypass capacitor.
- *Calculate* the cutoff frequency, output voltage, and phase angle of basic *RL* and *RC* filters.
- *Explain* the operation of bandpass and bandstop filters.
- *Explain* why log-log graph paper or semilog graph paper is used to plot a frequency response.
- *Define* the term *decibel*.
- *Explain* how resonant circuits can be used as bandpass or bandstop filters.
- *Describe* the function of a power-line filter and a television antenna filter.

## IMPORTANT TERMS IN THIS CHAPTER

| | | |
|---|---|---|
| ac component | cycle | octave |
| active filter | dc component | $\pi$-type filter |
| attenuation of filter | decade | piezoelectric effect |
| bandpass filter | decibels | pulsating dc values |
| bandstop filter | fluctuating dc values | ripple |
| bypass capacitor | graph cycles | semilog graph |
| capacitive coupling | high-pass filter | T-type filter |
| crystal filter | low-pass filter | transformer coupling |
| cutoff frequency | L-type filter | |

## TOPICS COVERED IN THIS CHAPTER

27-1   Examples of Filtering
27-2   Direct Current Combined with Alternating Current
27-3   Transformer Coupling
27-4   Capacitive Coupling
27-5   Bypass Capacitors
27-6   Filter Circuits
27-7   Low-Pass Filters
27-8   High-Pass Filters
27-9   Analyzing Filter Circuits
27-10   Decibels and Frequency Response Curves
27-11   Resonant Filters
27-12   Interference Filters

## 27-1 EXAMPLES OF FILTERING

Electronic circuits often have currents of different frequencies corresponding to voltages of different frequencies. The reason is that a source produces current with the same frequency as the applied voltage. As examples, the ac signal input to an audio circuit can have high and low audio frequencies; an RF circuit can have a wide range of radio frequencies in its input; the audio detector in a radio has both radio frequencies and audio frequencies in the output. Finally, the rectifier in a power supply produces dc output with an ac ripple superimposed on the average dc level.

In such applications where the current has different frequency components, it is usually necessary either to favor or to reject one frequency or a band of frequencies. Then an electrical filter is used to separate higher or lower frequencies.

The electrical filter can pass the higher-frequency component to the load resistance, which is the case of a high-pass filter, or a low-pass filter can be used to favor the lower frequencies. In Fig. 27-1a, the high-pass filter allows 10 kHz to produce output, while rejecting or attenuating the lower frequency of 100 Hz. In Fig. 27-1b, the filtering action is reversed to pass the lower frequency of 100 Hz, while attenuating 10 kHz. These examples are for high and low audio frequencies.

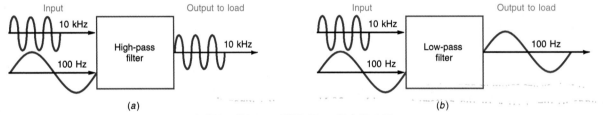

FIG. 27-1  Function of electrical filters. (a) High-pass filter couples higher frequencies out to the load. (b) Low-pass filter couples lower frequencies out to the load.

For the case of audio mixed with radio frequencies, a low-pass filter allows the audio frequencies in the output. Or a high-pass filter allows the radio frequencies to be passed to the load.

---
### TEST-POINT QUESTION 27-1
---

Answers at end of chapter.

A high-pass filter will pass which of the following:
**a.** 10 or 500 kHz.
**b.** 60 Hz or a steady dc level.


## 27-2 DIRECT CURRENT COMBINED WITH ALTERNATING CURRENT

Current that varies in amplitude but does not reverse in polarity is considered *pulsating* or *fluctuating* direct current. It is not a steady direct current because its value fluctuates. However, it is not alternating current because the polarity remains the same, either positive or negative. The same idea applies to voltages.

Figure 27-2 illustrates how a circuit can have pulsating direct current or voltage. Here, the steady dc voltage of the battery $V_B$ is in series with the ac voltage $V_A$. Since the two series generators add, the voltage across $R_L$ is the sum of the two applied voltages, as shown by the waveshape of $v_R$ in Fig. 27-2b.

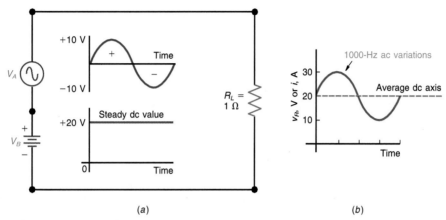

(a)                                          (b)

FIG. 27-2   An example of a pulsating or fluctuating direct current and voltage. (a) Circuit. (b) Graph of voltage across $R_L$. This $V$ equals $V_B$ of the battery plus $V_A$ of the ac source, with frequency of 1000 Hz.

If values are taken at opposite peaks of the ac variation, when $V_A$ is at $+10$ V, it adds to the $+20$ V of the battery to provide $+30$ V across $R_L$; when the ac voltage is $-10$ V, it bucks the battery voltage of $+20$ V to provide $+10$ V across $R_L$. When the ac voltage is at zero, the voltage across $R_L$ equals the battery voltage of $+20$ V.

The combined voltage $v_R$ then consists of the ac variations fluctuating above and below the battery voltage as the axis, instead of the zero axis for ac voltage. The result is a pulsating dc voltage, since it is fluctuating but always has positive polarity with respect to zero.

The pulsating direct current $i$ through $R_L$ has the same waveform, fluctuating above and below the steady dc level of 20 A. The $i$ and $v$ values are the same because $R_L$ is 1 Ω.

Another example is shown in Fig. 27-3. If the 100-Ω $R_L$ is connected across 120 V 60 Hz as in Fig. 27-3a, the current in $R_L$ will be $V/R_L$. This is an ac sine wave, with an rms value of 120/100 or 1.2 A.

Also, if you connect the same $R_L$ across the 200-Vdc source in Fig. 27-3b, instead of using the ac source, the steady direct current in $R_L$ will be 200/100, or 2 A. The battery source voltage and its current are considered steady dc values because there are no variations.

However, suppose that the ac source $V_A$ and dc source $V_B$ are connected in series with $R_L$, as in Fig. 27-3c. What will happen to the current and voltage for $R_L$? Will $V_A$ or $V_B$ supply the current? The answer is that both sources will. Each voltage source produces current as though the other were not there, assuming the sources have negligibly small internal impedance. The result then is the fluctuating dc voltage or current shown, with the ac variations of $V_A$ superimposed on the average dc level of $V_B$.

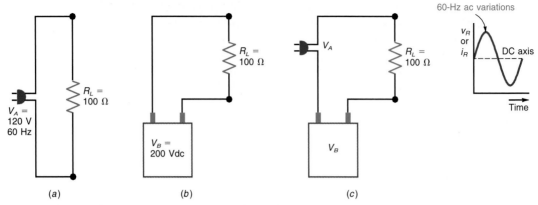

**FIG. 27-3** A combination of ac and dc voltage to provide fluctuating dc voltage across $R_L$. (*a*) An ac source alone. (*b*) A dc source alone. (*c*) The ac source and dc source in series for the fluctuating voltage across $R_L$.

**DC AND AC COMPONENTS**   The pulsating dc voltage $v_R$ in Fig. 27-3*c* is just the original ac voltage $V_A$ with its axis shifted to a dc level by the battery voltage $V_B$. In effect, a dc component has been inserted into the ac variations. This effect is called *dc insertion*.

Referring back to Fig. 27-2, if you measure across $R_L$ with a dc voltmeter, it will read the dc level of 20 V. An ac-coupled oscilloscope* will show only the peak-to-peak variations of $\pm 10$ V.

It is convenient, therefore, to consider the pulsating or fluctuating voltage and current in two parts. One is the steady dc component, which is the axis or average level of the variations; the other is the ac component, consisting of the variations above and below the dc axis. Here the dc level for $V_T$ is $+20$ V, while the ac component equals 10 V peak or 7.07 V rms value. The ac component is also called *ac ripple*.

It should be noted that with respect to the dc level the fluctuations represent alternating voltage or current that actually reverses in polarity. For example, the change of $v_R$ from $+20$ to $+10$ V is just a decrease in positive voltage compared with zero. However, compared with the dc level of $+20$ V, the value of $+10$ V is 10 V more negative than the axis.

**TYPICAL EXAMPLES OF DC LEVEL WITH AC COMPONENT**   As a common application, transistors always have fluctuating dc voltage or current when used for amplifying an ac signal. The transistor amplifier needs steady dc voltages to operate. The signal input is an ac variation, usually with a dc axis to establish the desired operating level. The amplified output is also an ac variation superimposed on a dc supply voltage that supplies the required power output. Therefore, the input and output circuits have fluctuating dc voltage.

The examples in Fig. 27-4 illustrate two possibilities, in terms of polarities with respect to chassis ground. In Fig. 27-4*a*, the waveform is always positive, as in the previous examples. This example could apply to collector voltage on an NPN transistor amplifier. Note the specific values. The average dc axis is the steady dc level. The positive peak equals the dc level plus the peak ac value. The

*See App. D for an explanation of how to use the oscilloscope.

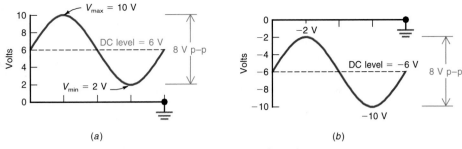

FIG. 27-4  Typical examples of a dc voltage access for an ac component. (*a*) Positive fluctuating dc values because of a large positive dc component. (*b*) Negative fluctuating dc values because of a large negative dc component.

minimum point equals the dc level minus the peak ac value. The peak-to-peak value of the ac component and its rms value are the same as for the ac signal alone. However, it is better to subtract the minimum from the maximum for the peak-to-peak value, in case the waveform is unsymmetrical.

In Fig. 27-4*b*, all the values are negative. Notice that here the positive peak of the ac component subtracts from the dc level because of the opposite polarities. Now the negative peak adds to the negative dc level to provide a maximum point of negative voltage.

**SEPARATING THE AC COMPONENT**   In many applications, the circuit has pulsating dc voltage, but only the ac component is desired. Then the ac component can be passed to the load, while the steady dc component is blocked, either with transformer coupling or with capacitive coupling. A transformer with a separate secondary winding isolates or blocks steady direct current in the primary. A capacitor isolates or blocks a steady dc voltage.

### TEST-POINT QUESTION 27-2

Answers at end of chapter.

For the fluctuating dc waveform in Fig. 27-4*a*, specify the following voltages:
**a.** Average dc level.
**b.** Maximum and minimum values.
**c.** Peak-to-peak of ac component.
**d.** Peak and rms of ac component.

# 27-3 TRANSFORMER COUPLING

Remember that a transformer produces induced secondary voltage just for variations in primary current. With pulsating direct current in the primary, the secondary has output voltage only for the ac variations, therefore. The steady dc component in the primary has no effect in the secondary.

In Fig. 27-5, the pulsating dc voltage in the primary produces pulsating primary current. The dc axis corresponds to a steady value of primary current that has a constant magnetic field, but only when the field changes can secondary voltage be induced. Therefore, only the fluctuations in the primary can produce output in the secondary. Since there is no output for the steady primary current, this dc level corresponds to the zero level for the ac output in the secondary.

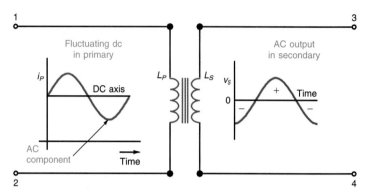

FIG. 27-5   Transformer coupling blocks the dc component. With fluctuating direct current in the primary $L_P$, only the ac component produces induced voltage in the secondary $L_S$.

When the primary current increases above the steady level, this increase produces one polarity for the secondary voltage as the field expands; when the primary current decreases below the steady level, the secondary voltage has reverse polarity as the field contracts. The result in the secondary is an ac variation having opposite polarities with respect to the zero level.

The phase of the ac secondary voltage may be as shown or 180° opposite, depending on the connections and direction of the windings. Also, the ac secondary output may be more or less than the ac component in the primary, depending on the turns ratio. This ability to isolate the steady dc component in the primary while providing ac output in the secondary applies to all transformers with a separate secondary winding, whether iron-core or air-core.

**TEST-POINT QUESTION 27-3**

Answers at end of chapter.
**a.** Is transformer coupling an example of a high-pass or low-pass filter?
**b.** In Fig. 27-5, what is the level of $v_S$ for the average dc level of $i_P$?

## 27-4 CAPACITIVE COUPLING

Capacitive coupling is probably the most common type of coupling in amplifier circuits. The coupling means connecting the output of one circuit to the input of the next. The requirements are to include all frequencies in the desired signal, while rejecting undesired components. Usually, the dc component must be blocked from the input to ac amplifiers. The purpose is to maintain a specific dc level for the amplifier operation.

In Fig. 27-6, the pulsating dc voltage across input terminals 1 and 2 is applied to the $RC$ coupling circuit. Capacitance $C_C$ will charge to the steady dc level, which is the average charging voltage. The steady dc component is blocked, therefore, since it cannot produce voltage across $R$. However, the ac component is developed across $R$, between the output terminals 3 and 4. The reason is that the ac voltage allows $C$ to produce charge and discharge current through $R$. Note that the zero axis of the ac voltage output corresponds to the average level of the pulsating dc voltage input.

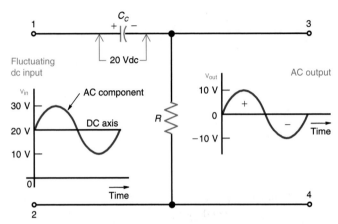

FIG. 27-6   The $RC$ coupling blocks the dc component. With fluctuating dc voltage applied, only the ac component produces charge and discharge current for the output voltage across $R$.

**THE DC COMPONENT ACROSS $C$**   The voltage across $C_C$ is the steady dc component of the input voltage because the variations of the ac component are symmetrical above and below the average level. Furthermore, the series resistance is the same for charge and discharge. As a result, any increase in charging voltage above the average level is counteracted by an equal discharge below the average.

In Fig. 27-6, for example, when $v_{in}$ increases from 20 to 30 V, this effect on charging $C_C$ is nullified by the discharge when $v_{in}$ decreases from 20 to 10 V. At all times, however, $v_{in}$ has a positive value that charges $C_C$ in the polarity shown.

The net result is that only the average level is effective in charging $C_C$, since the variations from the axis neutralize each other. After a period of time, depending on the $RC$ time constant, $C_C$ will charge to the average value of the pulsating dc voltage applied, which is 20 V here.

**THE AC COMPONENT ACROSS $R$**   Although $C_C$ is charged to the average dc level, when the pulsating input voltage varies above and below this level, the charge and discharge current produces $IR$ voltage corresponding to the fluctuations of the input. When $v_{in}$ increases above the average level, $C_C$ takes on charge, producing charging current through $R$. Even though the charging current may be too small to affect the voltage across $C_C$ appreciably, the $IR$ drop across

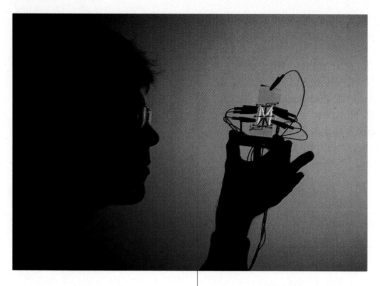

a large value of resistance can be practically equal to the ac component of the input voltage. In summary, a long $RC$ time constant is needed for good coupling.

If the polarity is considered, in Fig. 27-6, the charging current produced for an increase of $v_{in}$ produces electron flow from the low side of $R$ to the top, adding electrons to the negative side of $C_C$. The voltage at the top of $R$ is then positive with respect to the line below.

When $v_{in}$ decreases below the average level, $C$ loses charge. The discharge current then is in the opposite direction through $R$. The result is negative polarity for the ac voltage output across $R$.

When the input voltage is at its average level, there is no charge or discharge current, resulting in zero voltage across $R$. The zero level in the ac voltage across $R$ corresponds to the average level of the pulsating dc voltage applied to the $RC$ circuit.

The end result is that with positive pulsating dc voltage applied, the values above the average produce the positive half-cycle of the ac voltage across $R$; the values below the average produce the negative half-cycle. Only this ac voltage across $R$ is coupled to the next circuit, as terminals 3 and 4 provide the output from the $RC$ coupling circuit.

It is important to note that there is practically no phase shift. This rule applies to all $RC$ coupling circuits, since $R$ must be ten or more times $X_C$. Then the reactance is negligible compared with the series resistance, and the phase angle of less than 5.7° is practically zero.

**VOLTAGES AROUND THE $RC$ COUPLING CIRCUIT**    If you measure the fluctuating dc voltage across the input terminals 1 and 2 in Fig. 27-6 with a dc voltmeter, it will read the average dc level of 20 V. Across the same two points, if you connect an ac-coupled oscilloscope, it will show only the fluctuating ac component. These voltage variations have a peak value of 10 V, or a peak-to-peak value of 20 V, or an rms value of $0.707 \times 10 = 7.07$ V.

Across points 1 and 3 for $V_C$ in Fig. 27-6, a dc voltmeter reads the steady dc value of 20 V. An ac voltmeter across points 1 and 3 reads practically zero.

However, an ac voltmeter across the output $R$ between points 3 and 4 will read the ac voltage of 7 V, approximately, for $V_R$. Furthermore, a dc voltmeter across $R$ reads zero. The dc component of the input voltage is across $C_C$ but is blocked from the output across $R$.

**TYPICAL COUPLING CAPACITORS**    Common values of RF and AF coupling capacitors for different sizes of series $R$ are listed in Table 27-1. In all cases the coupling capacitor blocks the steady dc component of the input voltage, while the ac component is passed to the resistance.

The size of $C_C$ required depends on the frequency of the ac component. At each frequency listed at the left in Table 27-1, the values of capacitance in the horizontal row have an $X_C$ equal to one-tenth the resistance value for each column. The $R$ increases from 1.6 to 16 to 160 k$\Omega$ for the three columns, allowing

## TABLE 27-1    TYPICAL AUDIO FREQUENCY AND RADIO FREQUENCY COUPLING CAPACITORS*

| | VALUES OF $C_C$ | | | |
| FREQUENCY | R = 1.6 kΩ | R = 16 kΩ | R = 160 kΩ | FREQUENCY BAND |
|---|---|---|---|---|
| 100 Hz | 10 $\mu$F | 1 $\mu$F | 0.1 $\mu$F | Audio frequency |
| 1000 Hz | 1 $\mu$F | 0.1 $\mu$f | 0.01 $\mu$F | Audio frequency |
| 10 kHz | 0.1 $\mu$F | 0.01 $\mu$F | 0.001 $\mu$F | Audio frequency |
| 100 kHz | 0.01 $\mu$F | 0.001 $\mu$F | 100 pF | Radio frequency |
| 1 MHz | 0.001 $\mu$F | 100 pF | 10 pF | Radio frequency |
| 10 MHz | 100 pF | 10 pF | 1 pF | Radio frequency |
| 100 MHz | 10 pF | 1 pF | 0.1 pF | Very High frequency |

*For coupling circuit in Fig. 27-6; $X_{C_C} = \frac{1}{10}\,R$.

smaller values of $C_C$. Typical audio coupling capacitors, then, are about 0.1 to 10 $\mu$F, depending on the lowest audio frequency to be coupled and the size of the series resistance. Typical RF coupling capacitors are about 1 to 100 pF.

Values of $C_C$ more than about 1 $\mu$F are usually electrolytic capacitors, which must be connected in the correct polarity. These can be very small, many being ½ in. long, with a low voltage rating of 3 to 25 V for transistor circuits. Also, the small leakage current of electrolytic capacitors is not a serious problem in this application because of the low voltage and small series resistance for transistor coupling circuits.

### TEST-POINT QUESTION 27-4

Answers at end of chapter.
a. In Fig. 27-6, what is the level of $v_{out}$ across $R$ corresponding to the average dc level of $v_{in}$?
b. Which of the following is a typical audio coupling capacitor with a 1-kΩ $R$: 1 pF; 0.001 $\mu$F; or 5 $\mu$F?

## 27-5 BYPASS CAPACITORS

A bypass is a path around a component. In circuits, the bypass is a parallel or shunt path. Capacitors are often used in parallel with resistance to bypass the ac component of a pulsating dc voltage. The result, then, is steady dc voltage across the $RC$ parallel combination, if the bypass capacitance is large enough to have little reactance for the lowest frequency of the ac variations.

As illustrated in Fig. 27-7, the capacitance $C_1$ in parallel with $R_1$ is an ac bypass capacitor for $R_1$. For any frequency at which $X_{C_1}$ is one-tenth of $R_1$, or less, the ac component is bypassed around $R_1$ through the low reactance in the shunt path. The result is practically zero ac voltage across the bypass capacitor because of its low reactance.

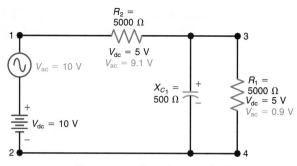

FIG. 27-7   Low reactance of bypass capacitor $C_1$ short-circuits $R_1$ for an ac component of fluctuating dc input voltage.

Since the voltage is the same across $R_1$ and $C_1$ because they are in parallel, there is also no ac voltage across $R_1$ for the frequency at which $C_1$ is a bypass capacitor. We can say that $R$ is bypassed for the frequency at which $X_C$ is one-tenth of $R$. The bypassing also applies to higher frequencies where $X_C$ is less than one-tenth of $R$. Then the ac voltage across the bypass capacitor is even closer to zero because of its lower reactance.

### BYPASSING THE AC COMPONENT OF A PULSATING DC VOLTAGE
The voltages in Fig. 27-7 are calculated by considering the effect of $C_1$ separately for $V_{dc}$ and for $V_{ac}$. For direct current, $C_1$ is practically an open circuit. Then its reactance is so high compared with the 5000-$\Omega$ $R_1$ that $X_{C_1}$ can be ignored as a parallel branch. Therefore, $R_1$ can be considered as a voltage divider in series with $R_2$. Since $R_1$ and $R_2$ are equal, each has 5 V, equal to one-half $V_{dc}$. Although this dc voltage division depends on $R_1$ and $R_2$, the dc voltage across $C_1$ is the same 5 V as across its parallel $R_1$.

For the ac component of the applied voltage, however, the bypass capacitor has very low reactance. In fact, $X_{C_1}$ must be one-tenth of $R_1$, or less. Then the 5000-$\Omega$ $R_1$ is so high compared with the low value of $X_{C_1}$ that $R_1$ can be ignored as a parallel branch. Therefore, the 500-$\Omega$ $X_{C_1}$ can be considered as a voltage divider in series with $R_2$.

With an $X_{C_1}$ of 500 $\Omega$, this value in series with the 5000-$\Omega$ $R_2$ allows approximately one-eleventh of $V_{ac}$ to be developed across $C_1$. This ac voltage, equal to 0.9 V here, is the same across $R_1$ and $C_1$ in parallel. The remainder of the ac applied voltage, equal to approximately 9.1 V, is across $R_2$. In summary, then, the bypass capacitor provides an ac short circuit across its shunt resistance, so that little or no ac voltage can be developed, without affecting the dc voltages.

Measuring voltages around the circuit in Fig. 27-7, a dc voltmeter reads 5 V across $R_1$ and 5 V across $R_2$. An ac voltmeter across $R_2$ reads 9.1 V, which is almost all the ac input voltage. Across the bypass capacitor $C_1$ the ac voltage is only 0.9 V.

In Table 27-2, typical sizes for RF and AF bypass capacitors are listed. The values of $C$ have been calculated at different frequencies for an $X_C$ one-tenth the shunt resistance given in each column. The $R$ decreases for the three columns, from 16 to 1.6 k$\Omega$ and 160 $\Omega$. Note that smaller values of $R$ require larger values of $C$ for bypassing. Also, when $X_C$ equals one-tenth of $R$ at one frequency, $X_C$ will be even less for higher frequencies, improving the bypassing action.

## DID YOU KNOW?

Crucial influences on the American electric power industry come from three sources: the need for reliable power to control sensitive electronics in business; regulations forcing transmission networks to be open to competitors; and the practice of bulk power sales.

| | VALUES OF C | | | |
|---|---|---|---|---|
| FREQUENCY | $R = 16\,k\Omega$ | $R = 1.6\,k\Omega$ | $R = 160\,\Omega$ | FREQUENCY BAND |
| 100 Hz | 1 $\mu$F | 10 $\mu$F | 100 $\mu$F | Audio frequency |
| 1000 Hz | 0.1 $\mu$F | 1 $\mu$F | 10 $\mu$F | Audio frequency |
| 10 kHz | 0.01 $\mu$F | 0.1 $\mu$F | 1 $\mu$F | Audio frequency |
| 100 kHz | 0.001 $\mu$F | 0.01 $\mu$F | 0.1 $\mu$F | Radio frequency |
| 1 MHz | 100 pF | 0.001 $\mu$F | 0.01 $\mu$F | Radio frequency |
| 10 MHz | 10 pF | 100 pF | 0.001 $\mu$F | Radio frequency |
| 100 MHz | 1 pF | 10 pF | 100 pF | Very high frequency |

*For $RC$ bypass circuit in Fig. 27-7; $X_{C_1} = \frac{1}{10} R$.

Therefore, the size of bypass capacitors should be considered on the basis of the lowest frequency to be bypassed.

It should be noted that the applications of coupling and bypassing for $C$ are really the same, except that $C_C$ is in series with $R$ and the bypass $C$ is in parallel with $R$. In both cases $X_C$ must be one-tenth or less of $R$. Then $C_C$ couples the ac signal to $R$. Or the shunt bypass short-circuits $R$ for the ac signal.

**BYPASSING RADIO FREQUENCIES BUT NOT AUDIO FREQUENCIES**   See Fig. 27-8. At the audio frequency of 1000 Hz, $C_1$ has a reactance of 1.6 M$\Omega$. This reactance is so much higher than $R_1$ that the impedance of the parallel combination is essentially equal to the 16,000 $\Omega$ of $R_1$. Then $R_1$ and $R_2$ serve as a voltage divider for the applied AF voltage of 10 V. Each of the equal resistances has one-half the applied voltage, equal to the 5 V across $R_2$ and 5 V across $R_1$. This 5 V at 1000 Hz is also present across $C_1$, since it is in parallel with $R_1$.

For the RF voltage at 1 MHz, however, the reactance of the bypass capacitor is only 1600 $\Omega$. This is one-tenth of $R_1$. Then $X_{C_1}$ and $R_1$ in parallel have a combined impedance equal to approximately 1600 $\Omega$.

Now, with a 1600-$\Omega$ impedance for the $R_1C_1$ bank in series with the 16,000 $\Omega$ of $R_2$, the voltage across $R_1$ and $C_1$ is one-eleventh the applied RF voltage. Then there is 0.9 V across the lower impedance of $R_1$ and $C_1$, with 9.1 V across the larger resistance of $R_2$. As a result, the RF component of the applied voltage can be considered bypassed. The capacitor $C_1$ is the RF bypass across $R_1$.

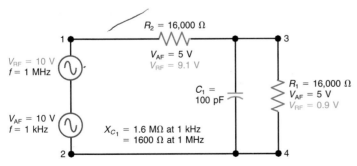

FIG. 27-8   Capacitor $C_1$ bypasses $R_1$ for the radio frequencies but not for the audio frequencies.

Answers at end of chapter.
**a.** In Fig. 27-8, is $C_1$ an AF or RF bypass?
**b.** Which of the following is a typical audio bypass capacitor across a 1-k$\Omega$ $R$: 1 pF; 0.001 $\mu$F; or 5 $\mu$F?

# 27-6 FILTER CIRCUITS

In terms of their function, filters can be classified as either low-pass or high-pass. A low-pass filter allows the lower-frequency components of the applied voltage to develop output voltage across the load resistance, while the higher-frequency components are attenuated, or reduced, in the output. A high-pass filter does the opposite, allowing the higher-frequency components of the applied voltage to develop voltage across the output load resistance.

The case of an $RC$ coupling circuit is an example of a high-pass filter because the ac component of the input voltage is developed across $R$ while the dc voltage is blocked by the series capacitor. Furthermore, with higher frequencies in the ac component, more ac voltage is coupled. For the opposite case, a bypass capacitor is an example of a low-pass filter. The higher frequencies are bypassed, but the lower the frequency, the less the bypassing action. Then lower frequencies can develop output voltage across the shunt bypass capacitor.

In order to make the filtering more selective in terms of which frequencies are passed to produce output voltage across the load, filter circuits generally combine inductance and capacitance. Since inductive reactance increases with higher frequencies, while capacitive reactance decreases, the two opposite effects improve the filtering action.

With combinations of $L$ and $C$, filters are named to correspond to the circuit configuration. Most common types of filters are the L, T, and $\pi$. Any one of the three can function as either a low-pass filter or a high-pass filter.

For either low-pass or high-pass filters with $L$ and $C$ the reactance $X_L$ increases with higher frequencies, while $X_C$ decreases. The frequency characteristics of $X_L$ and $X_C$ cannot be changed. However, the circuit connections are opposite to reverse the filtering action.

In general, high-pass filters use:

1. Coupling capacitance $C$ in series with the load. Then $X_C$ can be low for high frequencies to be passed to $R_L$, while low frequencies are blocked.
2. Choke inductance $L$ in parallel across $R_L$. Then the shunt $X_L$ can be high for high frequencies to prevent a short circuit across $R_L$, while low frequencies are bypassed.

The opposite characteristics for low-pass filters are:

1. Inductance $L$ in series with the load. The high $X_L$ for high frequencies can serve as a choke, while low frequencies can be passed to $R_L$.
2. Bypass capacitance $C$ in parallel across $R_L$. Then high frequencies are bypassed by a small $X_C$, while low frequencies are not affected by the shunt path.

For any filter, the ability to reduce the amplitude of undesired frequencies is called the attenuation of the filter. The frequency at which the attenuation reduces the output to 70.7 percent is the *cutoff frequency*, usually designated $f_c$.

## 27-7 LOW-PASS FILTERS

Figure 27-9 illustrates low-pass circuits from a single filter element with a shunt bypass capacitor in Fig. 27-9*a* or a series choke in *b*, to the more elaborate combinations of an L-type filter in *c*, a T type in *d*, and a $\pi$ type in *e* and *f*. With an applied input voltage having different frequency components, the low-pass filter action results in maximum low-frequency voltage across $R_L$, while most of the high-frequency voltage is developed across the series choke or resistance.

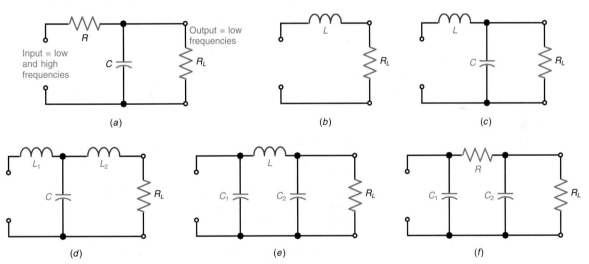

**FIG. 27-9** Low-pass filter circuits. (*a*) Bypass capacitor $C$ in parallel with $R_L$. (*b*) Choke $L$ in series with $R_L$. (*c*) Inverted-L type with choke and bypass capacitor. (*d*) The T type with two chokes and one bypass capacitor. (*e*) The $\pi$ type with one choke and bypass capacitors at both ends. (*f*) The $\pi$ type with a series resistor instead of a choke.

In Fig. 27-9*a*, the shunt capacitor $C$ bypasses $R_L$ for high frequencies. In Fig. 27-9*b*, the choke $L$ acts as a voltage divider in series with $R_L$. Since $L$ has maximum reactance for the highest frequencies, this component of the input voltage is developed across $L$, with little across $R_L$. For lower frequencies, $L$ has low reactance, and most of the input voltage can be developed across $R_L$.

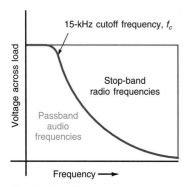

**FIG. 27-10** The response of a low-pass filter with cutoff at 15 kHz. The filter passes the audio signal but attenuates radio frequencies.

In Fig. 27-9c, the use of both the series choke and bypass capacitor improves the filtering by providing sharper cutoff between the low frequencies that can develop voltage across $R_L$ and the higher frequencies stopped from the load by producing maximum voltage across $L$. Similarly, the T-type circuit in Fig. 27-9d and the $\pi$-type circuits in e and f improve filtering.

Using the series resistance in Fig. 27-9f instead of a choke provides an economical $\pi$ filter needing less space.

**PASSBAND AND STOP BAND**    As illustrated in Fig. 27-10, a low-pass filter attenuates frequencies above the cutoff frequency $f_c$ of 15 kHz in this example. Any component of the input voltage having a frequency lower than 15 kHz can produce output voltage across the load. These frequencies are in the *passband*. Frequencies of 15 kHz or more are in the *stop band*. The sharpness of filtering between the passband and the stop band depends on the type of circuit. In general, the more $L$ and $C$ components, the sharper the response of the filter can be. Therefore, $\pi$ and T types are better filters than the L type and the bypass or choke alone.

The response curve in Fig. 27-10 is illustrated for the application of a low-pass filter attenuating RF voltages while passing audio frequencies to the load. This is necessary where the input voltage has RF and AF components but only the audio voltage is desired for the AF circuits that follow the filter.

A good example is filtering the audio output of the detector circuit in a radio receiver, after the RF-modulated carrier signal has been rectified. Another common application of low-pass filtering is where the steady dc component of pulsating dc input must be separated from the higher frequency 60-Hz ac component, as in the pulsating dc output of the rectifier in a power supply.

**CIRCUIT VARIATIONS**    The choice between the T-type filter with a series input choke and the $\pi$ type with a shunt input capacitor depends upon the internal resistance of the generator supplying input voltage to the filter. A low-resistance generator needs the T filter so that the choke can provide a high series impedance for the bypass capacitor. Otherwise, the bypass capacitor must have extremely large values to short-circuit the low-resistance generator for high frequencies.

The $\pi$ filter is more suitable with a high-resistance generator where the input capacitor can be effective as a bypass. For the same reasons, the L filter can have the shunt bypass either in the input for a high-resistance generator or across the output for a low-resistance generator.

For all the filter circuits, the series choke can be connected either in the high side of the line, as in Fig. 27-9, or in series in the opposite side of the line, without any effect on the filtering action. Also, the series components can be connected in both sides of the line for a *balanced filter* circuit.

**PASSIVE AND ACTIVE FILTERS**    All the circuits here are passive filters, as they use only capacitors, inductors, and resistors, which are passive components. An active filter, however, uses the operational amplifier (op amp) on an IC chip, with $R$ and $C$. The purpose is to eliminate the need for inductance $L$. This feature is important in filters for audio frequencies when large coils would be necessary. The operational amplifier is described in Chap. 32, "Integrated Circuits."

Answers at end of chapter.
**a.** Which diagrams in Fig. 27-9 show a $\pi$-type filter?
**b.** Does the response curve in Fig. 27-10 show low-pass or high-pass filtering?

## 27-8 HIGH-PASS FILTERS

As illustrated in Fig. 27-11, the high-pass filter passes to the load all frequencies higher than the cutoff frequency $f_c$, while lower frequencies cannot develop appreciable voltage across the load. The graph in Fig. 27-11a shows the response of a high-pass filter with a stopband of 0 to 50 Hz. Above the cutoff frequency of 50 Hz, the higher audio frequencies in the passband can produce AF voltage across the output load resistance.

The high-pass filtering action results from using $C_C$ as a coupling capacitor in series with the load, as in Fig. 27-11b. The L, T, and $\pi$ types use the inductance for a high-reactance choke across the line. In this way the higher-frequency components of the input voltage can develop very little voltage across the series

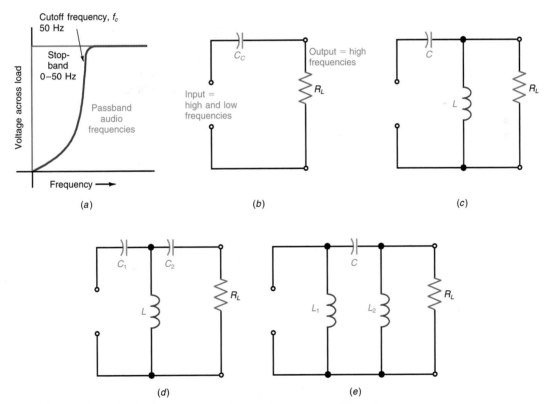

FIG. 27-11 High-pass filters. (a) The response curve for an audio-frequency filter cutting off at 50 Hz. (b) An RC coupling circuit. (c) Inverted-L type. (d) The T type. (e) The $\pi$ type.

capacitance, allowing most of this voltage to be produced across $R_L$. The inductance across the line has higher reactance with increasing frequencies, allowing the shunt impedance to be no lower than the value of $R_L$.

For low frequencies, however, $R_L$ is effectively short-circuited by the low inductive reactance across the line. Also, $C_C$ has high reactance and develops most of the voltage at low frequencies, stopping these frequencies from developing voltage across the load.

### TEST-POINT QUESTION 27-8

Answers at end of chapter.
**a.** Which diagram in Fig. 27-11 shows a T-type filter?
**b.** Does the response curve in Fig. 27-11*a* show high-pass or low-pass filtering?

## 27-9 ANALYZING FILTER CIRCUITS

Any low-pass or high-pass filter can be thought of as a frequency-dependent voltage divider, since the amount of output voltage is a function of frequency. Special formulas can be used to calculate the output voltage for any frequency of the applied voltage. What follows is a more mathematical approach in analyzing the operation of the most basic low-pass and high-pass filter circuits.

***RC* LOW-PASS FILTER**  Figure 27-12*a* shows a simple *RC* low-pass filter, while Fig. 27-12*b* shows how its output voltage, $V_{out}$, varies with frequency. Let's examine how the *RC* low-pass filter responds when $f = 0$ Hz (dc) and $f = \infty$ Hz. At $f = 0$ Hz, the capacitor *C* has infinite capacitive reactance $X_C$, calculated as:

$$\blacktriangleright \qquad X_C = \frac{1}{2\pi fC}$$

$$= \frac{1}{2 \times \pi \times 0 \text{ Hz} \times 0.01 \ \mu F}$$

$$= \infty \Omega$$

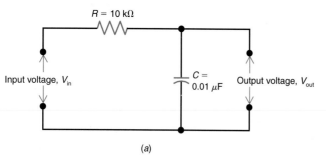

(a)                                                                                           (b)

**FIG. 27-12**  *RC* low-pass filter. (*a*) Circuit. (*b*) Graph of $V_{out}$ versus frequency.

Figure 27-13a shows the equivalent circuit for this condition. Notice that $C$ appears as an open. Since all of the input voltage appears across the open in a series circuit, $V_{out}$ must equal $V_{in}$ when $f = 0$ Hz.

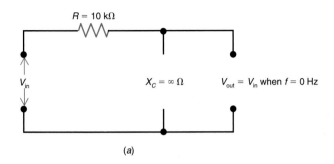

(a)

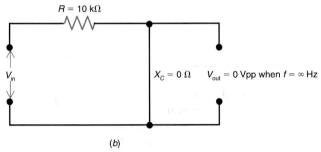

(b)

**FIG. 27-13** *RC* low-pass equivalent circuits. (*a*) Equivalent circuit for $f = 0$ Hz. (*b*) Equivalent circuit for very high frequencies, or $f = \infty$ Hz.

At the other extreme, consider the circuit when the frequency $f$ is very high or infinitely high. Then $X_C = 0 \ \Omega$, calculated as:

$$X_C = \frac{1}{2\pi f C}$$

$$= \frac{1}{2 \times \pi \times \infty \ \text{Hz} \times 0.01 \ \mu\text{F}}$$

$$= 0 \ \Omega$$

Figure 27-13b shows the equivalent circuit for this condition. Notice that $C$ appears as a short. Since the voltage across a short is zero, the output voltage for very high frequencies must be zero.

When the frequency of the input voltage is somewhere between zero and infinity, the output voltage can be determined by using Formula (27-1):

▶ $$V_{out} = \frac{X_C}{Z_T} \times V_{in} \qquad \textbf{(27-1)}$$

where

$$Z_T = \sqrt{R^2 + X_C^2}$$

**ABOUT ELECTRONICS**

Most supercomputers have up to 36 miles of wire to connect memory modules, as well as processors with memory. The Cray product line uses eZIPs instead—electric connectors of 400 contacts to send imped-ance-controlled signals be-tween modules. In these computers, wires are used only to provide external in-put and output.

For very low frequencies, where $X_C$ approaches infinity, $V_{out}$ is approximately equal to $V_{in}$. This is true because the ratio $X_C/Z_T$ approaches one as $X_C$ and $Z_T$ become approximately the same value. For very high frequencies, where $X_C$ approaches zero, the ratio $X_C/Z_T$ becomes very small, and $V_{out}$ is approximately zero.

With respect to the input voltage $V_{in}$, the phase angle $\theta$ of the output voltage $V_{out}$ can be calculated as:

$$\blacktriangleright \qquad \theta = \arctan\left(-\frac{R}{X_C}\right) \qquad \qquad \text{(27-2)}$$

At very low frequencies, $X_C$ is very large and $\theta$ is approximately 0°. For very high frequencies, however, $X_C$ is nearly zero and $\theta$ approaches $-90°$.

The frequency where $X_C = R$ is the *cutoff frequency*, designated $f_c$. At $f_c$ the series current $I$ is at 70.7 percent of its maximum value, because the total impedance $Z_T$ is 1.41 times larger than the resistance of $R$. The formula for the cutoff frequency $f_c$ of an $RC$ low-pass filter is derived as follows. Because $X_C = R$ at $f_c$, we have

$$\frac{1}{2\pi f_c C} = R$$

Solving for $f_c$ gives

$$\blacktriangleright \qquad f_c = \frac{1}{2\pi RC} \qquad \qquad \text{(27-3)}$$

The response curve in Fig. 27-12b shows that $V_{out} = 0.707V_{in}$ at the cutoff frequency $f_c$.

## Example

EXAMPLE 1    In Fig. 27-12a, calculate: **(a)** the cutoff frequency $f_c$; **(b)** $V_{out}$ at $f_c$; **(c)** $\theta$ at $f_c$. (Assume $V_{in} = 10$ Vpp for all frequencies.)

ANSWER

a.    To calculate $f_c$, use Formula (27-3).

$$f_c = \frac{1}{2\pi RC}$$

$$= \frac{1}{2 \times \pi \times 10\ k\Omega \times 0.01\ \mu F}$$

$$= 1.592\ kHz$$

b.    To calculate $V_{out}$ at $f_c$, use Formula (27-1). First, however, calculate $Z_T$ at $f_c$.

$$X_C = \frac{1}{2\pi f_c C}$$

$$= \frac{1}{2 \times \pi \times 1.592\ kHz \times 0.01\ \mu F}$$

$$= 10\ k\Omega$$

$$Z_T = \sqrt{R^2 + X_C^2}$$
$$= \sqrt{10^2 \text{ k}\Omega + 10^2 \text{ k}\Omega}$$
$$= 14.14 \text{ k}\Omega$$

Next,

$$V_{out} = \frac{X_C}{Z_T} \times V_{in}$$
$$= \frac{10 \text{ k}\Omega}{14.14 \text{ k}\Omega} \times 10 \text{ Vpp}$$
$$= 7.07 \text{ Vpp}$$

c. To calculate $\theta$, use Formula (27-2).

$$\theta = \arctan\left(-\frac{R}{X_C}\right)$$
$$= \arctan -\frac{10 \text{ k}\Omega}{10 \text{ k}\Omega}$$
$$= \arctan(-1)$$
$$= -45°$$

The phase angle of $-45°$ tells us that $V_{out}$ lags $V_{in}$ by 45° at the cutoff frequency $f_c$.

***RL* LOW-PASS FILTER**   Figure 27-14a shows a simple *RL* low-pass filter, while Fig. 27-14b shows how its output voltage $V_{out}$ varies with frequency. For the analysis that follows, it is assumed that the coil's dc resistance $r_s$ is negligible in comparison with the series resistance $R$.

Figure 27-15a shows the equivalent circuit when $f = 0$ Hz (dc). Notice that the inductor $L$ acts as a short, since $X_L$ must equal 0 $\Omega$ when $f = 0$ Hz. As a result, $V_{out} = V_{in}$ for very low frequencies and dc (0 Hz). For very high frequencies, $X_L$ approaches infinity and the equivalent circuit appears as in Fig. 27-15b. Since $L$ is basically equivalent to an open for very high frequencies, all of the

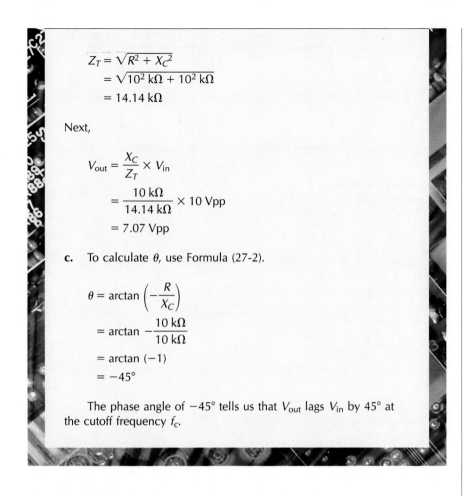
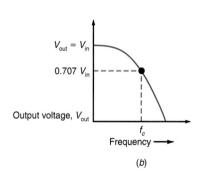

(a)                                                    (b)

FIG. 27-14   *RL* low-pass filter. (a) Circuit. (b) Graph of $V_{out}$ versus frequency.

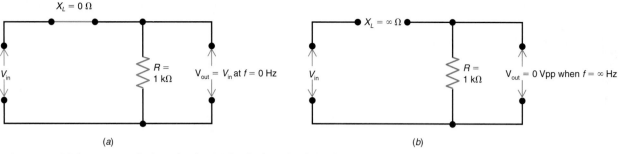

(a)

(b)

**FIG. 27-15** *RL* low-pass equivalent circuits. (*a*) Equivalent circuit for *f* = 0 Hz.
(*b*) Equivalent circuit for very high frequencies, or *f* = ∞ Hz.

input voltage will be dropped across *L* rather than *R*. Therefore, $V_{\text{out}} = 0$ Vpp for very high frequencies.

To calculate the output voltage at any frequency in Fig. 27-14*a*, use Formula (27-4).

$$\blacktriangleright \quad V_{\text{out}} = \frac{R}{Z_T} \times V_{\text{in}} \qquad\qquad (27\text{-}4)$$

where

$$Z_T = \sqrt{R^2 + X_L^2}$$

For very low frequencies, where $X_L$ is very small, $V_{\text{out}}$ is approximately equal to $V_{\text{in}}$. This is true because the ratio $R/Z_T$ approaches one as $Z_T$ and $R$ become approximately the same value. For very high frequencies the output voltage is approximately zero, because the ratio $R/Z_T$ becomes very small as $X_L$ and thus $Z_T$ approach infinity.

The phase angle $\theta$ between $V_{\text{in}}$ and $V_{\text{out}}$ can be determined using Formula (27-5).

$$\blacktriangleright \quad \theta = \arctan\left(-\frac{X_L}{R}\right) \qquad\qquad (27\text{-}5)$$

At very low frequencies, $X_L$ approaches zero and $\theta$ is approximately 0°. For very high frequencies, $X_L$ approaches infinity and $\theta$ is approximately −90°.

The frequency where $X_L = R$ is the cutoff frequency $f_c$. At $f_c$ the series current *I* is at 70.7 percent of its maximum value, since $Z_T = 1.41R$ when $X_L = R$. The formula for the cutoff frequency of an *RL* low-pass filter is derived as follows. Since $X_L = R$ at $f_c$, we have

$$2\pi f_c L = R$$

Solving for $f_c$ gives

$$\blacktriangleright \quad f_c = \frac{R}{2\pi L} \qquad\qquad (27\text{-}6)$$

The response curve in Fig. 27-14*b* shows that $V_{\text{out}} = 0.707 V_{\text{in}}$ at the cutoff frequency $f_c$.

## Example

EXAMPLE 2   In Fig. 27-14a, calculate: **(a)** the cutoff frequency $f_c$; **(b)** $V_{out}$ at 1 kHz; **(c)** $\theta$ at 1 kHz. (Assume $V_{in} = 10$ Vpp for all frequencies.)

**ANSWER**

a.   To calculate $f_c$, use Formula (27-6).

$$f_c = \frac{R}{2\pi L}$$

$$= \frac{1\ k\Omega}{2 \times \pi \times 50\ mH}$$

$$= 3.183\ kHz$$

b.   To calculate $V_{out}$ at 1 kHz, use Formula (27-4). First, however, calculate $X_L$ and $Z_T$ at 1 kHz.

$$X_L = 2\pi fL$$

$$= 2 \times \pi \times 1\ kHz \times 50\ mH$$

$$= 314\ \Omega$$

$$Z_T = \sqrt{R^2 + X_L^2}$$

$$= \sqrt{1^2\ k\Omega + 314^2\ \Omega}$$

$$= 1.05\ k\Omega$$

Next,

$$V_{out} = \frac{R}{Z_T} \times V_{in}$$

$$= \frac{1\ k\Omega}{1.05\ k\Omega} \times 10\ Vpp$$

$$= 9.52\ Vpp$$

Notice that $V_{out} \cong V_{in}$, since 1 kHz is in the passband of the low-pass filter.

c.   To calculate $\theta$ at 1 kHz, use Formula (27-5). Recall that $X_L = 314\ \Omega$ at 1 kHz.

$$\theta = \arctan\left(-\frac{X_L}{R}\right)$$

$$= \arctan\left(-\frac{314\ \Omega}{1\ k\Omega}\right)$$

$$= \arctan(-0.314)$$

$$= -17.4°$$

The phase angle of $-17.4°$ tells us that $V_{out}$ lags $V_{in}$ by 17.4° at a frequency of 1 kHz.

**_RC_ HIGH-PASS FILTER**   Figure 27-16*a* shows an _RC_ high-pass filter. Notice that the output is taken across the resistor $R$ rather than across the capacitor $C$. Figure 27-16*b* shows how the output voltage varies with frequency. To calculate the output voltage $V_{out}$ at any frequency, use Formula (27-7).

▷     $$V_{out} = \frac{R}{Z_T} \times V_{in} \qquad\qquad\qquad \textbf{(27-7)}$$

where

$$Z_T = \sqrt{R^2 + X_C^2}$$

For very low frequencies the output voltage approaches zero, because the ratio $R/Z_T$ becomes very small as $X_C$ and thus $Z_T$ approach infinity. For very high frequencies $V_{out}$ is approximately equal to $V_{in}$, because the ratio $R/Z_T$ approaches one as $Z_T$ and $R$ become approximately the same value.

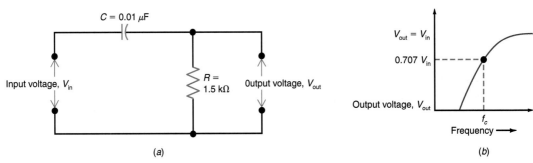

(a)                                    (b)

**FIG. 27-16**   _RC_ high-pass filter. (*a*) Circuit. (*b*) Graph of $V_{out}$ versus frequency.

The phase angle of $V_{out}$ with respect to $V_{in}$ for an _RC_ high-pass filter can be calculated using Formula (27-8).

▷     $$\theta = \arctan\left(\frac{X_C}{R}\right) \qquad\qquad\qquad \textbf{(27-8)}$$

For very low frequencies where $X_C$ is very large, $\theta$ is approximately 90°. For very high frequencies where $X_C$ approaches zero, $\theta$ is approximately 0°.

To calculate the cutoff frequency $f_c$ for an _RC_ high-pass filter, use Formula (27-3). Although this formula is used to calculate $f_c$ for an _RC_ low-pass filter, it can also be used to calculate $f_c$ for an _RC_ high-pass filter. The reason is that, for both circuits, $X_C = R$ at the cutoff frequency. In Fig. 27-16*b*, notice that $V_{out} = 0.707V_{in}$ at $f_c$.

**_RL_ HIGH-PASS FILTER**   An _RL_ high-pass filter is shown in Fig. 27-17*a*, while its response curve is shown in Fig. 27-17*b*. In Fig. 27-17*a*, notice that the output is taken across the inductor $L$ rather than across the resistance $R$.

To calculate the output voltage $V_{out}$ at any frequency, use Formula (27-9).

▷     $$V_{out} = \frac{X_L}{Z_T} \times V_{in} \qquad\qquad\qquad \textbf{(27-9)}$$

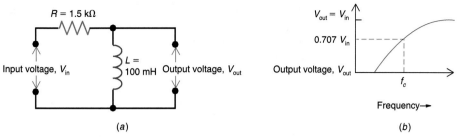

FIG. 27-17 *RL* high-pass filter. (*a*) Circuit. (*b*) Graph of $V_{out}$ versus frequency.

where

$$Z_T = \sqrt{R^2 + X_L^2}$$

For very low frequencies, where $X_L$ is very small, $V_{out}$ is approximately zero. For very high frequencies, $V_{out} = V_{in}$ because the ratio $X_L/Z_T$ is approximately one.

The phase angle $\theta$ of the output voltage $V_{out}$ with respect to the input voltage $V_{in}$ is

▶   $$\theta = \arctan\left(\frac{R}{X_L}\right) \qquad \textbf{(27-10)}$$

For very low frequencies $\theta$ approaches 90°, because the ratio $R/X_L$ becomes very large when $X_L$ approaches zero. For very high frequencies $\theta$ approaches 0°, because the ratio $R/X_L$ becomes approximately zero as $X_L$ approaches infinity. To calculate the cutoff frequency of an *RL* high-pass filter, use Formula (27-6).

## Example

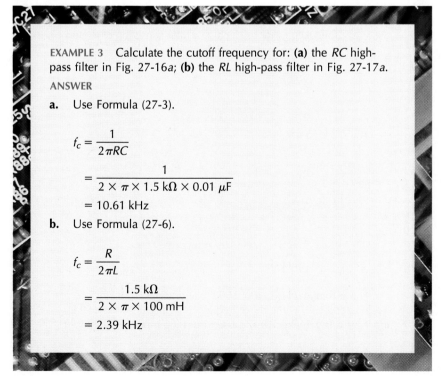

EXAMPLE 3   Calculate the cutoff frequency for: **(a)** the *RC* high-pass filter in Fig. 27-16*a*; **(b)** the *RL* high-pass filter in Fig. 27-17*a*.

ANSWER

**a.**   Use Formula (27-3).

$$f_c = \frac{1}{2\pi RC}$$

$$= \frac{1}{2 \times \pi \times 1.5 \text{ k}\Omega \times 0.01 \text{ }\mu\text{F}}$$

$$= 10.61 \text{ kHz}$$

**b.**   Use Formula (27-6).

$$f_c = \frac{R}{2\pi L}$$

$$= \frac{1.5 \text{ k}\Omega}{2 \times \pi \times 100 \text{ mH}}$$

$$= 2.39 \text{ kHz}$$

**RC BANDPASS FILTER**   A high-pass filter can be combined with a low-pass filter when it is desired to pass only a certain band of frequencies. This type of filter is called a *bandpass filter*. Figure 27-18a shows an *RC* bandpass filter, while Fig. 27-18b shows how its output voltage varies with frequency. In Fig. 27-18a, $R_1$ and $C_1$ constitute the high-pass filter, while $R_2$ and $C_2$ constitute the low-pass filter. To ensure that the low-pass filter does not load the high-pass filter, $R_2$ is usually made 10 or more times larger than the resistance of $R_1$. The cutoff frequency of the high-pass filter is designated $f_{c_1}$, while the cutoff frequency of the low-pass filter is designed $f_{c_2}$. These two frequencies can be found on the response curve in Fig. 27-18b. To calculate the values for $f_{c_1}$ and $f_{c_2}$, use the formulas given earlier for individual *RC* low-pass and *RC* high-pass filter circuits.

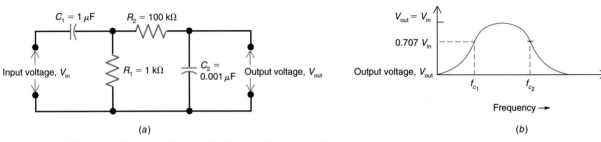

**FIG. 27-18**   *RC* bandpass filter. (*a*) Circuit. (*b*) Graph of $V_{out}$ versus frequency.

## Example

**EXAMPLE 4**   In Fig. 27-18a, calculate the cutoff frequencies $f_{c_1}$ and $f_{c_2}$.

**ANSWER**   Calculate $f_{c_1}$ for the high-pass filter consisting of $R_1$ and $C_1$.

$$f_{c_1} = \frac{1}{2\pi R_1 C_1}$$

$$= \frac{1}{2 \times \pi \times 1\ \text{k}\Omega \times 1\ \mu\text{F}}$$

$$= 159\ \text{Hz}$$

Next, calculate $f_{c_2}$.

$$f_{c_2} = \frac{1}{2\pi R_2 C_2}$$

$$= \frac{1}{2 \times \pi \times 100\ \text{k}\Omega \times 0.001\ \mu\text{F}}$$

$$= 1.59\ \text{kHz}$$

Those frequencies below 159 Hz and above 1.59 kHz are severely attenuated, while those frequencies lying between 159 Hz and 1.59 kHz are effectively passed from the input to the output.

**RC BANDSTOP FILTER**    A high-pass filter can also be combined with a low-pass filter when it is desired to block or severely attenuate a certain band of frequencies. Such a filter is called a *bandstop* or *notch filter*. Figure 27-19a shows an *RC* bandstop filter, while Fig. 27-19b shows how its output voltage varies with frequency. In Fig. 27-19a, the components identified as $2R_1$ and $2C_1$ constitute the low-pass filter section, while the components identified as $R_1$ and $C_1$ constitute the high-pass filter section. Notice that the individual filters are actually in parallel with each other. The frequency of maximum attenuation is called the *notch frequency* and is identified as $f_N$ in Fig. 27-19b. Notice that the maximum value of $V_{out}$ below $f_N$ is less than the maximum value of $V_{out}$ above $f_N$. The reason for this is that the series resistances $(2R_1)$ in the low-pass filter provide greater circuit losses than do the series capacitors $(C_1)$ in the high-pass filter.

To calculate the notch frequency $f_N$ in Fig. 27-19a, use Formula (27-11).

▶ $$f_N = \frac{1}{4\pi R_1 C_1} \qquad\qquad \textbf{(27-11)}$$

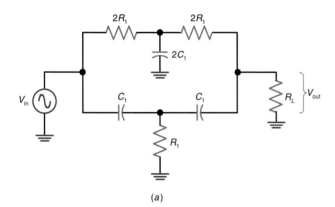

(a)

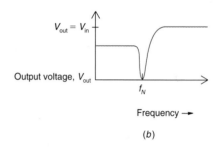

(b)

**FIG. 27-19**    Notch filter. (*a*) Circuit. (*b*) Graph of $V_{out}$ versus frequency.

## Example

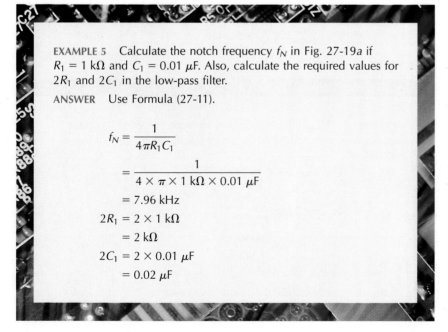

**EXAMPLE 5**    Calculate the notch frequency $f_N$ in Fig. 27-19a if $R_1 = 1\ k\Omega$ and $C_1 = 0.01\ \mu F$. Also, calculate the required values for $2R_1$ and $2C_1$ in the low-pass filter.

**ANSWER**    Use Formula (27-11).

$$f_N = \frac{1}{4\pi R_1 C_1}$$

$$= \frac{1}{4 \times \pi \times 1\ k\Omega \times 0.01\ \mu F}$$

$$= 7.96\ kHz$$

$$2R_1 = 2 \times 1\ k\Omega$$

$$= 2\ k\Omega$$

$$2C_1 = 2 \times 0.01\ \mu F$$

$$= 0.02\ \mu F$$

Answers at end of chapter.

Answer True or False.
a. Increasing the capacitance $C$ in Fig. 27-12$a$ raises the cutoff frequency $f_c$.
b. Decreasing the inductance $L$ in Fig. 27-14$a$ raises the cutoff frequency $f_c$.
c. Increasing the value of $C_2$ in Fig. 27-18$a$ reduces the passband.
d. In Fig. 27-17$a$, $V_{out}$ is approximately zero for very low frequencies.

# 27-10 DECIBELS AND FREQUENCY RESPONSE CURVES

In analyzing filters, the decibel (db) unit is often used to describe the amount of attenuation offered by the filter. In basic terms, the *decibel* is a logarithmic expression that compares two power levels. Expressed mathematically,

$$N_{db} = 10 \log \frac{P_{out}}{P_{in}} \qquad (27\text{-}12)$$

where

$$N_{db} = \text{gain or loss in decibels}$$
$$P_{in} = \text{input power}$$
$$P_{out} = \text{output power}$$

If the ratio $P_{out}/P_{in}$ is greater than one, the $N_{db}$ value is positive, indicating an increase in power from input to output. If the ratio $P_{out}/P_{in}$ is less than one, the $N_{db}$ value is negative, indicating a loss or reduction in power from input to output. A reduction in power, corresponding to a negative $N_{db}$ value, is referred to as *attenuation*.

*Example*

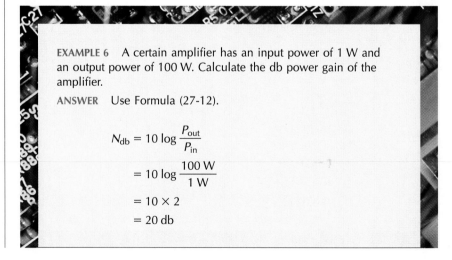

EXAMPLE 6    A certain amplifier has an input power of 1 W and an output power of 100 W. Calculate the db power gain of the amplifier.

ANSWER    Use Formula (27-12).

$$N_{db} = 10 \log \frac{P_{out}}{P_{in}}$$
$$= 10 \log \frac{100 \text{ W}}{1 \text{ W}}$$
$$= 10 \times 2$$
$$= 20 \text{ db}$$

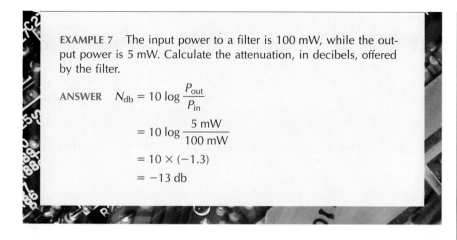

**EXAMPLE 7** The input power to a filter is 100 mW, while the output power is 5 mW. Calculate the attenuation, in decibels, offered by the filter.

**ANSWER**
$$N_{db} = 10 \log \frac{P_{out}}{P_{in}}$$

$$= 10 \log \frac{5 \text{ mW}}{100 \text{ mW}}$$

$$= 10 \times (-1.3)$$

$$= -13 \text{ db}$$

The power gain or loss in decibels can also be computed from a voltage ratio if the measurements are made across equal resistances.

$$\blacktriangleright \qquad N_{db} = 20 \log \frac{V_{out}}{V_{in}} \qquad\qquad \textbf{(27-13)}$$

where

$$N_{db} = \text{gain or loss in decibels}$$
$$V_{in} = \text{input voltage}$$
$$V_{out} = \text{output voltage}$$

For the passive filters discussed in this chapter, the $N_{db}$ value can never be positive, because $V_{out}$ can never be greater than $V_{in}$.

Consider the $RC$ low-pass filter in Fig. 27-20. The cutoff frequency $f_c$ for this circuit is 1.592 kHz, as determined by Formula (27-1). Recall that the formula for $V_{out}$ at any frequency is

$$V_{out} = \frac{X_C}{Z_T} \times V_{in}$$

Dividing both sides of the equation by $V_{in}$ gives

$$\frac{V_{out}}{V_{in}} = \frac{X_C}{Z_T}$$

Substituting $X_C/Z_T$ for $V_{out}/V_{in}$ in Formula (27-13) gives

$$N_{db} = 20 \log \frac{X_C}{Z_T}$$

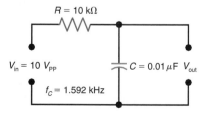

**FIG. 27-20** *RC* low-pass filter.

## Example

EXAMPLE 8   In Fig. 27-20, calculate the attenuation, in decibels, at the following frequencies: **(a)** 0 Hz; **(b)** 1.592 kHz; **(c)** 15.92 kHz. (Assume that $V_{in}$ = 10 Vpp for all frequencies.)

ANSWER

a.  At 0 Hz, $V_{out}$ = $V_{in}$ = 10 Vpp, since the capacitor $C$ appears as an open. Therefore,

$$N_{db} = 20 \log \frac{V_{out}}{V_{in}}$$

$$= 20 \log \frac{10 \text{ Vpp}}{10 \text{ Vpp}}$$

$$= 20 \log 1$$

$$= 20 \times 0$$

$$= 0 \text{ db}$$

b.  Since 1.592 kHz is the cutoff frequency $f_c$, $V_{out}$ will be 0.707 × $V_{in}$ or 7.07 Vpp. Therefore,

$$N_{db} = 20 \log \frac{V_{out}}{V_{in}}$$

$$= 20 \log \frac{7.07 \text{ Vpp}}{10 \text{ Vpp}}$$

$$= 20 \log 0.707$$

$$= 20 \times (-0.15)$$

$$= -3 \text{ db}$$

c.  To calculate $N_{db}$ at 15.92 kHz, $X_C$ and $Z_T$ must first be determined.

$$X_C = \frac{1}{2\pi f C}$$

$$= \frac{1}{2 \times \pi \times 15.92 \text{ kHz} \times 0.01 \text{ }\mu F}$$

$$= 1 \text{ k}\Omega$$

$$Z_T = \sqrt{R^2 + X_C^2}$$

$$= \sqrt{10^2 \text{ k}\Omega + 1^2 \text{ k}\Omega}$$

$$= 10.05 \text{ k}\Omega$$

Next,

$$N_{db} = 20 \log \frac{X_C}{Z_T}$$

$$= 10 \log \frac{1 \text{ k}\Omega}{10.05 \text{ k}\Omega}$$

$$= 20 \log 0.0995$$

$$= 20(-1)$$

$$= -20 \text{ db}$$

In Example 8, notice that $N_{db}$ is 0 db at a frequency of 0 Hz, which is in the filter's passband. This may seem unusual, but the 0-db value simply indicates that there is no attenuation at this frequency. For an ideal passive filter, $N_{db} = 0$ db in the passband. As another point of interest from Example 8, $N_{db}$ was determined to be $-3$ db at the cutoff frequency of 1.592 kHz. Since for any passive filter $V_{out} = 0.707V_{in}$ at $f_c$, $N_{db}$ is always $-3$ db at the cutoff frequency for a passive filter.

The $N_{db}$ value of loss can be determined for any filter if the values of $V_{in}$ and $V_{out}$ are known. Figure 27-21 shows the basic $RC$ and $RL$ low-pass and high-pass filters. For each filter the formula for calculating the $N_{db}$ loss is provided.

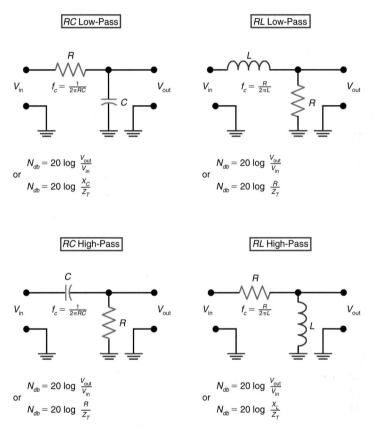

**FIG. 27-21** $RC$ and $RL$ filter circuits, showing formulas for calculating decibel attenuation.

**FREQUENCY RESPONSE CURVES**   The frequency response of a filter is typically shown by plotting its gain (or loss) versus frequency on logarithmic graph paper. The two types of logarithmic graph paper are log-log and semilog. On *semilog graph paper,* the divisions along one axis are spaced logarithmically, while the other axis has conventional linear spacing between divisions. On *log-log graph paper,* both axes have logarithmic spacing between divisions. Logarithmic spacing results in a scale that expands the display of smaller values and compresses the display of larger values. On logarithmic graph paper, a 2-to-1 range of frequencies is called an *octave,* and a 10-to-1 range of values is called a *decade.*

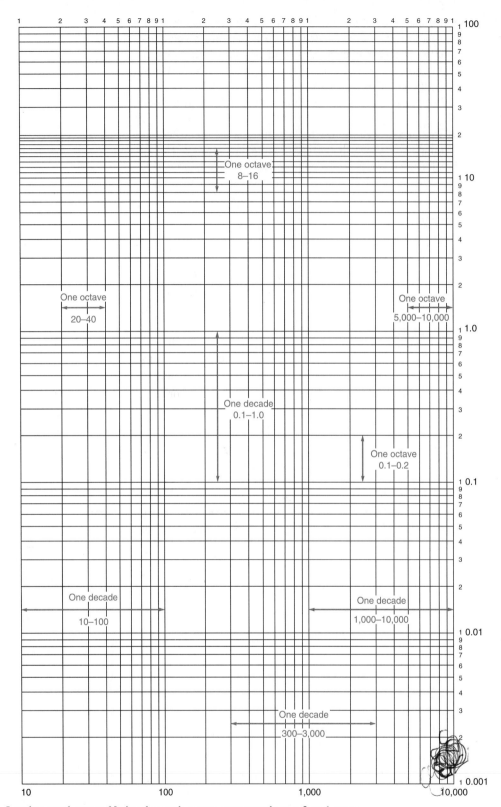

**FIG. 27-22** Log-log graph paper. Notice that each octave corresponds to a 2-to-1 range of values and each decade corresponds to a 10-to-1 range of values.

One advantage of logarithmic spacing is that a larger range of values can be shown in one plot without losing resolution in the smaller values. For example, if frequency values between 10 Hz and 100 kHz were plotted on 100 divisions of linear graph paper, each division would represent approximately 1000 Hz and it would be impossible to plot values in the decade between 10 Hz and 100 Hz. On the other hand, by using logarithmic graph paper, the decade between 10 Hz and 100 Hz would occupy the same space on the graph as the decade between 10 kHz and 100 kHz.

Log-log or semilog graph paper is specified by the number of decades it contains. Each decade is a *graph cycle*. For example, 2-cycle by 4-cycle log-log paper has two decades on one axis and four on the other. The number of cycles must be adequate for the range of data being plotted. For example, if the frequency response extends from 25 Hz to 40 kHz, 4 cycles are necessary to plot the frequency values corresponding to the decades 10 Hz to 100 Hz, 100 Hz to 1 kHz, 1 kHz to 10 kHz, and 10 kHz to 100 kHz. A typical sheet of log-log graph paper is shown in Fig. 27-22. Because there are three decades on the horizontal axis and five decades on the vertical axis, this graph paper is called 3-cycle by 5-cycle log-log paper. Notice that each octave corresponds to a 2-to-1 range in values and each decade corresponds to a 10-to-1 range in values. For clarity, several octaves and decades are shown in Fig. 27-22.

When semilog graph paper is used to plot a frequency response, the observed or calculated values of gain (or loss) must first be converted to decibels before plotting. On the other hand, since decibel voltage gain is a logarithmic function, the gain or loss values can be plotted on log-log paper without first converting to decibels.

### RC LOW-PASS FREQUENCY RESPONSE CURVE

Figure 27-23a shows an *RC* low-pass filter whose cutoff frequency $f_c$ is 1.592 kHz as determined by Formula (27-1). Figure 27-23b shows its frequency response curve plotted on semilog graph paper. Notice there are 6 cycles on the horizontal axis, which spans a frequency range extending from 1 Hz to 1 MHz. Notice the vertical axis specifies the $N_{db}$ loss, which is the amount of attenuation offered by the filter in decibels. Notice that $N_{db} = -3$ db at the cutoff frequency of 1.592 kHz. Above $f_c$, $N_{db}$ decreases at the rate of approximately 6 db/octave, which is equivalent to 20 db/decade.

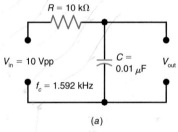

FIG. 27-23 *RC* low-pass filter frequency response curve. (a) Circuit. Continue on page 790 for part (b).

## Example

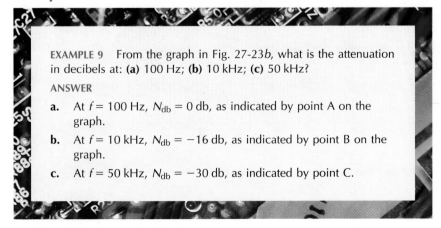

EXAMPLE 9    From the graph in Fig. 27-23b, what is the attenuation in decibels at: **(a)** 100 Hz; **(b)** 10 kHz; **(c)** 50 kHz?

ANSWER

a.    At $f = 100$ Hz, $N_{db} = 0$ db, as indicated by point A on the graph.

b.    At $f = 10$ kHz, $N_{db} = -16$ db, as indicated by point B on the graph.

c.    At $f = 50$ kHz, $N_{db} = -30$ db, as indicated by point C.

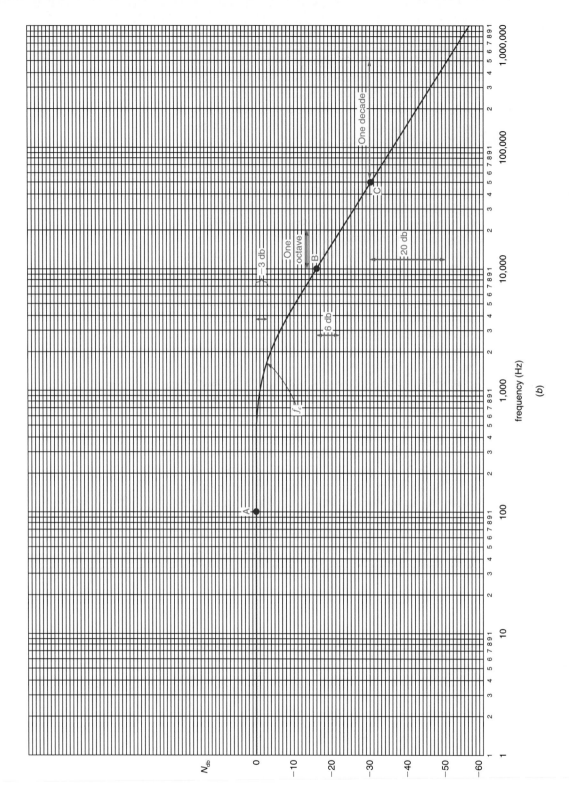

**FIG. 27-23 (*continued*)** *RC* low-pass filter frequency response curve. (*b*) Frequency response curve.

For filters such as the inverted-L, T, or $\pi$ type, the response curve rolloff is much steeper beyond the cutoff frequency $f_c$. For example, a low-pass filter with a series inductor and a shunt capacitor has a rate of rolloff of 12 db/octave or 40 db/decade above the cutoff frequency $f_c$. To increase the rate of rolloff, more inductors and capacitors must be used in the filter design. Filters are available whose rolloff rates exceed 36 db/octave.

---

### TEST-POINT QUESTIONS 27-10

Answers at end of chapter.

Answer True or False
a. For very low frequencies, a low-pass filter provides an attenuation of 0 db.
b. At the cutoff frequency, a low-pass filter has an $N_{db}$ loss of $-3$ db.
c. On logarithmic graph paper, one cycle is the same as one octave.
d. The advantage of semilog and log-log graph paper is that a larger range of values can be shown in one plot without losing resolution in the smaller values.

## 27-11 RESONANT FILTERS

Tuned circuits provide a convenient method of filtering a band of radio frequencies because relatively small values of $L$ and $C$ are necessary for resonance. A tuned circuit provides filtering action by means of its maximum response at the resonant frequency.

The width of the band of frequencies affected by resonance depends on the $Q$ of the tuned circuit, a higher $Q$ providing narrower bandwidth. Because resonance is effective for a band of frequencies below and above $f_r$, resonant filters are called *bandstop* or *bandpass* filters. Series or parallel $LC$ circuits can be used for either function, depending on the connections with respect to $R_L$. In the application of a bandstop filter to suppress certain frequencies, the $LC$ circuit is often called a *wavetrap*.

**SERIES RESONANCE FILTERS**    A series resonant circuit has maximum current and minimum impedance at the resonant frequency. Connected in series with $R_L$, as in Fig. 27-24a, the series-tuned $LC$ circuit allows frequencies at and near resonance to produce maximum output across $R_L$. Therefore, this is a case of bandpass filtering.

When the series $LC$ circuit is connected across $R_L$ as in Fig. 27-24b, however, the resonant circuit provides a low-impedance shunt path that short-circuits $R_L$. Then there is minimum output. This action corresponds to a shunt bypass capacitor, but the resonant circuit is more selective, short-circuiting $R_L$ just for frequencies at and near resonance. For the bandwidth of the tuned circuit, therefore, the series resonant circuit in shunt with $R_L$ provides band-stop filtering.

The series resistor $R_S$ in Fig. 27-24b is used to isolate the low resistance of the $LC$ filter from the input source. At the resonant frequency, practically all of the input voltage is across $R_S$, with little across $R_L$, because the $LC$ tuned circuit then has very low resistance due to series resonance.

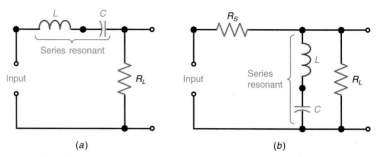

FIG. 27-24   The filtering action of a series resonant circuit. (*a*) Bandpass filter when *L* and *C* are in series with $R_L$. (*b*) Bandstop filter when *LC* circuit is in shunt with $R_L$.

**PARALLEL RESONANCE FILTERS**   A parallel resonant circuit has maximum impedance at the resonant frequency. Connected in series with $R_L$, as in Fig. 27-25*a*, the parallel-tuned *LC* circuit provides maximum impedance in series with $R_L$, at and near the resonant frequency. Then these frequencies produce maximum voltage across the *LC* circuit but minimum output voltage across $R_L$. This is a bandstop filter, therefore, for the bandwidth of the tuned circuit.

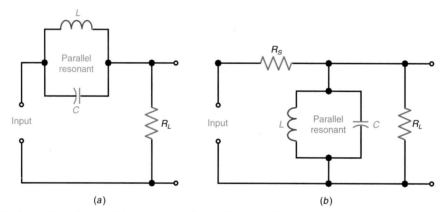

FIG. 27-25   The filtering action of a parallel resonant circuit. (*a*) Bandstop filter when *LC* bank is in series with $R_L$. (*b*) Bandpass filter when *LC* bank is in shunt with $R_L$.

The parallel *LC* circuit connected across $R_L$, however, as in Fig. 27-25*b*, provides a bandpass filter. At resonance, the high impedance of the parallel *LC* circuit allows $R_L$ to develop its output voltage. Below resonance, $R_L$ is short-circuited by the low reactance of *L*; above resonance, $R_L$ is short-circuited by the low reactance of *C*. For frequencies at or near resonance, though, $R_L$ is shunted by a high impedance, resulting in maximum output voltage.

The series resistor $R_S$ in Fig. 27-25*b* is used to improve the filtering effect. Note that the parallel *LC* combination and $R_S$ divide the input voltage. At the resonant frequency, though, the *LC* circuit has very high resistance for parallel resonance. Then most of the input voltage is across the *LC* circuit and $R_L$, with little across $R_S$.

**L-TYPE RESONANT FILTER**   Series and parallel resonant circuits can be combined in *L*, *T*, or $\pi$ sections for sharper discrimination in the frequencies to be filtered. Examples for an L-type filter are shown in Fig. 27-26.

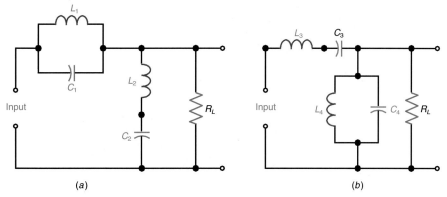

FIG. 27-26 Inverted-L filter with resonant circuits. (*a*) Bandstop filtering action. (*b*) Bandpass filtering action.

The circuit in Fig. 27-26*a* is a bandstop filter. The reason is that the parallel resonant $L_1C_1$ circuit is in series with the load, while the series-resonant $L_2C_2$ circuit is in shunt with $R_L$. There is a dual effect as a voltage divider across the input source voltage. The high resistance of $L_1C_1$ reduces voltage output to the load. Also, the low resistance of $L_2C_2$ reduces the output voltage.

For the opposite effect, the circuit in Fig. 27-26*b* is a bandpass filter. Now the series-resonant $L_3C_3$ circuit is in series with the load. Here the low resistance of $L_3C_3$ allows more output for $R_L$ at resonance. Also, the high resistance of $L_4C_4$ allows maximum output voltage.

**CRYSTAL FILTERS** A thin slice of quartz provides a resonance effect by mechanical vibrations at a particular frequency, like an *LC* circuit. The quartz crystal can be made to vibrate by a voltage input or produce voltage output when it is compressed, expanded, or twisted. This characteristic of some crystals is known as the *piezoelectric effect*. As a result, crystals are often used in place of resonant circuits. In fact, the *Q* of a resonant crystal is much higher than that of *LC* circuits. However, the crystal has a specific frequency that cannot be varied because of its stability. Crystals are used for radio frequencies, in the range of about 0.5 to 30 MHz. Figure 27-27 shows a crystal in its housing for the frequency of 3.579545 MHz, for use in the color oscillator circuit of a television receiver. Note the exact frequency. More details of the piezoelectric effect and crystal resonators are explained in Chap. 29.

Special ceramic materials, such as leads titanate, can also be used for crystal filters. They have the piezoelectric effect like quartz crystals. Ceramic crystals are smaller in size and cost less but they have lower *Q* than quartz crystals.

FIG. 27-27 Quartz crystal in holder. Size is ½ in wide.

**TEST-POINT QUESTION 27-11**

Answers at end of chapter.

Answer True or False.
**a.** A parallel-resonant *LC* circuit in series with the load is a bandstop filter.
**b.** A series resonant *LC* circuit in series with the load is a bandpass filter.
**c.** Quartz crystals can be used as resonant filters.

Voltage or current not at the desired frequency represents interference. Usually, such interference can be eliminated by a filter. Some typical applications are (1) low-pass filter to eliminate RF interference from the 60-Hz power-line input to a receiver, (2) high-pass filter to eliminate RF interference from the signal picked up by a television receiving antenna, and (3) resonant filter to eliminate an interfering radio frequency from the desired RF signal. As noted earlier, the resonant bandstop filter is called a wavetrap.

**POWER-LINE FILTER**  Although the power line is a source of 60-Hz voltage, it is also a conductor for interfering RF currents produced by motors, fluorescent lighting circuits, and RF equipment. When a receiver is connected to the power line, the RF interference can produce noise and whistles in the receiver output. To minimize this interference, the filter shown in Fig. 27-28 can be used. The filter is plugged into the wall outlet for 60-Hz power, while the receiver is plugged into the filter. An RF bypass capacitor across the line with two series RF chokes forms a low-pass balanced L-type filter. Using a choke in each side of the line makes the circuit balanced to ground.

The chokes provide high impedance for interfering RF current but not for 60 Hz, isolating the receiver input connections from RF interference in the power line. Also, the bypass capacitor short-circuits the receiver input for radio frequencies but not for 60 Hz. The unit then is a low-pass filter for 60-Hz power applied to the receiver while rejecting higher frequencies. The current rating means the filter can be used for equipment that draws 3 A or less from the power line without excessive heat in the chokes.

**TELEVISION ANTENNA FILTER**  When a television receiver has interference in the picture resulting from radio frequencies below the television broadcast band, picked up by the receiving antenna, this RF interference can be reduced by the high-pass filter shown in Fig. 27-29. The filter attenuates frequencies below 54 MHz, which is the lowest frequency for channel 2.

At frequencies lower than 54 MHz the series capacitances provide increasing reactance with a larger voltage drop, while the shunt inductances have less reactance and short-circuit the load. Higher frequencies are passed to the load as the series capacitive reactance decreases and the shunt inductive reactance increases.

Connections to the filter unit are made at the receiver end of the line from the antenna. Either end of the filter is connected to the antenna terminals on the receiver, with the opposite end connected to the antenna line.

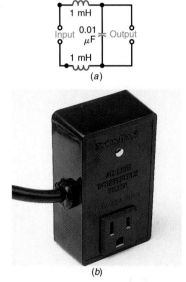

FIG. 27-28  Power-line filter unit. (*a*) Circuit of balanced L-type low-pass filter. (*b*) Filter unit.

FIG. 27-29  A television antenna filter to pass TV channel frequencies above 54 MHz but attenuate lower frequencies that can cause interference.

### TEST-POINT QUESTION 27-12

Answers at end of chapter.

Answer True or False.
**a.** A wavetrap is a band-stop filter.
**b.** The TV antenna filter in Fig. 27-29 is a high-pass filter with series capacitors.

# 27 SUMMARY AND REVIEW

- A filter separates high and low frequencies. With input of different frequencies, the high-pass filter allows the higher frequencies to produce output voltage across the load; a low-pass filter provides output voltage for the lower frequencies.
- Pulsating or fluctuating direct current varies in amplitude but does not reverse its direction. Similarly, a pulsating or fluctuating dc voltage varies in amplitude but maintains one polarity, either positive or negative.
- The pulsating direct current or voltage consists of a steady dc level, equal to the average value, and an ac component that reverses in polarity with respect to the average level. The dc and ac can be separated by filters.
- An $RC$ coupling circuit is effectively a high-pass filter for pulsating direct current. Capacitance $C_C$ blocks the steady dc voltage but passes the ac component.
- A transformer with an isolated secondary winding also is effectively a high-pass filter. With pulsating direct current in the primary, only the ac component produces output voltage in the secondary.
- A bypass capacitor in parallel with $R$ provides a low-pass filter.
- Combinations of $L$, $C$, and $R$ can be arranged as L, T, or $\pi$ filters for more selective filtering. All three arrangements can be used for either low-pass or high-pass action. See Figs. 27-9 and 27-11.
- In high-pass filters, the capacitance must be in series with the load as a coupling capacitor, with shunt $R$ or $L$ across the line.
- For low-pass filters, the capacitance is across the line as a bypass capacitor, while $R$ or $L$ then must be in series with the load.
- The cutoff frequency $f_c$ of a filter is the frequency at which the output voltage is reduced to 70.7 percent of its maximum value.
- For an $RC$ low-pass or high-pass filter, $X_C = R$ at the cutoff frequency. Similarly, for an $RL$ low-pass or high-pass filter, $X_L = R$ at the cutoff frequency. To calculate $f_c$ for an $RC$ low-pass or high-pass filter, use the formula $f_c = 1/2\pi RC$. To calculate $f_c$ for an $RL$ low-pass or high-pass filter, use the formula $f_c = R/2\pi L$.
- For an $RC$ or $RL$ filter, either low-pass or high-pass, the phase angle $\theta$ between $V_{in}$ and $V_{out}$ is approximately $0°$ in the passband. In the stop band, $\theta = \pm 90°$. The sign of $\theta$ depends on the type of filter.
- $RC$ low-pass filters can be combined with $RC$ high-pass filters when it is desired to either pass or block only a certain band of frequencies. These types of filters are called bandpass and band-stop filters, respectively.
- The decibel (dB) unit of measurement is used to compare two power levels. A passive filter has an attenuation of $-3$ db at the cutoff frequency.
- Semilog and log-log graph paper are typically used to show the frequency response of a filter. On semilog graph paper the vertical axis uses conventional linear spacing, while the horizontal axis uses logarithmically spaced divisions.

- The advantage of using semilog or log-log graph paper is that a larger range of values can be shown in one plot without losing resolution in the smaller values.
- A bandpass or bandstop filter has in effect two cutoff frequencies. The bandpass filter passes to the load those frequencies in the band between the cutoff frequencies, while attenuating all other frequencies higher and lower than the passband. A bandstop filter does the opposite, attenuating the band between the cutoff frequencies, while passing to the load all other frequencies higher and lower than the stop band.
- Resonant circuits are generally used for bandpass or bandstop filtering with radio frequencies.
- For bandpass filtering, the series resonant $LC$ circuit must be in series with the load, for minimum series opposition, while the high impedance of parallel resonance is across the load.
- For bandstop filtering, the circuit is reversed, with the parallel resonant $LC$ circuit in series with the load, while the series resonant circuit is in shunt across the load.
- A wavetrap is an application of the resonant bandstop filter.

## SELF-TEST

**ANSWERS AT BACK OF BOOK.**

Choose (a), (b), (c), or (d).

1. With input frequencies from direct current up to 15 kHz, a high-pass filter allows the most output voltage to be developed across the load resistance for which of the following frequencies? (a) Direct current; (b) 15 Hz; (c) 150 Hz; (d) 15,000 Hz.
2. With input frequencies from direct current up to 15 kHz a low-pass filter allows the most output voltage to be developed across the load resistance for which of the following frequencies? (a) Direct current; (b) 15 Hz; (c) 150 Hz; (d) 15,000 Hz.
3. An $R_C C_C$ coupling circuit is a high-pass filter for pulsating dc voltage because: (a) $C_C$ has high reactance for high frequencies; (b) $C_C$ blocks dc voltage; (c) $C_C$ has low reactance for low frequencies; (d) $R_C$ has minimum opposition for low frequencies.
4. A transformer with an isolated secondary winding is a high-pass filter for pulsating direct primary current because: (a) the steady primary current has no magnetic field; (b) the ac component of the primary current has the strongest field; (c) only variations in primary current can induce secondary voltage; (d) the secondary voltage is maximum for steady direct current in the primary.
5. Which of the following is a low-pass filter? (a) L type with series $C$ and shunt $L$; (b) $\pi$ type with series $C$ and shunt $L$; (c) T type with series $C$ and shunt $L$; (d) L type with series $L$ and shunt $C$.
6. A bypass capacitor $C_b$ across $R_b$ provides low-pass filtering because: (a) current in the $C_b$ branch is maximum for low frequencies; (b) voltage across $C_b$ is minimum for high frequencies; (c) voltage across $C_b$ is minimum for low frequencies; (d) voltage across $R_b$ is minimum for low frequencies.
7. An ac voltmeter across $R$ in Fig. 27-6 reads (a) practically zero; (b) 7.07 V; (c) 10 V; (d) 20 V.
8. Which of the following L-type filters is the best bandstop filter? (a) Series resonant $LC$ circuit in series with the load and parallel resonant $LC$ circuit in shunt; (b) parallel resonant

*LC* circuit in series with the load and series resonant *LC* circuit in shunt; (*c*) series resonant *LC* circuits in series and in parallel with the load; (*d*) parallel resonant *LC* circuits in series and in parallel with the load.

9. A 455-kHz wavetrap is a resonant *LC* circuit tuned to 455 kHz and connected as a (*a*) bandstop filter for frequencies at and near 455 kHz; (*b*) bandpass filter for frequencies at and near 455 kHz; (*c*) bandstop filter for frequencies from direct current up to 455 kHz; (*d*) bandpass filter for frequencies from 455 kHz up to 300 MHz.

10. A power-line filter for rejecting RF interference has (*a*) RF coupling capacitors in series with the power line; (*b*) RF chokes in shunt across the power line; (*c*) 60-Hz chokes in series with the power line; (*d*) RF bypass capacitors in shunt across the power line.

11. Which of the following will increase the cutoff frequency of an *RC* high-pass filter: (*a*) increasing *R*; (*b*) decreasing *C*; (*c*) increasing *C*; (*d*) both (*a*) and (*c*).

12. At the cutoff frequency of an *RL* low-pass filter: (*a*) $V_{out}$ is reduced to 70.7 percent of its maximum value; (*b*) $N_{db} = -10$ db; (*c*) $V_{out} = V_{in}$; (*d*) $V_{out} = 0$ Vpp.

13. On logarithmic graph paper, a 10-to-1 range of values is called a(n): (*a*) octave; (*b*) cycle; (*c*) decade; (*d*) both (*b*) and (*c*).

14. In the passband, an *RC* low-pass filter has a phase angle $\theta$ of approximately: (*a*) 0°; (*b*) −45°; (*c*) +90°; (*d*) −90°.

15. The decibel attenuation at the cutoff frequency of an *RC* low-pass filter equals: (*a*) 0 db; (*b*) −20 db; (*c*) −3 db; (*d*) −6 db.

# QUESTIONS

1. What is the function of an electrical filter?

2. Give two examples where the voltage has different frequency components.

3. (**a**) What is meant by pulsating direct current or voltage? (**b**) What are the two components of a pulsating dc voltage? (**c**) How can you measure the value of each of the two components?

4. Define the function of the following filters in terms of output voltage across the load resistance: (**a**) High-pass filter. Why is an $R_C C_C$ coupling circuit an example? (**b**) Low-pass filter. Why is an $R_b C_b$ bypass circuit an example? (**c**) Bandpass filter. How does it differ from a coupling circuit? (**d**) Bandstop filter. How does it differ from a bandpass filter?

5. Draw circuit diagrams for the following filter types. No values are necessary. (**a**) T-type high-pass and T-type low-pass; (**b**) $\pi$-type low-pass, balanced with a filter reactance in both sides of the line.

6. Draw the circuit diagrams for L-type bandpass and L-type bandstop filters. How do these two circuits differ from each other?

7. Draw the response curve for each of the following filters: (**a**) low-pass cutting off at 20,000 Hz; (**b**) high-pass cutting off at 20 Hz; (**c**) bandpass for 20 to 20,000 Hz; (**d**) bandpass for 450 to 460 kHz.

8. Give one similarity and one difference in comparing a coupling capacitor and a bypass capacitor.

9. Give two differences between a low-pass filter and a high-pass filter.

10. Explain briefly why the power-line filter in Fig. 27-28 passes 60-Hz alternating current but not 1-MHz RF current.

11. Explain the advantage of using semilog and log-log graph paper for plotting a frequency response curve.

12. Explain why an $RC$ bandstop filter cannot be designed by interchanging the low-pass and high-pass filters in Fig. 27-18a.

## PROBLEMS

### ANSWERS TO ODD-NUMBERED PROBLEMS AT BACK OF BOOK.

1. Refer to the $RC$ coupling circuit in Fig. 27-6, with $R$ equal to 16,000 $\Omega$. (a) Calculate the required value for $C_C$ at 1000 Hz. (b) How much is the average dc voltage across $C_C$ and across $R$? (c) How much is the ac voltage across $C_C$ and across $R$?

2. Refer to the $R_1C_1$ bypass circuit in Fig. 27-8. (a) Why is 1 MHz bypassed but not 1 kHz? (b) If $C_1$ were doubled in capacitance, what is the lowest frequency that could be bypassed, maintaining a 10:1 ratio of $R$ to $X_C$?

3. Calculate the $C_C$ needed to couple frequencies of 50 to 15,000 Hz with a 50-k$\Omega$ $R$.

4. Show the fluctuating collector current $i_c$ of a transistor that has an average dc axis of 24 mA and a square-wave ac component with a 10-mA peak value. Label the dc axis, maximum and minimum positive values, and the peak-to-peak alternating current.

5. Calculate the cutoff frequency $f_c$ for the filter in: (a) Fig. 27-30a; (b) Fig. 27-30b; (c) Fig. 27-30c; (d) Fig. 27-30d.

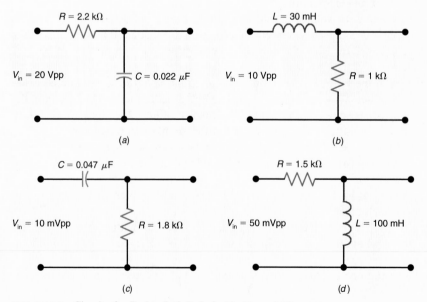

(a)

(b)

(c)

(d)

FIG. 27-30  Circuits for Probs. 5, 6, 7, 8, 9, 10, 11, and 15.

6. In Fig. 27-30a, calculate $V_{out}$ and the phase angle $\theta$ between $V_{in}$ and $V_{out}$ at the following frequencies: (a) 0 Hz; (b) 100 Hz; (c) $f_c$; (d) 5 kHz; (e) 15 kHz; (f) 100 kHz.

7. In Fig. 27-30b, calculate $V_{out}$ and the phase angle $\theta$ between $V_{in}$ and $V_{out}$ at the following frequencies: (a) 0 Hz; (b) 200 Hz; (c) $f_c$; (d) 10 kHz; (e) 53 kHz; (f) 1 MHz.

8. In Fig. 27-30c, calculate $V_{out}$ and the phase angle $\theta$ between $V_{in}$ and $V_{out}$ at the following frequencies: (a) 10 Hz; (b) 500 Hz; (c) $f_c$; (d) 5 kHz; (e) 20 kHz; (f) 500 kHz.

9. In Fig. 27-30d, calculate $V_{out}$ and the phase angle $\theta$ between $V_{in}$ and $V_{out}$ at the following frequencies: (a) 50 Hz; (b) 1.5 kHz; (c) $f_c$; (d) 6 kHz; (e) 50 kHz; (f) 1.5 MHz.

10. In Fig. 27-30a, calculate the attenuation in decibels ($N_{db}$) at the following frequencies: (a) 0 Hz; (b) $f_c$; (c) $10f_c$; (d) $20f_c$.

11. In Fig. 27-30d, calculate the attenuation in decibels ($N_{db}$) at the following frequencies: (a) 100 Hz; (b) $f_c$; (c) $5f_c$; (d) $100f_c$.

12. In Fig. 27-18a, calculate $f_{c_1}$ and $f_{c_2}$ for the following circuit values: $R_1 = 2.2$ k$\Omega$, $C_1 = 0.068$ $\mu$F, $R_2 = 47$ k$\Omega$, and $C_2 = 330$ pF.

13. In Fig. 27-19a, calculate the notch frequency $f_N$ if $R_1 = 18$ k$\Omega$ and $C_1 = 0.001$ $\mu$F.

14. In Fig. 27-31, calculate: (a) the maximum output voltage at low frequencies; (b) the dc voltage across $R_2$; (c) the value of $C_1$ required to effectively bypass $R_2$ if the lowest frequency of the applied voltage is 15 kHz; (d) the value of $C_1$ required to effectively bypass $R_2$ if the lowest frequency of the applied voltage is 100 kHz.

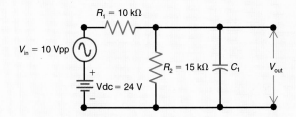

FIG. 27-31 Bypass circuit for Prob. 14.

15. The input power to an amplifier equals 1 W. Calculate the gain in decibels if the output power equals: (a) 2 W; (b) 10 W; (c) 20 W; (d) 100 W; (e) 1 kW; (f) 2 kW.

16. Using semilog graph paper, plot the frequency response curve for the filter in Fig. 27-30c. Mark the vertical axis in decibels. The frequency range on the horizontal axis should span the frequencies extending from 1 Hz to 100 kHz.

## CRITICAL THINKING

1. In Fig. 27-32 on page 800, calculate: (a) the cutoff frequency $f_c$; (b) the output voltage at the cutoff frequency $f_c$; (c) the output voltage at 50 kHz.

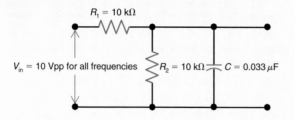

FIG. 27-32  Circuit for Critical Thinking Prob. 1.

2. In Fig. 27-33, calculate the values of $L$ and $C$ required to provide an $f_r$ of 1 Mhz and a bandwidth, $\Delta f$, of 40 kHz.

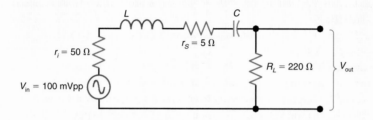

FIG. 27-33  Circuit for Critical Thinking Prob. 2.

3. In Fig. 27-34, calculate the values of $L$ and $C$ required to provide an $f_r$ of 1 MHz and a bandwidth, $\Delta f$, of 20 kHz.

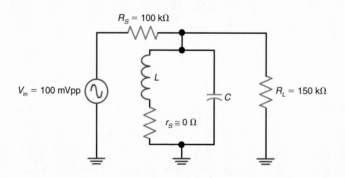

FIG. 27-34  Circuit for Critical Thinking Prob. 3.

## ANSWERS TO TEST-POINT QUESTIONS

| | | | | | | | |
|---|---|---|---|---|---|---|---|
| **27-1** | **a.** 500 kHz | **27-4** | **a.** 0 V | **27-8** | **a.** $d$ | **27-10** | **a.** T |
| | **b.** 60 Hz | | **b.** 5 $\mu$F | | **b.** high-pass | | **b.** T |
| **27-2** | **a.** 6 V | **27-5** | **a.** RF | **27-9** | **a.** F | | **c.** F |
| | **b.** 10 and 2 V | | **b.** 5 $\mu$F | | **b.** T | | **d.** T |
| | **c.** 8 V | **27-6** | **a.** high-pass | | **c.** T | **27-11** | **a.** T |
| | **d.** 4 and 2.8 V | | **b.** low-pass | | **d.** T | | **b.** T |
| **27-3** | **a.** high-pass | **27-7** | **a.** $e$ and $f$ | | | | **c.** T |
| | **b.** 0 V | | **b.** low-pass | | | **27-12** | **a.** T |
| | | | | | | | **b.** T |

# REVIEW: CHAPTERS 26 AND 27

## SUMMARY

- Resonance results when the reactances $X_L$ and $X_C$ are equal. In series, the net reactance is zero. In parallel, the net reactive branch current is zero. The specific frequency that makes $X_L = X_C$ is the resonant frequency $f_r = 1/(2\pi\sqrt{LC})$.
- Larger values of $L$ and $C$ mean lower resonant frequencies, as $f_r$ is inversely proportional to the square root of $L$ and $C$. If the value of $L$ or $C$ is quadrupled, for instance, $f_r$ will decrease by one-half.
- For a series resonant $LC$ circuit, the current is maximum. The voltage drop across the reactances is equal and opposite; the phase angle is zero. The reactive voltage at resonance is $Q$ times greater than the applied voltage.
- For a parallel resonant $LC$ circuit, the impedance is maximum with minimum line current, since the reactive branch currents cancel. The impedance at resonance is $Q$ times the $X_L$ value, but it is resistive with a phase angle of zero.
- The $Q$ of the resonant circuit equals $X_L/r_S$ for resistance in series with $X_L$, or $R_P/X_L$ for resistance in parallel with $X_L$.
- The bandwidth between half-power points if $f_r/Q$.
- A filter uses inductance and capacitance to separate high or low frequencies. A low-pass filter allows low frequencies to develop output voltage across the load; a high-pass filter does the same for high frequencies. Series inductance or shunt capacitance provides low-pass filtering; series capacitance or shunt inductance provides high-pass filtering.
- A fluctuating or pulsating dc is equivalent to an ac component varying in opposite directions around the average-value axis.
- An $RC$ coupling circuit is effectively a high-pass filter for pulsating dc voltage, passing the ac component but blocking the dc component.
- A transformer with an isolated secondary is a high-pass filter for pulsating dc, allowing ac in the secondary but no dc output level.
- A bypass capacitor in parallel with $R$ is effectively a low-pass filter, since its low reactance reduces the voltage across $R$ for high frequencies.
- The main types of filter circuits are $\pi$ type, L type, and T type. These can be high-pass or low-pass, depending on how $L$ and $C$ are connected.
- Resonant circuits can be used as bandpass or bandstop filters. For bandpass filtering, series resonant circuits are in series with the load or parallel resonant circuits are across the load. For bandstop filtering, parallel resonant circuits are in series with the load or series resonant circuits are across the load.
- A wavetrap is an application of a resonant bandstop filter.

- The cutoff frequency of a filter is the frequency at which the output voltage is reduced to 70.7 percent of its maximum value.
- The cutoff frequency of an $RC$ low-pass or high-pass filter can be calculated as $f_c = 1/2\pi RC$. Similarly, the cutoff frequency of an $RL$ low-pass or high-pass filter can be calculated as $f_c = R/2\pi L$.
- The decibel (db) is a logarithmic expression that compares two power levels. In the passband a passive filter provides 0 db of attenuation. At the cutoff frequency a passive filter provides an attenuation of $-3$ db.
- Semilog and log-log graph paper are typically used to show the frequency response of a filter. The advantage of using logarithmic graph paper is that a wide range of frequencies can be shown in one plot without losing resolution in the smaller values.

## REVIEW SELF-TEST

**ANSWERS AT BACK OF BOOK.**

Fill in the numerical answer.

1. An $L$ of 10 H and $C$ of 40 $\mu$F has $f_r$ of _____ Hz.
2. An $L$ of 100 $\mu$H and $C$ of 400 pF has $f_r$ of _____ MHz.
3. In question 2, if $C = 400$ pF and $L$ is increased to 400 $\mu$H, the $f_r$ decreases to _____ MHz.
4. In a series resonant circuit with 10 mV applied across a 1-$\Omega$ $R$, a 1000-$\Omega$ $X_L$, and a 1000-$\Omega$ $X_C$, at resonance the current is _____ mA.
5. In a parallel resonant circuit with a 1-$\Omega$ $r_S$ in series with a 1000-$\Omega$ $X_L$ in one branch and a 1000-$\Omega$ $X_C$ in the other branch, with 10 mV applied, the voltage across $X_C$ equals _____ mV.
6. In question 5, the $Z$ of the parallel resonant circuit equals _____ M$\Omega$.
7. An $LC$ circuit resonant at 500 kHz has a $Q$ of 100. Its total bandwidth between half-power points equals _____ kHz.
8. A coupling capacitor for 40 to 15,000 Hz in series with a 0.5-M$\Omega$ resistor has the capacitance of _____ $\mu$F.
9. A bypass capacitor for 40 to 15,000 Hz in shunt with a 1000-$\Omega$ $R$ has the capacitance of _____ $\mu$F.
10. A pulsating dc voltage varying in a symmetrical sine wave between 100 and 200 V has the average value of _____ V.
11. An $RC$ low-pass filter has the following values: $R = 1$ k$\Omega$, $C = 0.005$ $\mu$F. The cutoff frequency $f_c$ is _____.
12. The input voltage to a filter is 10 Vpp and the output voltage is 100 $\mu$Vpp. The amount of attenuation is _____ db.
13. On logarithmic graph paper, a 2-to-1 range of values is called a(n) _____, and a 10-to-1 range of values is called a(n) _____.
14. At the cutoff frequency, the output voltage is reduced to _____ percent of its maximum value.

Answer True or False.

**15.** A series resonant circuit has low $I$ and high $Z$.

**16.** A steady direct current in the primary of a transformer cannot produce any ac output voltage in the secondary.

**17.** A $\pi$-type filter with shunt capacitances is a low-pass filter.

**18.** An L-type filter with a parallel resonant $LC$ circuit in series with the load is a bandstop filter.

**19.** A resonant circuit can be used for a bandstop filter.

**20.** In the passband, an $RC$ low-pass filter provides approximately 0 db of attenuation.

**21.** The frequency response of a filter is never shown on logarithmic graph paper.

## REFERENCES

Bogart, T.: *Electric Circuits,* Glencoe/McGraw-Hill, Columbus, Ohio.

Grob, B.: *Electronic Circuits and Applications,* Glencoe/McGraw-Hill, Columbus, Ohio.

Kaufman, M., and A. H. Seidman: *Electronics Sourcebook: For Technicians and Engineers,* McGraw-Hill, New York.

Schuler, C., and R. Fowler: *Electric Circuit Analysis,* Glencoe/McGraw-Hill, Columbus, Ohio.

# CHAPTER 28

# ELECTRONIC DEVICES

For the most part, the subject of electronic devices means semiconductor components such as diodes, transistors, and integrated circuits. They are used for amplifiers, oscillators, rectifiers, and digital circuits, which include just about everything in electronics.

The semiconductors are a group of chemical elements with special electrical characteristics. Most common are silicon (Si) and germanium (Ge), with Si used for almost all semiconductor components. The semiconductors have a unique atomic structure that allows the addition of specific impurity elements to produce very useful features that can be applied in electronic circuits.

# CHAPTER OBJECTIVES

*Upon completion of this chapter, you should be able to:*

- *Explain* the difference between an intrinsic and an extrinsic semiconductor.
- *Explain* what a hole charge is and describe the concept of hole current flow.
- *Describe* the physical construction of a diode.
- *List* the approximate values of forward voltage $V_F$ for a silicon and germanium PN junction.
- *Name* the three terminals of a bipolar transistor.
- *State* the relationship among the three transistor currents.
- *Test* diodes and transistors using an ohmmeter.

# IMPORTANT TERMS IN THIS CHAPTER

| | | |
|---|---|---|
| anode and cathode | field-effect transistor (FET) | metal-oxide-semiconductor |
| bias, dc | forward voltage and current | FET (MOSFET) |
| bipolar transistor | hole charge | NPN and PNP transistors |
| bridge rectifier | insulated-gate FET (IGFET) | peak inverse voltage |
| covalent bond | junction FET (JFET) | rectifier |
| diode | junction transistor | reverse voltage |
| doping | leakage current | volt-ampere characteristic |

# TOPICS COVERED IN THIS CHAPTER

**28-1**   Semiconductors

**28-2**   The PN Junction

**28-3**   Semiconductor Diodes

**28-4**   PNP and NPN Transistors

**28-5**   Field-Effect Transistor (FET)

**28-6**   Testing Diodes and Transistors

# 28-1 SEMICONDUCTORS

The name *semiconductor* for materials such as silicon and germanium means that they are not as good as the metals as electrical conductors but they are not insulators. The reason is atomic structure.* All the semiconductor elements have atoms with an electron valence of $\pm 4$. With this valence, the atom has four electrons in the outermost shell, which can have eight for a stable ring.

As an example, silicon has the atomic number 14. This atom has 14 positive protons in the nucleus, balanced electrically by 14 negative electrons in three outer shells. The electrons are distributed in shells or rings of 2, 8, and 4. For germanium with atomic number 32, the electrons are in shells of 2, 8, 18, and 4.

With four electrons in the outermost shell, halfway to the goal of eight for stability, the atom does not easily gain or lose individual electrons. Instead, the semiconductor atoms share the four valence electrons with other groups of four. Such a combination of atoms sharing groups of valence electrons is called a covalent bond. As a result, pure semiconductors have the following resistance characteristics: (1) medium $R$ and (2) negative temperature coefficient $\alpha$. The negative $\alpha$ means that $R$ decreases with higher temperature. These characteristics apply just to the pure semiconductor, called *intrinsic,* which means without any added impurities.

Silicon itself is an element in most common rocks. Sand is silicon dioxide ($SiO_2$). The element Si was discovered in 1823 and Ge in 1886. Germanium is recovered from the ash of certain coals. The oxides of both Ge and Si are reduced chemically to produce the elements with almost perfect purity. Figure 28-1 shows a solid bar of silicon and the thin slices or disks that are used for semiconductor devices. The semiconductor must be very pure so that only the desired impurity elements are added. It can be noted that intrinsic Ge has only about $\frac{1}{1000}$ the resistance of Si, but silicon is generally used for semiconductor devices. It is the way that the semiconductors are altered electrically by added impurity elements that really makes it possible to have useful semiconductor devices.

**COVALENT BONDS AND CRYSTAL STRUCTURE**  Because of the covalent bonds between atoms, either in Si or Ge, the atoms form a network or lattice structure in a regular pattern that is characteristic of a crystal solid. This pattern is illustrated in Fig. 28-2 for Si atoms. A crystal has a definite geometrical form for the internal atoms. A diamond is an example of the crystalline structure for pure carbon which, incidentally, is also a semiconductor. When a crystal is broken into smaller segments, each has the same structure as the original crystal. With covalent bonds for the semiconductor elements Si and Ge and the crystal structure, it becomes possible to add impurity elements that result in the desired electrical characteristics. This process is called *doping* the pure semiconductor.

**N-TYPE AND P-TYPE SEMICONDUCTORS**  The production process involves vaporizing certain impurity elements under high heat in an oven with the semiconductor disk, such as the silicon disks shown in Fig. 28-1. For N-type material, the doping element is chosen to provide free electron charges. The P type

---

*More details of atomic structure for the chemical elements are described in Chap. 1.

FIG. 28-1    Pure silicon in the form of crystals, a solid bar, and wafer disks.

has free positive charges. The doped form is called an *extrinsic* semiconductor, as the opposite of the intrinsic or pure semiconductor.

For N-type, the doping element can be arsenic, antimony, or phosphorus. Each has an electron valence of 5. This value means one extra electron for each group of four in the outermost shell of the atom. As a result, each impurity atom provides an extra electron in the covalent bonds. Figure 28-3 illustrates silicon with atomic number 14 doped with phosphorus (P), which has atomic number 15. Note that P is the symbol for phosphorus and does not indicate positive polarity. The P atoms have five valence electrons. Four of these become part of covalent bond structure. The extra electron, however, can be considered as a free negative charge, since it is not needed for a covalent bond. The result is N-type doped silicon. Since many phosphorus atoms are added, the doping provides many free electrons. Remember that free charges can move with relative ease, when voltage is applied, to produce electric current.

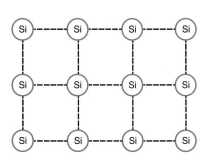

FIG. 28-2    Crystal lattice structure with covalent bonds between silicon (Si) atoms, for a pure semiconductor without doping.

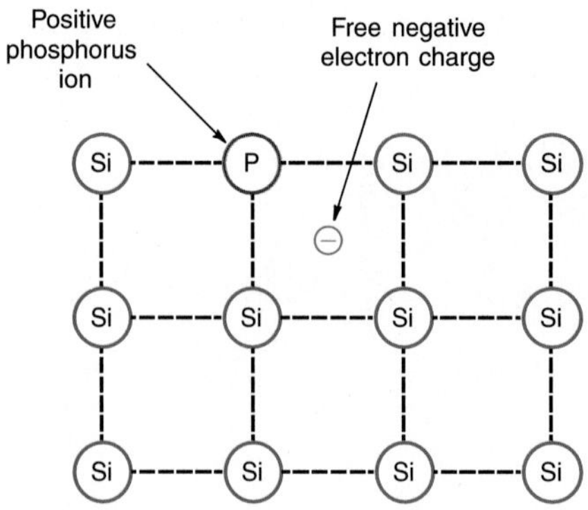

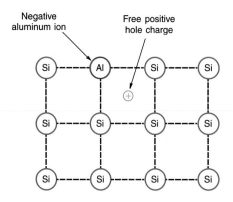

**FIG. 28-3** Crystal lattice structure of silicon (Si) atoms doped with phosphorus (P). The covalent bonds have one free electron for each phosphorus atom.

Positive phosphorus ion

Free negative electron charge

For P type, the doping element can be aluminum, boron, gallium, or indium, with a valence of 3. Each atom has three electrons in the outermost ring. Figure 28-4 illustrates silicon (Si) doped with aluminum (Al). The element aluminum has atomic number 13, which means three outer electrons. In the covalent bonds of Al with Si atoms, there are seven electrons instead of eight. The one missing electron in such a covalent bond can be considered as a free positive charge, called a *hole*. Remember that taking away a negative electron is equivalent to adding the same amount of positive charge. With many aluminum atoms added, the doping provides many hole charges. The holes are free charges that can move with relative ease to produce electric current. However, the free hole charges have slightly less mobility than electrons.

It should be noted that the doping really does not add or subtract charges. The semiconductor is still neutral with equal positive and negative charges. However, the doping redistributes the valence electrons so that more free charges are available.

**THE HOLE CHARGE** The hole is a new type of free charge that is present only in P-type semiconductors. The charge is the same amount as a proton, equal to that of an electron but with opposite polarity. A hole charge is not a proton, however. The proton is a stable, immobile charge in the nucleus where the proton is not free to move. The hole is a positive charge outside the nucleus, where it can be made to move by an applied voltage to produce electric current.

Negative aluminum ion

Free positive hole charge

**FIG. 28-4** Crystal lattice structure of silicon (Si) atoms doped with aluminum (Al). The covalent bonds have one free positive hole charge for each aluminum atom.

**HOLE CURRENT**    The idea of hole charges moving to produce current is illustrated in Fig. 28-5. Along the top row, a hole charge is shown at point 1, with some filled covalent bonds. Suppose that a valence electron from the filled bond at point 2 moves to point 1. Along the middle row, then, the bond at point 1 becomes filled and the hole charge moves to point 2. Similarly, along the bottom row, an electron can move from point 3 to point 2 to fill this bond and the hole charge is at point 3. With this sequence, the hole charge is moving from point 1 to point 6, from left to right in Fig. 28-5. To produce this current, a voltage could be applied across the semiconductor, with the positive terminal at point 1.

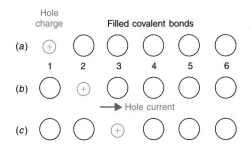

FIG. 28-5    An example of a hole charge moving in a P-type semiconductor to provide a hole current. Motion of the positive charge from location 1 to 2 to 3 is illustrated in (a), (b), and (c).

The direction of hole current is the same as conventional current, opposite from electron flow, because holes are positive charges. *All arrow symbols for the direction of current in semiconductor devices are shown for the direction of hole current.*

It should be noted, though, that hole current flows only in P-type semiconductors. The actual current is electron flow in N-type semiconductors and all wire conductors.

## MAJORITY AND MINORITY CHARGES IN SEMICONDUCTORS

With doping, an N-type semiconductor has a large supply of free electrons, a result of the added impurity atoms. Then the electrons become the dominant or *majority charges*. Still, there are *minority* charges of holes. The reason is that thermal energy, even at room temperatures, always gives a random motion to free charges.

Similarly, a P-type semiconductor has majority hole charges. The minority charges here are electrons. In any one type of semiconductor, the majority and minority charge carriers always have opposite polarities.

When the majority charges are made to move in a semiconductor by an applied voltage, the result is a relatively large amount of *forward* current or *easy current*. The forward current is motion of electrons in N-type semiconductors or hole charges in P-type semiconductors. The amount of $I$ is generally in the range of milliamperes to amperes.

When minority charges move, this current is in the reverse direction compared with the forward current of the majority charges. The reason is simply that the polarity of minority charges is the opposite of majority charges in the same conductor.

This very small current of minority charges is called *reverse current* or *leakage current*. The $I$ is in the order of microamperes.

Furthermore, the reverse current increases with higher temperatures. More minority charges are produced by an increase of thermal energy. This increase in the reverse current of minority charges is the reason why temperature is very important in the operation of NPN and PNP transistors.

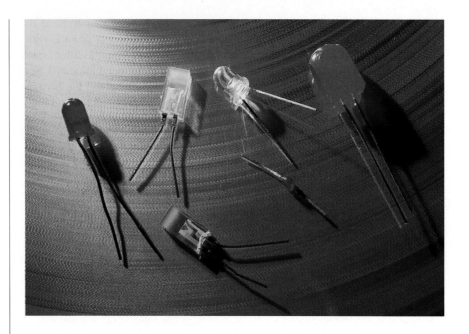

**FIXED ION CHARGES IN THE DOPED SEMICONDUCTOR**   The free charges in a doped semiconductor are balanced by ions of the impurity element. Two important features of ions in general are:

1. An ion is an atom, with its nucleus, where the atom has a net charge, either positive or negative.
2. Since an ion has the nucleus of the atom, the ions in a solid material are relatively immobile, meaning they cannot be moved as free charges.

As an example of ions resulting from the doping, refer to Fig. 28-3. Here the phosphorus ion is positive because it lacks one of its five valence electrons. As a result, the nucleus provides the charge of one proton in the phosphorus ion. For the example in Fig. 28-4, the aluminum ion is negative because effectively an extra electron has been added as part of its covalent bond structure.

The ions are fixed charges that are not easily moved in the solid crystal. Since the ions are impurity atoms, they are present only in the doped semiconductor. The fixed charges of the ions are important because they provide an internal contact potential that allows a junction to be formed where P and N materials meet. The PN or NP junction is the basis for the operation of all semiconductor devices.

## TEST-POINT QUESTION 28-1

Answers at end of chapter.
**a.** What is the electron valence for Si and Ge?
**b.** Is the Si doped with phosphorus in Fig. 28-3 N type or P type?
**c.** True or False? Hole current is in the same direction as electron flow.
**d.** Is forward current a flow of majority or minority charge carriers?

# 28-2 THE PN JUNCTION

It is interesting that doping increases the free charges in a semiconductor material but the real usefulness comes from having a junction between successive layers of P and N types. The reason is that the junction provides an internal contact potential, which is 0.7 V for Si and 0.3 V for Ge. Controlling this potential across a PN junction makes it possible to control the current in the semiconductor. The P-type and N-type materials then serve just as electrodes for applying an external voltage to the junction. Although labeled here as a PN junction, it could just as well be NP. The opposite polarities provide the internal junction potential.

In Fig. 28-6, the semiconductor materials are shown with a thin junction between successive layers of P-type and N-type formed in a single crystal. The junction itself has a width of only $10^{-4}$ cm. In the magnified view of the junction, the impurity ions are shown at opposite edges. The ions provide the contact potential across the two sides of a junction.

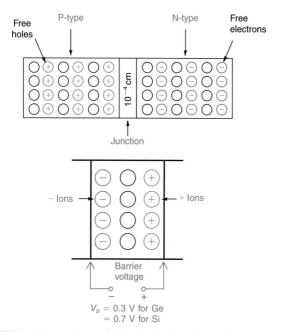

**FIG. 28-6** A PN junction with magnified view below of depletion zone to show how ion charges produce internal barrier voltage $V_b$.

Some of the free electrons in the N material at the junction are attracted toward the P material. At the same time, some of the free hole charges at the P side move the other way to the junction. These opposite charges combine to produce *electron-hole pairs* that are neutral. However, this effect at the junction uncovers the charged ions of the impurity atoms in the junction. The ions do not move. As a result, the ions provide an internal contact potential labeled $V_b$. This potential is considered a barrier voltage because it prevents any more free electrons or hole charges from crossing the junction. In effect, $V_b$ maintains the free electrons in the N-type semiconductor and the hole charges in the P-type to prevent opposite sides from neutralizing each other.

It should be noted that the junction is only an electrical boundary between the P and N semiconductors produced by alternate types of doping. There is actually no physical separation.

**THE INTERNAL BARRIER POTENTIAL $V_b$**   Note the polarity of $V_b$ at the junction in Fig. 28-6. The negative side of $V_b$ is at the edge with the P-type semiconductor. Here there are negative ions as a result of the P-type doping. This side of $V_b$ with negative polarity repels electrons from the N-type semiconductor, preventing them from crossing through the junction. Also, the positive side of $V_b$ is at the edge with the N-type material. The positive ions are produced by the N-type doping. This side of $V_b$ repels hole charges from the P-type semiconductor to prevent them from crossing through the junction.

Although $V_b$ is an internal contact potential that cannot be measured directly, its effect can be overcome by applying an external voltage of 0.3 V for Ge or 0.7 V for Si, in the correct polarity. The $V_b$ is higher for a silicon junction because its lower atomic number allows more stability in the covalent bonds.

The $V_b$ of the junction is a characteristic of the element. Therefore, the values given for Ge and Si apply to all PN junctions for semiconductors, diodes, and transistors of any size or power rating. Remember the values of 0.7 V for a silicon junction and 0.3 V for a germanium junction.

The barrier voltage is what makes the junction useful because the effect of $V_b$ can be controlled by applying an external voltage. With forward voltage applied in the polarity that neutralizes the effect of $V_b$, forward current can flow through the junction. For the opposite case, reverse voltage is applied in the polarity that does not cancel $V_b$.

**DEPLETION ZONE**   Because of its neutral electron-hole pairs, the junction area is considered as a depletion zone. It has no free charge carriers that can be moved. However, the junction still has the ion charges anchored in position to produce $V_b$.

**EFFECT OF TEMPERATURE**   The values of 0.3 V for Ge and 0.7 V for Si are at normal room temperature of 25°C. However, $V_b$ decreases at higher temperatures. The reason is that more minority charge carriers are produced by increased thermal energy. The decrease in $V_b$ is the reason why avoiding high temperature is an important precaution in the operation of circuits with NPN and PNP junction transistors.

**POLARITY OF FORWARD VOLTAGE AND REVERSE VOLTAGE**   Refer to Fig. 28-7a. The forward voltage $V_F$ is applied by wire conductors to the P and N electrodes. Such a connection without any barrier potential is called an *ohmic contact*. Then the external $V_F$ is applied through the bulk materials to the PN junction. Forward current $I_F$ flows as the forward voltage neutralizes the effect of the barrier voltage. The required polarity is

$$+V_F \text{ to the P electrode} \left. \right\}$$
$$-V_F \text{ to the N electrode} \qquad \text{forward voltage}$$

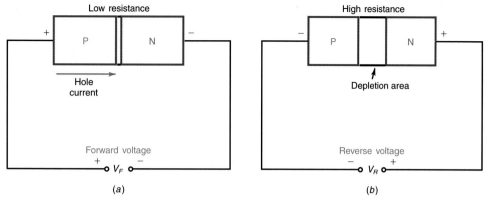

FIG. 28-7    (a) Forward voltage with $+V_F$ to the P side of the PN junction to produce forward current. (b) Reverse voltage with $+V_R$ to the N side of the junction. There is no forward current.

In other words, the polarity of $V_F$ corresponds to the semiconductor types.

The $+V_F$ at the P electrode repels hole charges to the side of the junction that has the negative ions of $V_b$. Then the effect of the negative ions is canceled. Also, the $-V_F$ at the N electrode repels electrons to the side of the junction that has the positive ions of $V_b$. Then the effect of the positive ions is canceled. The overall effect then is that $V_F$ cancels $V_b$.

The results of forward voltage are: (1) forward or easy current flows and (2) the junction has low resistance. All or part of $V_b$ can be neutralized, depending on the amount of $V_F$.

For reverse voltage $V_R$, see Fig. 28-7b. The polarity of $V_R$ is the opposite of $V_F$. Specifically,

$$\left.\begin{array}{l} -V_R \text{ to the P electrode} \\ +V_R \text{ to the N electrode} \end{array}\right\} \quad \text{reverse voltage}$$

In other words, the polarity of $V_R$ is the reverse of the semiconductor types.

The $-V_R$ at the P electrode attracts hole charges away from the junction. Also, the $+V_R$ at the N electrode attracts electrons away from the junction. As a result, the ion charges at the junction are not neutralized but remain intact to maintain $V_b$.

Because of the reverse voltage, no forward current can flow. The junction $R$ is practically infinite. A small reverse leakage current flows but this value is very low, in the order of $10^{-6}$ A for Ge and $10^{-9}$ A for Si.

Values of forward voltage are low, in millivolts or tenths of a volt. Too much $V_F$ causes excessive $I_F$, producing heat which can destroy the electrical characteristics of the junction. Values of reverse voltage can be much higher, in the order of 100 V to 10 kV or higher, since there is no forward current.

**FORWARD CURRENT $I_F$**    An important feature of $I_F$ is that it depends on the amount of $V_F$. Typical values of $V_F$ across the junction itself are 0.5 to 0.7 V for silicon. In Fig. 28-8a, the $V_F$ of 0.5 V is shown producing $I_F$ of 20 mA, just as examples. In Fig. 28-8b, the higher $V_F$ of 0.6 V increases $I_F$ to 30 mA. This effect of varying $V_F$ to control the amount of $I_F$ is the basis of transistor amplifiers.

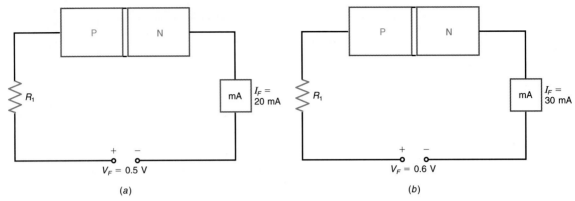

FIG. 28-8  Examples to show that more $V_F$ increases $I_F$. In (a), 0.5 V produces 20 mA; in (b), 0.6 V produces 30 mA.

More details of the forward current are illustrated in Fig. 28-9 so that the direction can be considered. The PN junction has the symbol shown with an arrow at the P side into the bar at the N side. Actually, any PN junction is a semiconductor diode. For all semiconductor symbols, the arrow shows the direction of hole current. In the P electrode, then, hole charges are moving into the junction. However, in the N electrode the equivalent effect is electrons flowing toward the junction. In the wire conductors and $R_1$, the current is indicated by dashed arrows for electron flow. Resistor $R_1$ is inserted to limit the amount of current. Note that the hole current and electron flow are in opposite directions. However, there is only one current in the circuit. The net effect is the same as conventional $I$ around the complete circuit in the direction shown. With the arrow symbol for hole current with semiconductors, it is usually simpler just to follow the current around the circuit in the direction of the arrow.

**VOLT-AMPERE CHARACTERISTICS**  A graphical plot of $I$ and $V$ for a PN junction is its volt-ampere characteristics. As shown in Fig. 28-10, the

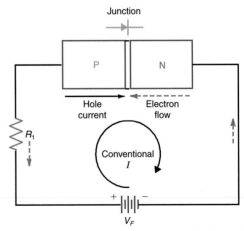

FIG. 28-9  Details of the forward current in a circuit with a PN junction. Note the symbol with an arrow in the direction of the hole current. The dashed arrow indicates the electron flow.

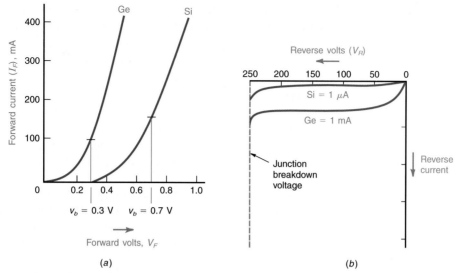

**FIG. 28-10**   Volt-ampere graphs of a PN junction for Ge and Si. (*a*) Forward characteristics in tenths of a volt and relatively high current. (*b*) Reverse voltage up to 250 V with very small reverse leakage current.

characteristic curves summarize the operation. Separate graphs are used here to illustrate forward voltage in Fig. 28-10*a* and reverse voltage in Fig. 28-10*b*.

In Fig. 28-10*a*, the graph plots low values of $V_F$, in tenths of 1 V, with relatively high values of $I_F$ in units of mA, which could also be in amperes. The reverse characteristics in Fig. 28-10*b* need a separate graph because relatively high values of $V_R$ up to 250 V are plotted. Also, the values of reverse leakage current are very small. Note that the polarities of $V_F$ and $V_R$ are opposite. Also, the forward current and reverse leakage current are in opposite directions.

In both Fig. 28-10*a* and *b*, separate curves are shown for germanium and silicon because they have different values for the internal barrier voltage $V_b$. Also, the reverse leakage current for Si is only 1 $\mu$A while Ge has 1 mA.

Consider the forward characteristic of Si in Fig. 28-10*a*, as it is used for most junction transistors. Forward current flows when $V_F$ approaches 0.5 V. More $V_F$ increases the $I_F$. At 0.7 V or more, the forward current increases sharply to its maximum value. A middle value is 0.6 V, which is a typical forward bias for Si junction transistors. Similarly, for a Ge junction, the range of $V_F$ for forward current is 0.1 to 0.3 V. The values of forward current can be in the range of 1 mA to as high as 20 A.

**REVERSE CURRENT**   With reverse voltage, only a small reverse current of minority charges can flow, as shown in Fig. 28-10*b*. The separate curves indicate typical leakage current of 1 mA for Ge and 1 $\mu$A for Si. Note the advantage of Si, with practically zero reverse current.

The reverse leakage current has the symbol $I_{CO}$ to indicate a small cutoff current. With reverse voltage, the junction is practically an open circuit, which cuts off the current, except for the small leakage current. As a comparison of forward and reverse characteristics, the $V_F$ makes the junction operate like a short circuit with high $I$ and low $V$, but for $V_R$ the junction is like an open circuit with just the small $I_{CO}$ and higher values of voltage.

The $I_{CO}$ is in the opposite direction from the forward current. They must be opposite because $I_F$ is the motion of majority charges but $I_{CO}$ consists of minority charges. Furthermore, the $I_{CO}$ increases with temperature. For every 10°C rise, the reverse leakage current doubles for either Ge or Si.

**JUNCTION BREAKDOWN VOLTAGE**    Refer to the reverse characteristics in Fig. 28-10b. The reverse current is constant at a very small value until $V_R$ reaches the junction breakdown voltage shown as 250 V here. Then a relatively large reverse current can flow. Most important, the reverse voltage across the junction is constant at the breakdown value. This effect is used for voltage regulator diodes.

What happens with the breakdown voltage is that the electrical characteristics are changed by the strong electric field of the reverse voltage. The value of 250 V may not seem so high but the junction is very thin. For a width of $1 \times 10^{-4}$ cm, the value of 25 V across the junction corresponds to $25 \times 10^4$ V/cm.

---

### TEST-POINT QUESTION 28-2

Answers at end of chapter.
**a.** How much is the barrier voltage $V_b$ for a silicon PN junction?
**b.** Does forward voltage $V_F$ have positive polarity at the P or N electrode of the junction?
**c.** Does reverse voltage $V_R$ have positive polarity at the P or N electrode of the junction?
**d.** Is typical reverse leakage current for a silicon PN junction equal to 5 mA or 1 $\mu$A?
**e.** In Fig. 28-10a, how much is the forward current $I_F$ for 0.7 V of forward voltage $V_F$?

## 28-3 SEMICONDUCTOR DIODES

A diode is essentially a PN junction. The standard symbol is an arrow to indicate the direction of hole current and a bar, as shown in Fig. 28-11. The arrow is at the anode, which must be positive for current flow, while the bar is the cathode. Conventional current is in the direction of the arrow for the flow of hole charges. Electron flow is the opposite way, against the arrow. The practical use of diodes is to serve as a one-way valve. Current can flow only when positive voltage at the anode with respect to cathode, provides forward voltage. With the reverse polarity, no forward current can flow. This feature is the basis for the general use of the diode as a rectifier to change ac input to dc output.

Two small semiconductor diodes are shown in Fig. 28-11. In Fig. 28-11a, the symbol is on the diode to indicate anode and cathode. For the diode in Fig. 28-11b, the colored band at one end indicates the cathode side. Some diodes may have a + sign at the cathode end to show this is where positive dc output can be obtained in a rectifier circuit. Any mark at one end indicates the cathode side. The cathode has positive dc output when the ac input is applied to the anode.

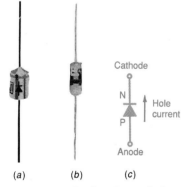

(a)        (b)        (c)

FIG. 28-11 Semiconductor diode rectifiers. Length is about ½ in. without leads. (a) Silicon power diode with current rating of 1 A. The arrow shows the direction of the hole current. (b) Germanium detector diode. The cathode end has a dark band. (c) Schematic symbol for diode.

**TYPE NUMBERS** The numbering system for diodes uses the letter N for semiconductors, the prefix 1 before the N and numbers after the N for individual types. The 1 means one junction. As an example, the 1N3196 is a popular silicon diode. The 1N indicates a semiconductor diode, while the 3196 specifies the individual characteristics, which are listed in semiconductor handbooks, specification sheets, and application notes. There is no special indication for Si or Ge, but practically all rectifier diodes are made of silicon. In schematic diagrams, diodes are usually labeled D, CR, or X and Y. The CR stands for crystal rectifier.

**DIODE APPLICATIONS** The following list summarizes the main uses for diodes:

1. *Power-supply rectifier.* This function is converting ac input from the 60-Hz power line to dc output. One diode is used for a half-wave rectifier. The full-wave rectifier needs two diodes. More details are described in Sec. 29-7.
2. *Signal detector.* The detector circuit uses a diode to rectify a modulated signal in order to recover the modulating signal. The circuit for an AM detector is explained in Chap. 29.
3. *Digital logic gates.* In these circuits, the diode functions as a switch. It is on when the diode conducts and off without conduction. More details of digital electronics are described in Chap. 31.

In addition, there are many different types of diodes for special applications. These include the capacitive diode for electronic tuning and the light-emitting diode used as a visual display. These diodes and other types are described in Sec. 28-8.

**RECTIFIER PACKAGING** The plastic package shown in Fig. 28-11 is very common with rectifiers for currents of about 1 A. Even smaller diodes can be used for less current. Two other types of rectifiers are shown in Fig. 28-12. The metal can in Fig. 28-12*a* is called "top-hat" style. The type in Fig. 28-12*b* uses a stud mount that screws directly into a metal mounting for the cathode connection. Note the diode symbols printed directly on the unit to indicate the anode and cathode terminals. The stud mount types generally have high current ratings.

**BRIDGE RECTIFIERS** This type of power supply is used very often, even though it requires four diodes. Connections for the bridge are shown in Fig. 28-13*a*, while typical packages are in Fig. 28-13*b* and *c*. Note that the bridge has four terminals. Two are connections for the ac input and two for the dc output.

**RECTIFIER RATINGS** The two most important ratings are for maximum forward current $I_F$ and maximum peak inverse voltage (PIV). Ratings for maximum $I_F$ can be a fraction of one ampere up to 25 A or more. The PIV rating for popular diodes is typically about 1000 V. The peak inverse voltage is the value that can be used across the diode in reverse polarity, negative at the anode, without disrupting the electrical characteristics of the junction. The PIV rating is usually chosen to be at least double the value of the dc voltage output.

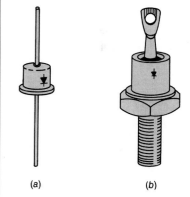

(a)          (b)

**FIG. 28-12** Rectifier packages. (*a*) "Top-hat" style. Height is ⅜ in. without leads. (*b*) Heavy-duty rectifier for stud mounting. Height without stud is ½ in.

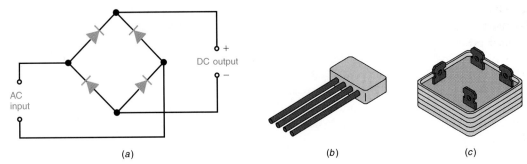

**FIG. 28-13** The bridge rectifier. (*a*) Schematic with four diodes as a full-wave bridge. (*b*) Typical package. Length is ¾ in. (*c*) Heavy-duty package for mounting on heat sink. Size is 1 in. square.

---

**TEST-POINT QUESTION 28-3**

Answers at end of chapter.
**a.** Is the anode of a diode positive or negative for conduction?
**b.** Does the arrow symbol for a diode show the direction of hole charges or electron flow?
**c.** Does a band marked at the end of a plastic diode package indicate the anode or cathode?
**d.** How many diodes are used in a half-wave rectifier power supply?
**e.** In a rectifier circuit, is positive dc output voltage taken from the anode or cathode?

## 28-4 PNP AND NPN TRANSISTORS

PNP and NPN transistors consist of a P or N semiconductor between opposite types, as shown in Fig. 28-14. The purpose is to have three electrodes with two junctions. In operation, the first section at one end supplies free charges, either holes or electrons, to be collected by the third section at the opposite end, through the middle section. The middle electrode controls the current. The names and functions of the electrodes are

Emitter—supplies free charges
Base—controls the flow of charges
Collector—collects the charges from the emitter

Note that the base electrode in the middle has a junction with the emitter and another junction with the collector.

With an N-type base, the transistor is PNP. A P-type base is used for an NPN transistor. The letters correspond to the polarities for emitter, base and collector. Both PNP and NPN transistors operate the same way but they take opposite polarities of dc supply voltage. Most small transistors are the NPN type and made of silicon.

In the schematic symbols, the emitter has an arrow at the junction with the base. The arrow indicates this electrode is the emitter. The third electrode is the

**DID YOU KNOW?**

A new microprocessor can sense a tornado's sound and alert a household 30 to 90 seconds before the twister hits.

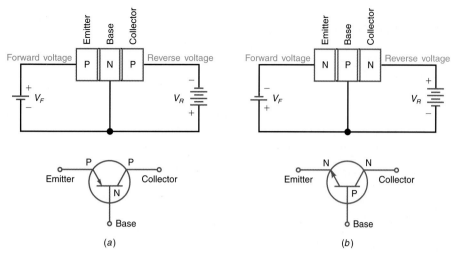

FIG. 28-14 Schematic symbols and dc bias voltages for junction transistors. (*a*) PNP. (*b*) NPN.

collector. As in all semiconductor symbols, the arrow is in the direction of hole current. In Fig. 28-14*a*, the emitter arrow shows that hole charges can move from the P emitter into the N base. Therefore, this transistor is PNP. In Fig. 28-14*b*, the arrow is in the opposite direction to show that hole charges can move from the P base to the N emitter. This transistor is NPN, therefore. Electron flow can be considered to be in the direction from the N emitter to the P base. In short, an arrow into the base means PNP; an arrow out from the base indicates an NPN transistor.

The NPN and PNP types are called *junction transistors.* Also, they can be considered *bipolar transistors* because they have the two opposite polarities of doped semiconductor.

With three electrodes, the transistor is a *triode.* Compared with the diode as a two-terminal device, a triode has one more electrode that can control the current. In a transistor, the base electrode controls the current from emitter to collector, which makes it possible to have amplification. Practically all amplifiers in electronic circuits use transistors. Figure 28-15 shows a simple transistor amplifier circuit as it would appear on a lab prototype board and on a surface-mount circuit board. Either discrete transistors can be used, or the transistor is part of an integrated circuit (IC). Transistors are the main components in IC chips.

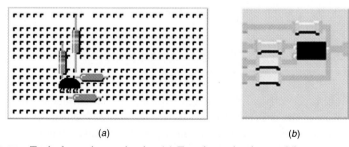

FIG. 28-15 Typical transistors circuits. (*a*) Transistor circuit on a lab prototype board. (*b*) Transistor circuit on a surface-mount circuit board.

The transistor was invented in 1948 at the Bell Telephone Laboratories, as part of research on semiconductor materials. Its name is derived from "trans resistor," meaning that it can transfer its internal resistance from low $R$ in the emitter-base circuit to a much higher $R$ in the collector-base circuit.

**THE EMITTER-BASE JUNCTION**   This junction has forward voltage applied across the PN or NP junction in order to allow the free charges of the emitter to move into the base. As shown in Fig. 28-14a, positive voltage is applied to the P emitter of the PNP transistor, with the negative side of $V_F$ to the N base. The $V_F$ is forward bias for the transistor. These polarities are for the PNP type. In Fig. 28-14b, the NPN transistor has forward bias, with $-V_F$ to the N emitter, just the opposite of the PNP type.

Typical values of forward bias are 0.2 V for Ge or 0.6 V for Si in transistor amplifiers. The required bias voltage is the same for any size transistor.

It is important to realize that the forward bias is necessary for the transistor to operate. No current can come out of the collector unless $V_F$ allows the emitter to inject free charges into the base. In short, the junction transistor is a normally off device. It needs forward voltage applied to start conducting.

**THE COLLECTOR-BASE JUNCTION**   The function of the collector-base junction is to remove charges from the base. Then current can flow in the collector return circuit to the emitter. However, to accomplish this result, the collector must have reverse voltage with respect to the base. As shown in Fig. 28-14a, the P collector of the PNP transistor is connected to the negative side of $V_R$, with $+V_R$ to the N base. These polarities for reverse voltage are opposite in Fig. 28-14b with the NPN transistor. In both Fig. 28-14a and b, though, the collector has reverse voltage.

In short, NPN transistors take positive dc supply voltage at the collector for reverse voltage; PNP transistors require negative dc collector voltage. Typical values are 9 to 100 V, depending on the power rating of the transistor.

The reverse voltage across the collector-base junction means that no majority charges can flow from collector to base. However, in the opposite direction from base to collector, the collector voltage attracts the charges in the base supplied by the emitter.

**TRANSISTOR ACTION**   The requirement is to have the collector current controlled by the emitter-base circuit. There are three factors:

1. The emitter has heavy doping to supply free charges.
2. The base has only light doping and is very thin.
3. The collector voltage is relatively high.

As a result, practically all the charges supplied by the emitter to the base are made to flow in the collector circuit. Typically, 98 to 99 percent or more of the emitter charges provide collector current $I_C$. The remaining charges become the small base current $I_B$.

Consider the currents for an NPN transistor as illustrated in Fig. 28-16. The N emitter supplies electrons to the P base with forward voltage across the junction. In the P base, the electrons are minority charges. Because of the light doping in the base, though, very few of the electrons can recombine with hole charges.

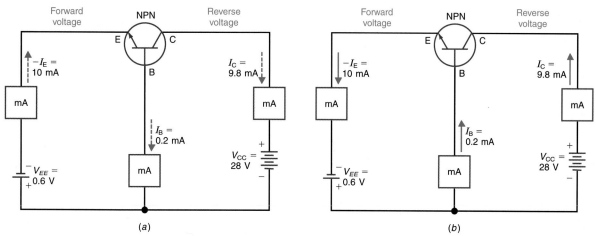

FIG. 28-16 Electrode currents $I_E$, $I_B$, and $I_C$ for an NPN transistor. (a) Dashed arrows for $I$ show the direction of the electron flow. (b) Solid arrows for $I$ show the direction of the conventional current for the same NPN transistor as in (a).

Some electrons in the base return through the external base circuit to the emitter to provide the very small $I_B$. However, almost all the electrons move through the thin base to the collector junction. Here the N collector has reverse voltage of positive polarity. For electrons moving from the base, though, the positive collector voltage attracts these free electron charges. Therefore, the electrons supplied from the emitter side of the base move to the collector side of the base and are attracted into the collector electrode. The result is collector current in the external circuit, where $I_C$ returns to the emitter.

For a PNP transistor, all voltage polarities are the opposite of Fig. 28-16, for the reverse and forward voltages. Also, the $I_C$ at the collector electrode consists of hole charges.

### ELECTRODE CURRENTS

For the example in Fig. 28-16, the emitter supplies 10 mA of forward current. This is $I_E$. Consider that 98 percent or 9.8 mA is injected into the collect circuit. This current is $I_C$. Only 2 percent, equal to 0.2 mA or 200 $\mu$A of $I_B$, flows through the base terminal to return to the emitter. As a formula,

$$I_E = I_C + I_B \qquad \textbf{(28-1)}$$

In Fig. 28-16a, the direction of the currents is shown with dashed arrows for electron flow. The opposite direction for conventional current is indicated by the solid arrows in Fig. 28-16b. For either direction of current, the values are still the same, with 10 mA of $I_E$ supplying 9.8 mA for $I_C$ and 0.2 mA for $I_B$.

Incidentally, note that the supply voltage for each electrode is labeled with double subscripts, as in $V_{EE}$ and $V_{CC}$. This notation is standard practice. It is useful for typical amplifiers, where the actual electrode voltage may have a lower value than the supply voltage because of voltage drops in the circuit.

Note that $I_E$ in Fig. 28-16 is marked negative, only to indicate that its direction is opposite from that of $I_C$ and $I_B$. The $I_E$ is into its electrode, while the $I_C$ and $I_B$ are out from their respective electrodes. *It is standard practice to consider hole current into a semiconductor as the positive direction of I.* This rule is only an arbitrary definition. As an application in Fig. 28-16a, the $I_E$ is electron flow into the transistor. Electron flow moving in corresponds to hole charges moving out, which is the negative direction for $I$. Also $I_C$ and $I_B$ as electron flow are out from the transistor, which is the positive direction corresponding to hole charges moving in. The same signs for $I$ apply in Fig. 28-16b where the currents are shown for the direction of hole charges or conventional current. Algebraically, the values of current in Fig. 28-16 can be stated as

$$-I_E + I_C + I_B = 0$$
$$-10 \text{ mA} + 9.8 \text{ mA} + 0.2 \text{ mA} = 0$$

In practical terms, the formula states that the collector and base currents must add to equal the emitter current, which is the source.

## Example

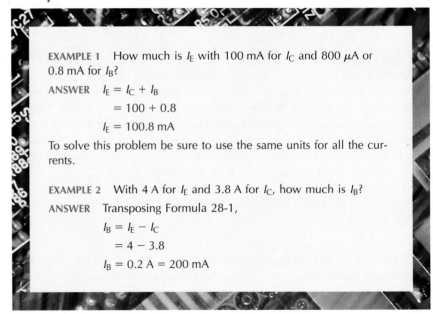

**EXAMPLE 1**   How much is $I_E$ with 100 mA for $I_C$ and 800 $\mu$A or 0.8 mA for $I_B$?

**ANSWER**   $I_E = I_C + I_B$

$\phantom{I_E}= 100 + 0.8$

$I_E = 100.8 \text{ mA}$

To solve this problem be sure to use the same units for all the currents.

**EXAMPLE 2**   With 4 A for $I_E$ and 3.8 A for $I_C$, how much is $I_B$?

**ANSWER**   Transposing Formula 28-1,

$I_B = I_E - I_C$

$\phantom{I_B}= 4 - 3.8$

$I_B = 0.2 \text{ A} = 200 \text{ mA}$

For most transistors, the $I_B$ is in microamperes or milliamperes. The $I_C$ and $I_E$ are in milliamperes, usually, or in amperes for power transistors. In all cases, $I_E$ and $I_B$ return through the external circuit to the emitter, as the source of the free charges for all the currents.

## THE BASE CURRENT CONTROLS THE COLLECTOR CURRENT

This factor is the reason why a transistor can amplify the signal input. When $I_B$ is increased by more forward voltage, this effect means more majority charges are in the base to be injected into the collector. Therefore, increasing $I_B$ means more $I_C$. For the opposite variation with less forward voltage and less $I_B$, the collector current is reduced. As a result, the signal variations of amplitude in the base circuit produce equivalent variations in the collector circuit.

It is important to remember that there must be at least enough forward voltage across the emitter-base junction to produce current. For silicon, typical values for $V_{BE}$ are 0.5 to 0.7 V. For lower voltages down to zero, the transistor is off, without any conduction. With enough $V_{BE}$ to provide emitter current, then the transistor can produce amplification.

All these features apply to both PNP and NPN transistors. See Table 28-1 for a summary of the two types of junction transistors.

**TABLE 28-1  JUNCTION TRANSISTORS**

| TYPE | SYMBOL | ELECTRODES | NOTES |
|------|--------|-----------|-------|
| NPN | | C = collector<br>B = base<br>E = emitter | Needs $+V_C$ reverse voltage for collector; forward bias of 0.6 V for Si or 0.2 V for Ge typical values; Si more common for NPN<br>Hole current out from base into emitter |
| PNP | | C = collector<br>B = base<br>E = emitter | Needs $-V_C$ reverse voltage for collector; forward bias $V_{BE}$ of 0.2 V for Ge or 0.6 V for Si typical values; Ge more common for PNP<br>Hole current into base from emitter |

**TEST-POINT QUESTION 28-4**

Answers at end of chapter.
**a.** Does the base-emitter junction have forward or reverse bias?
**b.** Does the collector-base junction have forward or reverse voltage?
**c.** If $I_C$ is 1 mA and $I_B$ is 50 $\mu$A, how much is $I_E$?
**d.** A Si transistor has 0.1-V forward bias. Is it conducting or cut off?
**e.** A transistor symbol shows the emitter arrow out from base. Is the transistor PNP or NPN?

# 28-5 FIELD-EFFECT TRANSISTOR (FET)

The field-effect transistor (FET) is an amplifier with the same function as a junction transistor, but FET construction is different. As a result, the FET has the following features:

1. The input resistance is very high. A typical value is 15 M$\Omega$.
2. The input circuit can take several volts for the input signal, compared with tenths of a volt for junction transistors.

As illustrated in Fig. 28-17*a*, the FET operation depends on controlling current through a semiconductor channel of N or P polarity. One side of the channel is the *source electrode* and the other end is the *drain electrode.* An N channel is shown here, but a P channel can be used instead. For either type, current flows from the source to the drain. The voltage applied to the gate electrode controls the current through the channel. The bulk or substate material is neutral or lightly doped silicon. It only serves as a platform on which the other electrodes are diffused.

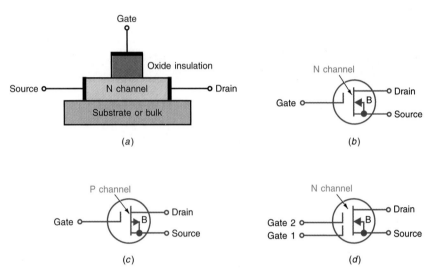

FIG. 28-17 Insulated-gate field-effect transistor, or IGFET. (*a*) Construction. (*b*) Schematic symbol for N-channel with arrow in. B is bulk or substrate connected internally to source. (*c*) Symbol for P-channel with arrow out. (*d*) N-channel IGFET with two-gate inputs.

The terms anode and cathode are not used for the FET because the channel can be either N or P. An FET is a unipolar device, as the charge carriers in the channel have only one polarity.

Compared with junction transistors, the FET has much higher input resistance, from gate to source, and can take more input signal voltage. Also, the FET is less sensitive to the effects of temperature, x-rays, and cosmic radiation. These energy sources can produce minority carriers in junction transistors. In addition, the FET has less internal noise as an amplifier. The disadvantages are less gain for a given bandwidth and smaller power ratings than the NPN or PNP type. Finally, the switching speed of the FET is slower.

In summary, the electrodes of an FET correspond to the emitter, base, and collector in a junction transistor as follows:

1. *Source.* This is the terminal where the charge carriers enter the channel bar to provide current through the channel. Source current is $I_S$. The source corresponds to the emitter.
2. *Drain.* This is the terminal where current leaves the channel. Drain current is $I_D$. The drain corresponds to the collector.
3. *Gate.* This electrode controls the conductance of the channel between the source and the drain. Input signal voltage is generally applied to the gate. The gate voltage is $V_G$. The gate corresponds to the base, but the gate voltage controls

the electric field in the channel, while the base current controls the collector current in a junction transistor.

In the schematic symbol, an arrow for hole charges into the channel indicates an N channel, as in Fig. 28-17b. For a P channel, the arrow direction is out, as in Fig. 28-17c. The source and drain have no polarity, since they are just ohmic contacts. An N channel takes positive drain voltage to provide drain current.

**FUNCTION OF THE GATE**    In the input circuit, the gate and channel act like two plates of a capacitor. A charge of one polarity on the gate induces an equal and opposite charge in the channel. As a result, the conductivity of the channel can be increased or decreased by the gate voltage. With an N channel, positive voltage at the gate induces negative charges in the channel to allow more electron flow from source to drain.

**IGFET**    This abbreviation is for the insulated-gate FET, with the construction illustrated in Fig. 28-17a. The IGFET consists of a metal electrode for the gate separated from the channel by a thin layer of silicon dioxide. This material is an insulator, like glass. However, by electrostatic induction a voltage applied to the gate can induce charges in the channel to control the current from source to drain. There is no PN junction. The IGFET construction is also used for transistors in integrated circuits. This type is a metal-oxide-semiconductor field-effect transistor (MOSFET). Either name, IGFET or MOSFET, is used for these transistors.

In the FET symbols in Fig. 28-17, an N channel is shown in b, and a P channel in c. For the FET in Fig. 28-17d, the symbol shows an N channel with dual gate electrodes for two input signals to control the drain current.

Because of its very high input resistance, an IGFET not connected in a circuit may require a shorting ring on the leads to protect against a buildup of static charge. Also, a grounded iron is used for soldering the leads. Excess charge can produce enough voltage to puncture the thin glass insulation of the gate electrode. However, many FETs have internal protective diodes for the gate.

**DEPLETION OR ENHANCEMENT MODE**    IGFETs come as either depletion or enhancement types, depending on the amount of doping used for the channel construction. For the depletion type:

1. The channel has free charge carriers.
2. Current can be produced in the channel with voltage applied between drain and source, but no gate voltage.
3. The gate voltage can deplete the charge carriers in the channel to a greater or lesser extent to control the drain current.

As a result of these characteristics, the depletion type of IGFET is a normally on device. Drain current flows with zero gate voltage but usually a reverse voltage of about 1 V is used as dc bias for the desired operating characteristics as an amplifier.

For the enhancement type of IGFET, the channel has very little doping. Then gate voltage must be applied to enhance the amount of charge carriers in the channel to produce drain current. Therefore, the enhancement type is a normally off device. A forward voltage of about 5 to 7 V is applied to the gate as dc bias for the amplifier. With an N channel, forward voltage at the gate is positive and reverse voltage is negative.

A comparison between the on and off conditions is illustrated in Fig. 28-18 for these two types. The gate electrode is open for the condition of zero gate voltage. In Fig. 28-18a, the meter shows drain current produced by the voltage between drain and source for the depletion type. However, the enhancement type in Fig. 28-18b has no drain current.

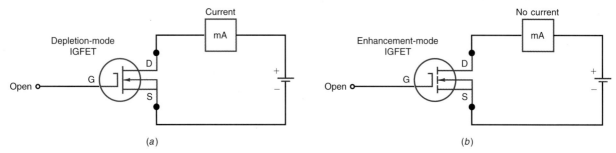

(a)                                                    (b)

**FIG. 28-18**   (a) Depletion-mode N-channel IGFET operating as a normally on device. (b) Enhancement-mode N-channel IGFET operating as a normally off device.

Note the IGFET schematic symbols in Fig. 28-18a and b, which show an N channel with the arrow for hole current directed into the channel. In Fig. 28-18b, however, the channel is shown as a broken line in order to indicate that this is the enhancement type.

Another mode for the IGFET is the depletion-enhancement type, as a compromise between both characteristics. In this type, drain current flows with zero gate voltage, but less than the amount for a depletion type. As a result, the depletion-enhancement IGFET can be used in an amplifier circuit without any dc bias for the gate.

**EIA TYPES**   The Electronic Industries Association (EIA) classifies the types of IGFET in three groups labeled A, B, and C. For an N channel, the depletion type A takes negative gate bias for a middle value of drain current $I_D$. With the same $I_D$, depletion-enhancement type B can operate with zero gate bias. Finally, enhancement type C requires positive gate bias.

**JFET**   This abbreviation is for junction field-effect transistor. Instead of an insulated gate in an IGFET, the JFET uses a PN junction between the gate and channel. This construction is illustrated in Fig. 28-19. However, reverse bias is

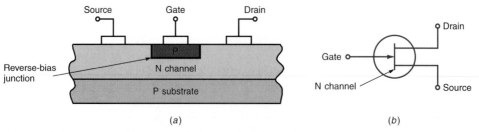

(a)                                                    (b)

**FIG. 28-19**   Junction field-effect transistor, or JFET. (a) Construction. Note the reverse bias for junction of gate and source. (b) Schematic symbol for N-channel with arrow in.

used at the gate so that the input resistance is very high as in the IGFET. In the schematic symbol, the arrow is on the gate electrode. The arrow directed inward shows an N channel. All the different types of FETs, including the JFET, are summarized in Table 28-2, with symbols, electrodes, and characteristics.

## TABLE 28-2  TYPES OF FIELD-EFFECT TRANSISTOR

| TYPE | SYMBOL | ELECTRODES | NOTES |
|------|--------|-----------|-------|
| JFET | Channel<br>G — D, S | D = drain<br>G = gate<br>S = source | Junction-type FET; arrow pointing to channel indicates P gate and N channel; reverse bias at junction |
| IGFET or MOSFET N channel | G — D, B, S | D = drain<br>G = gate<br>S = source | Insulated gate; depletion or depletion-enhancement type; B is bulk or substrate connected internally to source |
| IGFET or MOSFET P channel | G — D, B, S | D = drain<br>G = gate<br>S = source | Arrow pointing away from channel indicates P channel |
| IGFET or MOSFET, N channel, enhancement | G — D, B, S | D = drain<br>G = gate<br>S = source | Broken lines for channel show enhancement type |
| Dual-gate IGFET or MOSFET, N-channel | $G_2$ — D, B<br>$G_1$ — S | D = drain<br>$G_2$ = gate 2<br>$G_1$ = gate 1<br>S = source | Either or both gates control amount of drain current $I_D$ |

### TEST-POINT QUESTION 28-5

Answers at end of chapter.

Answer True or False.
**a.** The IGFET has high input resistance.
**b.** The gate electrode on an FET compares with the emitter electrode on a junction transistor.
**c.** The schematic symbol in Fig. 28-17b is for an N-channel depletion-mode IGFET.
**d.** The IGFET is unipolar while junction transistors are bipolar.

# 28-6 TESTING DIODES AND TRANSISTORS

An ohmmeter can be used to check a PN junction either for an open circuit or a short circuit. The short is indicated by R of practically zero ohms. A very high R of many megohms, in the direction of infinite ohms, means an open circuit. Power is off in the circuit for ohmmeter readings. Preferably, the device is out of the circuit to eliminate any parallel paths that can affect the resistance readings.

Figure 28-20 illustrates the idea of testing a diode with an ohmmeter. In Fig. 28-20*a*, the forward resistance should be low, perhaps 100 to 1000 Ω, with the positive battery lead of the ohmmeter at the anode side of the diode. Next, the ohmmeter leads are reversed to provide reverse voltage across the diode. Then the reverse resistance should be very high, near infinity for silicon diodes. These measurements also show which end of the diode is the anode. There are the following possibilities in the measurements:

1. When the ratio of reverse to forward $R$ is very high, the diode is probably good.
2. When both the forward and reverse $R$ are very low, close to zero, the diode junction is short-circuited.
3. When both the forward and reverse $R$ are very high, close to infinity, the diode probably has an open at the terminal.

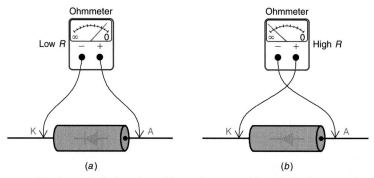

FIG. 28-20   Testing a diode junction with an ohmmeter. Normal $R$ values are shown here. (*a*) Forward bias results in very low resistance. (*b*) Reverse leads for reverse bias and very high resistance.

These tests should not be made on the $R \times 1$ position of the ohmmeter because it may supply too much current. Use the $R \times 10$ or $R \times 100$ position.

When the ohmmeter has a low-ohms position, only about 0.3 V is used for the ohmmeter leads. This voltage is not high enough to turn on a silicon junction for testing. However, this type of meter usually has a *diode test* position. The meter then indicates the normal junction voltage of approximately 0.7 V for Si or 0.3 V for Ge. Current for testing the junction is provided by the meter.

For testing PNP and NPN transistors, the same diode test can be used for each junction. Check the emitter-base junction as a diode, in one polarity and then the opposite way. Similarly, the collector-base junction can be checked as a diode. Remember that an NPN transistor takes positive voltage at the base for forward bias. More detailed tests on transistors, including their electrical characteristics, can be checked with a transistor tester.

With junction transistors that are not marked, some practical points can help identify the type. In a circuit where the dc supply voltage is positive for the collector or negative for the emitter, the transistor is NPN. This polarity is needed as reverse voltage for $V_{CE}$. When the forward voltage for $V_{BE}$ is 0.6 to 0.7 V, the transistor is silicon. Germanium transistors take 0.2 to 0.3 V.

Consider a transistor by itself, out of the circuit. Some ohmmeter tests can determine which leads are for the emitter, base, and collector. On the $R \times 100$ or $R \times 10,000$ scale for small transistors, measure the resistance for the three combinations between two pins. Then reverse the ohmmeter leads and repeat the measurements. The lowest reading is the resistance between base and emitter in the forward direction. With an NPN type, the base has the positive side of $V_{BE}$. The next-to-lowest reading is between collector and base, also in the forward direction. Incidentally, the reverse readings for silicon are practically infinite ohms.

To check a field-effect transistor, the resistance of the channel between source and drain should be about 10,000 $\Omega$. The $R$ between gate and channel should be infinitely high for an MOSFET, in either polarity. With a JFET check the gate-to-channel junction as a diode.

It should be noted that the red lead of the ohmmeter is usually the positive side of the internal battery. However, check the polarity by using another voltmeter to measure the voltage across the ohmmeter leads.

---

### TEST-POINT QUESTION 28-6

Answers at end of chapter.

Answer True or False.
**a.** An ohmmeter test across a diode should show low $R$ in one polarity and very high $R$ in the opposite polarity.
**b.** The same test as in **a** across the base-collector junction of a transistor should show the same results.
**c.** The $R$ of the channel between source and drain of an FET should measure infinitely high.

# 28 SUMMARY AND REVIEW

- The semiconductor elements used for electronic devices are silicon (Si) and germanium (Ge). Doped semiconductors are P type or N type. All semiconductor devices are solid-state components, generally using Si.
- A PN junction allows forward current with forward voltage $V_F$ applied. The polarity of $V_F$ is the same as the P and N electrodes. Reverse voltage of the opposite polarity prevents forward current.
- A semiconductor diode has a PN junction. The P side is the anode and the N side is the cathode. Positive voltage at the anode allows diode current. The diode is used as a one-way conductor for a rectifier to convert ac input to dc output.
- Both the NPN and the PNP transistors have two junctions for the three electrodes: emitter, base, and collector. The emitter supplies free charges through the base to be received at the collector. The collector requires reverse voltage, while the base-emitter junction needs forward bias. Typical forward bias is 0.6 V for Si or 0.2 V for Ge. The features of NPN and PNP transistors are summarized in Table 28-1.
- The field-effect transistor (FET) is an amplifier like junction transistors, but the FET has very high input resistance. The FET electrodes are a source corresponding to an emitter, a gate like the base electrode, and a drain corresponding to a collector. Features of the FET are summarized in Table 28-2.
- A semiconductor diode can be tested with an ohmmeter for low $R$ in the forward direction and high $R$ in the reverse direction. The same tests apply to the junctions in PNP and NPN transistors.

## SELF-TEST

### ANSWERS AT BACK OF BOOK.

1. Give the electron valence for the semiconductor elements.
2. How much is the internal barrier voltage for a silicon PN junction?
3. Is hole current in the same or opposite direction as electron flow?
4. Does an arrow on the emitter out from the base show a PNP or NPN transistor?
5. Which electrode controls the output current for junction transistors?
6. Is $V_{BE}$ forward or reverse voltage?
7. Is $V_{CB}$ forward or reverse voltage?
8. Do NPN transistors take positive or negative collector voltage?
9. In a rectifier circuit, is positive dc output taken from the diode anode or cathode?

10. Does the arrow in symbols for semiconductor devices show the direction of hole current or electron flow?
11. When $I_C$ in a junction transistor is 99.9 mA and $I_B$ is 0.1 mA, how much is $I_E$?
12. Which electrode in an FET corresponds to the emitter in junction transistors?
13. In schematic symbols for the FET, does an arrow directed into the channel show an N channel or P channel?
14. Give the abbreviations for three types of FET.
15. Does an FET have higher or lower input resistance than a junction transistor?
16. An ohmmeter test on a PN junction shows close to zero ohms with forward and reverse voltage. Is the junction shorted or open?
17. True or False? The normal resistance of the channel in an FET is infinitely high.

## QUESTIONS

1. Define the following: (**a**) doping; (**b**) N-type silicon; (**c**) P-type silicon; (**d**) PN junction; (**e**) internal barrier potential; (**f**) depletion zone.
2. For a PN junction, show a battery applying: (**a**) forward voltage; (**b**) reverse voltage.
3. Give two comparisons between electron flow and hole current.
4. Compare hole charges to ion charges.
5. Draw the schematic symbols for NPN and PNP transistors and label the electrodes.
6. Give the functions for the three electrodes in a junction transistor.
7. Explain the biasing on the emitter-base junction and base-collector junctions of NPN and PNP transistors.
8. Draw the schematic symbols for an N-channel MOSFET, depletion type and enhancement type.
9. Compare the functions of the three electrodes in an FET with a junction transistor.
10. Give two comparisons between junction transistors and the FET.
11. Explain briefly how to test a PN junction with an ohmmeter for a short or open.
12. Identify the majority and minority charges in a(n): (**a**) N-type semiconductor; (**b**) P-type semiconductor.
13. Draw a schematic for a bridge rectifier which will produce a negative output voltage.
14. Explain what is meant when a depletion-type IGFET is said to be normally on.

## PROBLEMS

**ANSWERS TO ODD-NUMBERED PROBLEMS AT BACK OF BOOK.**

1. Calculate the resistance of a silicon diode that has 0.5 A of current through it with a 0.8-V drop across the two terminals.

2. In a junction transistor, $I_C$ is 1 mA and $I_B$ is 20 $\mu$A. Calculate $I_E$.
3. In a junction transistor, $I_E$ is 5.82 mA and $I_B$ is 120 $\mu$A. Calculate $I_C$.
4. Refer to the graph in Fig. 28-10. How much is $I_F$ with (a) $V_F$ of 0.7 V for Si; (b) $V_F$ of 0.3 V for Ge?
5. Refer to the electrode currents in Fig. 28-16. If $I_B$ increases to 0.3 mA and $I_C$ increases to 50 mA, how much is the higher value of $I_E$?
6. For each of the circuits in Fig. 28-21, indicate whether the diodes and transistors are cut off or conducting. Note the difference of potential for the voltage in each case.

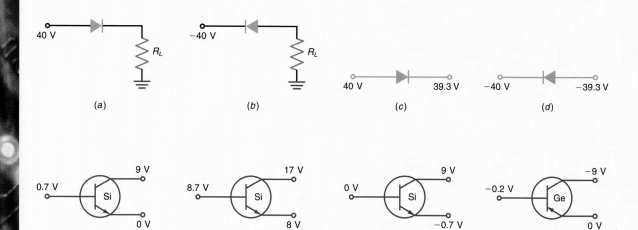

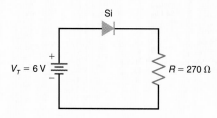

FIG. 28-21   Circuits for Prob. 6.

7. In Fig. 28-22, calculate the current $I$ in the circuit. (Assume that $V_F = 0.6$ V.)
8. In Fig. 28-22, how much is the current $I$ if the diode is reversed?

FIG. 28-22   Circuit for Probs. 7 and 8.

## CRITICAL THINKING

1. In Fig. 28-23, calculate the forward current $I_F$ in diode $D_1$. (Assume that $V_F = 0.6$ V.) Hint: Apply Thevenin's theorem.

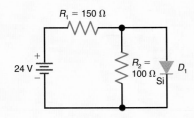

FIG. 28-23   Circuit for Critical Thinking Prob. 1.

## ANSWERS TO TEST-POINT QUESTIONS

**28-1 a.** ±4
    **b.** N-type
    **c.** F
    **d.** majority charges

**28-2 a.** 0.7 V
    **b.** P
    **c.** N
    **d.** 1 $\mu$A
    **e.** 150 mA

**28-3 a.** positive
    **b.** hole current
    **c.** cathode
    **d.** one
    **e.** cathode

**28-4 a.** forward
    **b.** reverse
    **c.** 1.05 mA
    **d.** cut off
    **e.** NPN

**28-5 a.** T
    **b.** F
    **c.** T
    **d.** T

**28-6 a.** T
    **b.** T
    **c.** F

# CHAPTER 29

# ELECTRONIC CIRCUITS

Transistors and diodes are two common types of semiconductor devices that make it possible to have so many applications of electronics. One of the main applications of transistors is in amplifier circuits. An amplifier increases the magnitude or amplitude of signal variations to make the desired signal stronger.

Without electronic amplification, not much could be done with audio, radio, video, or control systems. An amplified audio signal makes the reproduced sound loud enough. In television, the amplified video signal makes the reproduced picture have enough contrast and brightness.

Another important function of electronic circuits is switching, with either diodes or transistors. When the device is conducting current, the internal resistance is low. The $R$ can be low enough, less than 1 $\Omega$, to be considered a short circuit. This low resistance corresponds to a closed switch. For the opposite case, a diode or transistor can be cut off, meaning no current in the device. For this condition, the $R$ is practically infinity. The high resistance corresponds to an open switch. The electronic switching, therefore, means making the diode or transistor change between conduction and cutoff.

The integrated circuit (IC) chip combines transistors and diodes in one unit, often with resistance and capacitance also. Inductors are not included, since they take up too much space. The semiconductor element silicon (Si) is used for most transistors, diodes, and IC chips. A transistor or diode not in an IC chip is called a *discrete component* because the part is complete in itself. Discrete transistors and diodes generally have higher power ratings than IC chips.

# CHAPTER OBJECTIVES

*Upon completion of this chapter, you should be able to:*

- *Explain* the difference between an analog and a digital signal.
- *Give* examples of analog and digital signals.
- *Calculate* the voltage gain, current gain, and power gain of an amplifier or a chain of amplifiers.
- *Explain* the roles of resistors, capacitors, and inductors in an amplifier circuit.
- *Explain* what is meant by *positive feedback*.
- *Describe* the operation of an RF feedback oscillator.
- *List* three different types of multivibrators.
- *Define amplitude modulation* and *frequency modulation* and list the main characteristics of each.
- *Explain* the operation of a half-wave power supply.
- *Troubleshoot* a defective half-wave power supply.

# IMPORTANT TERMS IN THIS CHAPTER

| | | |
|---|---|---|
| active device | detector circuit | integrated circuit |
| amplifier | dc supply | isolation transformer |
| amplitude modulation (AM) | digital signal | modulation |
| analog signal | discrete component | multivibrator |
| anode | feedback | oscillator circuit |
| baseband signal | flip-flop circuit | passive device |
| binary numbers | frequency modulation (FM) | power supply |
| bit | full-wave rectifier | rectifier |
| byte | gain of amplifier | semiconductor device |
| carrier wave | half-wave rectifier | sidebands |
| cascaded amplifiers | Hartley oscillator | signal variations |
| Colpitts oscillator | hum | transistor |
| crystal oscillator | IC chip | |

# TOPICS COVERED IN THIS CHAPTER

**29-1** Analog and Digital Signals
**29-2** Amplifier Gain
**29-3** Characteristics of Amplifier Circuits
**29-4** Oscillators

**29-5** Multivibrators
**29-6** Modulation
**29-7** Diode Rectifiers
**29-8** Troubleshooting the DC Supply Voltage

# 29-1 ANALOG AND DIGITAL SIGNALS

The world of electronics is divided into two broad areas—analog and digital—because they are so different. Analog circuits consist mainly of amplifiers for voltage or current variations that are smooth and continuous. Transistors and IC chips are generally used for the amplification. Digital circuits provide electronic switching of voltage pulses. A pulse has abrupt changes between two distinctly different amplitude levels. Diodes and transistors in digital IC chips are generally used. Just to indicate the division between the digital and analog areas, the manufacturers of IC chips have separate catalogs or handbooks for their digital and analog products. The analog form is generally called a *linear* type of IC unit because analog information deals with proportional values.

What do we mean by the signal? In general, the signal variations for electronic circuits are changes in voltage and current that correspond to the desired information. In an analog signal, the electrical variations have a direct relation to the changes that represent the information. Analog examples include audio signal for sound and video signal for the picture in television. As another practical example, a radio or television broadcast station transmits radio-frequency variations in an electromagnetic field that forms an RF signal. All analog signals have continuous variations, with smooth changes between many different values. For the opposite case, the pulses in a digital signal have abrupt changes between two levels, representing only two values. It is the combinations of pulses that provide the desired information.

As a specific example of analog signals, Fig. 29-1 shows sine-wave variations

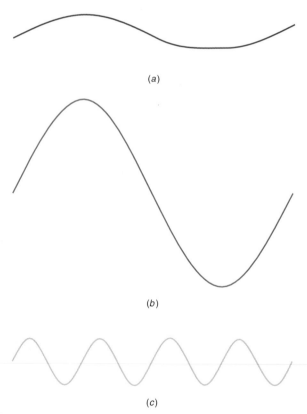

(a)

(b)

(c)

FIG. 29-1    Examples of analog signals. (*a*) Sine wave. (*b*) More amplitude. (*c*) Higher frequency.

in voltage or current. In Fig. 29-1*a*, note that the amplitude variations are smooth and continuous, without any abrupt transitions in amplitude. The sine wave is shown with higher amplitude in Fig. 29-1*b*, representing a stronger value of the corresponding voltage and current. In Fig. 29-1*c*, more cycles for the sine waves show a higher frequency. In all cases, these waveforms are analog signals, as the variations in the electrical values are similar to the changes in the desired information.

A digital signal consists of a train of pulses for the voltage or current, as illustrated in Fig. 29-2. The pulses all have the same amplitude with abrupt changes between the maximum level at 5 V here and the minimum level at 0 V. The voltages between the two extremes have no meaning in terms of information for the signal. The reason is that the pulses operate with a switching circuit, which is turned either on or off.

Since the digital signal in Fig. 29-2 has only two significant levels, either HIGH or LOW, it is useful to represent the pulses in a binary number system with the digits 1 and 0. The high level is generally indicated as binary 1 and the low level with 0. Then the binary numbers correspond to the digital pulse signal. For instance, the binary values in Fig. 29-2 represent the four pulses in each signal as follows:

$$1010 = \text{HIGH, LOW, HIGH, LOW (Fig. 29-2}a)$$
$$0101 = \text{LOW, HIGH, LOW, HIGH (Fig. 29-2}b)$$
$$1100 = \text{HIGH, HIGH, LOW, LOW (Fig. 29-2}c)$$
$$0011 = \text{LOW, LOW, HIGH, HIGH (Fig. 29-2}d)$$

The binary values are usually in groups of eight. Each pulse is a *bit* of information. The group of bits is a *word*. The words can have 4, 8, 16, or 32 bits. An 8-bit word is called a *byte*.

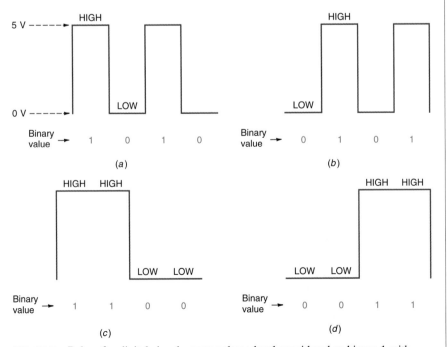

FIG. 29-2  Pulses for digital signals. HIGH voltage level considered as binary 1 with zero level as 0. Information is in the combinations of 1 and 0.

Answers at end of chapter.

Answer True or False.

**a.** The sine wave is an example of an analog signal.

**b.** The digits used in a binary number system are 1 and 2.

**c.** The pulses for the binary word 0111 are *not* shown in Fig. 29-2.

## 29-2 AMPLIFIER GAIN

The ability of an amplifier circuit to increase the amount of signal is measured by the gain, defined as the ratio of output signal to input signal. For example, when the output is 50 times more than the input, the gain of the amplifier equals 50.

General symbols for an amplifier circuit are shown in Fig. 29-3. The triangle is a general form that just shows terminals 1 and 2 for input and output signals. The square block indicates that two *pairs* of connections are needed. Note that one input terminal and one output terminal are tied together for a return path to the common terminal 3. The ground connection here does not necessarily mean earth ground but is just a common return. The block diagram is a simplified method of indicating an amplifier circuit.

**DID YOU KNOW?**

An endless depth of field is possible in a camera that has a motorized unit to pan several images. The camera's computer analyzes the images and selects the sharpest image of each, giving a picture that is a composite of the sharpest focus for all elements.

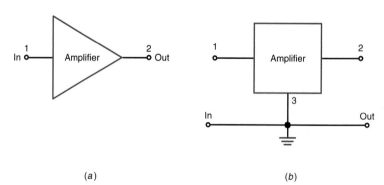

(a)                                    (b)

**FIG. 29-3** Block symbols for amplifier circuit. (*a*) Triangle as general symbol with input and output terminals. (*b*) Square block with details for two pairs of connections. Note common return for low side of input and output circuits.

**VOLTAGE GAIN**   In terms of signal voltage, the gain with the symbol $A_V$ is

$$A_V = \frac{\text{output signal voltage}}{\text{input signal voltage}} \qquad (29\text{-}1)$$

The output and input signal voltages can be in any units but they must be the same for the ratio. Peak-to-peak (p–p) values are usually best, in case the signal waveform is not symmetrical. Typical values of voltage gain for transistor amplifier circuits are about 10 to 2000.

An example for a voltage gain of 40 is illustrated in Fig. 29-4. Here, the input signal equals 0.1 V, p–p. This signal is amplified to the value of 4 V p–p in the output. To calculate the voltage gain

$$A_V = \frac{4 \text{ V}}{0.1 \text{ V}} = 40$$

There are no units for $A_V$ because it is a ratio of the same units, which cancel.

To do this problem on a calculator, just punch in 4 on the numerical keyband, press the division key ⊕ at the side, enter the .1, and press the ⊜ key for the answer of 40.

This example is for an audio circuit amplifying a signal with the audio frequency of 400 Hz, as noted in the diagram in Fig. 29-4. Note that the frequency of the output signal voltage is the same as the input signal. The 400 Hz is only one example. Almost any frequency can be amplified.

For the output signal voltage in Fig. 29-4, note that the phase is shown opposite from the input signal, meaning a phase inversion of 180°. The amplifier can then be considered as an *inverter* circuit also, because of the reversed polarity. The phase inversion does not affect the gain, however. Many amplifiers can invert the polarity of the signal, depending on the type of output circuit.

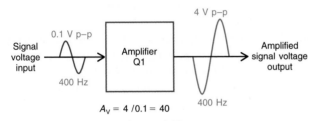

FIG. 29-4    Amplifier with voltage gain $A_V$ of 40.

**CURRENT GAIN**    With transistor amplifiers, the gain in current for the output signal compared with the input signal is probably more important than the voltage gain. The reason is that the amount of ac signal voltage for the input circuit is limited to ±0.1 V, approximately, but the input current can be in microamperes, milliamperes, or even as high as an ampere. This limitation applies to junction transistors such as the PNP and NPN types.

The amount of current gain, with the symbol $A_I$, is

▶   $$A_I = \frac{\text{output signal current}}{\text{input signal current}} \qquad\qquad \textbf{(29-2)}$$

For the example in Fig. 29-5 the input signal current of 200 $\mu$A is equal to 0.2 mA. The output is 6 mA. Then

$$A_I = \frac{\text{output } I}{\text{input } I}$$

$$A_I = \frac{6 \text{ mA}}{0.2 \text{ mA}} = 30$$

There are no units for $A_I$ because it is a ratio of the same two units of current.

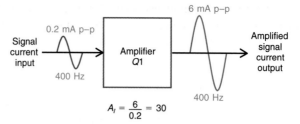

FIG. 29-5   Amplifier with current gain $A_I$ of 30.

Note that no phase inversion occurs with the signal current. Only the amplified signal voltage can be inverted in the output circuit. Typical values of current gain with transistors are about 1 to 500.

**POWER GAIN**   This quantity, with the symbol $A_P$, is the product of the voltage gain times the current gain, or

▶   $$A_P = A_V \times A_I \qquad\qquad (29\text{-}3)$$

For the examples of $A_V$ equal to 40 and $A_I$ of 30, the power gain is

$$A_P = 40 \times 30 = 1200$$

There are still no units for $A_P$ because it is the product of two gain values without any units. A high value of power gain for an amplifier means it can drive a load that requires appreciable current and voltage. It may be noted that discrete transistors generally have higher power ratings than IC chips for applications that require appreciable power gain.

**OVERALL GAIN FOR AMPLIFIERS IN CASCADE**   Most applications require more than one amplifier stage in order to provide enough gain. The reason is that the original signal to be amplified usually has low amplitude and a strong signal is needed for the desired output. As an example for audio signals, the output from a record player or magnetic tape may be just a few millivolts. However, a loudspeaker requires much more signal. Sufficient amplification is needed in order to hear the sound.

Actually, it is practical to have almost any amount of gain with transistors and IC chips because these semiconductor devices are so small. One IC chip can easily have two, three, or more transistor amplifiers.

A specific example is shown in Fig. 29-6 for the two amplifier stages $Q1$ and $Q2$ connected in cascade. Each amplifier circuit with one transistor is called

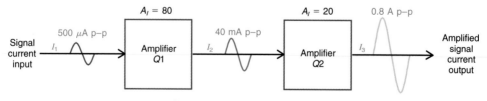

FIG. 29-6   Amplifiers in cascade to multiply the gain. Here, $A_I = 80 \times 20 = 1600$.

a *stage*. When the output terminal of one stage drives the input terminal of the next stage, the two stages are connected in *cascade*. Just to indicate how the circuit might be different, it should be noted that transistors can be connected in series or in parallel. When the amplifier stages are in cascade, the total gain equals the product of the individual gains for each stage.

Figure 29-6 shows cascaded values of gain to illustrate a practical example with transistors such as the PNP or NPN types. In the second amplifier $Q2$, this transistor needs signal input variations with an amplitude of 40 mA p–p in order to provide output of 0.8 A p–p. This current gain of $Q2$ is 0.8 A or 800 mA divided by 40 mA, for $A_I$ of 20. However, the variation of current in the original signal has a magnitude of only 500 $\mu$A or 0.0005 A p–p. Therefore, this signal is fed into amplifier $Q1$, with a current gain of 80, to provide enough signal current for the input to $Q2$. The calculations for the current amplitudes in Fig. 29-6 are as follows:

$$I_2 = 80 \times I_1$$
$$= 80 \times 500 \ \mu A$$
$$I_2 = 40,000 \ \mu A = 40 \ mA$$
$$I_3 = 20 \times I_2$$
$$= 20 \times 40 \ mA$$
$$I_3 = 800 \ mA = 0.8 \ A$$

The overall gain for the two stages in cascade in Fig. 29-6 is $80 \times 20 = 1600$ for the total $A_I$. This value can also be calculated as the ratio of the 0.8 A output to the 500 $\mu$A input. Then converting 0.8 A to 800,000 $\mu$A gives

$$A_I = \frac{800,000 \ \mu A}{500 \ \mu A} = 1600$$

The multiplication of gain values for stages in cascade also applies to $A_V$ and $A_P$.

---

### TEST-POINT QUESTION 29-2

Answers at end of chapter.
a. Calculate the gain $A_V$ for output of 10 V with input of 50 mV.
b. Calculate the gain $A_I$ for output of 1 mA with input of 20 $\mu$A.
c. For a transistor amplifier stage, $A_V$ equals 200 and $A_I$ is 50. Calculate its power gain.
d. Three stages in cascade each have $A_I$ of 30. Calculate the total current gain.

# 29-3 CHARACTERISTICS OF AMPLIFIER CIRCUITS

There must be hundreds of different kinds of amplifiers but a few basic features can reduce the problem of analysis. Referring to the amplifier circuit in Fig. 29-7, note the following:

1. The transistor $Q1$ is the amplifying device.

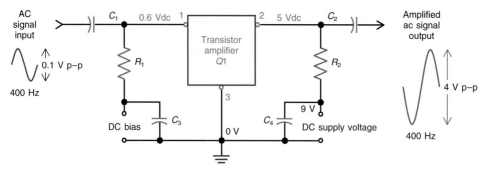

**FIG. 29-7** Schematic diagram of an amplifier with a transistor as active device.

2. Resistors and capacitors are used. Inductors can also be included, although they are not shown here.

3. The frequency of 400 Hz for the ac signal indicates this circuit is for audio amplification.

4. Both dc and ac voltages are shown. The dc voltages are needed for electrode voltages on $Q1$, to make it conduct current. The ac voltages apply to the desired signal input and output, generally in peak-to-peak values.

These characteristics can be applied to all types of amplifier circuits.

The transistor is called an *active device* because it can amplify the signal. Diodes also are active devices since conduction depends on the polarity of the input voltage. The $R$, $L$, and $C$ components are considered *passive devices.*

**$R$, $C$, AND $L$ COMPONENTS IN AN AMPLIFIER**  Each of these passive components has its own characteristics, whether in an electric circuit or in an amplifier circuit. However, the special effects for dc and ac voltages become more important because an amplifier circuit has both.

Resistance reduces the amount of current. The $R$ provides a voltage drop equal to $IR$. In terms of dc voltage, the voltage drop reduces the amount of voltage for $Q1$. Referring to Fig. 29-7, note that the dc voltage at terminal 2 of $Q1$ is 5 V, from the 9-Vdc supply, because of an $IR$ drop of 4 V across $R_2$. The voltage drop across $R_2$ is even more important for ac signal voltage. Actually the ac voltage across $R_2$ in the amplifier output circuit provides the desired signal output. In Fig. 29-7, $R_2$ is the output load resistor for signal voltage from terminal 2 of $Q1$ to the next stage. Also, for the input circuit, $R_1$ is the load resistor that develops ac signal input to terminal 1 of $Q1$. It should be noted that a resistor has the same $R$ for a steady current or a varying current. Also, $R$ is constant for all frequencies in an ac signal.

Because a capacitor can charge and discharge with changes in voltage, it has capacitive reactance $X_C$. For steady dc voltage, however, a capacitor is practically an open circuit. Furthermore, $X_C$ decreases for higher frequencies. Also, $X_C$ is less with a higher value of $C$. The amount of $X_C$ can easily be made less than 10 Ω, for a circuit path with very little opposition to the current. As a result, capacitors are often used in electronic circuits for the following important functions:

1. They block dc voltage but pass the ac signal. In this application, $C$ is a coupling capacitor. In Fig. 29-7, $C_1$ and $C_2$ are coupling capacitors. $C_2$ passes

the ac signal output from terminal 2 of $Q1$ to the next stage, but blocks the dc voltage in the output circuit. For the input circuit, $C_1$ couples the ac signal input to terminal 1 of $Q1$ but blocks any dc voltage from the previous stage.

2. The $C$ provides lower $X_C$ for high frequencies compared with lower frequencies. This factor means more ac signal voltage can be passed for the higher frequencies. As an example, a division between radio frequencies for high values and audio frequencies for lower values is provided.

3. The same frequency characteristics of $X_C$ can be applied to bypass capacitors as well as coupling capacitors. The only difference is that a coupling capacitor is a series component in the high side of the signal circuit to pass along the desired information, while a bypass capacitor is a parallel component to shunt the ac signal away from a part of the circuit where the signal is not desired. Usually, the shunt path of a bypass capacitor connects the ac signal to the common terminal of the return path for the low side of the circuit. In Fig. 29-7, $C_4$ at the low side of $R_2$ is a bypass capacitor to keep the ac signal from producing current in the source of the 9-Vdc supply voltage. This dc voltage is needed to produce current in the transistor. Similarly, $C_3$ at the low side of $R_1$ for the input current is a bypass capacitor for the 0.6-Vdc bias. The dc bias for the input circuit is needed to provide the desired operating characteristics for the transistor amplifier $Q1$.

In summary, the three main functions of capacitors in amplifier circuits are to block the dc supply voltage, couple the ac signal to the points in the circuit where the signal is needed, and bypass the ac signal around the components where the signal should not be. As typical values, 5 $\mu$F is commonly used for a coupling or bypass capacitor in audio amplifiers, while 100 pF is a typical size for RF circuits with frequencies of 0.5 to 10 MHz, approximately. Figure 29-8 shows how the electronic components look on a printed-circuit board.

Since an inductor is just a coil of wire, it allows direct current with dc voltage applied. The dc value depends on the resistance of the wire in the coil. However, because of the magnetic field around the coil with current, the inductor also has inductive reactance $X_L$ for alternating current. The amount of $X_L$ increases with higher frequencies and more $L$. These reactance effects for $X_L$ are

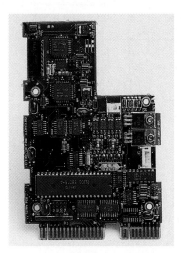

**FIG. 29-8** Components for electronic circuits mounted on a printed-circuit board.

the opposite of $X_C$. Inductors are used where it is desired to have high impedance for alternating current, with less opposition for lower frequencies down to 0 Hz for direct current. A common application is an RF or AF choke to isolate an ac component from the signal variations or to provide an ac load impedance that still allows direct current to flow. It should be noted that no $L$ is shown in Fig. 29-7 because this circuit does not use any chokes.

Keep in mind that both $L$ and $C$ can be used for resonant circuits, particularly for RF signals, as in a tuned RF amplifier. The higher the resonant frequency the smaller the values of $L$ and $C$ required.

**DC AND AC VOLTAGES IN AMPLIFIER CIRCUITS** An important practical feature of amplifiers is that they generally use ac and dc voltages in the same circuit. This characteristic makes the circuits interesting but the combined effect may not be so easy to visualize. The reason for having the ac–dc combination is very specific. An active device such as a transistor needs operating voltages applied to its electrodes in order to operate at all. The operation means it must be conducting current. Furthermore, the dc voltage must have a specific polarity. For instance, with an NPN transistor the dc supply voltage must be positive for the output electrode. A PNP transistor takes negative dc supply voltage. In addition, as far as amplification is concerned, the desired variations are usually in the form of an ac signal.

The way that an amplifier circuit diagram looks in terms of dc electrode voltages is illustrated in Fig. 29-9a. The dc supply voltage is 9 V, and terminal 2 has 5 V because of the 4-V drop across $R_2$. The input terminal has 0.6 V for dc bias to provide the desired operating characteristic for the amplifier $Q1$. Without any ac signal input at all, the amplifier $Q1$ is conducting direct current. In other words, the amplifier $Q1$ is ready for amplification.

It should be noted that any path for dc operating voltage cannot have any series capacitor, since capacitors block the dc voltage. However, series chokes can be used because they pass direct current. A practical example of the need for dc voltage is the fact that in a small portable transistor radio, the 9-V battery is the dc supply for all the circuits.

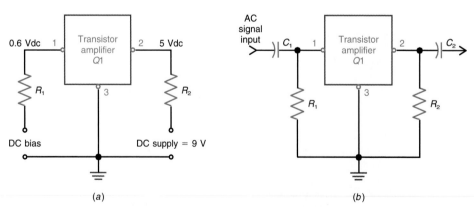

FIG. 29-9 The dc and ac voltages for the amplifier circuit in Fig. 29-7, shown separately in two diagrams. (a) The dc supply voltages without any ac signal. (b) Equivalent circuit for the ac signal without the dc supply voltages. The bypass $C_3$ and $C_4$ in Fig. 29-7 provide ac ground returns (not shown in diagram).

The circuit in Fig. 29-9b shows how the circuit looks for ac signal only, without any dc voltages indicated. The common ground return at terminal 3 of Q1 is only an equivalent ground for the ac signal. The dc voltages are really necessary but the low side of the actual circuit has bypass capacitors to ground. The bypass capacitors are chosen with enough C to have such low reactance at the operating frequency that they can be considered as a short circuit for the ac signal. In summary, the bypassing provides an effective ac ground for the signal without affecting the dc voltage. If ac signal were applied to the circuit without its dc operating voltages, the signal could not be amplified.

The complete amplifier circuit in Fig. 29-7 has ac signal input and the required dc operating voltages. The 0.1 V signal applied to the input is amplified up to 4 V for the output signal. However, the amplified output at terminal 2 is actually a fluctuating dc voltage, as shown in Fig. 29-10. The waveform has an ac component of 4 V p–p riding on the average dc level of 5 V. For instantaneous values, the output voltage is varying from 5 V down to 3 V and then from 5 V up to 7 V. These signal variations of $\pm2$ V, or 4 V p–p, are much larger than the input signal of 0.1 V p–p. This amplification by transistor Q1 is accomplished by allowing the small signal at the input to control the output circuit with its dc supply, where current and voltage variations can be produced with much greater amplitude.

Consider the fluctuating dc voltage in Fig. 29-10 as the output at terminal 2 of the amplifier in Fig. 29-7. Then the dc and ac components are separated as follows:

1. The coupling capacitor $C_2$ blocks the 5-Vdc level by developing this voltage across the two terminals of the capacitor.

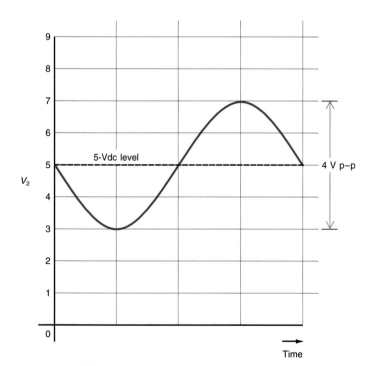

FIG. 29-10  Graph of fluctuating dc voltage with ac component at output terminal 2 of amplifier in Fig. 29-7.

2. The 4-Vac p–p signal is coupled to the next amplifier as the ac voltage across its input circuit.

**SIGNAL FREQUENCIES IN AMPLIFIERS**   An amplifier can be used for audio frequencies or radio frequencies and sometimes for both in wideband amplifiers. The range of audio frequencies is 20 to 20,000 Hz but 50 to 15,000 Hz is generally the frequency range for high-fidelity audio equipment. A narrower AF range can be used and still be suitable. In telephone applications, the range of audio frequencies is usually 100 to 3000 Hz.

Radio frequencies extend from 30 kHz up to the megahertz ($10^6$ Hz) and gigahertz ($10^9$ Hz) ranges. The values between 20 kHz at the top of the AF range and 30 kHz for RF can be considered ultrasonic audio frequencies.

The RF range includes the following four bands that are used for many RF applications, such as radio and television:

Medium frequencies (MF), 0.3 to 3 MHz
High frequencies (HF), 3 to 30 MHz
Very high frequencies (VHF), 30 to 300 MHz
Ultra-high frequencies (UHF), 300 to 3000 MHz

As examples, the AM radio broadcast service is 535 to 1605 kHz in the HF band; the FM commercial radio service is 88 to 108 MHz in the VHF band; television broadcast stations use 6 MHz channels in the VHF and UHF bands.

Amplifiers for AF signals are untuned, using a resistance load that is constant for all audio frequencies. The circuit shown before in Fig. 29-7 is for an audio amplifier. RF amplifiers are usually tuned with $LC$ circuits resonant at the desired frequency. A wideband amplifier is a special case for amplifying audio and radio frequencies. An example is the video amplifier used in television for the broad range of video frequencies from 30 Hz up to 4 MHz.

An example of a tuned RF amplifier is shown in Fig. 29-11. This circuit is similar to the basic amplifier in Fig. 29-7, except that the parallel resonant circuit with $L_1$ and $C_1$ is used for the output load instead of a resistor. No bypass capacitors for the dc voltages are shown in Fig. 29-11 because this bypassing is not always necessary.

The values for $L_1$ and $C_1$ are chosen for resonance at 1 MHz in this example. The amplifier is tuned to this frequency therefore. Only 1 MHz and a narrow band of frequencies around it can be amplified. Other frequencies do not

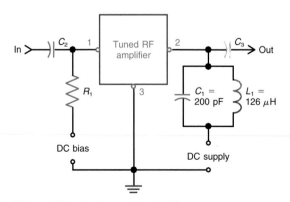

FIG. 29-11   An RF amplifier circuit tuned to 1 MHz.

have any gain. The reason for gain at 1 MHz is that the tuned circuit has high impedance for parallel resonance. A high impedance as the output load is necessary for the amplifier to provide high voltage gain. Frequencies off resonance have low impedance and little or no gain. The tuned RF amplifier then is able to select the frequency to be amplified. The amount of gain in a tuned RF amplifier is its *sensitivity*. How narrow the response is in terms of the band of frequencies that are amplified is the *selectivity*.

Answer True or False.
**a.** Coupling and bypass capacitors have low reactance at the frequency of the ac signal.
**b.** A resistor has the same $R$ for dc or ac voltages.
**c.** The dc voltage in Fig. 29-10 has an ac component of 4 V p–p.
**d.** Audio amplifiers usually have resonant $LC$ circuits for the load impedance.

# 29-4 OSCILLATORS

The process of oscillation means that variations in amplitude are repeated continuously at a specific frequency. A mechanical example is a swinging pendulum. In electronic circuits, an oscillator generates ac signal output without any ac signal input from an external source. Essentially, the oscillator is an ac generator for audio or radio frequencies, with many useful applications. This important function is accomplished by using an amplifier in a circuit where part of the output is fed back to the input. The feedback then corresponds to input signal. An example is shown in Fig. 29-12.

The oscillator output cannot be generated without using energy. This energy comes from the dc voltage for the circuit. In effect, the oscillator circuit converts the energy of the dc power supply into ac signal variations.

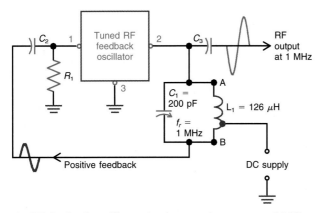

**FIG. 29-12** An RF feedback oscillator circuit generating output at 1 MHz.

**POSITIVE FEEDBACK**    The positive polarity means that the ac signal for oscillator feedback must be in the same phase that an ac input signal would have for amplification. Usually, the positive feedback results from two phase reversals of 180° each. The amplifier itself has one phase inversion of 180°. Then another 180° phase reversal is provided by the circuit that feeds signal from the output back to the input.

**TUNED RF FEEDBACK OSCILLATORS**    This name is given to the type of circuit in Fig. 29-12. It is tuned to the radio frequency of 1 MHz in this example by the resonant circuit with $C_1$ and $L_1$. Note that $C_1$ is shown variable to serve as a tuning capacitor that sets the oscillator frequency. Actually, the oscillating part of an oscillator circuit is the $L_1 C_1$ circuit. Any tuned circuit can produce sine-wave oscillations of current and voltage at its natural resonant frequency $f_r$. The oscillator ac output signal is at the $f_r$ of the tuned circuit. The only function of the amplifier in an oscillator circuit is to provide feedback that supplies energy to prevent the oscillations from decaying to zero. The tuned circuit is often called a *tank circuit* because it stores energy.

The functions of the components in the oscillator circuit of Fig. 29-12 can be summarized as follows:

$C_2$ is a coupling capacitor for the feedback signal into terminal 1.
$R_1$ provides the ac feedback signal coupled by $C_2$.
$C_3$ is a coupling capacitor for the output signal to the next stage.
$C_1$ is the tuning capacitor to set the frequency of the oscillator output.
$L_1$ is the inductance for the tuned circuit.

The resonant frequency of the tuned circuit can be calculated as

$$\blacktriangleright \quad f_r = \frac{1}{2\pi\sqrt{LC}}$$

For the values of 126 $\mu$H and 200 pF in Fig. 29-12,

$$f_r = \frac{1}{2\pi\sqrt{126 \times 10^{-6} \times 200 \times 10^{-12}}} = \frac{0.159}{\sqrt{126 \times 200}} \times 10^9$$

$$= \frac{0.159}{1590} \times 10^9$$

$$f_r = 0.001 \times 10^9 = 1 \times 10^6 = 1 \text{ MHz}$$

How to do a problem like this with a calculator is explained in Chap. 26 on resonant circuits.

The RF oscillator circuit in Fig. 29-12 is very similar to the RF amplifier in Fig. 29-11, except for the feedback. Note that the coil $L_1$ is tapped for the connection to the dc supply. This point is effectively an ac ground. Therefore, the two opposite ends of the coil at A and B have opposite polarities of ac signal, with respect to the tap. The feedback for point B then is opposite in phase to the amplified output signal for point A. As a result, positive feedback is provided because the two phase inversions of 180° add to equal 360°.

The amount of feedback voltage is determined by the tap on $L_1$ in Fig. 29-12. Generally, about one-third of the output voltage is taken for feedback. Most of the oscillator voltage is used for the ac output coupled by $C_3$ to the next stage.

Note that no dc bias source is shown for the input circuit at terminal 1 where the feedback signal is applied. The reason is that an oscillator circuit usually makes its own bias by rectifying the feedback signal at the input. In this way, the bias regulates itself since the amount of bias depends on the amount of feedback. In fact, a practical method of testing whether an oscillator circuit is oscillating is to measure its dc bias. No dc bias means no ac output from the oscillator.

**HARTLEY AND COLPITTS OSCILLATORS**  These are named for the inventors of the two main types of circuits for an RF feedback oscillator. In the Hartley circuit, the feedback is provided by a tapped coil as in Fig. 29-12. Then the coil serves as an ac voltage divider for the output voltage and feedback signal. In a Colpitts circuit, similar results are obtained with a capacitive voltage divider, as shown in Fig. 29-13. Here the voltage across $C_2$ is the feedback. The coil $L_T$ is made variable for tuning the oscillator. There are many modifications in the circuits, but all RF feedback oscillators can fit into these two classifications.

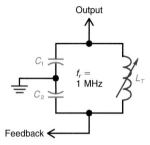

FIG. 29-13  Tuned circuit with capacitive voltage divider to provide feedback for Colpitts oscillator circuit.

**CRYSTAL OSCILLATORS**  In this type, a piezoelectric crystal is used as a resonant circuit, replacing an $LC$ circuit. The crystal is a thin slice of natural quartz or a synthetic material. An example is shown in Fig. 29-14. The piezoelectric effect means the crystal can vibrate mechanically when excited electrically and produce ac voltage output. The resonant frequency is fixed by the size of the crystal. Typical values of $f_r$ are 0.5 to 30 MHz. The advantages of the crystal is its very high $Q$ as a resonant circuit, which results in good frequency stability for the oscillator.

FIG. 29-14  A 3.58-MHz crystal in its housing, commonly used for the color oscillator in television receivers.

**$RC$ FEEDBACK OSCILLATORS**  This type of circuit, shown in Fig. 29-15, is used for audio oscillators. At audio frequencies, the $LC$ values for a tuned circuit would be too large. In Fig. 29-15 on the next page, three $RC$ networks are used to provide feedback. Each can provide a phase shift of 60°. Then $3 \times 60° = 180°$, which when added to the 180° for phase inversion in $Q1$ is able to provide positive feedback. Resistor $R_3$ is made variable to tune the oscillator for the required frequency. The circuit oscillates at the frequency that provides the required phase shift for positive feedback. Typical frequencies for the oscillator output are 20 Hz to 200 kHz.

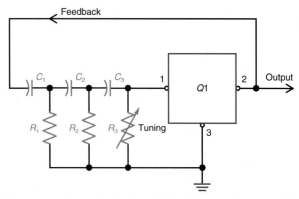

**FIG. 29-15** The ac equivalent circuit of an *RC* feedback oscillator for AF, with three *RC* networks in feedback circuit. The dc supply voltage is not shown.

**TEST-POINT QUESTION 29-4**

Answers at end of chapter.
**a.** Is a tapped coil for feedback used in the Hartley or the Colpitts oscillator?
**b.** Does an oscillator circuit use positive or negative feedback?
**c.** For the circuit in Fig. 29-12, if $C_1$ is reduced to 50 pF, what will the oscillator frequency be?

## 29-5 MULTIVIBRATORS

The multivibrator (MV) circuit is in a class by itself as an oscillator because it is so important as a pulse generator in digital electronics. In this application, the MV serves as a *reference clock* to synchronize the timing in a digital system for the switching of pulses. Instead of generating sine waves, the MV produces oscillations between the HIGH and LOW voltage levels at the output electrode. One cycle includes the time for a HIGH and a LOW. When each level takes the same time, the output is a symmetrical square wave. With unequal times, the circuit produces unsymmetrical pulses. The voltage levels oscillate between the HIGH and LOW levels because of the changes between conduction and cutoff in the MV circuit. This type is sometimes called a *relaxation oscillator* because of the periods of cutoff.

Figure 29-16 shows the block diagram of an ac equivalent circuit, without dc supply voltages, for a free-running MV circuit. This MV operates as an oscillator without the need for any input signal. The same circuit with more details is shown in Fig. 29-17. Referring to the block diagram in Fig. 29-16, note the following:

1. This MV circuit consists of two cross-coupled amplifier stages $Q1$ and $Q2$.
2. The MV oscillator is a pulse generator.
3. Operation can be over a wide range of audio or radio frequencies. The output is shown here at 1 MHz only as an example. The frequency is determined by the time constants in the *RC* coupling circuits.

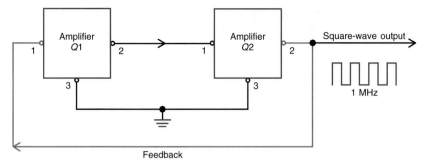

FIG. 29-16 Block diagram of MV circuit with two cross-coupled amplifier stages. The dc supply voltage is not shown.

The multivibrator is a very compact circuit, using transistors, diodes, resistors, and capacitors but without the need for any coils or transformers for feedback.

The cross-coupling means that the output of each stage drives the input of the other. Since each stage produces a phase inversion of 180°, the two inversions result in the positive feedback needed for oscillations.

The oscillations are in the conducting and cutoff conditions for $Q1$ and $Q2$ in Fig. 29-16. Conduction in a stage means it is turned ON with driving voltage at the input; the OFF means that the stage is not conducting because of cutoff voltage at the input. When one stage is ON, the other is OFF. In fact, it is the conduction in one stage that makes the other stage cut off because of the feedback. The ON–OFF times depend on the stage that is cut off. How long it is OFF is controlled by the $RC$ time constant in the input circuit. When it starts to conduct, the drop in its output voltage cuts off the other stage. The action is almost instantaneous, resulting in sharp changes in voltage for the output pulses.

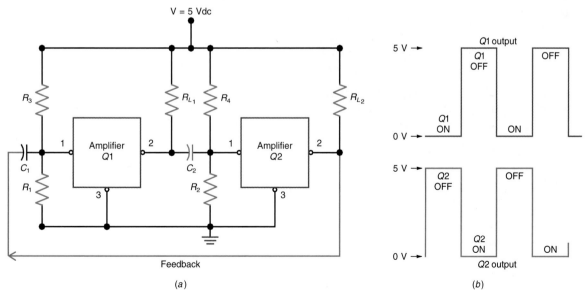

FIG. 29-17 (a) Details of a free-running MV circuit with dc operating voltage. (b) Waveform at output terminal 2 for $Q1$ above and $Q2$ below.

**MV CIRCUIT** More details can be seen from the schematic diagram in Fig. 29-17a. Note that the output electrode 2 of $Q1$ drives the input terminal of $Q2$ through the $R_2C_2$ coupling circuit. Also, in the feedback path shown at the bottom of the diagram, output terminal 2 of $Q2$ drives input terminal 1 of $Q1$ through the $R_1C_1$ coupling circuit. For the other components in the circuit, $R_{L_1}$ is the output load resistor for $Q1$ while $R_{L_2}$ has the same function for $Q2$. The output pulses are obtained from terminal 2 of either $Q1$ or $Q2$ but with opposite polarities, as shown in Fig. 29-17b. Resistors $R_3$ and $R_4$ provide dc bias for the input circuit of $Q1$ and $Q2$.

The drop in voltage at terminal 2 for the output from either $Q1$ or $Q2$ depends on conduction of current. When either stage is cut off, the output voltage at terminal 2 equals the dc supply of 5 V. The reason is that without any current, no $IR$ drop is produced across the output load resistor. When the stage conducts, the result is an $IR$ drop of 5 V across the load resistor, resulting in zero volts at terminal 2. Then the output drops from 5 V to 0 V.

For either $Q1$ or $Q2$, the input voltage cuts off the stage because of the drop in voltage at the output of the previous stage. How long the cutoff stage remains nonconducting depends on the $RC$ time constant of the input coupling circuit. When the cutoff stage starts conducting, it cuts off the other stage.

When the two stages have the same values of components, they are cut off for the same amount of time. The output voltage then is a symmetrical square wave, as shown in Fig. 29-17b. One cycle includes the period of cutoff and conduction for either stage. Output can be obtained from terminal 2 of either $Q1$ or $Q2$, but with opposite polarities. The reason is that one stage has HIGH output voltage when the other is LOW. When the two stages are not symmetrical, one is HIGH for a longer time than the other. Then the output consists of unsymmetrical pulses.

To summarize the action of each stage of the MV in producing pulses of voltage in the output:

OFF = no conduction = HIGH output voltage

ON = conduction = LOW output voltage

**TYPES OF MULTIVIBRATORS** The circuits in Figs. 29-16 and 29-17 show the type called an *astable MV,* meaning it is not stable in terms of the ON and

OFF states for either stage. This circuit is a free-running oscillator. It does not need any input signal.

Another type is the *bistable MV*. By the choice of component values, the MV circuit can be made to remain stable with either stage OFF and the other ON. It has two stable states. For instance $Q1$ can remain OFF with $Q2$ conducting, or for the opposite condition, $Q2$ can be OFF with $Q1$ conducting. The circuit stays in one of these states until an input pulse is applied to the OFF stage to make it conduct. This function of forcing the stage into conduction is called *triggering*. Then the ON stage drives the other stage into the OFF condition. The circuit then stays in this condition until another input pulse reverses the states. The name *flip-flop* is used for the bistable MV circuit to describe this idea of switching the ON–OFF states one way and then the opposite way by means of input trigger pulses.

A third type is the *monostable* or *one-shot MV*. This circuit has only one stable state. An input pulse is needed to trigger the OFF stage into conduction. Then the MV goes through one cycle of changes and back to its original condition. The original OFF stage is again in the nonconducting condition, ready for another trigger pulse.

**TEST-POINT QUESTION 29-5**

Answers at end of chapter.

Answer True or False.
**a.** An astable MV circuit is a free-running oscillator.
**b.** In Figs. 29-16 and 29-17, the amplifiers $Q1$ and $Q2$ must be conducting at the same time.
**c.** The flip-flop circuit is a bistable MV.
**d.** The output electrode has high output voltage from the dc supply when the stage is not conducting.

# 29-6 MODULATION

The process of modulation in electronic circuits can be defined as modifying the characteristics of one waveform with the variations in another signal. The purpose is to transmit the information in a desired signal as the variations of another waveform that is better for transmission. Common examples are amplitude modulation and frequency modulation used in radio and television broadcasting. In these applications, a basic RF waveform serves as the *carrier wave* for the modulating information. The frequency of the carrier wave must be much higher than the modulating frequencies for minimum distortion in the modulating process. In AM radio broadcasting, AF signals modulate an RF carrier wave.

The lower-frequency signal for the modulation is called the *baseband signal*. In AM and FM radio broadcasting, the baseband modulation is an audio signal. For television, a video signal is used as the baseband modulation.

The baseband modulation can vary three characteristics of the carrier wave. These are peak-to-peak amplitude, instantaneous frequency, and phase angle.

**AMPLITUDE MODULATION (AM)** Figure 29-18 illustrates this process. The carrier input to the modulator comes from an RF oscillator. For modulation, the baseband signal is from an audio amplifier. The modulator stage can be a diode or a nonlinear amplifier. Nonlinear amplification means that the output amplitudes are not exactly proportional to the input signal. Otherwise the two input signals would just be mixed in the output. In Fig. 29-18, the modulator stage amplifies the 1-MHz RF input, but the amount of gain is controlled by the audio modulating signal. Then the amplitudes of the RF output cycles vary in step with the variations in the audio modulating signal. The result is the amplitude-modulated signal shown for the output.

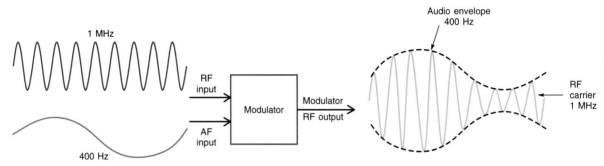

FIG. 29-18 Illustrating the process of amplitude modulation (AM). The 1-MHz RF carrier wave is modulated by the 400-Hz audio signal.

In the AM output signal, the RF peak-to-peak amplitudes have variations that correspond to the audio modulation. As shown in Fig. 29-18, the outline of varying amplitudes is the *modulation envelope.* The envelope is the same top and bottom or positive and negative, since the RF amplitude variations are symmetrical around the zero axis. Note that the envelope is shown as a dotted waveform because it is not actually a separate signal in itself. The reason is that the AM carrier signal has equal audio variations in opposite directions. The modulated signal must be detected by rectification to eliminate the symmetry and filtered in order to recover the audio modulation.

Important applications of amplitude modulation are the standard AM radio broadcast service and the picture signal for television. The AM radio service uses RF carrier frequencies spaced every 10 kHz in the band of 535 to 1605 kHz. Examples of the carrier frequencies for AM radio broadcast stations are 540, 880, 1010, and 1560 kHz. The 10-kHz spacing is needed for the bandwidth of $\pm 5$ kHz with an AF baseband signal of 50 to 5000 Hz.

In the television service, 6-MHz channels are used for broadcasting, starting with 54 to 60 MHz for channel 2. The 6-MHz bandwidth is needed for a video baseband signal of 0 to 4 MHz. The sound associated with the picture is broadcast as a separate FM signal.

**SIDEBANDS** A modulated signal needs more bandwidth than the carrier wave itself, in order to allow for the variations produced by the modulation. The necessary bandwidth is at least equal to the frequencies in the baseband signal, in a band just above and below the carrier frequency. As an example, for a 1000-kHz carrier modulated by 5 kHz, the extra bandwidth is $\pm 5$ kHz for a total of 10 kHz.

Then the modulated signal includes frequencies from 995 to 1005 kHz. The 10-kHz range of frequencies around 1000 kHz then become the sidebands of the 1000-kHz carrier wave. This example is illustrated in Fig. 29-19.

**PERCENT MODULATION**    This figure measures how much the carrier is changed by the baseband signal. In Fig. 29-18, the amplitudes are shown with approximately 50 percent modulation. With 100 percent modulation, the RF amplitudes go up to double the unmodulated level and down to zero. More than 100 percent modulation cannot be used in an AM signal because then part of the baseband signal would be missing while the carrier amplitude is zero.

**FREQUENCY MODULATION (FM)**    In this method, the instantaneous *frequency* of the carrier wave is made to vary in step with the variation of *voltage* in the baseband signal. There are many types of FM modulator circuits for this process. An example of an FM signal is shown in Fig. 29-20. Here the RF carrier frequency is 1 MHz or 1000 kHz. This value is the *center frequency*. Because of the modulation, though, the instantaneous frequency is made to deviate 75 kHz by the audio baseband signal. This change from center is the *frequency deviation*. In this example, the deviation is 75 kHz and the total swing is ±75 kHz or 150 kHz.

The peak values of the audio modulation produce the maximum frequency deviation of ±75 kHz. Smaller AF values produce less frequency deviation in the RF carrier wave. When the audio modulating voltage is at its zero value, the FM signal is at its center frequency. In summary, the amplitude values in the audio baseband signal are indicated by the instantaneous frequency values of the FM carrier signal. The information about the frequencies in the baseband signal is indicated by the rate at which the frequency swings are produced in the FM signal.

The frequency deviation of 75 kHz is chosen in Fig. 29-20 to illustrate the value that is the maximum allowed for 100 percent modulation in the commercial FM radio broadcast band. In an FM signal, the percentage of modulation is

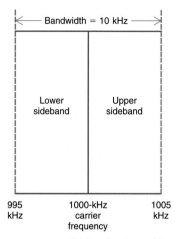

FIG. 29-19    Sidebands of a 1000-kHz carrier wave.

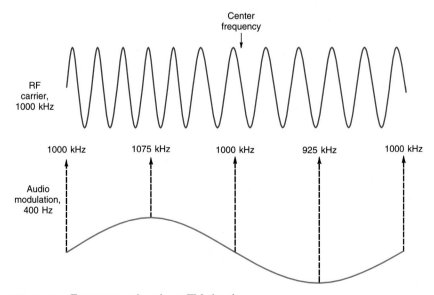

FIG. 29-20    Frequency swings in an FM signal.

in the amount of frequency change for the carrier wave. The 75-kHz deviation is for the loudest audio signal with the greatest amplitude in the baseband modulating signal. Lower values of audio amplitude result in less frequency deviation.

The value of 75 kHz for 100 percent modulation applies only to the FM radio broadcast band. In the FM sound signal in television broadcasting, the value is 25-kHz maximum deviation for 100 percent modulation. The FM range for the baseband signal is 50 to 15,000 Hz for FM radio and TV sound. It should be noted that in narrowband FM systems for communications radio, 5 kHz can be used for the maximum deviation, with a baseband audio signal of 300 to 3000 Hz.

The FM radio broadcast band is 88 to 108 MHz, with stations spaced every 200 kHz or 0.2 MHz for the center frequency of the transmitted carrier. Examples of carrier frequencies for FM broadcast stations are 92.1, 96.3, and 104.5 MHz. The 200-kHz spacing between carrier frequencies is needed to allow for a total frequency swing of 150 kHz, with a guard band of 25 kHz on each side to prevent interference between adjacent stations.

**PHASE MODULATION**   In this method, the instantaneous phase angle of the RF carrier wave is made to vary in step with the modulating voltage. Actually, the PM is similar to FM, since any change in frequency affects the phase. Therefore, phase modulation produces *equivalent FM* or *indirect FM*. However, one important factor is that a change in phase angle produces a larger change in the RF carrier frequency for higher audio modulating frequencies. This relation can be corrected, though, by a predistortion network for the audio modulation. Many FM transmitters use a phase-modulator circuit with a crystal-controlled oscillator for good frequency stability of the center frequency for the carrier wave.

**PULSE MODULATION**   This method is necessary with the pulses representing digital information. Typical systems of pulse modulation are:

PAM or pulse-amplitude modulation
PFM or pulse-frequency modulation
PWM or pulse-width modulation
PCM or pulse-code modulation

Pulse modulation is efficient because the carrier power is on for only the time of the pulses. However, greater bandwidth may be needed for the harmonic frequency components of sharp pulses.

### TEST-POINT QUESTION 29-6

Answers at end of chapter.
**a.** In Fig. 29-20, is 400 Hz the baseband signal or the carrier frequency?
**b.** Is the carrier frequency of 880 kHz in the AM or FM radio band?
**c.** In an FM signal, the carrier frequency deviates from a center frequency of 96,000 kHz to 96,050 kHz. Give the frequency deviation.
**d.** Do the sidebands of a modulated signal increase or decrease the necessary bandwidth?
**e.** Is phase modulation similar to AM or FM?

## 29-7 DIODE RECTIFIERS

In Fig. 29-21, the ac input to the anode (terminal 1) of a diode has positive and negative half-cycles. However, current can flow in a diode only during the time when the anode is positive. Therefore, only the positive half-cycles of the input at terminal 1 can produce output at terminal 2. The negative half-cycles of the input are just not used. The nonconducting diode then is practically an open circuit, without any conduction because the anode is negative.

Although the output at terminal 2 in Fig. 29-21 has fluctuations in the positive half-cycles, it is still a dc waveform. In terms of voltage, it has only one polarity. For the current, there is only one direction, whether we consider conventional current or electron flow. Actually, the variations in the fluctuating dc voltage can be smoothed out by filter capacitors and chokes.

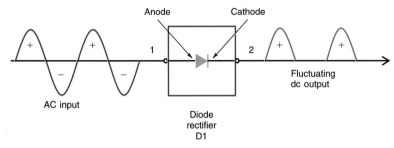

**FIG. 29-21** The diode rectifier converts its ac input to fluctuating dc output.

**THE DIODE AS A SWITCH**   A diode can operate in such a way that it really serves as an electronic switch. It can be ON with very low resistance because of conduction. Then the diode switch is closed. The resistance may be less than 1 Ω. Or the diode can be OFF because no current flows. Then the diode switch is open with infinitely high resistance. The ON–OFF conditions can be summarized as follows:

1.  Anode positive. Current flows. Diode is ON as a closed switch with very low $R$.
2.  Anode negative. No current. Diode is OFF as an open switch with very high $R$.

Even as a rectifier, the diode can be considered as a switch. The diode connects the output to the input only for the polarity that makes the anode positive. As a result, the output has only one polarity. This action is called *commutating,* meaning a process of switching in accordance with a specific polarity.

**HALF-WAVE POWER SUPPLY**   One of the most common applications of the diode rectifier is to provide dc supply voltage from the 60-Hz ac power line. The circuit is a dc power supply. Its function can very well be to supply the dc operating voltages needed for the amplifiers and oscillators on an electronic circuit board. In portable electronic equipment, the dc supply voltage is provided by batteries. For electronic equipment that operates from the ac power line, though, a dc power supply is necessary.

In Fig. 29-22, D1 is the diode rectifier. One diode is always a half-wave rectifier because only one-half of the ac input cycles are used for dc output. These waveforms were shown before in Fig. 29-21. However, the fluctuations in dc output are not shown in Fig. 29-22 because the ac ripple is almost completely eliminated by the filter capacitors $C_1$ and $C_2$ with the smoothing choke $L_1$. The frequency of the ac ripple component in the dc output is 60 Hz, with ac input at this frequency.

Operation of the power supply depends on the diode. When the anode is positive, current flows and the ac input voltage charges $C_1$ and $C_2$ for dc output voltage. Capacitor $C_1$ is at the input side of the filter. It can charge through D1 but without $L_1$. Capacitor $C_2$ is the output filter for $R_L$. When the anode of the diode is negative, no current flows.

In the diode input circuit, $R_1$ is a surge-limiting resistor. It prevents excessive current through the diode when the input filter capacitor $C_1$ is charging. The output resistor $R_L$ represents the combined resistance of all the load currents connected to the output of the dc power supply.

The dc output voltage may be higher than the rms value of the ac input voltage because the input filter capacitor $C_1$ can charge to the peak value. In Fig. 29-22, the dc output of 140 V is between 120 V as the rms value and 170 V as the peak value of the ac input. Remember that the peak of a sine wave equals 1.414 times the rms value. Then 120 V × 1.414 = 169.68 or approximately 170 V.

The value of dc output voltage, compared to the ac input voltage, depends on the amount of dc load current, represented by the 500-$\Omega$ value of $R_L$ in Fig. 29-22. Since the load current represents discharge of $C_1$ and $C_2$, less current means the capacitors can charge to a higher voltage. The value of 140 Vdc with $R_L$ of 500 $\Omega$ is typical for a load current $I_L$ of 280 mA. This $I_L$ can be calculated as

$$I_L = \frac{V_{dc}}{R_L} = \frac{140 \text{ V}}{500 \text{ } \Omega}$$

$$I_L = 0.28 \text{ A} = 280 \text{ mA}$$

In Fig. 29-22, the dc output voltage has positive polarity because it is taken from the diode cathode. In general, ac input at the anode produces positive dc

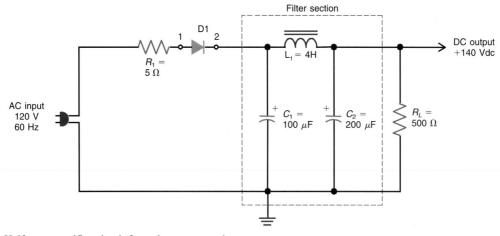

**FIG. 29-22**   Half-wave rectifier circuit for a dc power supply.

output at the cathode. Even though the dc voltage output makes the cathode positive, the ac input voltage makes the anode more positive to allow conduction. Basically, the cathode terminal in Fig. 29-22 must provide positive output because the output at terminal 2 is connected to the input at terminal 1 of the diode only when the source voltage at the input is positive.

For the opposite polarity of dc output, the ac input can be connected to the cathode for negative dc output at the anode. This circuit is sometimes called an *inverted power supply.* Both positive and negative polarities are commonly used as dc supply voltage for transistor circuits.

**FILTER SECTION**    Note that $C_1$ and $C_2$ in Fig. 29-22 are marked with a polarity sign, indicating they are electrolytic capacitors. The filter capacitors in a 60-Hz power supply are always electrolytics because of the high capacitance required. Typical values are 80 to 1000 $\mu$F. The filters are essentially shunt bypass capacitors that must have very low reactance at the frequency of the ac ripple, usually at 60 Hz or 120 Hz. Larger filter capacitors are needed with larger values of load current, corresponding to a smaller value of $R_L$. The filter $L_1$ is an iron-core choke used as a series component. It must have high reactance at the frequency of the ac ripple. In many cases, a series filter resistor of 100 to 1000 $\Omega$ may be used instead of $L_1$, for economy and to save space.

**TYPES OF POWER SUPPLIES**    The half-wave rectifier with one diode is the basic power supply but combinations are used with more diodes. Two diodes can be arranged in a *full-wave rectifier* circuit. It provides dc output for both cycles of the ac input. The advantage is that more load current can be supplied. Also, the frequency of the ac ripple on the output becomes 120 Hz instead of 60 Hz. The higher ripple frequency is easier to filter, allowing smaller values of $C$.

Other combinations include the voltage doubler with two diodes and the voltage tripler with three diodes. These circuits are used for higher dc output voltage with small values of load current.

**DIODE DETECTOR CIRCUIT**    Another important function of the diode rectifier is detecting a modulated signal to recover the modulation. Half-wave rectification is generally used. A detector is just a rectifier circuit for small values of signal voltage, usually about 1 to 10 V. Diodes for detectors are made of silicon (Si) or germanium (Ge). The Ge diodes have less resistance.

In Fig. 29-23, an AM signal is shown for input to the diode detector D1. The signal must be rectified for detection, in order to eliminate the symmetry in the modulation with positive and negative envelopes that are essentially the same. The load resistor $R_L$ has the rectified output voltage, which consists of half-cycles of the rectified carrier signal. The polarity of the rectified output does not matter in this application for an audio signal. In the rectified output across $R_L$, the amplitudes vary in accordance with the changes in the envelope of the AM signal. The individual cycles of rectified carrier signal are not shown, however, because they are eliminated by the bypass capacitor $C_1$. It has very low reactance for the RF carrier frequency but not for the lower frequencies in the audio modulation. As a result, the output of the AM detector circuit is the desired audio signal, coupled by $C_2$ to the next stage.

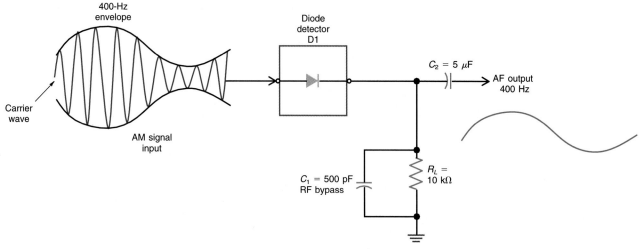

FIG. 29-23   Diode detector circuit to recover audio modulation in an AM signal.

Answers at end of chapter.

Answer True or False.
a. The anode must be positive for current in a diode.
b. The diode symbol shows the direction of electron flow.
c. One diode can be used as a half-wave rectifier.
d. An ac input at the anode of a diode results in positive dc output voltage.
e. Filter capacitors in a power supply are generally electrolytic capacitors.
f. A diode can be used for detection of an AM signal.

## 29-8 TROUBLESHOOTING THE DC SUPPLY VOLTAGE

Although electronic circuits are used mainly for ac signals, most troubles in operation result from incorrect dc supply voltages. Remember that transistors and IC chips need dc electrode voltages so that they can conduct current and function. No dc supply voltage means no ac output, even with ac signal input. Low values of dc voltage also can cause troubles in the operation of the circuit.

Very common is the problem of no dc supply voltage. If a supply voltage problem appears in battery-powered portable equipment, first try a new battery. An old battery may appear to have its normal voltage when measured with a dc voltmeter, but the output drops drastically with load current.

When a power supply is used, as illustrated in Fig. 29-24, the first step in troubleshooting is to check the dc output voltage to see if it is normal. The measurement can be made between point C in the diagram to chassis ground. A dc voltmeter should read 170 V at C and 140 V at D. Normal values are generally within ±10 percent. If the dc output voltage is not correct, then additional voltage and resistance tests can be made to isolate the trouble. The procedure may

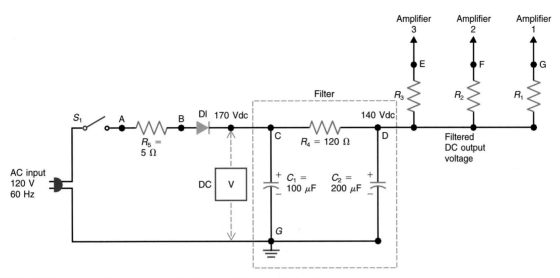

**FIG. 29-24** Half-wave rectifier power supply illustrated for troubleshooting procedures explained in the text.

seem complicated, but usually the purpose is simply to find a component that is either open or shorted.

Use a multimeter, either the digital or analog type, in its three functions:

1. *AC voltmeter.* To check the 60-Hz ac voltage input.
2. *Ohmmeter.* To check for an open circuit, short circuit, or incorrect $R$ value. A short circuit reads $0\,\Omega$. With an open circuit, the ohms reading is infinitely high.
3. *DC voltmeter.* Measure dc voltages in the output of the rectifier, from different points in the circuit to chassis ground. The negative lead of the voltmeter stays connected to ground and the positive lead is moved to the check points, assuming positive dc supply voltage.

**CHECKING THE AC VOLTAGE INPUT**   The meter function is set for ac voltages, on a range for 120 V. With power turned on by the switch $S_1$, measure from point A in Fig. 29-24 to G, across the ac power plug. Zero voltage here means no input power, probably because of a blown fuse or open circuit breaker in the power line. The switch $S_1$ could be defective, but this is not a common trouble. Also measure the ac input voltage at point B to G. If there is ac voltage at A but not at B, then $R_5$ must be open.

When the diode anode at point B has ac input voltage but there is no dc output voltage at point C at the diode cathode, either the diode is defective or the output circuit has a trouble.

**OHMMETER MEASUREMENTS**   Power is off, preferably with the plug disconnected. First measure the resistance of the dc output circuit, from point C to G, to see if it is shorted. A power supply with a short circuit in the dc output will produce excessive current in the ac input, if the power is turned on.

The ohmmeter is really the meter that finds the defective component that needs replacement. Measure across $R_5$ to see if it is $5\,\Omega$. An open here means no ac input voltage for the diode rectifier. Measure across $R_4$ for $120\,\Omega$. An open here means the dc output of 170 V at point C cannot be available as 140 V at D. There is normally an *IR* drop of 40 V across $R_4$. Also the resistance across $R_1$, $R_2$, and $R_3$ can be measured for the dc supply of each amplifier. If one of these resistors is open, this stage will not have dc operating voltage while the other stages do. All the amplifiers are in parallel for dc voltage from the power supply. Finally, and maybe most important, the ohmmeter can be used to check the diode rectifier D1 and the filter capacitors $C_1$ and $C_2$.

**CHECKING FILTER CAPACITORS WITH AN OHMMETER**   These capacitors are the electrolytic type with large values of *C*. First, discharge the capacitor with a jumper lead across its two terminals. Then check the resistance with the ohmmeter leads. The capacitor charging action from the battery in the ohmmeter should be very definite, starting with a very low *R* and backing off to a high value for its normal *R*. Typical values are 100 k$\Omega$ to 500 k$\Omega$, which is much lower than for other capacitor types. Check an electrolytic capacitor with the ohmmeter leads in one polarity and then reverse the leads. Use the higher readings. The following capacitor troubles can be indicated:

1.  No charging action with zero ohms of *R* means the capacitor is shorted.
2.  No charging action with a very high *R* means the capacitor is open.
3.  Very little charging action may mean lower *C* than normal.
4.  Too small a reading for the highest *R* may indicate the capacitor has leakage across its terminals.

For all these cases, the capacitor is defective and should be replaced. Install the new electrolytic in the same polarity as the old one. Also, with electrolytic capacitors, the replacement should have approximately the same voltage rating.

**TESTING DIODES WITH AN OHMMETER**   When the internal battery of the ohmmeter makes the diode anode positive, this polarity is called forward voltage because current can flow easily. The result is a low value of forward *R*. Typical values may be 10 to 1000 $\Omega$. For the opposite polarity, when the ohmmeter leads are reversed, the resistance of a silicon diode is almost infinitely high, practically an open circuit. Therefore, a good diode has very much more *R* with one polarity of the ohmmeter leads, compared with the opposite polarity. The ratio of reverse to forward *R* should be at least 100:1 and usually 1000:1. A defective diode is indicated by the following:

1.  The diode resistance is low in both directions. This diode has an internal short circuit.
2.  The diode resistance is very high in both directions. This diode has an open circuit, probably at the electrode leads.

In either case, the diode is defective and must be replaced. Install the new diode in the same polarity as the old one.

Several points about ohmmeters should be kept in mind. Many ohmmeters have a *low-ohms* position with very low battery voltage. Do *not* use this position for testing diodes because there is not enough voltage to produce forward current. Also, many multimeters have a *diode test* position. This test is not for *R* but provides normal forward voltage across the diode terminals, typically 0.6 to 0.7 V for silicon diodes. A higher or lower value indicates a defective diode.

**HUM** When the filters in a power supply do not have enough capacitance, the result is too much of the ac ripple component in the dc output voltage. The effect is excessive *hum* in the sound output from an audio system. With a half-wave power supply, the hum is at 60 Hz. In a full-wave supply, the sound of the hum at 120 Hz has a little higher pitch. The problem with hum voltage is that it becomes part of the ac signal in the amplifier circuits.

With a hum component in the video signal for a television picture, the effect is horizontal dark and light bars across the screen. They usually appear to roll slowly upward. With 60 Hz, the screen has one pair of hum bars; for 120 Hz two pairs of bars are produced.

**ISOLATION TRANSFORMER** A power-supply circuit like the one in Fig. 29-24 is *line-connected* or *nonisolated*. This type has one side of the dc output connected directly to the 60-Hz power line. The result can be dangerous; it can present the hazard of a severe electrical shock. For safety in testing such a supply, an isolation transformer should be used (Fig. 29-25). It has separate primary and secondary windings to isolate the ac input and dc output circuits. The turns ratio may be 1:1, or the transformer can have adjustable values of ac input for testing with different values of input voltage.

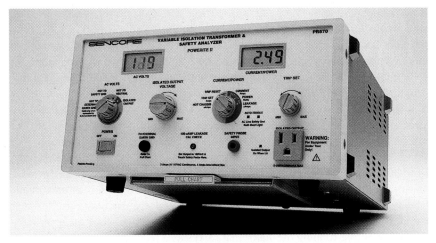

FIG. 29-25   Isolation transformer for safe bench work.

## TEST-POINT QUESTION 29-8

Answers at end of chapter.

Refer to the diagram in Fig. 29-24.
**a.** Which open resistor can cause no ac input voltage?
**b.** Which open resistor can cause no filtered dc output voltage?
**c.** Which components can cause excessive hum?
**d.** Which component converts the ac input to dc output?
**e.** Which open resistor can cause no dc supply voltage for amplifier 3?

# 29  SUMMARY AND REVIEW

- A sine wave of $V$ or $I$ is an analog signal with continuous variations that are proportional to changes in the information of the signal.
- Amplification means increasing the magnitude or amplitude. The voltage gain $A_V$ of an amplifier is given in Formula 29-1; current gain $A_I$ is defined by Formula 29-2, and power gain $A_P$ by Formula 29-3.
- Amplifiers in cascade have signal from the output of one stage driving the input of the next stage. The overall gain of the amplifiers equals the product of the individual gain values.
- Amplifiers use transistors and integrated circuit chips. These active electronic devices need dc supply voltage to provide current so that the ac signal can be amplified.
- Passive components in electronic circuits are resistors, capacitors, and inductors. Resistance is used to provide an $IR$ voltage drop. Capacitance is used for coupling and bypass capacitors. Inductance is used for chokes and transformers. Inductance and capacitance are combined for resonant circuits at radio frequencies.
- An electronic oscillator circuit is an amplifier with positive feedback to sustain oscillations. No input signal is necessary because the feedback from the output circuit provides the input. The oscillator generates its own ac output, converted from the power of the dc voltage supply. For special applications, AF oscillators and RF oscillators are used.
- RF feedback oscillators use tuned circuits to determine the oscillator frequency. Two main types are the Hartley and the Colpitts. A Hartley oscillator uses a tapped coil as an ac voltage divider for feedback. In the Colpitts circuit, a capacitive voltage divider is used.
- The multivibrator is a circuit to produce voltage output that oscillates between HIGH and LOW states. The astable MV is a free-running oscillator that serves as a pulse generator. The bistable MV is stable in either the HIGH or LOW state but can be triggered into the reverse state.
- Modulation means modifying the characteristics of one waveform in accordance with the variations in another signal that has a lower frequency. Common applications are in radio and television broadcasting where an RF carrier wave is modulated by audio or video signal. For amplitude modulation, the amplitude of the RF carrier varies with the modulation. In frequency modulation, the frequency of the RF carrier varies with the modulation.
- In a power supply, the 60-Hz ac input from the power line is converted to dc output, generally for dc supply voltage to amplifier circuits. Electrolytic filter capacitors are used to eliminate the ac ripple in the dc fluctuations of the rectified output. The basic half-wave rectifier circuit uses one diode. A full-wave rectifier uses two diodes.
- An ac ripple in the fluctuating dc output of a power supply is called hum, from the way it sounds in an audio system. In a television picture, the ripple produces horizontal hum bars across the screen. The hum frequency is 60 Hz for a half-wave rectifier or 120 Hz in a full-wave rectifier. Hum is generally caused by defective filter capacitors in the power supply.
- Troubles in a power supply are generally no dc output, insufficient dc output, and hum.

1. Is the transistor an active or inactive device?
2. Does a coupling capacitor have high or low reactance at the frequency of the signal?
3. Is the sine wave a digital or analog waveform?
4. With 0.05 V input and 5 V output, calculate the voltage gain.
5. For 600-$\mu$A input and 30-mA output, how much is the current gain?
6. Which component blocks dc voltage, $R$, $L$, or $C$?
7. Give the radio frequencies in the very high frequency (VHF) band.
8. Is a resistance load in the output circuit more likely to be used in an AF or RF amplifier?
9. Is a tapped coil for feedback used in the Hartley or Colpitts oscillator?
10. Which circuit can be used as a pulse generator, the multivibrator or the Hartley oscillator?
11. Which circuit is a free-running oscillator, the astable MV or the flip-flop?
12. True or False? The sidebands in a modulated signal increase the bandwidth?
13. Does the standard radio band of 535 to 1605 kHz use AM or FM?
14. Is the baseband signal for the picture in television a video or audio signal?
15. Is phase modulation similar to AM or FM?
16. In the symbol for a diode, does the arrow point to the anode or cathode?
17. In order for a diode to conduct, which of its electrodes must be more positive?
18. In a half-wave rectifier circuit, is the hum frequency 60 or 120 Hz?
19. How many diodes would be necessary for a full-wave rectifier circuit?
20. True or False? In Fig. 29-24, if the diode is open, the trouble will be no dc output.
21. In Fig. 29-24, if filter capacitor $C_2$ is open, will the trouble be no dc output or excessive hum?
22. True or False? In testing a diode with an ohmmeter, the reverse $R$ should be much higher than the forward $R$.
23. True or False? A filter capacitor that shows no charging action when tested with an ohmmeter should be replaced.

## QUESTIONS

1. Define active device and passive device for electronic circuits. Give two examples of each.
2. Give two differences between analog and digital signals. Would you consider the audio signal that drives a loudspeaker an analog or digital signal?
3. Draw the waveform of a pulse signal representing the binary values 1010.
4. Define the terms bit, byte, and word for digital signals.
5. What is meant by amplification of an ac signal?
6. Why is dc supply voltage needed in a transistor amplifier circuit for ac signals?
7. Compare the terms voltage gain and current gain.
8. Give the definitions for the gain values $A_V$, $A_I$, and $A_P$.
9. What does the term *in cascade* mean for amplifiers?
10. Give two methods of calculating the gain for amplifiers in cascade.
11. Give one difference and one similarity in a comparison of coupling and bypass capacitors.

12. State the frequencies in the VHF and UHF bands.
13. Show a sine wave for the signal waveform as a fluctuating dc voltage. Label the average dc axis and the peak-to-peak value of the ac component.
14. Which of the following components can block dc voltage: RF choke; AF coupling capacitor; RF bypass capacitor; load resistor?
15. Compare the frequencies in AF and RF signals. Why are *LC* tuned circuits generally used for RF signals rather than AF signals?
16. Compare a tuned RF amplifier stage with an audio amplifier.
17. Give a definition of an oscillator circuit.
18. What is meant by feedback? How would positive feedback be different from negative feedback?
19. What is the main difference between the Hartley and Colpitts oscillator circuits?
20. What is meant by an *RC* feedback oscillator?
21. Give a definition for the multivibrator (MV) oscillator.
22. What is the difference between the astable and bistable MV?
23. What is meant by modulation of an RF carrier wave?
24. Define AM, FM, and PM. Give two commercial applications.
25. What is meant by the baseband signal in the modulation process? Give two examples of baseband signals.
26. Define center frequency and the frequency deviation for an FM signal.
27. Draw the schematic symbol for a silicon diode and label the anode and cathode. Indicate the direction of hole current and electron flow.
28. What is meant by a rectifier? Why is the diode a good example? Give two applications of diode rectifiers.
29. Describe briefly how you can test a diode with an ohmmeter.
30. What is the purpose of a filter capacitor in a power supply?
31. What is the function of a dc power supply in electronic circuits?
32. What is a flip-flop circuit?
33. Describe briefly how you would test an electrolytic filter capacitor with an ohmmeter.
34. Draw the circuit of a power supply using a half-wave rectifier with filter. Give the function of each component.
35. For the circuit in Question 34, list three possible troubles caused by defective components.

## PROBLEMS

**ANSWERS TO ODD-NUMBERED PROBLEMS AT BACK OF BOOK.**

1. A transistor amplifier has input signal of 0.02 V and 400 $\mu$A p–p. The amplified output signal is 6 V and 36 mA, also p–p. Calculate the voltage gain $A_V$, current gain $A_I$, and power gain $A_p$.
2. With input signal of 600 $\mu$A p–p and a current gain of 80, calculate the peak-to-peak output current.
3. Three amplifier stages in cascade have current gain values of 50, 20, and 10 respectively. Calculate the total current gain.
4. In Prob. 3, when the input signal to the first stage is 200 $\mu$A p–p, how much is the output from the last stage?

5. Calculate the capacitive reactance $X_C$ of a 5-$\mu$F audio coupling capacitor at 200 Hz.
6. What size $C$ is needed for an RF bypass capacitor at 88 MHz?
7. For a filter capacitor in a power supply calculate $C$ needed for 8 $\Omega$ of $X_C$ at: (a) 60 Hz; (b) 120 Hz.
8. What $L$ is needed for an RF choke with 10 k$\Omega$ of $X_L$ at 1.6 MHz?
9. An RF feedback oscillator has an $LC$ circuit with 30 pF for $C$ and 320 $\mu$H for $L$. Calculate the oscillator frequency.
10. In Prob. 9, what $C$ is needed for an oscillator frequency of 995 kHz?
11. Refer to Fig. 29-26. What value of $R_L$ is needed for the 7 V at terminal 2 of $Q1$?
12. What value of $R_L$ would be needed in Fig. 29-26 if $I$ were 4 mA?

## CRITICAL THINKING

1. In Fig. 29-27, how much dc voltage exists at point A with respect to ground?
2. In Fig. 29-27, how much dc voltage exists at point A if the ground connection is removed from the center tap (C.T.) connection on the transformer secondary? Why?

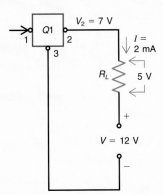

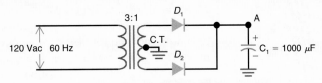

FIG. 29-27   Circuit for Critical Thinking Probs. 1 and 2.

FIG. 29-26   Circuit for Probs. 11 and 12.

## ANSWERS TO TEST-POINT QUESTIONS

29-1 a. T
  b. F
  c. T

29-2 a. 200
  b. 50
  c. 10,000
  d. 27,000

29-3 a. T
  b. T
  c. T
  d. F

29-4 a. Hartley
  b. positive
  c. 2 MHz

29-5 a. T
  b. F
  c. T
  d. T

29-6 a. baseband
  b. AM
  c. 50 kHz
  d. increase
  e. FM

29-7 a. T
  b. F
  c. T
  d. T
  e. T
  f. T

29-8 a. $R_5$
  b. $R_4$
  c. $C_1$ and $C_2$
  d. D1
  e. $R_3$

# CHAPTER 30

# TRANSISTOR AMPLIFIERS

More details of exactly how a transistor amplifies its input signal are analyzed in this chapter. In general, any amplifier operates by having a small input able to control more power in the output circuit. The dc supply for electrode voltages provides the power. As a result, amplifier circuits for ac signals operate with a combination of ac and dc values.

Another question in amplifiers is which electrodes are used for input and output signals. These connections determine the circuit configuration for the amplifier. The features of amplifiers are described here for NPN and PNP transistors and the field-effect transistor (FET). The amplifiers can be discrete units or part of an integrated circuit (IC) chip.

# CHAPTER OBJECTIVES

*Upon completion of this chapter, you should be able to:*

- *List* the three different amplifier configurations for bipolar transistors.
- *Define* class A, class B, and class C operation of a transistor amplifier and list the characteristics of each.
- *Analyze* a common-emitter amplifier in terms of biasing voltages and signal variations.
- *Define* the terms *alpha* ($\alpha$) and *beta* ($\beta$).
- *Explain* the term *transconductance* ($g_m$) as it relates to an FET amplifier.
- *Troubleshoot* a transistor amplifier circuit.

# IMPORTANT TERMS IN THIS CHAPTER

alpha characteristic ($\alpha$)
beta characteristic ($\beta$)
bias current
bias stabilization
common-base (CB) circuit
common-collector (CC) circuit

common-drain (CD) circuit
common-emitter (CE) circuit
common-gate (CG) circuit
common-source (CS) circuit
Darlington circuit

emitter bias
emitter follower
self-bias
source-follower
transconductance ($g_m$)

# TOPICS COVERED IN THIS CHAPTER

30-1  Circuit Configurations
30-2  Class A, B, or C Operation
30-3  Analysis of Common-Emitter (CE)
        Amplifier

30-4  Collector Characteristic Curves
30-5  Letter Symbols for Transistors
30-6  FET Amplifiers
30-7  Troubleshooting Amplifier Circuits

# 30-1 CIRCUIT CONFIGURATIONS

The circuit configuration specifies which electrodes in the amplifier are used for input and output signals. Actually, though, the configuration is named for the electrode that is the common return connection. The common electrode usually is the one that does not have any signal.

Since a PNP or NPN transistor is a triode with only three electrodes, there are only three possible configurations: the base common; the emitter common; or a common collector. Figure 30-1 shows these circuits. The general example in Fig. 30-1a would apply to any amplifier device with three terminals. For transistors specifically, the common-base circuit is in Fig. 30-1b, the common-emitter circuit is in Fig. 30-1c, and the common-collector circuit is in Fig. 30-1d. Although the common electrode is shown grounded here, it need not be connected to chassis ground. The main characteristics of these circuits are compared in Table 30-1. All the circuits have reverse voltage for the collector and forward bias for the emitter-base junction.

The common-emitter (CE) circuit is the one generally used for amplifiers because it has the best combination of current gain and voltage gain. However, each type of circuit has special features.

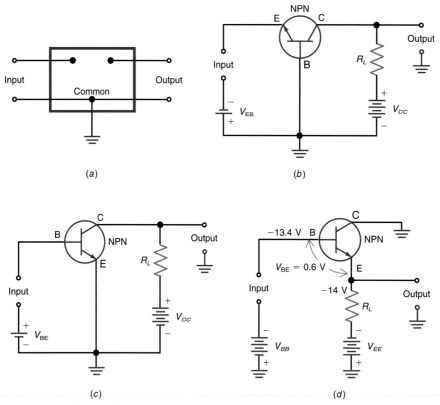

FIG. 30-1   Circuit configurations for amplifiers shown with NPN transistors. All polarities are reversed for PNP. (a) General case of a common terminal for two pairs of connections. (b) Common-base circuit. (c) Common-emitter circuit. (d) Common-collector circuit or emitter-follower.

## TABLE 30-1 COMPARISON OF CIRCUITS FOR JUNCTION TRANSISTORS

| CHARACTERISTIC | COMMON BASE (CB) | COMMON EMITTER (CE) | COMMON COLLECTOR (CC) |
|---|---|---|---|
| Signal into | Emitter | Base | Base |
| Signal out of | Collector | Collector | Emitter |
| Advantage | Stability | High gain | High $r_i$ |
| Phase inversion | No | Yes | No |
| Input resistance* $r_i$ | 20 $\Omega$ | 1000 $\Omega$ | 150 k$\Omega$ |
| Output resistance* $r_o$ | 1 M$\Omega$ | 50 k$\Omega$ | 80 $\Omega$ |

*Typical values of $r$ for small-signal transistor with $I_E$ of 1.5 mA.

**COMMON-BASE (CB) CIRCUIT**   In Fig. 30-1*b*, the input voltage is applied to the emitter, with respect to the grounded base. The amplified output is taken from the collector. Resistance $R_L$ is in series with the collector supply $V_{CC}$.

In the CB circuit, the emitter input has low resistance $r_i$ because $I_E$ is high. The output resistance $r_o$ for the collector is high because of the reverse voltage. Typical values for a small-signal transistor with $I_E$ of 1.5 mA are 20 $\Omega$ for $r_i$ and 1 M$\Omega$ for $r_o$. These values are for the internal resistance of each electrode to the common base.

The CB circuit is seldom used. It has no current gain from input to output because $I_C$ must be less than $I_E$. The voltage gain can be high, but the output is shunted by the low input resistance of the next stage. The only advantage of the CB circuit is that it has the best stability with an increase in temperature. The reason is that reverse leakage current from collector to base is not amplified in the CB circuit.

**COMMON-EMITTER (CE) CIRCUIT**   See Fig. 30-1*c*. Input voltage is applied to the base instead of to the emitter, which is now the grounded electrode. Note that the emitter is shown at the bottom of the schematic symbol. The input circuit here involves the small $I_B$ instead of $I_E$. As a result, the $r_i$ for the CE circuit is much higher than for the CB circuit. A typical value is 1000 $\Omega$ for $r_i$.

The output voltage is still taken from the collector with its $R_L$. A typical value for $r_o$ in the collector output circuit is 50 k$\Omega$.

In the input circuit, the forward bias $V_{BE}$ is applied to the base instead of the emitter. Note the polarity. Positive $V_{BE}$ to the P base corresponds to negative $V_{EB}$ at the negative emitter. Both are forward-bias voltages, with the polarity the same as the N or P electrode.

Furthermore, the positive $V_{BE}$ at the base for forward bias uses the same voltage polarity as positive $V_{CC}$ for reverse voltage at the N collector. This feature allows the practical convenience of using one voltage supply for both forward bias in the input and reverse bias in the output.

The CE circuit has current gain because $I_C$ is much larger than $I_B$. The voltage gain is the same as for the CB circuit. With a higher $r_i$, however, the CE circuit can be used in cascaded amplifiers where the collector output of one stage drives the base input of the next. The CE circuit is the amplifier generally used

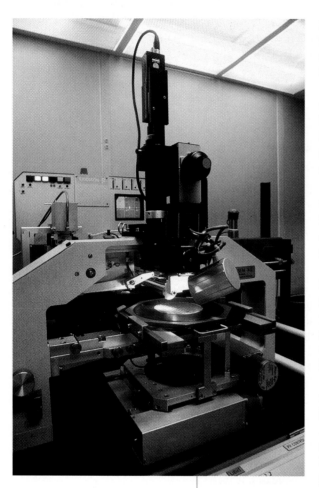

for transistors, therefore, because it has the best combination of voltage gain and current gain. The disadvantage is that reverse leakage current is amplified in the CE circuit, but bias stabilization methods can be used.

Only the CE amplifier inverts the polarity of signal voltage. This phase inversion of 180° is neither good nor bad, but just a result of the circuit connections. When the base input signal increases the forward voltage, the collector voltage of the same polarity decreases because of the voltage drop across $R_L$.

**COMMON-COLLECTOR (CC) CIRCUIT**    See Fig. 30-1$d$. Signal input is applied to the base, as in the CE circuit. However, the collector is grounded, instead of the emitter. Therefore, the emitter has the $R_L$ for the output signal.

Now there are two questions for the electrode voltages: how to apply reverse voltage for the grounded collector and forward bias for the base. Note that the emitter is at $-14$ V with respect to chassis ground. The collector is at chassis ground. In effect, the collector is connected to the positive side of the emitter supply voltage. This makes the N collector positive with respect to the emitter, as reverse voltage for $V_{CE}$.

For forward voltage, the base must be more positive than the emitter. In this example $V_E$ is $-14$ V. Therefore $V_B$ is made $-13.4$ V. The actual bias $V_{BE}$ then is $+0.6$ V.

In the CC circuit, the input circuit has high $r_i$. A typical value is 150 k$\Omega$. The output in the emitter circuit has low $r_o$ of about 80 $\Omega$. Note that for the CC circuit, the input resistance is high and output resistance is low, compared with low $r_i$ and high $r_o$ for the other circuits.

There is no voltage gain in the CC circuit because the output signal across $R_L$ in the emitter circuit provides negative feedback to the base input circuit. However, there is appreciable current gain.

The name *emitter-follower* is generally used for the CC circuit. The output signal at the emitter follows the polarity of the input signal at the base. The emitter-follower circuit is often used for impedance matching, from a high-impedance source to a low-impedance load. The circuit also provides isolation between a load in the emitter circuit and a source in the base circuit.

**DARLINGTON PAIR**    This circuit consists of two emitter followers connected in cascade. The two stages are usually in one package, with dc coupling internally and just three external leads. The package provides higher input resistance and more current gain than just one stage.

**TEST-POINT QUESTION 30-1**

Answers at end of chapter.
**a.** Which circuit has the most gain?
**b.** Which circuit has input signal to the base and output from the collector?
**c.** Give another name for the CC circuit.

# 30-2 CLASS A, B, OR C OPERATION

The amplifier class of operation is defined by the percentage of the input signal that is able to produce output current. In other words, is any part of the input cycle cut off in the output? The class of operation depends on two amplitudes: (1) the dc bias compared with the cutoff value and (2) the peak ac signal compared with the dc bias.

The input and output waveforms for class A, B, and C amplifiers are illustrated in Fig. 30-2. The output current is labeled $I_O$. This is collector current for junction transistors, or drain current for the FET. The class of operation determines the power efficiency and how much distortion of the signal may be produced by the amplifier.

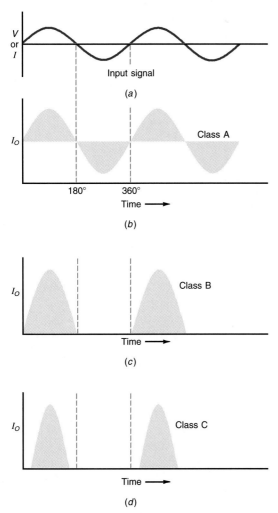

FIG. 30-2 Class of operation for amplifiers in terms of output current $I_O$. (a) Cycles of sine-wave ac input signal. (b) Class A with $I_O$ for full cycle of 360°. (c) Class B with $I_O$ for half-cycle of 180°. (d) Class C with $I_O$ for less than 180°, typically 120°.

**CLASS A**    The output current $I_O$ flows for the full cycle of 360° of input signal. This operation is shown by the waveform in Fig. 30-2b. An audio amplifier stage operates this way to follow the signal variations without too much distortion.

For class A operation, the dc bias allows an average $I_O$ of about one-half the maximum value. Then the ac signal swings $I_O$ around that middle value. The output current $I_O$ can vary up to its maximum value, and close to zero, but is never cut off.

**CLASS B**    The $I_O$ flows for 180°, or approximately one-half of the input cycle, as shown in Fig. 30-2c. The dc bias is at or near the cutoff value. $I_O$ is at or close to zero, then, without any signal input. However, the positive half-cycle of signal can swing $I_O$ up to its maximum value. The negative half-cycles of input signal are cut off in the output, because $I_O$ then is zero. Class B operation requires more dc bias and more ac signal drive than class A.

Class B operation with a single stage corresponds to half-wave rectification of the ac signal input. However, two stages can be used to provide opposite half-cycles of the signal in the output.

**CLASS C**    In Class C operation the output current $I_O$ flows for less than one-half the input cycle. Typical operation is 120° of $I_O$ during the positive half-cycle of input, as shown in Fig. 30-2d. This result is produced by doubling the class B bias and using twice as much ac signal drive. Because of its high efficiency, class C operation is used for tuned RF power amplifiers.

**CHARACTERISTICS OF EACH CLASS**    Which class of operation is used for an amplifier depends on the requirements for minimum distortion, maximum ac power output, and efficiency. The degree by which the output signal waveshape differs from the input signal waveshape is known as distortion. The ac power output is signal output. Efficiency is the ratio of ac power output to the dc power dissipated at the output electrode of the amplifier.

In class A operation, distortion is lowest, but so also are ac power output and efficiency. Typical values are less than 1 to 5 percent distortion and an efficiency of 5 to 25 percent. At the opposite extreme, class C operation offers the highest efficiency, of about 90 percent, and allows the greatest ac power output but with the most distortion. Class B operation lies between A and C in distortion, power, and efficiency.

With audio amplifiers, class A must be used in a single stage for minimum distortion. Otherwise, the sound would be garbled. Also, an RF stage amplifying an amplitude-modulated signal must operate class A for minimum distortion of the modulation. In general, most small-signal amplifiers operate class A.

The reason for low efficiency in class A operation is that the middle value of $I_C$ flows all the time, with or without ac signal input and for weak or strong signals. As a result, the dc power dissipation at the output electrode is high. Furthermore, relatively little ac signal drive can be applied without exceeding the cutoff voltage.

Class B amplifiers are usually connected in pairs, each stage of which supplies opposite half-cycles of the signal input. Such a circuit is called a *push-pull amplifier.* The results approximate the low distortion of class A, but more drive can be used for more ac power output with higher efficiency. The push-pull circuit arrangement is often used for audio power output to a loudspeaker.

Class C operation is generally used for RF amplifiers with a tuned circuit in the output. Then the *LC* circuit can provide a full sine-wave cycle of output for each pulse of $I_O$. Class C amplifiers have high efficiency because the average $I_O$ is very low compared with the peak signal amplitude. The result is relatively low dc power dissipated at the output electrode compared with the amount of ac power output. In addition, a pulse clipper circuit operates as a class C amplifier.

**TEST-POINT QUESTION 30-2**

Answers at end of chapter.

Give the class of operation for the following:
a. Output current flows for the full ac cycle of the input signal.
b. Output current flows for one-half the input cycle.
c. Output current flows for 120° of the ac input cycle.
d. With a silicon NPN transistor, cutoff is 0.5 V, the dc bias is 0.6 V and the ac signal is ±50 mV.

# 30-3 ANALYSIS OF COMMON-EMITTER (CE) AMPLIFIER

Typical values of $V_{BE}$ are in tenths of a volt for a junction transistor. The required bias at the base for a class A amplifier is 0.6 to 0.7 V for Si or 0.2 to 0.3 V for Ge. Class A operation means that the amplifier conducts current for 360° of the signal cycle, for minimum distortion. Furthermore, the maximum ac input signal without overload distortion is ±0.1 V. These values are summarized in Table 30-2. Note that 0.1 V is 100 mV.

Without any forward bias a junction transistor is cut off by its own internal barrier potential. The cut-in voltage in the first column of Table 30-2 is the lowest $V_{BE}$ that allows appreciable $I_C$.

The saturation voltage in the second column of Table 30-2 is the highest $V_{BE}$ that allows it to produce proportional changes in $I_C$. At saturation, the maximum $I_C$ does not increase with an increase of forward voltage.

The input voltages listed in Table 30-2 apply to all junction transistors, regardless of size and power rating. However, the difference is in the amount of base current $I_B$ and collector current $I_C$. As an example, a small-signal transistor may have $I_B$ of 60 $\mu$A with $V_{BE}$ of 0.6 V at the input, for $I_C$ output of 3 mA. In a medium-power transistor $I_B$ could be 20 mA for the same $V_{BE}$ of 0.6 V, to produce $I_C$ of 1 A.

| TABLE 30-2 | INPUT VOLTAGES $V_{BE}$ AT 25°C FOR JUNCTION TRANSISTORS | | | |
|---|---|---|---|---|
| | CUT-IN VOLTAGE | SATURATION VOLTAGE | ACTIVE REGION | AVERAGE BIAS VOLTAGE |
| Ge | 0.1 | 0.4 | 0.1–0.4 | 0.2–0.3 |
| Si | 0.5 | 0.8 | 0.5–0.8 | 0.6–0.7 |

**CIRCUIT COMPONENTS** The transistor amplifier itself is usually labeled $Q$, as for $Q1$ in Fig. 30-3. The 2.2-k$\Omega$ $R_L$ is the collector load. It is in series with the positive $V_{CC}$ of 12 V for reverse collector voltage on the NPN transistor.

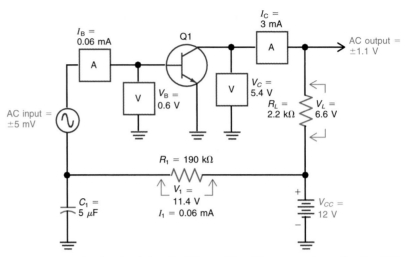

**FIG. 30-3** Example of a circuit for the CE amplifier. The meters shown for $V$ and $I$ indicate average dc values. This circuit is analyzed in the text.

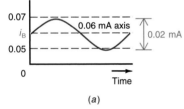

(a)

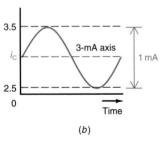

(b)

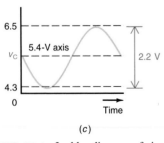

(c)

**FIG. 30-4** Ladder diagram of signal waveforms for the circuit in Fig. 30-3. (a) Base current $i_B$. (b) Collector current $i_C$. (c) Collector output voltage $v_C$.

One supply voltage is used for both collector and base in the CE circuit, as positive base bias and positive collector voltage are needed. However, the collector voltage is too high for base bias. Therefore, the 190-k$\Omega$ $R_1$ is connected in series as a voltage-dropping resistor for the base.

The required forward-bias voltage for Si is 0.6 V. The corresponding bias current for this transistor is taken as 60 $\mu$A or 0.06 mA, as an example. The voltage drop across $R_1$ is 0.06 mA $\times$ 190 k$\Omega$ = 11.4 V. Then $12 - 11.4 = 0.6$ V remains for $V_{BE}$ as forward voltage for the base.

The bypass capacitor $C_1$ allows the ac input signal voltage to vary the base current without the series resistance of $R_1$. Then very small changes of input voltage can produce appreciable changes in base current. We are assuming an ac input of $\pm 5$ mV for the base input signal, or 10 mV p–p.

**SIGNAL VARIATIONS** The input signal of base current $i_B$ is shown in Fig. 30-4a. This waveform shows $i_B$ varies by 10 $\mu$A above the 60-$\mu$A bias axis, up to the peak of 70 $\mu$A. On the down side, $i_B$ decreases by 10 $\mu$A, from 60 to 50 $\mu$A. Positive signal voltage in the forward direction increases $i_B$, while negative signal voltage reduces $i_B$. The peak-to-peak signal in $i_B$ then is $70 - 50 = 20$ $\mu$A, or 0.02 mA.

The variations in $i_B$ cause corresponding variations in $i_C$, as shown in the waveform in Fig. 30-4b. Let the current transfer ratio be 50, meaning that this is the ratio of collector output current to base input current. Then the $i_B$ variations of $\pm 10$ $\mu$A swing $i_C$ by $50 \times 10 = 500$ $\mu$A or 0.5 mA.

The average dc level for $I_C$ is taken as 3 mA for a small-signal low-power transistor. Then the ac signal swing of $i_C$ is $\pm 0.5$ mA above and below the axis of 3 mA. In $i_C$, the p–p signal for the output current is $3.5 - 2.5 = 1$ mA.

The signal changes in $i_C$ produce variations in the voltage drop $i_C R_L$ across the collector load for the output circuit. As a result, $V_C$ varies because it is the difference between $V_{CC}$ of the supply and the voltage drop across $R_L$. As a formula,

$$\blacktriangleright \quad V_C = V_{CC} - i_C R_L \qquad\qquad (30\text{-}1)$$

For example, with an average level of 3-mA $I_C$ through the 2.2-k$\Omega$ $R_L$, this voltage drop is $0.003 \times 2200 = 6.6$ V. Subtracting 6.6 V from 12 V, the difference is 5.4 V for the average $V_C$.

The variations of $V_C$ are in the waveform in Fig. 30-4c. This shows the amplified signal output voltage. The average dc level or axis is 5.4 V. When $i_B$ increases, the $v_C$ decreases to 4.3 V because of a larger voltage drop across $R_L$. On the next half-cycle $i_C$ decreases. Then less voltage across $R_L$ allows $v_C$ to rise to 6.5 V. Then peak-to-peak signal voltage is $6.5 - 4.3 = 2.2$ V for $v_C$ at the collector. This amplified output voltage is 180° out of phase with the signal input voltage at the base.

The basis for Formula (30-1) is just the fact that $R_L$ and the collector-emitter circuit of the transistor are in series with each other as a voltage divider from the high side of $V_{CC}$ to chassis ground. The equivalent collector circuit is shown in Fig. 30-5 with $R_L$ as the external load resistor. The $R_Q$ is the internal resistance of the transistor conducting current from emitter to collector. In this example, $Q_1$ is conducting 3 mA, resulting in 5.4 V for $V_{CE}$ in the divider with $V_L$. Note that $V_Q$ is the same as $V_{CE}$. These values are $12 - 6.6 = 5.4$ V for $V_Q$. Voltages $V_C$ and $V_{CE}$ are the same here because the emitter is grounded.

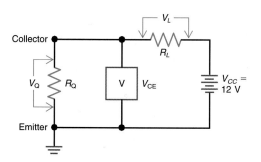

FIG. 30-5   Equivalent voltage divider circuit for $R_Q$ in series with $R_L$ across the supply voltage $V_{CC}$.

**TYPICAL BASE BIAS VOLTAGE**   In a class A amplifier with collector output current for the full signal cycle, the general requirements are to have the value of $I_C$ that allows the voltage drop $I_C R_L$ to equal about one-half the dc supply voltage. Then the average dc collector voltage $V_C$ is also approximately $V_{CC}/2$. *The base bias $V_{BE}$ is made the value, around 0.6 to 0.7 V, that produces the required $I_C$ with the specified $R_L$.*

**GAIN**   To calculate the voltage amplification, or gain, with peak-to-peak values for Fig. 30-3,

$$\blacktriangleright \quad A_V = \frac{V_{\text{out}}}{V_{\text{in}}} \qquad\qquad (30\text{-}2)$$

$$A_V = \frac{2.2 \text{ V}}{0.01 \text{ V}} = 220$$

The current amplification is

$$A_I = \frac{i_{out}}{i_{in}}$$
(30-3)

$$A_I = \frac{i_C}{i_B} = \frac{1 \text{ mA p–p}}{0.02 \text{ mA p–p}} = 50$$

The power amplification is

$$A_P = A_V \times A_I$$
(30-4)

$$A_P = 220 \times 50 = 11,000$$

Since the CE circuit has both voltage and current amplification, the power gain is high. Power gain is desirable because it means the voltage output can drive a low-impedance circuit without too much loss of voltage amplification.

**CASCADED STAGES**   As shown in Fig. 30-6, the amplifiers $Q1$, $Q2$, $Q3$, and $Q4$ are in cascade. With CE amplifiers, the collector output of one stage drives the base input of the next. It is important to realize that the voltage amplification need not build up the signal to a level greater than $\pm 0.1$ V. This is the maximum signal swing without distortion for junction transistors. However, the cascaded stages provide enough signal current to drive the base of the output stage $Q4$.

**FIG. 30-6**   Amplifier stages in cascade. Drive increases for each successive stage.

As an example, suppose that $Q4$ is a power output stage to drive a loudspeaker that needs 5 A as the load. With an average level of 5 A for $I_C$ in $Q4$, its $I_B$ would be of the order of 250 mA or 5 A/20, with a current transfer ratio of 20. This $I_B$ of 250 mA can be supplied by the collector output of the driver stage $Q3$. Similarly, $Q3$ with an $I_C$ of 250 mA would have $I_B$ of 12.5 mA with a current ratio of 20. Also, with a current ratio of 50 for $Q2$, its $I_B$ would be 12.5 mA/50 = 0.25 mA, or 250 $\mu$A. This drive for base current in $Q3$ can be provided by the collector current of the input stage $Q1$. In summary, each of the cascaded amplifiers increases the signal current enough to drive the next stage.

### TEST-POINT QUESTION 30-3

Answers at end of chapter.
**a.** In Fig. 30-3, how much is the base-bias $V_{BE}$?
**b.** In Fig. 30-5, how much is $V_Q$ with $V_L$ of 5.5 V?
**c.** In Fig. 30-4, how much is the peak-to-peak signal output in $i_C$?
**d.** In Fig. 30-4, how much is the peak-to-peak signal input for $i_B$?

## 30-4 COLLECTOR CHARACTERISTIC CURVES

The curves in Fig. 30-7 show the volt-ampere characteristics for the collector. $I_C$ on the vertical axis is plotted against $V_{CE}$ on the horizontal axis. Each curve is for a specific $I_B$. The different curves specify how $I_C$ increases with increases in $I_B$.

The characteristic curves are provided by the manufacturer in a transistor manual or application notes. For the CE circuit, the collector curves are for different values of $I_B$; for a CB circuit, they would be for different values of $I_E$.

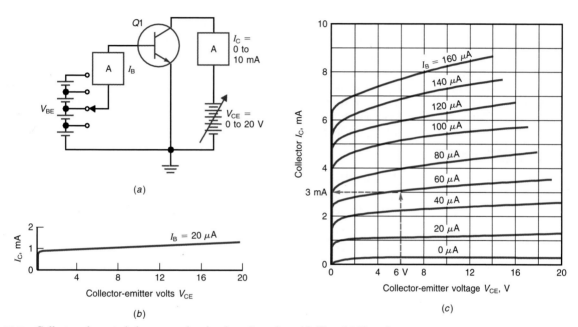

**FIG. 30-7** Collector characteristic curves showing how $I_C$ varies with $V_{BE}$. (*a*) Experimental CE circuit to determine values. The circuit does not have any load. (*b*) A single collector curve for a single value of 20 $\mu$A for $I_B$. (*c*) Family of collector curves for different values of $I_B$. The dashed arrows indicate the example in the text.

**AN EXPERIMENTAL CIRCUIT FOR $I_C$**    Figure 30-7*a* is a circuit in which the transistor voltages can be varied experimentally in order to determine the effect on $I_C$. One value of base voltage is used for a specific $I_B$ while $V_{CE}$ is varied to see how much $I_C$ changes. Then the base voltage is set for another value of $I_B$ and $V_{CE}$ is varied again while $I_C$ is measured. The $V_{CE}$ and $I_C$ values for each $I_B$ setting are used for one curve.

The collector and base voltages are labeled $V_{CE}$ and $V_{BE}$ for the general case of a potential difference with respect to emitter. However, they are the same as $V_C$ and $V_B$ with the emitter grounded.

Note that no load resistance is used for the experimental circuit of Fig. 30-7*a*. Also, there is no signal input or output. The circuit is not an amplifier for signal voltage; it is only an experimental arrangement for measuring the volt-ampere characteristics of the transistor itself without any load.

**ONE TYPICAL CURVE**    The results for one value of $I_B$ at 20 $\mu$A are shown by the curve in Fig. 30-7$b$. $I_C$ rises from 0 to 1 mA when $V_C$ is increased from 0 to 1 V, approximately, but there is only a slight rise in $I_C$ to about 1.3 mA when $V_C$ is further increased to 20 V. The reason for the small second increase in $I_C$ is that the increase is limited by the value of $I_B$ permitted by the forward voltage at the base junction. For more $I_C$, the transistor needs more base current. As an example of reading values from the curve, $I_C$ is exactly 1 mA when $V_{CE}$ is 4 V.

**THE FAMILY OF CURVES**    The results of different values of base current are shown by the family of collector characteristics in Fig. 30-7$c$. Each curve represents the relationship of $I_C$ and $V_C$ for a specific $I_B$. Note that the curve for 20 $\mu$A of $I_B$ is the same as Fig. 30-7$b$.

There are several curves, but only one is read at a time. As an example, arrows are shown for the fourth curve up from the bottom, for $I_B$ of 60 $\mu$A. The values there are 3 mA of collector current with 6 V at the collector.

The family of curves really shows how the values of $I_C$ and $I_B$ are related for the same collector voltage. If the vertical arrow in Fig. 30-7$c$ is extended up to the next curve, for 80 $\mu$A of $I_B$, the $I_C$ reading will increase to slightly less than 4 mA with the same 6 V at the collector. For the opposite change, when $I_B$ decreases to 40 $\mu$A, the $I_C$ is reduced to 2.2 mA, all with 6 V for $V_{CE}$.

**BETA ($\beta$) CHARACTERISTIC**    This specification for a junction transistor indicates the amount of current gain in the common-emitter circuit, since $\beta$ compares the collector current $I_C$ to the base current $I_B$. Specifically,

$$\beta = \frac{I_C}{I_B} \tag{30-5}$$

As an example, when 60 $\mu$A of $I_B$ produces 3 mA of $I_C$,

$$\beta = \frac{I_C}{I_B} = \frac{3 \text{ mA}}{60 \text{ }\mu\text{A}} = \frac{3000 \text{ }\mu\text{A}}{60 \text{ }\mu\text{A}}$$

$$\beta = 50$$

There are no units for $\beta$ because it is a ratio of two currents. Note that 3 mA here is converted to 3000 $\mu$A. This example gives the static or dc value of $\beta$. The dynamic or ac value is calculated for changes in the current values. Then the ac value of beta gives the current gain in the CE circuit.

The $\beta$ value can be used two ways to relate $I_C$ and $I_B$:

$$I_C = \beta \times I_B$$

or

$$I_B = \frac{I_C}{\beta}$$

For instance, when $I_B$ is 2 mA and $\beta$ equals 90, then the $I_C$ is $2 \times 90 = 180$ mA. Typical values of $\beta$ are 40 to 300 for small-signal transistors and 10 to 30 for power transistors.

**ALPHA ($\alpha$) CHARACTERISTIC**   This ratio compares collector current to emitter current:

▶  $$\alpha = \frac{I_C}{I_E} \qquad\qquad (30\text{-}6)$$

As an example, for a transistor with 3 mA of $I_C$ and 3.06 mA of $I_E$, the calculations are

$$\alpha = \frac{I_C}{I_E} = \frac{3 \text{ mA}}{3.06 \text{ mA}}$$

$$\alpha = 0.98 \qquad \text{approximately}$$

There are no units for $\alpha$ because it is a ratio of two currents. The $\alpha$ must always be less than 1 because $I_C$ cannot be larger than $I_E$. The value of 0.98 is typical for $\alpha$.

---

### TEST-POINT QUESTION 30-4

Answers at end of chapter.
**a.** What is the $I_B$ for the curve in Fig. 30-7b?
**b.** From the family of curves in Fig. 30-7c, what is $I_C$ for 8 V of $V_{CE}$ and 140 mA of $I_B$?
**c.** Calculate $\beta$ for 80 $\mu$A of $I_B$ and 4 mA of $I_C$.
**d.** The $I_B$ is 80 $\mu$A and $\beta$ is 100. Calculate $I_C$.

## 30-5 LETTER SYMBOLS FOR TRANSISTORS

Because of the combination of an ac component on a dc axis, it is important to distinguish between the different voltages and currents in a transistor amplifier. In general, there are letter symbols for three kinds of values:

1. Average dc values
2. Instantaneous values of the fluctuating dc waveform
3. Values for the ac signal variations alone

All these are summarized in Table 30-3, which shows how the various letters are used to indicate the different voltages or currents.

The capital letters $V$ and $I$ and their subscripts are used for average dc values. The subscript also is a capital letter. An example is $V_C$ for average dc collector voltage.

Double subscripts that are repeated, as in $V_{CC}$, indicate the supply voltage that does not change. Also, $V_{EE}$ is used to denote the dc supply voltage for the emitter.

The small letters $v$ and $i$ are used for instantaneous values that vary with the fluctuating dc waveform. As an example, $v_C$ is an instantaneous value of the varying dc collector voltage.

A small letter in the subscript indicates the ac component.

## TABLE 30-3   LETTER SYMBOLS FOR TRANSISTORS

| SYMBOL | DEFINITION | NOTES |
|---|---|---|
| $V_{CC}$ | Collector supply voltage | Same system for collector currents; also for base or emitter voltages and currents. Also applies to drain, gate, and source of field-effect transistors |
| $V_C$ | Average dc voltage | |
| $v_c$ | AC component | |
| $v_C$ | Instantaneous value | |
| $V_c$ | RMS value of ac component | |
| $I_{CBO}$ | Collector cutoff current, emitter open | Reverse leakage current |
| $BV_{CBO}$ | Breakdown voltage, collector to base, emitter open | Ambient temperature $T_A$ is 25°C |
| $h_{fe}$ | Small-signal forward-current transfer ratio in CE circuit | Same as ac $\beta$ for CE circuit |

The rms value, or effective value, of the ac component is a capital letter. However, its subscript is a small letter. As an example, $V_c$ is the rms value of the ac component of collector voltage.

At the bottom of Table 30-3, additional letter symbols for transistors are listed. For example, $I_{CBO}$ denotes reverse leakage current. The letter $O$ shows which electrode is open when leakage current between the other two electrodes is measured. Therefore, $I_{CBO}$ is leakage current between collector and base with the emitter open.

In the symbol $h_{fe}$, the $h$ stands for *hybrid parameters*, which are combinations of voltage and current ratios in the forward and reverse directions. In the subscripts, $f$ indicates a forward characteristic from the base input to collector output. The $e$ indicates the common-emitter circuit. The symbol $h_{fe}$ is used often, therefore, because its forward current-transfer ratio is the same as the small-signal or ac $\beta$ of the transistor in the CE circuit.

---

### TEST-POINT QUESTION 30-5

Answers at end of chapter.

Give the letter symbol for the following:
**a.** Collector dc supply voltage.
**b.** Instantaneous value of collector voltage.
**c.** The ac component of base current.

## 30-6 FET AMPLIFIERS

Just like the configurations with junction transistors, there are three types of circuit connections for the FET. As shown in Fig. 30-8, these are:

1. *Common-source (CS) circuit.* This circuit corresponds to the common-emitter with junction transistors. With an FET, input signal is applied to

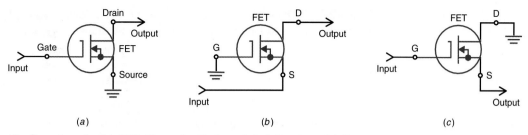

FIG. 30-8 Configurations for the FET. Shown for N-channel depletion type. (*a*) Common-source circuit. (*b*) Common-gate circuit. (*c*) Common-drain circuit.

the gate, which is the control electrode (Fig. 30-8*a*). Amplified output signal is taken from the drain. The source is the common electrode.

2. *Common-gate (CG) circuit.* As shown in Fig. 30-8*b*, the input signal is applied to the source, with output from the drain. The gate is the common electrode.

3. *Common-drain (CD) circuit.* As shown in Fig. 30-8*c*, input signal is applied to the gate, with output from the source. The drain is the common electrode. With the output load impedance in the source circuit, this configuration is a *source follower,* corresponding to the emitter follower with junction transistors.

Of the three types of circuits, the common-source configuration is probably used most often for FET amplifiers, just as the common-emitter circuit is the main type for junction transistors.

**FET AMPLIFIER**    Refer to Fig. 30-9 for a common-source circuit using an N-channel depletion-type FET. The input signal is applied to the gate by the $R_1C_1$ coupling circuit. In the output circuit, $R_L$ is the load resistor for amplified output signal. The $R_L$ is in series with $V_{DD}$ of 20 V for the drain supply voltage.

The source is the common electrode, even though it is not directly grounded. Actually, the bypass capacitor $C_2$ provides an effective ac ground for the source electrode.

The combination of $R_2$ with $C_2$ provides source bias for the amplifier. Drain current $I_D$ returning to the source through $R_2$ produces a dc voltage drop that biases the source with respect to the gate. The bypass $C_2$ provides a steady value for the dc bias. This method is called *self-bias* because it is produced by the $I_D$ of the transistor itself.

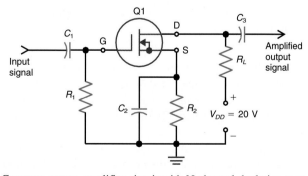

FIG. 30-9   Common-source amplifier circuit with N-channel depletion type of FET.

**TRANSCONDUCTANCE $g_m$**    This factor is important for the FET because it specifies how the gate voltage $V_G$ controls the drain current $I_D$. Specifically,

▶     $$g_m = \frac{\Delta I_D}{\Delta V_G} \tag{30-7}$$

The delta sign ($\Delta$) means a change in value. As an example, suppose that a change of 0.5 V in the gate voltage can increase or decrease the drain current by 4 mA. Then

$$g_m = \frac{\Delta I_D}{\Delta V_G} = \frac{4 \times 10^{-3}\ A}{0.5\ V}$$
$$= 8 \times 10^{-3} = 8000 \times 10^{-6}\ S$$
$$g_m = 8000\ \mu S$$

Note that the unit for $g_m$ is the seimens for conductance because it is a ratio of $I/V$. Since the conductance is less than 1 S, the $g_m$ values are usually given in microsiemens. The $g_m$ symbol indicates a mutual conductance relation of how the effect of the input voltage at the gate is transferred to the output current in the drain circuit.

---

### TEST-POINT QUESTION 30-6

Answers at end of chapter.
a. Which FET circuit corresponds to the CE amplifier?
b. Which FET circuit is a source follower?
c. Calculate $g_m$ in microsiemens when $V_G$ of 1 V changes $I_D$ by 10 mA.

## 30-7 TROUBLESHOOTING AMPLIFIER CIRCUITS

With all the advances in modern electronic equipment, troubles are still caused most of the time by a short circuit, open circuit, or low dc supply voltage. The open circuit can be in the transistor itself, resistors, capacitors, coils, or the wiring, especially at plugs, sockets, and connectors. A short circuit can occur in transistors and capacitors. It is a good idea to check the dc supply voltage first, especially with batteries.

**TRANSISTOR TROUBLES**    Failures generally result from an open weld at the wire leads to the semiconductor, a short circuit at a junction caused by momentary overloads, and circuit failures that cause transistor overheating. In most cases, a defective transistor is internally short-circuited or open, and simple tests will reveal the trouble.

The cause of some problems, like an increase in leakage, a drop in breakdown voltage, or excessive noise, is more difficult to detect, and direct substitution may be the easiest way to localize the fault. Transistor testers are available to check the transistor in or out of the circuit for an open circuit, short circuit, leakage, and $\beta$. However, open and short circuits in a transistor can also be checked by using a multimeter to test each junction as a diode. If a DMM has a diode test position, it can be used for a dynamic test of the junction.

**IN-CIRCUIT TESTS**    These tests are helpful because transistors are usually soldered into the circuit board. Measurements for dc voltage can determine if the junctions are intact and if the transistor is conducting normal current.

Refer to Fig. 30-10 for examples in a CE amplifier. This circuit is typical because of the method of obtaining base-emitter bias $V_{BE}$. In the emitter circuit, self-bias of 2 V is obtained as the voltage drop of $I_E$ through the 470-$\Omega$ $R_E$. This voltage is *self-bias* because $V_E$ depends on the transistor's own emitter current. However, $V_E$ biases $Q1$ in the reverse direction, as this voltage is positive at the N emitter. The purpose of $R_E$ is to provide *bias stabilization,* by preventing $I_C$ from increasing with more leakage current.

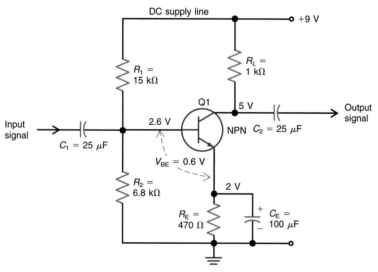

FIG. 30-10    Typical audio amplifier circuit for troubleshooting analysis in the text.

In order to provide forward bias on $Q1$, the voltage divider with $R_1$ and $R_2$ is used. The divider provides 2.6 V for $V_B$. It should be noted that $I_B$ returns to the emitter through $R_1$. Both $V_B$ and $V_E$ are dc bias voltages, positive with respect to chassis ground. The net voltage for $V_{BE}$, then, is $2.6 - 2.0 = 0.6$ V, which provides forward bias for the transistor amplifier.

In the collector circuit of $Q1$, the 1-k$\Omega$ $R_L$ is the collector load resistor connected to the V$^+$ supply of 9 V. $R_L$ has a dc voltage drop of 4 V, which allows 5 V for the collector voltage to chassis ground. The actual $V_{CE}$, though, is $5 - 2 = 3$ V because the emitter has 2 V.

The collector has a positive dc supply for reverse voltage on the NPN transistor. As a CE amplifier, $Q1$ has input signal from the coupling capacitor $C_1$, with amplified output signal coupled by $C_2$.

**CHECKING FORWARD BIAS**   Measure the base-to-emitter voltage by putting the dc voltmeter leads directly across these terminals. In Fig. 30-10, as an example, $V_{BE}$ should read 0.6 V.

If the reading for $V_{BE}$ is zero, the base-emitter junction is short-circuited. For the opposite case, if $V_{BE}$ is 0.8 V or higher, the junction is probably open. One word of caution, though. These voltage readings apply to class A amplifiers, which require a middle value of forward bias. However, in pulse circuits it may be normal to have reverse bias of several volts for $V_{BE}$ in order to cut off $I_C$ until the input pulse drives the transistor into conduction.

**CHECKING $I_C R_L$ VOLTAGE**   To check for correct collector current, put the voltmeter between the collector and the supply voltage to read the voltage drop across the load. In Fig. 30-10, a VOM across the 1-k$\Omega$ $R_L$ should read 4 V. Then divide this reading by the dc resistance in the collector circuit to calculate the current $I_C$. For this example, the normal $I_C$ value is 4 V/1 k$\Omega$ = 4 mA.

If there is no voltage drop across $R_L$, then $I_C$ must be zero. Then $V_C$ at the collector will have the same 9-V value as the supply voltage $V_{CC}$. For the opposite trouble, excessive $I_C$ can cause excessive voltage across $R_L$, resulting in zero or very low $V_C$.

If $I_C$ is zero or very low, the transistor may be open. However, check for opens in the emitter circuit before making a replacement.

If excessive $I_C$ is flowing, short-circuit the base-to-emitter voltage and repeat the test. Under these conditions only the small leakage current should flow. Remember that a junction transistor is cut off without any forward bias. If $I_C$ is still high, the transistor is probably short-circuited.

**MEASURING $I_C$**   Calculation of collector current may be difficult if the collector circuit contains little resistance or an unknown value, such as a transformer primary. In this case, current measurements may be better. You can open the collector circuit by cutting the foil of the printed-circuit board with a razor blade. Then put the leads of your VOM, set to read milliamperes or amperes, across the cut. You can bridge the cut with solder when the test is finished.

**CHECKING THE EMITTER CIRCUIT**   You can check current by measuring the voltage drop across the emitter resistance and dividing by the value of the resistor. Be careful in your analysis. This voltage will read almost normal even if the emitter resistor is open because the voltmeter resistance then completes the emitter circuit. So check the value of the emitter resistor first.

---

### TEST-POINT QUESTION 30-7

Answers at end of chapter.

Refer to the CE amplifier in Fig. 30-10.
**a.** How much is the normal dc voltage across $R_E$ to ground?
**b.** How much is the normal forward bias $V_{BE}$?
**c.** How much is $V_C$ when $R_L$ is open?

# 30 SUMMARY AND REVIEW

- The three types of circuits for junction transistors are the common-emitter, common-collector or emitter follower, and common-base configurations. See Table 30-1.
- In class A operation, output current flows for 360° of the cycle, class B for 180°, and class C for less than 180°. Class A operation has the least distortion, while class C has the best efficiency.
- Typical forward bias for $V_{BE}$ with NPN Si transistors as a class A amplifier is 0.6 V, with higher reverse voltage at the collector. The transistor is cut off without the forward bias. See Table 30-2.
- For junction transistors, $\beta$ is the ratio of $I_C$ to $I_B$. The $\beta$ determines the current gain in a CE circuit. Typical values of $\beta$ are 10 to 300. The $\alpha$ is the ratio of $I_C$ to $I_E$. Typical values are 0.98 or 0.99; it must be less than 1.
- In letter symbols for transistors, double subscripts are used for dc supply voltage, as in $V_{CC}$ or $V_{DD}$. Small letters are used for instantaneous values. See Table 30-3.
- In FET amplifiers, the common-source circuit corresponds to the common-emitter circuit for junction transistors; the common drain circuit corresponds to the common-collector circuit; the source follower corresponds to the emitter follower; the common-gate circuit corresponds to the CB circuit. See Fig. 30-8 for this comparison. The circuit of a common-source FET amplifier circuit is shown in Fig. 30-9.

## SELF-TEST

**ANSWERS AT BACK OF BOOK.**

1. Which is the most common type of amplifier circuit, CB, CE, or CC?
2. Does the CB, CE, or CC circuit have the most gain?
3. Is the current gain for cascaded stages multiplied or added?
4. Which is an emitter follower, the CB, CE, or CC circuit?
5. Which FET circuit corresponds to the CE circuit?
6. Is dc bias of 0.6 V typical for an Si or Ge transistor?
7. Which type of amplifier operation has the least distortion, class A, B, or C?
8. In a class A amplifier, is $V_{BE}$ forward or reverse voltage?
9. Is forward or reverse voltage needed at the collector?
10. Does the N-channel FET take positive or negative drain supply voltage?
11. Is positive collector supply voltage used for a PNP or NPN transistor?
12. Is the letter symbol for collector supply voltage $V_{CC}$ or $V_C$?
13. With an FET, is the CG, CS, or CD circuit a source follower?
14. Is the current gain in the CE circuit indicated by the $\alpha$ or $\beta$ of the transistor?

15. Is the value of $\alpha$ or $\beta$ always less than 1?
16. With $I_B$ of 50 $\mu$A and $\beta$ of 50, how much is $I_C$?
17. Would class A or C operation be used for an audio amplifier?
18. Without forward bias, is a junction transistor off or on?
19. Does zero ohms across the base-emitter junction indicate a short circuit or an open circuit?
20. In an amplifier with $R_L$ in the collector circuit, should $V_C$ be more or less than $V_{CC}$?
21. Would a stage for impedence matching use the CB, CC, or CE circuit?
22. Is the forward bias for a CE amplifier a dc or ac voltage?
23. In Fig. 30-10, is self-bias provided by $R_E$ or $R_L$?

## QUESTIONS

1. Make three drawings to illustrate the CB, CE, and CC circuits.
2. Give an application for the CE and CC circuits.
3. Compare the emitter-follower and source-follower circuits.
4. Which FET circuits correspond to the CB, CE, and CC circuits?
5. Show a circuit diagram for an FET amplifier.
6. Specify what the following letter symbols indicate: $V_{CC}$, $V_{DD}$, $V_{EE}$, $V_C$, $h_{fe}$, and $I_{CBO}$.
7. Give two conditions that would cause a junction transistor to be cut off without any current.
8. Define the following classes of operation for amplifiers: A, B, and C.
9. Why would you say that the characteristic curves in Fig. 30-7 apply to the common-emitter circuit?
10. Why are the waveshapes in Fig. 30-4 called a *ladder diagram.*
11. How could a transistor amplifier circuit be used as a switch to operate in the on-off conditions?
12. What is meant by the cutoff condition of a transistor?
13. Refer to the waveform of $i_c$ in Fig. 30-4b. How much current would a dc milliammeter read in the collector circuit?
14. Refer to the collector curves in Fig. 30-7c. Approximately how much bias current $I_B$ would be used for a class A amplifier?
15. For the CE class A amplifier in Fig. 30-10 give the following values: **(a)** $V_E$; **(b)** $V_B$; **(c)** $V_{BE}$; **(d)** $V_{CC}$; **(e)** $V_C$; **(f)** $V_{CE}$.

## PROBLEMS

**ANSWERS TO ODD-NUMBERED PROBLEMS AT BACK OF BOOK.**

1. A CE amplifier has the following values for ac signal: $v_b = \pm 60$ mV and $i_b = \pm 40$ $\mu$A; $v_c = \pm 3$ V and $i_c = \pm 3.2$ mA. Calculate **(a)** voltage gain $A_V$. **(b)** Current gain $A_I$. **(c)** Power gain $A_P$.
2. Three cascaded stages have $A_I$ values of 70, 50, and 15. Calculate the total current gain.

3. An FET amplifier has input signal of $\pm 0.8$ V and output of $\pm 9$ V. Calculate the voltage gain $A_V$.
4. Base current is 220 mA. Collector current is 3.4 A. Calculate $\beta$.
5. A CE amplifier with an $R_L$ of 2 k$\Omega$ has the following dc voltages: $V_{CC} = 9$ V, $V_C = 5$ V. Calculate (a) Voltage across $R_L$. (b) Value of $I_C$.
6. $I_E = 10.2$ mA, $I_C = 10.098$ mA, and $I_B = 102$ $\mu$A. Calculate $\alpha$ and $\beta$.
7. With an FET in the CS circuit, $V_{DD}$ is 20 V, $V_D$ is 12 V, and $R_L$ is 4 k$\Omega$. (a) How much is $V_{RL}$? (b) Calculate $I_D$. (c) What value of $R_S$ would be needed for a source bias voltage of 2 V?
8. In an emitter-bias circuit, $V_E$ is 0.8 V and $I_E$ is 0.6 A. Calculate the required value of $R_E$.
9. Refer to the collector characteristic curves in Fig. 30-7c. For $V_{CE}$ of 8 V and $I_B$ variations of $\pm 40$ $\mu$A around a bias current of 80 $\mu$A: (a) How much is the variation in $i_c$? (b) Calculate $\beta$.

## CRITICAL THINKING

1. Derive the formula

$$\beta = \frac{\alpha}{1 - \alpha}$$

2. Derive the formula

$$\alpha = \frac{\beta}{\beta + 1}$$

## ANSWERS TO TEST-POINT QUESTIONS

**30-1 a.** CE
  **b.** CE
  **c.** emitter follower

**30-2 a.** class A
  **b.** class B
  **c.** class C
  **d.** class A

**30-3 a.** 0.6 V
  **b.** 6.5 V
  **c.** 1 mA
  **d.** 0.02 mA

**30-4 a.** 20 $\mu$A
  **b.** 7 mA
  **c.** 50
  **d.** 8 mA

**30-5 a.** $V_{CC}$
  **b.** $v_C$
  **c.** $i_b$

**30-6 a.** CS
  **b.** CD
  **c.** 10,000

**30-7 a.** 2V
  **b.** 0.6 V
  **c.** zero

# REVIEW: CHAPTERS 28 TO 30

## SUMMARY

- Analog signals have continuous variations, as in a sine wave of $V$ or $I$. Digital signals consist of combinations of pulses.
- An amplifier circuit increases the amplitude of the signal. The ratio of output signal to input signal is the gain of the amplifier.
- An oscillator is an amplifier circuit with positive feedback to generate ac output from the dc power supply. The oscillator can produce audio or radio frequencies.
- In tuned RF feedback oscillators, the two main types are the Hartley and Colpitts circuits. The former has a tapped coil for feedback; the latter uses a capacitive voltage divider.
- The multivibrator (MV) circuit is used as a pulse generator. The astable MV is a free-running oscillator often used to produce timing pulses for digital circuits.
- Modulation means varying the characteristics of a carrier wave. The modulation is the baseband signal. The main types are amplitude, frequency, and phase modulation (PM).
- A semiconductor diode is a PN junction. The P terminal is the anode, the N side is the cathode. Electron flow is in the direction from cathode to anode, when the anode is positive. Therefore, the diode is used as a rectifier to convert ac input to dc output.
- One diode can serve as a half-wave rectifier. Two diodes are needed for the full-wave rectifier circuit. A bridge rectifier uses four diodes.
- An ac ripple in the fluctuating dc output of a rectifier causes hum interference. With 60-Hz ac input, the hum frequency is 60 Hz for a half-wave rectifier or 120 Hz for a full-wave circuit.
- Digital logic gates are used to control the flow of binary pulses in digital circuits.
- Junction transistors are the NPN and PNP types. There are three electrodes: emitter, base, and collector. The emitter supplies charges to the base to be received by the collector. Forward bias is necessary at the emitter-base junction. The collector-base junction needs reverse voltage. Positive collector voltage is used for NPN transistors.
- The field-effect transistor (FET) has three electrodes: source, gate, and drain, corresponding to emitter, base, and collector in junction transistors. Both types are commonly used for transistor amplifiers. See Table 28-2 for a summary of FET types.
- A semiconductor diode can be tested with an ohmmeter. The reverse $R$ should be much higher than the forward $R$. This test also applies to the junctions for NPN and PNP transistors.
- The three circuits for junction transistors are common base, common emitter, and common collector. The CE circuit is used most often because it has the most gain. See Table 30-1.
- The corresponding circuits for the FET are common gate, common source, and common drain, also called a source follower.
- In class A operation of amplifiers, the output current flows for the complete input cycle of 360°; class B is 180°; class C is 120°.

- The $\beta$ characteristic for junction transistors compares collector current to base current. Typical values of $\beta$ are 10 to 300.
- The $\alpha$ characteristic for junction transistors compares collector current to emitter current. Typical values are 0.98 to 0.99. It must be less than 1.
- The transconductance $g_m$ for the FET compares drain current to gate voltage. Typical values of $g_m$ are about 8000 $\mu$mhos.

# REVIEW SELF-TEST

**ANSWERS AT BACK OF BOOK.**

Answer True or False.

1. Transistors are active devices because they can amplify signals.
2. A coupling capacitor has low reactance but a bypass capacitor needs high reactance.
3. With 200-$\mu$A input signal and 8-mA output signal, the current gain is 200.
4. An RF choke also blocks direct current.
5. The VHF band of radio frequencies is 30 to 300 MHz.
6. The astable multivibrator circuit is a pulse generator.
7. The reverse resistance of a silicon diode is very high.
8. In a class A amplifier the output current flows for the full 360° of the input cycle.
9. In a class B amplifier the output current flows for 180° of the input cycle.
10. An electrolytic filter capacitor that shows no charging action with an ohmmeter is open.
11. Hole current is a motion of positive charges.
12. An N-channel FET takes positive drain supply voltage.
13. Hole current and electron flow are in opposite directions.
14. Normal voltage across a conducting silicon diode is about 0.7 V.
15. An NPN transistor takes a negative collector voltage.
16. The emitter supplies charges to the base electrode.
17. The emitter-base junction must have forward voltage to have the transistor conduct current.
18. The gate electrode in the FET corresponds to the emitter electrode in junction transistors.
19. A PNP transistor symbol has the emitter arrow into the base.
20. The emitter-follower circuit has high input resistance and low output resistance for impedance matching.
21. The common-source circuit with an FET corresponds to an emitter-follower.
22. With $\beta$ of 60 and $I_B$ of 400 $\mu$A, the $I_C$ equals 2.4 mA.
23. Class A operation in an amplifier provides maximum efficiency and distortion.
24. The unit for transconductance $g_m$ is the ohm.
25. The $\alpha$ characteristic of a transistor must be less than 1.

# REFERENCES

Malvino, A.: *Electronic Principles,* Glencoe/ McGraw-Hill, Columbus, Ohio.

Schuler, C.: *Electronics: Principles and Applications,* Glencoe/McGraw-Hill, Columbus, Ohio.

# CHAPTER 31

# DIGITAL ELECTRONICS

Digital electronic circuits operate using only two voltage levels for all of their input and output signals. The two voltage levels most commonly used are 0 V and +5 V. Regardless of the voltage levels used, all input and output signals encountered in digital circuits will be at one of two distinctly different voltage levels. This two-state design allows us to use the binary number system when working with digital circuits. The binary number system uses only two digits, which are 0 and 1. In most digital circuits, binary 0 is used to represent 0 V, and binary 1 is used to represent +5 V.

Modern calculators and computers that process binary numbers use decision-making elements called *logic gates*. There are several different types, such as the AND gate and the OR gate. Logic gates can have many input signals, but they have only one output signal.

Digital logic circuits are often classified into two very broad categories: combinational logic circuits and sequential logic circuits. Generally, a circuit is considered a combinational logic circuit if its output goes either LOW or HIGH with a specified combination of input signals. The order or sequence in which the inputs are applied is not important. What is important, though, is that the correct combination of inputs exists for the desired output. Sequential logic circuits, on the other hand, must have a definite order or sequence for their inputs before the desired output is obtained. The basic building block in combinational logic circuits is the logic gate; the basic building block of the sequential logic circuit is the flip-flop.

# CHAPTER OBJECTIVES

*Upon completion of this chapter, you should be able to:*

- *Count* using the binary and hexadecimal number systems.
- *Convert* from the binary and hexadecimal number systems to the decimal number system and vice versa.
- *Understand* the BCD system and ASCII code.
- *Describe* the operation of and construct truth tables for the inverter, AND, OR, NAND, NOR, XOR, and XNOR logic gates.
- *Understand* boolean algebra and DeMorgan's theorem.
- *Define* what is meant by the terms *active high* and *active low*.
- *Explain* how to handle unused inputs on logic gates.
- *Derive* a boolean expression from a truth table.
- *Simplify* boolean expressions.
- *Describe* the operation of *RS* flip-flops, *D*-type flip-flops, and *JK* flip-flops.
- *Understand* binary counters.
- *Identify* the new rectangular logic symbols.

## IMPORTANT TERMS IN THIS CHAPTER

| | | |
|---|---|---|
| active HIGH | counter | nibble |
| active LOW | DeMorgan's theorem | NOR gate |
| AND gate | flip-flop | OR gate |
| base | hexadecimal | radix |
| binary | inverter | reset |
| bit | least significant bit (LSB) | set |
| boolean algebra | minterm | truth table |
| byte | most significant bit (MSB) | XNOR gate |
| chunking | NAND gate | XOR gate |

## TOPICS COVERED IN THIS CHAPTER

| | | | |
|---|---|---|---|
| **31-1** | Comparing Binary and Decimal Numbers | **31-8** | DeMorgan's Theorem |
| **31-2** | Decimal to Binary Conversion | **31-9** | Active HIGH/Active LOW Terminology |
| **31-3** | Hexadecimal Numbers | **31-10** | Treating Unused Inputs on Logic Gates |
| **31-4** | Binary Coded Decimal System | **31-11** | Combinational Logic Circuits |
| **31-5** | The ASCII Code | **31-12** | Flip-Flops |
| **31-6** | Logic Gates, Symbols, and Truth Tables | **31-13** | Binary Counters |
| **31-7** | Boolean Algebra | **31-14** | New Logic Symbols |

# 31-1 COMPARING BINARY AND DECIMAL NUMBERS

In the binary number system there are only two digits, 0 and 1. Binary numbers, then, are just strings of 0s and 1s. In a moment we will see how to determine the decimal equivalent of a binary number, such as 1001. How to count with binary numbers will be explained later in this section.

All number systems have a *base* or *radix,* which specifies how many digits can be used in each place count. For binary numbers, the base is 2, with 0 and 1 as the only two digits. In the decimal system, the base is 10, so there are ten digits that can be used for each place count. The digits are 0, 1, 2, 3, 4, 5, 6, 7, 8, and 9. The decimal number system is familiar because it is used by all of us in our everyday world.

Each digit position in both the binary and decimal number systems has a specified weight in the value of the number. For binary numbers, the position represents a power of 2, such as 2, 4, 8, and 16. For decimal numbers, each digit position represents a power of 10, such as 100 and 1000.

The weight distribution for digit positions in the binary number system is illustrated in Fig. 31-1. Notice that the value, or weight, in each position doubles as we move left, because the base is 2. We know that $2^0 = 1$ is true, because any number raised to the zero power* equals 1. For the digit positions in the binary number 1001, the decimal value is $8 + 0 + 0 + 1 = 9$. Notice that the procedure is to add only those bit positions that contain a 1 in the original binary number.

| | $2^7$ | $2^6$ | $2^5$ | $2^4$ | $2^3$ | $2^2$ | $2^1$ | $2^0$ |
|---|---|---|---|---|---|---|---|---|
| ← etc. | 128 | 64 | 32 | 16 | 8 | 4 | 2 | 1 |

FIG. 31-1  Weight distribution for binary numbers.

Typical binary numbers are often written in groups of four or eight digits. Examples are 1001 and 10010110. Each digit, either 0 or 1, is referred to as a *bit.* A string of four bits is called a *nibble,* and eight bits make a *byte.* Thus, 1001 is a nibble and 10010110 is a byte.

The weight distribution for digit places in the decimal system is shown in Fig. 31-2. Each positional value, or weight, increases by a factor of 10. Notice that as we move to the left, the place values are 10, 100, 1000, 10,000, and 100,000. Consider 2367 as a typical decimal number. This value is determined as

$$(2 \times 1000) + (3 \times 100) + (6 \times 10) + (7 \times 1) = 2367$$

| | $10^5$ | $10^4$ | $10^3$ | $10^2$ | $10^1$ | $10^0$ |
|---|---|---|---|---|---|---|
| ← etc. | 100,000 | 10,000 | 1000 | 100 | 10 | 1 |

FIG. 31-2  Weight distribution for decimal numbers.

For either binary or decimal numbers, the rightmost digit is referred to as the least significant digit, or LSD, because its positional value, or weight, is the

---

*See Grob, *Mathematics for Basic Electronics* for an explanation of exponents.

lowest. For the decimal number 2367, the 7 is the LSD. In the binary number 1001, the 1 at the right is the LSD.

The left-most digit is the most significant digit, or MSD, because its positional value, or weight, is the highest. For the decimal number 2367 the 2 is the MSD with a value of 2000. In the binary number 1001, the 1 at the left is the MSD with the value of 8 in decimal terms.

The method for counting with binary numbers is illustrated in Fig. 31-3. Only four places are shown here, but the same idea applies to more places, with the positional values shown in Fig. 31-1. For the numbers in the bottom row of Fig. 31-3 the values are

$$(1111)_2 = 8 + 4 + 2 + 1 = (15)_{10}$$

Note that the subscripts indicate that 1111 is to base 2 (and therefore a binary number), and 15 is to base 10 (so it's a decimal number).

**Positional values**

| $2^3$ | $2^2$ | $2^1$ | $2^0$ | Decimal count |
|---|---|---|---|---|
| 8 | 4 | 2 | 1 | |
| 0 | 0 | 0 | 0 | $= 0 + 0 + 0 + 0 = 0$ |
| 0 | 0 | 0 | 1 | $= 0 + 0 + 0 + 1 = 1$ |
| 0 | 0 | 1 | 0 | $= 0 + 0 + 2 + 0 = 2$ |
| 0 | 0 | 1 | 1 | $= 0 + 0 + 2 + 1 = 3$ |
| 0 | 1 | 0 | 0 | $= 0 + 4 + 0 + 0 = 4$ |
| 0 | 1 | 0 | 1 | $= 0 + 4 + 0 + 1 = 5$ |
| 0 | 1 | 1 | 0 | $= 0 + 4 + 2 + 0 = 6$ |
| 0 | 1 | 1 | 1 | $= 0 + 4 + 2 + 1 = 7$ |
| 1 | 0 | 0 | 0 | $= 8 + 0 + 0 + 0 = 8$ |
| 1 | 0 | 0 | 1 | $= 8 + 0 + 0 + 1 = 9$ |
| 1 | 0 | 1 | 0 | $= 8 + 0 + 2 + 0 = 10$ |
| 1 | 0 | 1 | 1 | $= 8 + 0 + 2 + 1 = 11$ |
| 1 | 1 | 0 | 0 | $= 8 + 4 + 0 + 0 = 12$ |
| 1 | 1 | 0 | 1 | $= 8 + 4 + 0 + 1 = 13$ |
| 1 | 1 | 1 | 0 | $= 8 + 4 + 2 + 0 = 14$ |
| 1 | 1 | 1 | 1 | $= 8 + 4 + 2 + 1 = 15$ |

FIG. 31-3 Counting in the binary system.

## TEST-POINT QUESTION 31-1

Answers at end of chapter.
a. What digits are used in the binary number system?
b. What digits are used in the decimal number system?
c. How many bits are in a byte?
d. What binary number follows 0111?

# 31-2 DECIMAL TO BINARY CONVERSION

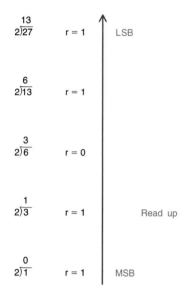

FIG. 31-4 Double-dabble method of converting a decimal number to its binary equivalent, using the remainders (r) 0 or 1.

It may be desirable or necessary to convert a decimal number to its binary equivalent. The method described here is called *double-dabble,* because it requires successive divisions by 2. When converting a decimal number to its binary equivalent, be sure to write down each quotient and its remainder, as shown for the example (decimal 27) in Fig. 31-4. First, divide 27 by 2, which is 13 with a remainder of 1. This bit of 1 is the least significant bit (LSB) in the resultant binary number. Next, divide the quotient of 13 by 2 to obtain a new quotient of 6 with a remainder of 1 again. This 1 is the next bit in the resultant binary number. Notice that you read the bits upward in Fig. 31-4.

Continue the process of dividing the new quotient by 2 and noting whether the remainder is 0 or 1 until you have performed as many divisions as possible (i.e., until you have obtained a quotient of 0 with a remainder of 1). The final remainder of 1 is the most significant bit (MSB) in the binary equivalent number. Reading the remainders in Fig. 31-4 from bottom to top we have 11011 as the binary equivalent of decimal 27. The values are $16 + 8 + 0 + 2 + 1$. Remember that when looking at the divisions and their remainders, the LSB appears at the top and the MSB is at the bottom.

## TEST-POINT QUESTION 31-2

Answers at end of chapter.
**a.** Convert the decimal number 30 to its binary equivalent.
**b.** What is the decimal value of binary 11110?
**c.** Convert decimal 127 to binary form.

# 31-3 HEXADECIMAL NUMBERS

Hexadecimal numbers are used extensively in the microcomputer field. As we will see, binary numbers start to get very lengthy and therefore become quite cumbersome to work with. However, hexadecimal numbers, with a base of 16, are much shorter and, therefore, much easier to work with. The first ten digits in the hexidecimal system are represented by the numbers 0 through 9, and the letters A through F are used to represent the numbers 10, 11, 12, 13, 14, and 15 respectively.

As is true for binary and decimal numbers, each digit in the hexidecimal system has a positional value or weight. For the right-most digit, the positional value, or weight, corresponds to $16^0$ or 1, the next digit to the left corresponds to $16^1$ or 16, and so on. Each digit to the left has a positional value, or weight, that increases in ascending powers of 16. The weight distribution for the hexadecimal number system is shown in Fig. 31-5.

| ← etc. | $16^5$ | $16^4$ | $16^3$ | $16^2$ | $16^1$ | $16^0$ |
|---|---|---|---|---|---|---|
| | 1,048,576 | 65,536 | 4096 | 256 | 16 | 1 |

FIG. 31-5 Weight distribution for a hexadecimal number system.

**HEXADECIMAL COUNTING**    Figure 31-6 shows the counting sequence. Start with 0 in the $16^0$, or 1s, column and proceed down until the digit "F" appears. Then, for the next count, the digit in the 1s column returns to 0, and the digit in the $16^1$, or 16s, column advances by 1. This process continues until the digits "FF" are reached. For the next count we start over with 0s in the $16^1$ and $16^0$ columns and add 1 to the $16^2$ column.

Positional values

| $16^3$ | $16^2$ | $16^1$ | $16^0$ | Decimal count |
|---|---|---|---|---|
| 4096 | 256 | 16 | 1 | |
| | | | 0 | = 0 |
| | | | 1 | = 1 |
| | | | 2 | = 2 |
| | | | 3 | = 3 |
| | | | 4 | = 4 |
| | | | 5 | = 5 |
| | | | 6 | = 6 |
| | | | 7 | = 7 |
| | | | 8 | = 8 |
| | | | 9 | = 9 |
| | | | A | = 10 |
| | | | B | = 11 |
| | | | C | = 12 |
| | | | D | = 13 |
| | | | E | = 14 |
| | | | F | = 15 |
| | | 1 | 0 | 16 + 0 = 16 |
| | | F | F | 240 + 15 = 255 |
| | 1 | 0 | 0 | 256 + 0 + 0 = 256 |
| | F | F | F | 3840 + 240 + 15 = 4095 |
| 1 | 0 | 0 | 0 | 4096 + 0 + 0 + 0 = 4096 |

FIG. 31-6    Counting in the hexadecimal system.

**HEXADECIMAL TO DECIMAL CONVERSIONS**    It is sometimes necessary or desirable to convert a hexadecimal number to its decimal equivalent. To convert hexadecimal number $B49F_{16}$, for example, start by writing the positional values, or weights, above each digit in the hexadecimal number:

$$16^3 \qquad 16^2 \qquad 16^1 \qquad 16^0$$
$$B \qquad\quad 4 \qquad\quad 9 \qquad\quad F$$

Next, multiply each digit by its positional value and add them all together. The resultant number is the decimal equivalent of the hexadecimal number. This can be shown as

$$(11 \times 4096) + (4 \times 256) + (9 \times 16) + (15 \times 1)$$
$$45{,}046 \quad + \quad 1024 \quad + \quad 144 \quad + \quad 15 \quad = 46{,}239$$

Thus, $B49F_{16} = 46{,}239_{10}$.

**DECIMAL TO HEXADECIMAL CONVERSIONS**   To convert from a decimal number to a hexadecimal number, we can use hex-dabble. The idea is the same as double-dabble, but with hex-dabble we have successive divisions by 16 rather than 2. You know the process is complete when you obtain a quotient of 0 and a remainder ranging anywhere from 1 to F. The example in Fig. 31-7 illustrates how the hex-dabble technique is used to obtain the hexadecimal equivalent of decimal number $6666_{10}$.

The first step is to divide 6666 by 16 to obtain a quotient of 416 with a remainder of 10. Next, we divide the quotient of 416 by 16 to obtain a quotient of 26 with a remainder of 0. Next 26 is divided by 16 to obtain a quotient of 1 with a remainder of 10. Finally 1 is divided by 16 to obtain a quotient of 0 with a remainder of 1. Therefore $6666_{10} = 1A0A_{16}$. Notice that the last indicated remainder is the MSD in the final answer, while the first remainder obtained is the LSD. Notice also that when remainders of 10, 11, 12, 13, 14, and 15 are obtained, we substitute the equivalent hexadecimal digit (A, B, C, D, E, and F, respectively) as the remainder.

**HEXADECIMAL TO BINARY CONVERSIONS**   To convert a hexadecimal number to a binary number, change each hexadecimal digit to its 4-bit binary equivalent. As an example, let's convert $FAF_{16}$ to its binary equivalent.

$$F \qquad\qquad A \qquad\qquad F$$
$$1111 \qquad 1010 \qquad 1111$$

Therefore, we can say that $FAF_{16} = 111110101111_2$. However for easier reading, it is appropriate to show the binary number with spaces between each 4-bit nibble, such as:

$$FAF_{16} = 1111\ 1010\ 1111_2$$

**BINARY TO HEXADECIMAL CONVERSIONS**   To go from a binary to a hexadecimal number, simply reverse the process. For example, to convert binary $10100001001_2$ to its hexadecimal equivalent, break the binary number into 4-bit groups. You must begin grouping from the far *right*. Then convert each 4-bit group to its hexidecimal equivalent. That is:

$$0101 \qquad\quad 0000 \qquad\quad 1001$$
$$5 \qquad\qquad\quad 0 \qquad\qquad\quad 9$$

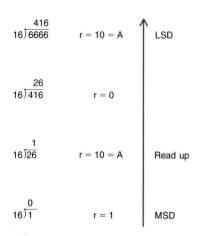

$$\begin{array}{lll}
\dfrac{416}{16\,\overline{)\,6666}} & r = 10 = A & \text{LSD} \\[3ex]
\dfrac{26}{16\,\overline{)\,416}} & r = 0 & \\[3ex]
\dfrac{1}{16\,\overline{)\,26}} & r = 10 = A & \text{Read up} \\[3ex]
\dfrac{0}{16\,\overline{)\,1}} & r = 1 & \text{MSD}
\end{array}$$

**FIG. 31-7**   Hex-dabble method of converting a decimal number to its hexadecimal equivalent.

(Notice that the 4-bit group on the left begins with a zero. When the MSB of the binary equivalent is 0, it can be dropped without affecting the value of the binary number.) Thus, $10100001001_2 = 509_{16}$.

You can see how much shorter it is to say, think, and write $509_{16}$ than one, zero, one, zero, zero, zero, zero, one, zero, zero, one. Hexadecimal numbers are simply much easier for technicians and engineers to deal with. The process of replacing long strings of data such as 10100001001 with a much shorter string, such as $509_{16}$, is known as *chunking*. See Table 31-1 for a comparison of binary, decimal, and hexadecimal numbers.

## TEST-POINT QUESTION 31-3

Answers at end of chapter.
**a.** List the digits used in the hexadecimal number system.
**b.** Convert hexadecimal number D104 to its decimal equivalent.
**c.** Find the binary equivalent for hexadecimal 2C14.
**d.** Find the hexadecimal equivalent of binary 101110011.

### TABLE 31-1  BINARY, DECIMAL, AND HEXADECIMAL NUMBERS COMPARED

| BINARY | DECIMAL | HEXADECIMAL |
|--------|---------|-------------|
| 0000 | 0 | 0 |
| 0001 | 1 | 1 |
| 0010 | 2 | 2 |
| 0011 | 3 | 3 |
| 0100 | 4 | 4 |
| 0101 | 5 | 5 |
| 0110 | 6 | 6 |
| 0111 | 7 | 7 |
| 1000 | 8 | 8 |
| 1001 | 9 | 9 |
| 1010 | 10 | A |
| 1011 | 11 | B |
| 1100 | 12 | C |
| 1101 | 13 | D |
| 1110 | 14 | E |
| 1111 | 15 | F |

# 31-4 BINARY CODED DECIMAL SYSTEM

Another very commonly used number system in the field of digital electronics is the binary coded decimal (BCD) system. This system is different from the ordinary number system in that it expresses each decimal digit as a 4-bit nibble. For example, it may be desirable or necessary to convert $489_{10}$ to a binary coded decimal. It is done as follows:

$$
\begin{array}{ccc}
4 & 8 & 9 \\
0100 & 1000 & 1001
\end{array}
$$

Note that the highest BCD value that a 4-bit nibble could represent is 9, which would be $1001_2$ in binary. See Table 31-2 for decimal numbers and their equivalent BCD values. When using the BCD number system, remember that all zeros must be retained, unlike a binary number where leading zeros can be dropped.

The BCD number system is used when it is necessary to transfer decimal information into or out of a digital machine. Examples of digital machines include digital clocks, calculators, digital voltmeters, and frequency counters.

## TABLE 31-2  BINARY CODED DECIMAL (BCD) VALUES

| DECIMAL | BINARY CODED DECIMAL |
|:---:|:---:|
| 0 | 0000 |
| 1 | 0001 |
| 2 | 0010 |
| 3 | 0011 |
| 4 | 0100 |
| 5 | 0101 |
| 6 | 0110 |
| 7 | 0111 |
| 8 | 1000 |
| 9 | 1001 |
| 10 | 0001 0000 |
| 11 | 0001 0001 |
| 12 | 0001 0010 |
| ↓ | ↓ |
| 128 | 0001 0010 1000 |
| 129 | 0001 0010 1001 |

Answers at end of chapter.
**a.** Convert the decimal number 245 to a binary coded decimal (BCD).
**b.** Write the BCD equivalent of decimal number 1056.
**c.** What is the decimal value for the BCD number 0101 1000 0111 0100?

# 31-5 THE ASCII CODE

For information to be transferred into or out of a computer, numbers, letters, and several other symbols must be translated into binary code. The system used is the American Standard Code for Information Interchange, or ASCII (pronounced "ask-key"). The ASCII code is an alphanumeric code; it has binary values for each letter, number, and symbol. The ASCII code has been used to standardize codes for numbers, letters, and symbols in equipment such as printers, keyboards, and computer displays. Each keystroke on an ASCII keyboard produces a corresponding binary code for the designated character.

The breakdown of the ASCII code is shown in Table 31-3. Each number, letter, and symbol is represented by a 7-bit binary word in the form of $X_6$, $X_5$, $X_4$, $X_3$, $X_2$, $X_1$, $X_0$, where $X_6$ is the first bit. As an example, the ASCII code for the

## TABLE 31-3  BINARY VALUES IN THE ASCII CODE

| $X_3X_2X_1X_0$ | $X_6X_5X_4$ 010 | 011 | 100 | 101 | 110 | 111 |
|---|---|---|---|---|---|---|
| 0000 | SP | 0 | @ | P |   | p |
| 0001 | ! | 1 | A | Q | a | q |
| 0010 | " | 2 | B | R | b | r |
| 0011 | # | 3 | C | S | c | s |
| 0100 | $ | 4 | D | T | d | t |
| 0101 | % | 5 | E | U | e | u |
| 0110 | & | 6 | F | V | f | v |
| 0111 | ' | 7 | G | W | g | w |
| 1000 | ( | 8 | H | X | h | x |
| 1001 | ) | 9 | I | Y | i | y |
| 1010 | * | : | J | Z | j | z |
| 1011 | + | ; | K |   | k |   |
| 1100 | , | < | L |   | l |   |
| 1101 | — | = | M |   | m |   |
| 1110 | . | > | N |   | n |   |
| 1111 | / | ? | O |   | o |   |

capital letter "W" is 1010111. Table 31-3 shows that the $X_6, X_5, X_4$ bits are 101 and the $X_3, X_2, X_1, X_0$ bits are 0111.

---

### TEST-POINT QUESTION 31-5

Answers at end of chapter.
**a.** What capital letter corresponds to 1000101 in the ASCII code?
**b.** What is the binary ASCII code for a question mark?

## 31-6 LOGIC GATES, SYMBOLS, AND TRUTH TABLES

A logic gate is a circuit that has one or more input signals but only one output signal. All logic gates can be analyzed by constructing a truth table. Truth tables list all input possibilities and the corresponding output for each input.

**INVERTERS**    The inverter is the simplest of all logic gates. It has only one input and one output, where the output is the opposite of the input. The schematic symbol for a logic inverter is shown in Fig. 31-8a and b. (The small bubble on the inverter diagram represents inversion. Notice that the bubble can be shown on either the input or output side without affecting the way the inverter operates. The reason why the bubble is shown on one or the other side for logic diagrams will be discussed in Sec. 31-9.)

A binary 0 represents 0 V, and a binary 1 represents +5 V. It is common to refer to a binary 0 as a LOW input or output, and a binary 1 as a HIGH input or output. The logic inverter works like this: When the input $A$ is LOW, or a 0 V, the output $X$ is HIGH, or at +5 V. Also, when the input $A$ is HIGH, or at +5 V, the output $X$ is LOW, or at 0 V.

The number of input possibilities for the truth table in Fig. 31-8c is $2^1$ or 2, because the logic gates in Fig. 31-8a and b have only one input. We know the input can be either 0 or 1. In general, the number of possibilities listed in the truth table is $2^N$, where $N$ is the number of inputs to the logic gate.

**OR GATES**    Another commonly used logic gate is the OR gate. An OR gate has two or more inputs but only one output. The logic symbol for a 2-input OR gate and its truth table are shown in Fig. 31-9.

For any OR gate, the output $X$ is LOW when *all* inputs are LOW. However, the output $X$ of any OR gate is HIGH if any or all inputs are HIGH. The OR gate in Fig. 31-9 will have a HIGH $X$ output if either or both inputs $A$ and $B$ are HIGH. The output $X$ will be LOW when both inputs $A$ and $B$ are LOW. Notice that for a 2-input truth table there are $2^2$ (or 4) input combinations of 0s and 1s.

Now look at Fig. 31-10, which shows a 3-input OR gate and its corresponding truth table. Notice in the truth table that the number of different input combinations equals $2^3$, or 8. The output $X$ in the truth table of Fig. 31-10 is LOW only when all inputs $A$, $B$, and $C$ are LOW. When any or all inputs $A$, $B$, and $C$ are HIGH, the output $X$ is HIGH. The logic symbol for a multiple-input OR gate is basically the OR gate symbol drawn with the required number of inputs.

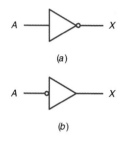

| $A$ | $X$ |
|:---:|:---:|
| 0 | 1 |
| 1 | 0 |

(c)

FIG. 31-8    Inverter logic gates. (a) Logic symbol with bubble at output. (b) Bubble at input. (c) Truth table.

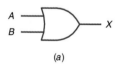

| $A$ | $B$ | $X$ |
|:---:|:---:|:---:|
| 0 | 0 | 0 |
| 0 | 1 | 1 |
| 1 | 0 | 1 |
| 1 | 1 | 1 |

(b)

FIG. 31-9    Two-input OR gate. (a) Logic symbol. (b) Truth table.

## AND GATES

**AND GATES**   The AND gate is another logic gate. An AND gate has two or more inputs but only one output. The logic symbol for a 2-input AND gate and its truth table are shown in Fig. 31-11. For any AND gate, the output $X$ is HIGH when *all* inputs are HIGH. However, the output $X$ of any AND gate is LOW if any or all inputs are LOW. For the 2-input AND gate in Fig. 31-11, the output $X$ is HIGH only when both inputs $A$ and $B$ are HIGH. The output $X$ is LOW if either or both inputs $A$ and $B$ are LOW.

Figure 31-12 shows the logic symbol and truth table for a 3-input AND gate. Notice from the truth table that the output is HIGH only when all inputs $A$, $B$, and $C$ are HIGH. Also notice that the output is LOW for all other input combinations because at least one of the inputs $A$, $B$, or $C$ is LOW.

The logic symbol for a multiple-input AND gate uses a basic AND gate symbol drawn with the required number of inputs.

**NOR GATES**   The NOR gate has two or more inputs but only one output. The logic symbol for a 2-input NOR gate and its truth table are shown in Fig. 31-13a on page 904. The output $X$ is LOW if either or both inputs $A$ and $B$ are HIGH. The output $X$ is HIGH only when both inputs $A$ and $B$ are LOW.

The NOR gate actually performs a logic function identical to that of an OR gate followed by an inverter. This is shown in Fig. 31-13b. Notice that the output of the OR gate is connected to the input of the inverter. If the output of the OR gate is HIGH, then the inverter output $X$ is LOW. If the output of the OR gate is LOW, then the output $X$ is HIGH. Therefore, the truth table for the logic circuit in Fig. 31-13b is the same as for the NOR gate in Fig. 31-13a.

A NOR gate with three or more inputs reacts the same way as a 2-input NOR gate. That is, the output $X$ is LOW if any or all inputs are HIGH, and the output $X$ is HIGH only when *all* inputs are LOW.

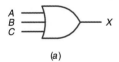

| A | B | C | X |
|---|---|---|---|
| 0 | 0 | 0 | 0 |
| 0 | 0 | 1 | 1 |
| 0 | 1 | 0 | 1 |
| 0 | 1 | 1 | 1 |
| 1 | 0 | 0 | 1 |
| 1 | 0 | 1 | 1 |
| 1 | 1 | 0 | 1 |
| 1 | 1 | 1 | 1 |

(b)

FIG. 31-10   Three-input OR gate. (a) Logic symbol. (b) Truth table.

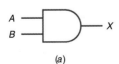

| A | B | X |
|---|---|---|
| 0 | 0 | 0 |
| 0 | 1 | 0 |
| 1 | 0 | 0 |
| 1 | 1 | 1 |

(b)

FIG. 31-11   Two-input AND gate. (a) Logic symbol. (b) Truth table.

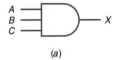

| A | B | C | X |
|---|---|---|---|
| 0 | 0 | 0 | 0 |
| 0 | 0 | 1 | 0 |
| 0 | 1 | 0 | 0 |
| 0 | 1 | 1 | 0 |
| 1 | 0 | 0 | 0 |
| 1 | 0 | 1 | 0 |
| 1 | 1 | 0 | 0 |
| 1 | 1 | 1 | 1 |

(b)

FIG. 31-12   Three-input AND gate. (a) Logic symbol. (b) Truth table.

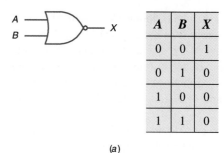

| A | B | X |
|---|---|---|
| 0 | 0 | 1 |
| 0 | 1 | 0 |
| 1 | 0 | 0 |
| 1 | 1 | 0 |

(a)

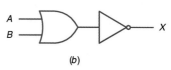

(b)

**FIG. 31-13** The NOR gate. (*a*) Logic symbol with truth table. (*b*) Equivalent logic circuit for a NOR gate.

**NAND GATES**   The NAND gate also has two or more inputs but only one output. The logic symbol for a 2-input NAND gate and its truth table are shown in Fig. 31-14*a*. Notice that the output $X$ is HIGH if either or both inputs $A$ and $B$ are LOW. The output $X$ is LOW only when both inputs $A$ and $B$ are HIGH. The NAND gate actually performs a logic function identical to that of an AND gate followed by an inverter. This is shown in Fig. 31-14*b*.

Figure 31-14*b* shows that the output $X$ of the AND gate is connected to the input of the inverter. If the output of the AND gate is HIGH, then the output $X$ is LOW. If the output of the AND gate is LOW, then the output $X$ is HIGH. Therefore, the truth table for the logic circuit in Fig. 31-14*b* is the same as for the NAND gate in Fig. 31-14*a*.

A NAND gate with three or more inputs reacts the same way as a 2-input NAND gate. That is, the output $X$ is HIGH when any or all inputs are LOW, and the output $X$ is LOW only when *all* inputs are HIGH.

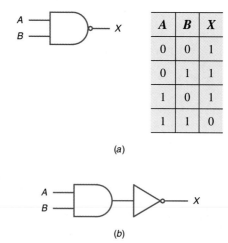

| A | B | X |
|---|---|---|
| 0 | 0 | 1 |
| 0 | 1 | 1 |
| 1 | 0 | 1 |
| 1 | 1 | 0 |

(a)

(b)

**FIG. 31-14** The NAND gate. (*a*) Logic symbol with truth table. (*b*) Equivalent logic circuit for a NAND gate.

**EXCLUSIVE OR (XOR) AND EXCLUSIVE NOR (XNOR) GATES**   Two other logic gates are exclusive OR and exclusive NOR gates. The logic symbols and truth tables for each are shown in Fig. 31-15. Notice that for the XOR gate in Fig. 31-15a the output X is HIGH only when the inputs A and B are different. For a multiple-input XOR gate with three or more inputs, the output X will be HIGH only if an odd number of 1s is applied to the inputs. If an even number of 1s is applied to the inputs of an XOR gate, then the output X is LOW.

For the XNOR gate in Fig. 31-15b the output X is HIGH only when both inputs are the same. The XNOR gate is equivalent to an XOR gate followed by an inverter. For a multiple-input XNOR gate with three or more inputs, the output x will be HIGH only when an even number of 1s is applied to the inputs. If an odd number of 1s is applied to the inputs of an XNOR gate, the output x will be LOW. It is important to note that zero 1s is an even number when looking at the truth tables.

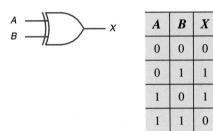

| A | B | X |
|---|---|---|
| 0 | 0 | 0 |
| 0 | 1 | 1 |
| 1 | 0 | 1 |
| 1 | 1 | 0 |

(a)

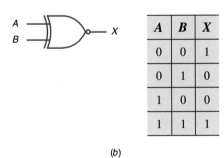

| A | B | X |
|---|---|---|
| 0 | 0 | 1 |
| 0 | 1 | 0 |
| 1 | 0 | 0 |
| 1 | 1 | 1 |

(b)

**FIG. 31-15**   The XOR and NXOR gates. (a) Logic symbol and truth table for a 2-input XOR gate. Note the extra curved line at the front of the symbol. (b) Logic symbol and truth table for a 2-input XNOR gate.

## TEST-POINT QUESTION 31-6

Answers at end of chapter.

Answer True or False.
**a.** A HIGH input applied to an inverter produces a LOW output.
**b.** A 4-input AND gate will have a HIGH output only when all inputs are HIGH.
**c.** The output of an OR gate will be LOW if any or all inputs are HIGH.
**d.** A 2-input NAND gate has a LOW output when both inputs are HIGH.
**e.** A 3-input NOR gate has a HIGH output when all inputs are LOW.
**f.** A XNOR gate with two inputs has a HIGH output when both inputs are the same.
**g.** A XOR gate with two inputs has a LOW output when both inputs are the same.

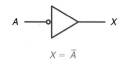

FIG. 31-16   Inverter logic gate. Boolean expression is $X = \bar{A}$.

It is very common to express the operation of a logic gate, or combination of logic gates, using boolean algebra. For the basic logic inverter in Fig. 31-16, the boolean expression would be $X = \bar{A}$. The overbar or "not sign" above the input variable $A$ represents inversion, or complementing. To *invert*, or *complement*, a binary number means to change it to the opposite state, such as changing a 0 to a 1, or a 1 to a 0. For the inverter in Fig. 31-16, $X = $ not $A$, or $X = \bar{A}$. Then,

$$\text{If } A = 0, \text{ then } X = \bar{0}, \text{ or } X = 1 \quad \text{and}$$
$$\text{If } A = 1, \text{ then } X = \bar{1}, \text{ or } X = 0$$

**BOOLEAN ALGEBRA FOR OR GATES**   The boolean expression for the OR gate in Fig. 31-17a is $A + B = X$. The "+" sign stands for OR addition. The following truth table shows all of the possibilities for the inputs.

| $A + B = X$ |
|:---:|
| $0 + 0 = 0$ |
| $0 + 1 = 1$ |
| $1 + 0 = 1$ |
| $1 + 1 = 1$ |

According to the truth table, when 0 is ORed with 0, the result equals 0. Also, any variable ORed with 1 equals 1.

In Fig. 31-17b we see that when $A$ is ORed with 0, the output will be whatever $A$ is. If $A = 0$, then $0 + 0 = 0$. If $A = 1$, then $1 + 0 = 1$.

We see in Fig. 31-17c that when $A$ is ORed with 1, the output will be 1. If $A = 0$, then $0 + 1 = 1$. If $A = 1$, then $1 + 1 = 1$.

In Fig. 31-17d we see that when $A$ is ORed with $A$, then the output will be whatever $A$ is. If $A = 0$, then $0 + 0 = 0$. If $A = 1$, then $1 + 1 = 1$.

In Fig. 31-17e we see that if $A$ is ORed with its complement, then the output is 1. If $A = 0$, then $\bar{A} = 1$. If $A = 1$, then $\bar{A} = 0$. The output must be 1 because any variable ORed with 1 equals 1.

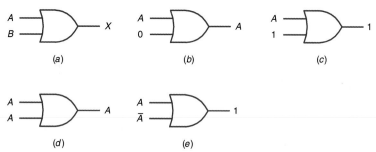

FIG. 31-17   Boolean algebra for OR gates. (a) $A + B = $ X. (b) $A + 0 = A$. (c) $A + 1 = 1$. (d) $A + A = A$. (e) $A + \bar{A} = 1$.

To summarize Fig. 31-17:

0 ORed with 0 equals 0

0 ORed with 1 equals 1

1 ORed with 1 equals 1

$$A + 0 = A$$

$$A + 1 = 1$$

$$A + A = A$$

$$A + \overline{A} = 1$$

**BOOLEAN ALGEBRA FOR AND GATES**   The boolean expression for the AND gate in Fig. 31-18a is $A \cdot B = X$, where the multiplication dot stands for the AND operation. (Note that the multiplication dot is often omitted, so the expression may appear as $AB = X$.) For Fig. 31-18a we have the following input possibilities:

| $A \cdot B$ | $X$ |
|-------------|-----|
| $0 \cdot 0$ | $= 0$ |
| $0 \cdot 1$ | $= 0$ |
| $1 \cdot 0$ | $= 0$ |
| $1 \cdot 1$ | $= 1$ |

The truth table for an AND gate tells us that 0 ANDed with any variable equals 0. Also, 1 ANDed with 1 equals 1.

In Fig. 31-18b we see that when $A$ is ANDed with 0, the output will be 0. If $A = 0$, then $0 \cdot 0 = 0$. If $A = 1$, then $1 \cdot 0 = 0$.

We see in Fig. 31-18c that when $A$ is ANDed with 1, the output will be whatever $A$ is. If $A = 0$, then $0 \cdot 1 = 0$. If $A = 1$, then $1 \cdot 1 = 1$.

In Fig. 31-18d we see that when $A$ is ANDed with $A$, then the output will be whatever $A$ is. If $A = 0$, then $0 \cdot 0 = 0$. If $A = 1$, then $1 \cdot 1 = 1$.

In Fig. 31-18e we see that if $A$ is ANDed with its complement, then the output is 0. If $A = 0$, then $\overline{A} = 1$. If $A = 1$, then $\overline{A} = 0$. The output must be 0 because any variable ANDed with 0 equals 0.

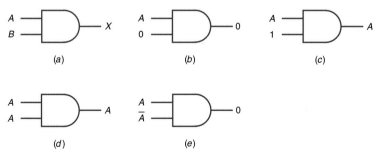

**FIG. 31-18**   Boolean algebra for AND gates. (a) $AB = X$. (b) $A \cdot 0 = 0$. (c) $A \cdot 1 = A$. (d) $A \cdot A = A$. (e) $A \cdot \overline{A} = 0$.

To summarize Fig. 31-18:

$$0 \text{ ANDed with } 0 \text{ equals } 0$$
$$0 \text{ ANDed with } 1 \text{ equals } 0$$
$$1 \text{ ANDed with } 1 \text{ equals } 1$$
$$A \cdot 0 = 0$$
$$A \cdot 1 = A$$
$$A \cdot A = A$$
$$A \cdot \overline{A} = 0$$

FIG. 31-19  The NOR gate. $\overline{A + B} = X$.

FIG. 31-20  The NAND gate. $\overline{A \cdot B} = X$.

FIG. 31-21  The XOR gate. $A \oplus B = X$. Note the $\oplus$ symbol used for the XOR and NXOR gates.

**BOOLEAN ALGEBRA FOR OTHER LOGIC GATES**  The boolean expression for the NOR gate in Fig. 31-19 is $\overline{A + B} = X$, which can be read as $X =$ not $A$ or $B$. To perform the boolean algebra operation, it is important to perform the OR portion first, and then invert the OR sum. For Fig. 31-19 we have:

| $\overline{A + B}$ | = | $X$ |
|---|---|---|
| $\overline{0 + 0}$ = $\overline{0}$ | = | 1 |
| $\overline{0 + 1}$ = $\overline{1}$ | = | 0 |
| $\overline{1 + 0}$ = $\overline{1}$ | = | 0 |
| $\overline{1 + 1}$ = $\overline{1}$ | = | 0 |

The boolean expression for the NAND gate in Fig. 31-20 is $\overline{A \cdot B} = X$, which can be read as $X =$ not $A \cdot B$. To perform the boolean algebra operation, first the inputs must be ANDed, and then the inversion is performed. For Fig. 31-20 we have:

| $\overline{A \cdot B}$ | = | $X$ |
|---|---|---|
| $\overline{0 \cdot 0}$ = $\overline{0}$ | = | 1 |
| $\overline{0 \cdot 1}$ = $\overline{0}$ | = | 1 |
| $\overline{1 \cdot 0}$ = $\overline{0}$ | = | 1 |
| $\overline{1 \cdot 1}$ = $\overline{1}$ | = | 0 |

The boolean expression for the exclusive OR gate in Fig. 31-21 is $A \oplus B = X$, which can be read as $A$ XOR $B = X$. For Fig. 31-21 we have:

| $A \oplus B = X$ |
|---|
| $0 \oplus 0$ = 0 |
| $0 \oplus 1$ = 1 |
| $1 \oplus 0$ = 1 |
| $1 \oplus 1$ = 0 |

This table tells us that the output $X$ is HIGH, or 1, only when the inputs are different.

For XOR addition with more than 2-input variables, simply obtain the XOR sum of two variables and then XOR this sum with the other input variable. As an example: $1 \oplus 0 \oplus 1 = 0$. First find the XOR sum of $0 \oplus 1$, which is shown as $0 \oplus 1 = 1$. Then take this XOR sum of 1 and XOR it with 1 to obtain the following: $1 \oplus 1 = 0$.

The boolean expression for the exclusive NOR gate shown in Fig. 31-22 is $\overline{A \oplus B} = X$, which can be read as $X$ = not $A$ XOR $B$. For Fig. 31-22 we have:

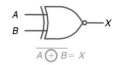

FIG. 31-22   The NXOR gate. $\overline{A \oplus B} = X$.

| $\overline{A \oplus B}$ | $X$ |
|---|---|
| $\overline{0 \oplus 0} = \overline{0} = 1$ | |
| $\overline{0 \oplus 1} = \overline{1} = 0$ | |
| $\overline{1 \oplus 0} = \overline{1} = 0$ | |
| $\overline{1 \oplus 1} = \overline{0} = 1$ | |

Looking at this table we can see that the output $X$ is HIGH only when the inputs are the same. Regardless of the number of input variables, first the XOR operation must be performed, followed by the inversion.

---

### TEST-POINT QUESTION 31-7

Answers at end of chapter.
**a.** Write the boolean expression for a 3-input OR gate.
**b.** Write the boolean expression for a 3-input AND gate.
**c.** Write the boolean expression for a 2-input NOR gate.
**d.** Write the boolean expression for a 2-input NAND gate.
**e.** Write the output for each of the following:
   $A + 0$
   $A \cdot 0$
   $A + A$
   $A \cdot 1$
   $A + \overline{A}$
   $A \cdot \overline{A}$
   $1 \oplus 1 \oplus 1$
   $0 \oplus 1 \oplus 1$

## 31-8 DEMORGAN'S THEOREM

Two very important principles of boolean algebra, known as DeMorgan's theorem, can help to greatly simplify expressions in which a product or sum is inverted. The first theorem states that the complement of a sum equals the product of the complements. Expressed as an equation, we have:

$$\overline{A + B} = \overline{A} \cdot \overline{B}$$

In terms of the algebra itself, it is important to realize that if the overbar is broken directly above the OR operation sign for $\overline{A + B}$, then each variable remains complemented, but the operation sign changes from OR (+) to AND (·). This basically means that the output of a NOR gate and the output of an AND gate with inverted inputs will be the same, provided both gates have the same inputs.

The logic symbols and truth tables for the NOR and the AND gate with inverted inputs are shown in Fig. 31-23. The truth tables prove the equivalency for the statement $\overline{A + B} = \overline{A} \cdot \overline{B}$.

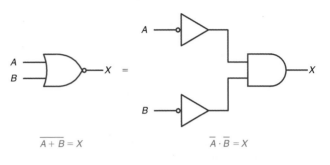

$$\overline{A + B} = X \qquad\qquad \overline{A} \cdot \overline{B} = X$$

Truth table
for NOR gate

Truth table
for AND gate
with inverted
inputs

| A | B | X |
|---|---|---|
| 0 | 0 | 1 |
| 0 | 1 | 0 |
| 1 | 0 | 0 |
| 1 | 1 | 0 |

=

| A | B | X |
|---|---|---|
| 0 | 0 | 1 |
| 0 | 1 | 0 |
| 1 | 0 | 0 |
| 1 | 1 | 0 |

**FIG. 31-23** Logic symbols and truth tables for a NOR gate, and for an AND gate with inverted inputs.

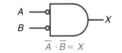

$$\overline{A} \cdot \overline{B} = X$$

**FIG. 31-24** Bubbled AND gate.

The AND gate with inverted inputs is usually shown with just the bubbles on the input leads. Figure 31-24 shows the schematic symbol of a bubbled AND gate. This symbol is actually an alternate way of showing a NOR gate.

DeMorgan's second theorem states that the complement of a product equals the sum of the complements. Expressed as an equation, we have:

$$\overline{A \cdot B} = \overline{A} + \overline{B}$$

As far as the algebra is concerned, when the overbar is broken directly above the AND operation sign for $A \cdot B$ the individual variables remain complemented, but the operation sign changes from AND ($\cdot$) to OR ($+$). This basically means that the output of a NAND gate is the same as for an OR gate with inverted inputs, provided both gates have the same inputs. The logic symbols and truth tables for the NAND gate and the OR gate with inverted inputs are shown in Fig. 31-25. The truth tables prove the equivalency for the statement $\overline{A \cdot B} = \overline{A} + \overline{B}$.

The OR gate with inverted inputs is usually shown with just the bubbles on the input leads, as in Fig. 31-26. This symbol is actually an alternate symbol for a NAND gate. (Note that there are many times when the alternate symbols for both NAND gates and NOR gates will be used to help simplify interpretation of a given logic circuit.)

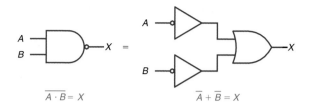

$$\overline{A \cdot B} = X \qquad \overline{A} + \overline{B} = X$$

|  | Truth table for NAND gate |  |  |  | Truth table for OR gate with inverted inputs |  |  |
|---|:---:|:---:|:---:|:---:|:---:|:---:|:---:|
|  | **A** | **B** | **X** |  | **A** | **B** | **X** |
|  | 0 | 0 | 1 |  | 0 | 0 | 1 |
| = | 0 | 1 | 1 | = | 0 | 1 | 1 |
|  | 1 | 0 | 1 |  | 1 | 0 | 1 |
|  | 1 | 1 | 0 |  | 1 | 1 | 0 |

**FIG. 31-25** Logic inputs and truth tables for a NAND gate, and for an OR gate with inverted inputs.

Two other important concepts in boolean algebra should be understood. First, if a variable is double complemented, the variable appears uncomplemented at the output. As examples, $\overline{\overline{A}} = A$, $\overline{\overline{AB}} = AB$, $\overline{\overline{A + B}} = A + B$, and so on. Second, complementing both sides of an equation does not destroy its equality. As an example, if we complement $A + B = X$, we have $\overline{A + B} = \overline{X}$, and this simplifies to $A + B = \overline{\overline{X}}$. As another example, we can complement $AB = X$ to get $\overline{\overline{AB}} = \overline{X}$, which simplifies to $AB = \overline{X}$.

Figure 31-27 shows the standard and alternate logic symbols used for the various logic gates. The way a logic gate is drawn can help simplify interpretation of a given logic circuit when troubleshooting. For Fig. 31-27, look at the boolean expression for each logic gate in the left column and confirm that the logic gate and boolean expression in the right column is correct. Remember that when the overbar is broken directly above the operation sign, the individual variables remain complemented but the operation sign changes.

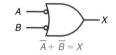

$$\overline{A} + \overline{B} = X$$

**FIG. 31-26** Bubbled OR gate.

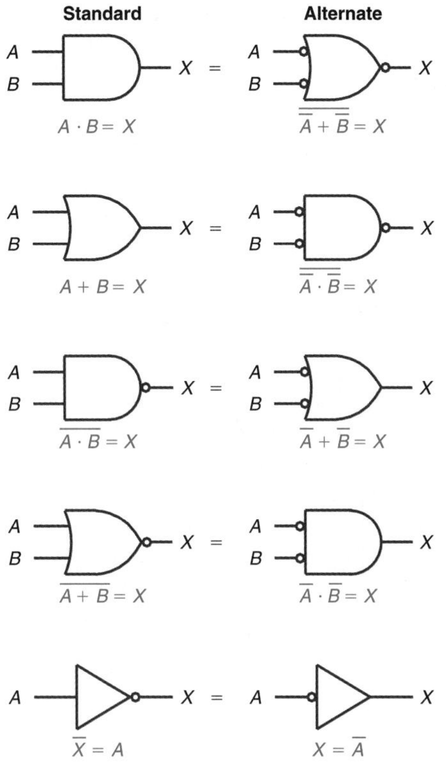

**Standard**                 **Alternate**

$A \cdot B = X$              $\overline{\overline{A} + \overline{B}} = X$

$A + B = X$              $\overline{\overline{A} \cdot \overline{B}} = X$

$\overline{A \cdot B} = X$              $\overline{A} + \overline{B} = X$

$\overline{A + B} = X$              $\overline{A} \cdot \overline{B} = X$

$\overline{X} = A$              $X = \overline{A}$

**FIG. 31-27** Standard and alternate logic symbols used for the common logic gates.

## 31-9 ACTIVE HIGH/ACTIVE LOW TERMINOLOGY

When an input or output line on a logic gate symbol does not show a bubble, it indicates that these lines are active HIGH. When an input or output line does show a bubble, these lines are said to be active LOW. Therefore, the presence or absence of a bubble on the inputs and outputs of logic gates indicates whether a line is considered to be active HIGH or active LOW. When an input variable or an output in a boolean expression has no overbar (or "not sign"), it means that the input variables or outputs are active HIGH. However, if an input or an output in a boolean expression does have an overbar, it means that the input variable or the output variable is active LOW.

Now that we can identify active HIGH and active LOW inputs and outputs on logic gates and in boolean expressions, let's examine what is really meant by the terminology "active HIGH" and "active LOW." An example (see Fig. 31-28) will best illustrate the idea. In this circuit, the LED turns on when the output $X$ goes HIGH. The reason is that the $X$ output is connected to the LED anode, which needs positive voltage to turn on. Also, the output $X$ will only go HIGH if the input $A$ is LOW. Because the bubble appears on the input line of the inverter, the input $A$ is said to be active LOW. Likewise, because there is no bubble on the output line, it is said to be active HIGH. For Fig. 31-28, we can say that the output $X$ is active HIGH when the input $A$ is active LOW. We call the output $X$ active HIGH because it is this HIGH signal that causes action in the circuitry being driven by the output $X$. Likewise we call the input $A$ active LOW because when this input signal is LOW it causes action in the circuitry driven by the inverter output. For Fig. 31-28 the

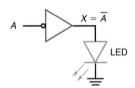

**FIG. 31-28** Inverter logic gate with output $X$ connected to the anode of the LED. The input $A$ must be active LOW to produce an active HIGH output. The circuit is active when the LED comes on.

action is the LED being turned on. The logic gate symbol describes how the circuit functions.

Notice that the boolean expression $X = \overline{A}$ describes how the inverter functions. Because $X$ has no overbar it is said to be active HIGH. The input variable $A$ is complemented and is said to be active LOW. Technicians and engineers looking at the logic circuit in Fig. 31-28 and its corresponding boolean expression would realize that the output $X$ is active HIGH only when the input $A$ is active LOW. They would also know that the output $X$ is inactive LOW when the input $A$ is inactive HIGH. This condition is called inactive, because the LED does not light. The logic symbol for an inverter with the bubble on the output would not be appropriate, as it does not represent how the circuit operates.

For another example, see Fig. 31-29. Here we see there is no bubble on the input line, which means the input $A$ is active HIGH. The bubble on the output indicates that $X$ is active LOW. We can say that the output $X$ is active LOW when the input $A$ is active HIGH because now the $X$ output is connected to the LED cathode.

It is common to see the boolean expression for this circuit as $A = \overline{X}$, rather than $X = \overline{A}$. (Here we have simply complemented both sides of the equation $X = \overline{A}$. Remember, complementing does not destroy the equality of the equation.) Notice how the boolean expression matches the logic symbol. For Fig. 31-29 the LOW output $X$ causes the LED to turn on; this is the action. Likewise, when the input $A$ is HIGH, the output $X$ is LOW, which causes action in the circuit by lighting the LED. Thus, it is common practice to write the boolean expression for the circuit in Fig. 31-29 as $A = \overline{X}$, because the expression matches the inverter logic symbol.

Another example is shown in Fig. 31-30. Here we see both inputs are active HIGH and the output $X$ is active LOW. Either, or both inputs must be active HIGH in order for the output $X$ to be active LOW. The most appropriate boolean expression is $A + B = \overline{X}$. It is obtained by complementing both sides of the equation $\overline{A + B} = X$. Notice that the boolean expression and the logic diagram clearly describe how the logic circuit is functioning. Remember, that the turned on LED is the action.

Suppose we have a circuit like the one shown in Fig. 31-31. For this logic circuit we can say that both inputs $A$ and $B$ must be active LOW to produce an active HIGH output. It is important to realize that the logic gate in Fig. 31-31 is a NOR gate. The alternate logic symbol, rather than the standard logic symbol, is used to clarify circuit operation. The boolean expression that is most appropriate is $\overline{A} \cdot \overline{B} = X$, not $\overline{A + B} = X$. Notice how the boolean expression matches the logic diagram. The standard logic symbol for a NOR gate is not used here because it does not clearly represent how the circuit operates.

Any logic gate can be shown or represented by either of two symbols: standard or alternate. The logic symbol and boolean expression used should provide the clearest description of how the circuit operates.

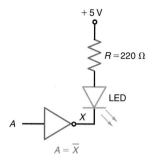

FIG. 31-29   Inverter logic gate with output $X$ connected to the cathode of the LED. The input $A$ must be active HIGH to produce an active LOW output.

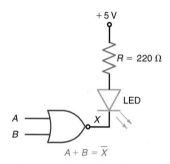

FIG. 31-30   A NOR logic gate with output $X$ connected to the cathode of the LED. Either or both inputs $A$ and $B$ must be active HIGH to produce an active LOW output.

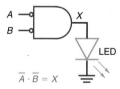

FIG. 31-31   A NOR logic gate drawn using the alternate symbol. Output $X$ is connected to the anode of the LED. Inputs $A$ and $B$ must be active LOW to produce an active HIGH output.

### TEST-POINT QUESTION 31-9

Answers at end of chapter.
**a.** True or False? A bubble on the output of a logic gate indicates that the output is active HIGH.
**b.** True or False? Bubbles on the input lines of logic gates indicate that these inputs are active LOW.

**c.** True or False? The boolean expression for a logic circuit is $\overline{A} + \overline{B} = X$. This tells us both inputs are active LOW and the output is active HIGH.

**d.** Draw the logic gate symbol that would match the following boolean expression: $\overline{A} + \overline{B} = X$.

**e.** Draw the logic gate symbol that would match the following boolean expression: $AB = \overline{X}$.

# 31-10 TREATING UNUSED INPUTS ON LOGIC GATES

Digital circuits often include inputs that are not needed in the final wiring. Unused inputs on logic gates should never be left disconnected or floating, because they can act as small antennas and pick up noise, causing erratic or unpredictable operation of logic circuits.

Unused inputs on AND gates should be connected directly to $V_{CC}$ (+5 V), as in Fig. 31-32a, or tied to another input that is being used. Note that since the unused input is always HIGH, inputs A and B must then be made HIGH to obtain a HIGH output at X. Furthermore, the unused input should never be tied to ground for an AND gate because then the output X would always be LOW even if all other inputs are HIGH. Figure 31-32b shows the unused input connected to another input, which is also acceptable.

Unused inputs on OR gates should be tied to ground, as in Fig. 31-33a, or tied to another input that is being used. In Fig. 31-33a, the output X will be HIGH if either or both inputs A and B are HIGH. Figure 31-33b shows the unused input connected to another input, which is also acceptable. The unused input should never be tied to $V_{CC}$ for an OR gate because this would cause the output X to remain HIGH regardless of the conditions of the other inputs.

Figure 31-34 shows how to handle unused inputs on NAND gates. Notice that this is the same method used with AND gates. The output X will be LOW only when inputs A and B are HIGH. The output X will be HIGH if either or both inputs A and B are LOW.

Figure 31-35 shows how to handle unused inputs on NOR gates, which is the same method used with OR gates. The output X will be HIGH only when inputs A and B are LOW. The output X will be LOW if either or both inputs A and B are HIGH.

It is also possible to use NAND and NOR gates as inverters, in which case, all inputs are tied together and used as one input. To summarize:

1. All unused inputs of AND gates and NAND gates should be tied to $V_{CC}$ or to other used inputs.
2. All unused inputs of OR gates and NOR gates should be tied to ground or to other used inputs.
3. NAND and NOR gates can be used as inverters if all inputs are tied together.

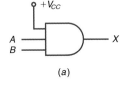

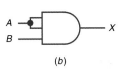

**FIG. 31-32** Treating unused inputs on AND gates. (a) Tie unused input to $V_{CC}$. (b) Connect unused input to another used input.

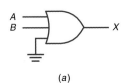

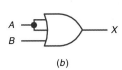

**FIG. 31-33** Treating unused inputs on OR gates. (a) Tie unused input to ground. (b) Connect unused input to another used input.

**TEST-POINT QUESTION 31-10**

Answers at end of chapter.

**a.** A 3-input AND gate is to be used as a 2-input AND gate. Show how to connect the unused input.

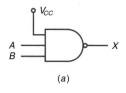

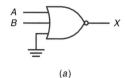

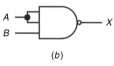

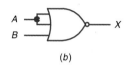

**FIG. 31-34** Treating unused inputs on NAND gates. (*a*) Tie unused input to $V_{CC}$. (*b*) Connect unused input to another used input.

**FIG. 31-35** Treating unused inputs on NOR gates. (*a*) Tie unused input to ground. (*b*) Connect unused input to another used input.

**b.** A 4-input NOR gate is to be used as a 2-input NOR gate. Show how to connect the unused inputs.

**c.** A 4-input NAND gate is to be used as an inverter. Show how to wire the inputs.

# 31-11 COMBINATIONAL LOGIC CIRCUITS

Digital circuits often consist of several different logic gates, interconnected in such a way as to perform a specific logic function. Figure 31-36*a* shows a logic circuit that uses one OR gate and one AND gate. The boolean expression for this logic circuit is $A \cdot (B + C) = X$, or just $A(B + C) = X$. The parentheses around the $B + C$ sum indicates that the input variable $A$ is being ANDed with the $B + C$ sum. The truth table in Fig. 31-36*b* lists all input possibilities and the corresponding output for each input condition. According to the truth table, the output $X$ is LOW when $A$ is LOW. This must be true because any variable ANDed with 0 equals 0. The output $X$ is HIGH only when $A$ is HIGH *and* either or both inputs $B$ and $C$ are HIGH.

As another example, see Fig. 31-37*a*. This logic circuit also uses one OR gate and one AND gate. The boolean expression for this logic circuit is $A + BC = X$. The truth table in Fig. 31-37*b* lists all input possibilities and the corresponding output for each input condition. From the truth table we see that the output $X$ is HIGH if $A$ is HIGH *or* if $B$ and $C$ are both HIGH. This must be true because any variable ORed with 1 equals 1.

## DERIVING A BOOLEAN EXPRESSION FROM A TRUTH TABLE
When designing digital circuits, we begin by constructing a truth table. For example, suppose we have to construct a logic circuit that will produce an output in accordance with the truth table in Fig. 31-38. The boolean expression for this truth table would be

$$\overline{A}\,\overline{B}C + A\overline{B}C + AB\overline{C} + ABC = X$$

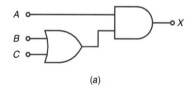

| $A$ | $B$ | $C$ | $X$ |
|-----|-----|-----|-----|
| 0 | 0 | 0 | 0 |
| 0 | 0 | 1 | 0 |
| 0 | 1 | 0 | 0 |
| 0 | 1 | 1 | 0 |
| 1 | 0 | 0 | 0 |
| 1 | 0 | 1 | 1 |
| 1 | 1 | 0 | 1 |
| 1 | 1 | 1 | 1 |

(*b*)

**FIG. 31-36** Combinational logic circuit. (*a*) Logic diagram with OR gate feeding AND gate. (*b*) Truth table.

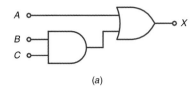

(a)

| A | B | C | X |
|---|---|---|---|
| 0 | 0 | 0 | 0 |
| 0 | 0 | 1 | 0 |
| 0 | 1 | 0 | 0 |
| 0 | 1 | 1 | 1 |
| 1 | 0 | 0 | 1 |
| 1 | 0 | 1 | 1 |
| 1 | 1 | 0 | 1 |
| 1 | 1 | 1 | 1 |

(b)

FIG. 31-37 Combinational logic circuit. (a) Logic diagram with AND gate feeding OR gate. (b) Truth table.

| A | B | C | X |
|---|---|---|---|
| 0 | 0 | 0 | 0 |
| 0 | 0 | 1 | 1 |
| 0 | 1 | 0 | 0 |
| 0 | 1 | 1 | 0 |
| 1 | 0 | 0 | 0 |
| 1 | 0 | 1 | 1 |
| 1 | 1 | 0 | 1 |
| 1 | 1 | 1 | 1 |

FIG. 31-38 Truth table used for obtaining boolean expression.

This is called a sum of products, or *minterm* boolean expression. Each AND product is ORed together. Let's examine each term in the minterm boolean expression and see how it is obtained from the truth table.

From the second row in the truth table we see that when $A = 0$, $B = 0$, and $C = 1$, the output $X$ is HIGH. The boolean expression for this condition is $\overline{A}\,\overline{B}C$, which is the first term shown in the minterm boolean expression. Using the rules of boolean algebra we have $\overline{0} \cdot \overline{0} \cdot 1 = 1$, or $1 \cdot 1 \cdot 1 = 1$. Then from the sixth row in the truth table we see that $X$ is HIGH when $A = 1$, $B = 0$, and $C = 1$. The boolean expression for this term is $A\overline{B}C = X$, the second term in the minterm boolean expression. Using the rules of boolean algebra we have $1 \cdot \overline{0} \cdot 1 = 1$, or $1 \cdot 1 \cdot 1 = 1$. The other two terms in the minterm boolean expression are obtained using the same method.

As a general rule, when designing a digital circuit from a truth table, write each of the AND products that will produce a HIGH output, and OR these AND products together. When a variable is 0 for an AND product that produces a HIGH output, indicate the variable as complemented. When a variable is 1 for an AND product that produces a HIGH output, the variable should appear uncomplemented.

**SIMPLIFYING BOOLEAN EXPRESSIONS** Before building the logic circuit that would implement the boolean expression $\overline{A}\,\overline{B}C + A\overline{B}C + AB\overline{C} + ABC = X$, it should be determined whether or not the boolean expression can be simplified. Here we can apply the rules of boolean algebra. Remember that a simpler boolean expression means a simpler overall logic circuit that requires fewer ICs.

One way to simplify the boolean expression $\overline{A}\,\overline{B}C + A\overline{B}C + AB\overline{C} + ABC = X$ is to factor the boolean expression if possible. Notice that the first two terms have $\overline{B}C$ as common factors. The factoring can be shown as:

$$\overline{A}\,\overline{B}C + A\overline{B}C$$
$$\overline{B}C(A + \overline{A})$$

$A + \overline{A} = 1$, and $\overline{B}C \cdot 1$ simplifies to $\overline{B}C$. Therefore, the first two terms $\overline{A}\,\overline{B}C + A\overline{B}C$ simplify to $\overline{B}C$. The second two terms $AB\overline{C} + ABC$ have $AB$ as common factors. The factoring can be shown as:

$$AB\overline{C} + ABC$$
$$AB(C + \overline{C})$$

$C + \overline{C} = 1$, and $AB \cdot 1$ simplifies to $AB$. Therefore, the second two terms can be simplified to $AB$. Thus,

$$\overline{A}\,\overline{B}C + A\overline{B}C + AB\overline{C} + ABC = AB + \overline{B}C$$

Again, not only is the boolean expression simplified, but so is the resultant logic circuit.

To build the logic circuit for $AB + \overline{B}C = X$, we use the configuration shown in Fig. 31-39a. Notice how the boolean expression and logic circuit match. Inputs $A$ and $B$ are active HIGH inputs for the upper AND gate, while the lower AND gate uses an active LOW input $B$ and an active HIGH input $C$. The output $X$ is also active HIGH.

**REDUCING THE NUMBER OF ICs REQUIRED TO IMPLEMENT A BOOLEAN EXPRESSION**    The compactness of an electronic device is extremely important in today's world. In digital electronic circuitry it is desirable to perform a specific logic function using as few ICs as possible. In digital electronics, ICs known as *TTL* (transistor-transistor logic) *circuits* are often used. For a complete listing of all TTL devices, refer to the TTL data book published by Texas Instruments. The logic circuit in Fig. 31-39a will require three different ICs, using one 7404 hex inverter (IC1), one 7408 quad 2-input AND gate (IC2), and one 7432 quad 2-input OR gate (IC3). IC pin numbers are shown for each logic gate. Although not shown in Fig. 31-39a, each IC is connected to $V_{CC}$ and ground through the appropriate pins.

The same logic function that would implement the boolean expression $AB + \overline{B}C = X$ could be built using only one 7400 quad 2-input NAND gate. This is shown in Fig. 31-39b. IC pin numbers are shown for each gate inside the 7400 device. The inverter symbol in Fig. 31-39b is a NAND gate wired to work as an inverter. The boolean expression for this circuit would be $\overline{\overline{AB}} + \overline{\overline{BC}} = X$, which simplifies to $AB + \overline{B}C = X$. The idea shown in Fig. 31-39b is that the logic circuit uses only one IC instead of three to perform the exact same logic function. This, of course, means less cost, less space, and less weight for the electronic device.

In Fig. 31-39b the circuit uses all NAND gates. NAND gates are often referred to as the universal logic gate because they can be used to implement any boolean expression. The right most NAND gate (numbered 4 in the diagram) is performing the OR function and is, therefore, drawn using the alternate symbol. The middle NAND gates (numbered 2 and 3) perform the AND function and are, therefore, drawn using the standard symbol. Notice the double inversion from the outputs of NAND gates 2 and 3 to the inputs of NAND gate 4. Whenever possible, connect bubbled outputs to bubbled inputs and nonbubbled outputs to nonbubbled inputs. This makes it much easier for technicians and engineers to follow the signal flow through the circuit and to determine the input conditions that are required to produce an active output, as explained in Sec. 31-9. Double inversion is the same as no inversion at all!

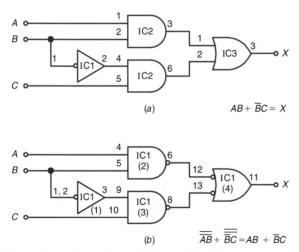

FIG. 31-39    Constructing a logic diagram from the simplified boolean expression. (*a*) Circuit built using three ICs. (*b*) Circuit built using one 7400 IC. Both figures *a* and *b* implement the boolean expression $AB + \overline{B}C$.

Any logic circuit of AND gates and OR gates can be replaced with equivalent NAND gates. This can be accomplished by adding circles at the outputs of each AND gate and circles at the inputs of each OR gate. This converts all AND gates and OR gates to NAND gates. If two bubbles appear in series, they have no effect on the overall operation of the circuit. If converting AND gates and OR gates to NAND gates causes a single bubble to appear at an input or output, then an inverter must be added to the input or output to produce an equivalent boolean expression like that of the original AND/OR logic circuit. Using these rules, the boolean expression of the resultant logic circuit, consisting of NAND gates, will always simplify to the same equation shown for the original logic circuit consisting of AND's and OR's.

---

### TEST-POINT QUESTION 31-11

Answers at end of chapter.

Answer True or False.
**a.** The NAND gate is considered a universal logic gate.
**b.** Boolean expressions can be simplified using boolean algebra.
**c.** Two bubbles in series provide inversion.

## 31-12 FLIP-FLOPS

A *flip-flop* is a digital circuit that has two stable states. A flip-flop will stay in one of its two stable states until an input pulse forces the flip-flop to switch to its other stable state. The flip-flop can remain in either stable state indefinitely. Flip-flops are used to store binary information. Digital memory circuits that can store bits of data are an essential part of any computer system.

*RS* **FLIP-FLOPS**   The most basic type of flip-flop is the reset/set type, hence the name *RS* flip-flop. The basic *RS* flip-flop can be built using either two NOR gates, as shown in Fig. 31-40a, or two NAND gates, as shown in Fig. 31-40b. Notice that for either type, the inputs are labeled $R$ for reset, and $S$ for set. Also each flip-flop has two outputs labeled $Q$ and $\overline{Q}$. The flip-flop is said to be set when $Q = 1$ and $\overline{Q} = 0$. When $Q = 0$ and $\overline{Q} = 1$, the flip-flop is said to be reset.

Let's analyze the NOR gate flip-flop and its truth table in Fig. 31-40a. When $S_1$ is in the up position, $R = 1$ and $S = 0$. For this condition $Q = 0$ and $\overline{Q} = 1$; therefore, the flip-flop is reset. This condition is shown in the third row of the truth table. When $S_1$ is in the down position, $R = 0$ and $S = 1$. For this condition $Q = 1$ and $\overline{Q} = 0$; therefore, the flip-flop is set. This condition is shown in the second row of the truth table. When $S_1$ is moved to its middle position, the flip-flop output does not change. In fact, moving $S_1$ back and forth between its middle and set positions will not change the $Q$ and $\overline{Q}$ outputs. The only way to reset the flip-flop is to move $S_1$ to its up position, where $R = 1$ and $S = 0$. Again, once the flip-flop is reset, moving $S_1$ back and forth between its middle and reset positions does not change the condition of the $Q$ and $\overline{Q}$ outputs. When $S_1$ is in its middle position, $R = 0$ and $S = 0$. This condition is shown in the first row of the truth table. Notice that for this condition, no change (NC) occurs in the flip-flop outputs. Resistors $R_1$ and $R_2$ are called *pull-down resistors*.

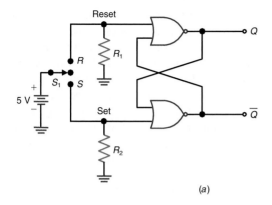

| R | S | Q | Comment |
|---|---|---|---|
| 0 | 0 | NC | No change |
| 0 | 1 | 1 | Set |
| 1 | 0 | 0 | Reset |
| 1 | 1 | * | Illegal |

(a)

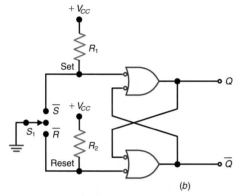

| R | S | Q | Comment |
|---|---|---|---|
| 0 | 0 | * | Illegal |
| 0 | 1 | 0 | Reset |
| 1 | 0 | 1 | Set |
| 1 | 1 | NC | No change |

(b)

FIG. 31-40 (a) Set/reset flip-flop with active HIGH inputs. (b) Set/reset flip-flop with active LOW inputs.

These resistors pull the TTL inputs to ground for binary 0. The maximum resistance value for either $R_1$ or $R_2$ should not exceed 500 Ω. This is determined by the following relationship:

$$R_{\text{pull-down (max)}} = V_{\text{IL}}/I_{\text{IL}}$$
$$= 0.8 \text{ V}/1.6 \text{ mA}$$
$$R_{\text{pull-down (max)}} = 500 \text{ Ω}$$

This basically says that $R$ must not be so large that its voltage drop exceeds 0.8 V. Remember, logic gates will recognize an input as LOW if the voltage is 0.8 V or less. Also remember that a low TTL input could draw as much as 1.6 mA of current.

One more thing. The inputs without bubbles in Fig. 31-40a are active HIGH. This flip-flop will only respond to HIGH inputs. For example, in Fig. 31-40a assume that the flip-flop is reset, where $Q = 0$ and $\overline{Q} = 1$. If we move $S_1$ to its set position, the flip-flop outputs change to $Q = 1$ and $\overline{Q} = 0$. It is the HIGH $S$ input, not the LOW $R$ input, that causes the flip-flop outputs to change, hence the term active HIGH. To reset the flip-flop, we move $S_1$ to its reset position to obtain $Q = 0$ and $\overline{Q} = 1$. It is the HIGH $R$ input, not the LOW $S$ input, that causes the flip-flop outputs to change.

The bottom row of the truth table in Fig. 31-40a shows that $R = 1$ and $S = 1$. If this were possible (it is not with the circuit in Fig. 31-40a), both $Q$ and $\overline{Q}$ would equal 0. This is commonly referred to as an illegal or prohibited state for the outputs.

An $RS$ flip-flop built with NAND gates is shown in Fig. 31-40b. The truth table describes the operation. When $S_1$ is in the up position, $\overline{R} = 1$ and $\overline{S} = 0$. This causes the flip-flop to set, where $Q = 1$ and $\overline{Q} = 0$, as shown in the third row of the truth table. When $S_1$ is in the down position, $\overline{R} = 0$ and $\overline{S} = 1$. For this condition $Q = 0$ and $\overline{Q} = 1$, as shown in the second row of the truth table. If the flip-flop is reset, moving $S_1$ back and forth between the middle and reset positions will not affect the condition of the outputs. Likewise, if the flip-flop is set, moving $S_1$ back and forth between the set and middle positions will not change the condition of the flip-flop outputs. When $S_1$ is in the middle position, $\overline{R} = 1$ and $\overline{S} = 1$. This condition is shown in the last row of the truth table. Notice for this condition that no change occurs in the flip-flop outputs. Resistors $R_1$ and $R_2$ are called *pull-up resistors*. When $S_1$ is in the middle position, $R_1$ and $R_2$ pull the TTL inputs up to $+V_{CC}$ for a binary 1.

One more thing. The alternate logic symbol is used for the NAND gates because the $\overline{R}$ and $\overline{S}$ inputs are active LOW. For example, in Fig. 31-40b assume that the flip-flop is reset where $Q = 0$ and $\overline{Q} = 1$. If we move $S_1$ to the set position where $\overline{R} = 1$ and $\overline{S} = 0$, the flip-flop outputs change to $Q = 1$ and $\overline{Q} = 0$. It is the LOW $\overline{S}$ input, not the HIGH $\overline{R}$ input, that causes the flip-flop to set, hence the name active LOW. To reset the flip-flop, we move $S_1$ to the reset position where $Q = 0$ and $\overline{Q} = 1$. It is the LOW $\overline{R}$ input, not the HIGH $\overline{S}$ input, that resets the flip-flop.

$RS$ flip-flops are often shown using the schematic symbols in Fig. 31-41a and b. If the inputs are active HIGH, then Fig. 31-41a is used, where no bubbles appear on the input lines. If the inputs are active LOW, then the symbol shown with bubbles in Fig. 31-41b is used to indicate the active LOW characteristic. From now on $RS$ flip-flops will be shown using these symbols.

**CLOCKED $RS$ FLIP-FLOPS**  Figure 31-42a shows an $RS$ flip-flop that has a clock (CLK) input. The clock voltage is a square wave that has a maximum value of $+5$ V and a minimum value of 0 V. The truth table in Fig. 31-42b explains the operation. When the clock is LOW, the outputs will not change regardless of the conditions of the $R$ and $S$ inputs. When the clock input is HIGH, the flip-flop will set if $R = 0$ and $S = 1$. When the clock input is HIGH and $R = 1$ and $S = 0$, the flip-flop will reset. Once the flip-flop is set, or perhaps reset, the inputs $R$ and $S$ can be pulled LOW and the flip-flop will remain in its last stable state even though the clock is HIGH. The last row in the truth table shows CLK $= 1$, $R = 1$, and $S = 1$. This is an illegal, or prohibited, state because both $Q$ and $\overline{Q}$ would equal 1.

Figure 31-43 shows a clocked $RS$ flip-flop with a timing diagram depicting how the $Q$ output responds to inputs applied to the $R$, $S$, and clock inputs. When analyzing the $Q$ output in the timing diagram, refer back to the truth table in Fig. 31-42b.

It should be pointed out that computers use literally thousands of flip-flops. To coordinate the overall circuit action inside of a computer, a clock signal is sent to each and every flip-flop. This clock input signal prevents the flip-flop outputs from changing until exactly the right time.

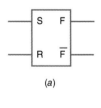

(a)

(b)

**FIG. 31-41**  Logic symbols for set/reset flip-flops. (a) $RS$ flip-flop with active HIGH inputs. (b) $RS$ flip-flop with active LOW inputs.

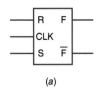

(a)

| CLK | R | S | Q |
|-----|---|---|---|
| 0 | 0 | 0 | NC |
| 0 | 0 | 1 | NC |
| 0 | 1 | 0 | NC |
| 0 | 1 | 1 | NC |
| 1 | 0 | 0 | NC |
| 1 | 0 | 1 | 1 |
| 1 | 1 | 0 | 0 |
| 1 | 1 | 1 | Illegal* |

(b)

**FIG. 31-42** Clocked *RS* flip-flop. (a) Logic diagram. (b) Truth table.

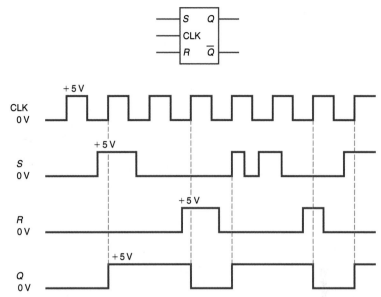

**FIG. 31-43** Clocked *RS* flip-flop with timing diagram to show how the *Q* output responds to *R*, *S*, and CLK inputs.

**D-TYPE FLIP-FLOPS** Another commonly used flip-flop is the edge-triggered *D*-type flip-flop. The logic symbol and truth table for the *D*-type flip-flop are shown in Fig. 31-44a and b. The presence of a small triangle on the clock input indicates that the flip-flop is edge-triggered. Also the *X*s in the truth table of Fig. 31-44b are called "don't care's" because if the clock is LOW, HIGH, or on it's negative edge, the flip-flop is inactive. Therefore, we "don't care" what the data input value is for these conditions of the clock. The flip-flop is edge-triggered because the flip-flop only responds when the clock is changing states.

For the *D*-type flip-flop in Fig. 31-44a, the *Q* and $\overline{Q}$ outputs change only on the positive-going edge of the incoming clock pulse. In the truth table, arrows are used to indicate whether we have a positive- or negative-going clock edge. The up arrow ( ↑ ) indicates a positive-going clock edge, and the down arrow ( ↓ ) indicates a negative-going clock edge. A positive edge-triggered flip-flop is inactive if the clock is LOW, HIGH, or on its negative-going edge. This is shown in the first three rows of the truth table. The last two rows indicate an output change on the positive-going edge of the incoming clock pulse. If *D* = 0 when the positive-going clock edge appears, then *Q* = 0 and $\overline{Q}$ = 1. If *D* = 1 when the positive-going clock edge appears, then *Q* = 1 and $\overline{Q}$ = 0. The data input and output are the same after a positive-going pulse. In other words, the input data *D* is stored only on the positive-going edge of the incoming clock pulse.

Figure 31-45 shows a clocked *D*-type flip-flop with a timing diagram depicting how the *Q* output responds to the *D* and clock inputs. When analyzing the *Q* output in the timing diagram, refer to the truth table in Fig. 31-44b.

(a)

| CLK | D | Q |
|-----|---|---|
| 0 | X | NC |
| 1 | X | NC |
| ↓ | X | NC |
| ↑ | 0 | 0 |
| ↑ | 1 | 1 |

(b)

**FIG. 31-44** Positive edge-triggered *D*-type flip-flop. (a) Logic diagram. (b) Truth table.

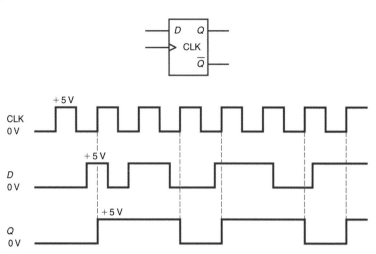

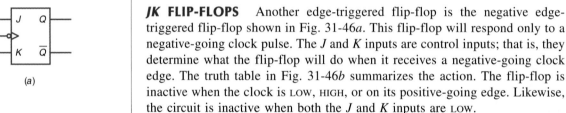

**FIG. 31-45** Positive edge-triggered *D*-type flip-flop with timing diagram to show how the *Q* output responds to *R*, *S*, and CLK inputs.

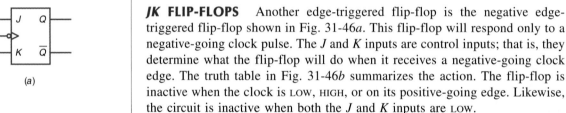

(a)

| CLK | J | K | Q |
|:---:|:---:|:---:|:---:|
| 0 | X | X | NC |
| 1 | X | X | NC |
| ↑ | X | X | NC |
| X | 0 | 0 | NC |
| ↓ | 0 | 1 | 0 |
| ↓ | 1 | 0 | 1 |
| ↓ | 1 | 1 | Toggle |

(b)

**FIG. 31-46** Negative edge-triggered *JK* flip-flop. (*a*) Logic diagram. (*b*) Truth table.

**JK FLIP-FLOPS**   Another edge-triggered flip-flop is the negative edge-triggered flip-flop shown in Fig. 31-46*a*. This flip-flop will respond only to a negative-going clock pulse. The *J* and *K* inputs are control inputs; that is, they determine what the flip-flop will do when it receives a negative-going clock edge. The truth table in Fig. 31-46*b* summarizes the action. The flip-flop is inactive when the clock is LOW, HIGH, or on its positive-going edge. Likewise, the circuit is inactive when both the *J* and *K* inputs are LOW.

When $J = 0$ and $K = 1$, the negative-going edge of the clock pulse puts the outputs at $Q = 0$ and $\overline{Q} = 1$. When $J = 1$ and $K = 0$, the negative-going edge of the clock pulse puts the *Q* outputs at $Q = 1$ and $\overline{Q} = 0$. When $J = 1$ and $K = 1$, the *Q* and $\overline{Q}$ outputs toggle, or alternate, with each negative-going clock edge. Figure 31-47 shows a clocked *JK* flip-flop with the diagram depicting how the *Q* outputs respond to the *J*, *K*, and clock inputs.

**TEST-POINT QUESTION 31-12**

Answers at end of chapter.

Answer True or False.
**a.** A flip-flop is set when $Q = 0$ and $\overline{Q} = 1$.
**b.** For a positive edge-triggered *D*-type flip-flop, the *Q* output will equal the *D* input after a positive-going clock edge is applied.
**c.** A *JK* flip-flop will operate in the toggle mode when $J = 1$ and $K = 1$.
**d.** Pull-down resistors for standard TTL inputs should not exceed 500 Ω.

## 31-13 BINARY COUNTERS

*JK* flip-flops can also be connected together to form a binary counter. Binary counters are used when it is necessary to count the number of clock pulses that

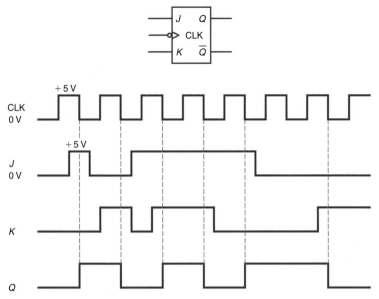

FIG. 31-47 Negative edge-triggered *JK* flip-flop with timing diagram to show how the *Q* output responds to *R*, *S*, and CLK inputs.

arrive at a clock input. Figure 31-48*a* shows a binary counter built using four *JK* flip-flops. Notice that for each flip-flop, the *J* and *K* inputs are tied HIGH. This means that each flip-flop will toggle when its clock input receives a negative-going clock pulse. The MSB of the counter is $Q_3$, and the LSB is $Q_0$.

Although not mentioned earlier, all *D* and *JK* flip-flops have clear and pre-set inputs. These inputs override all other inputs on the flip-flop. The flip-flops in Fig. 31-48 have an active LOW "clear input." When $\overline{CLR}$ is pulled LOW, all flip-flop *Q* outputs return to 0. Notice the overbar above $\overline{CLR}$. This is to indicate the active LOW condition. When the flip-flops are counting, the $\overline{CLR}$ input is pulled HIGH to its inactive state.

Figure 31-48*b* shows how the *Q* outputs of each flip-flop respond to each negative-going clock edge. Notice that with each negative-going clock edge, the count increases by 1. Initially the count is $Q_3Q_2Q_1Q_0 = 0000$. As shown in the diagram, the LSB flip-flop sets on the first negative-going edge of the clock input, increasing the count to 0001. The HIGH-going $Q_0$ output is fed to the clock input of the next most significant flip-flop. This HIGH-going clock pulse does not cause the $Q_1$ output to change. However, the second negative-going clock edge applied to the LSB flip-flop causes the $Q_0$ output to toggle from 1 to 0. This negative-going clock edge causes the $Q_1$ output to go from 0 to 1, changing the count to 0010. The count continues until 1111 is reached. Then on the next negative-going clock edge, all flip-flop outputs toggle back to 0 for a count of 0000.

Notice that each flip-flop divides the incoming clock pulse frequency by a factor of 2. The frequency of the $Q_0$ output is one-half that of the clock input. Likewise the $Q_1$ output is one-fourth the frequency of the clock input. The $Q_2$ output is one-eighth the frequency of the clock input, and the $Q_3$ output is one-sixteenth the frequency of the clock input. The counter in Fig. 31-48 is called a *ripple counter* because the output of one flip-flop is fed to the clock input of another. When the clock input to the counter receives a negative-going clock pulse, the count changes. In effect, pulses are fed down the line to the left like a ripple in water.

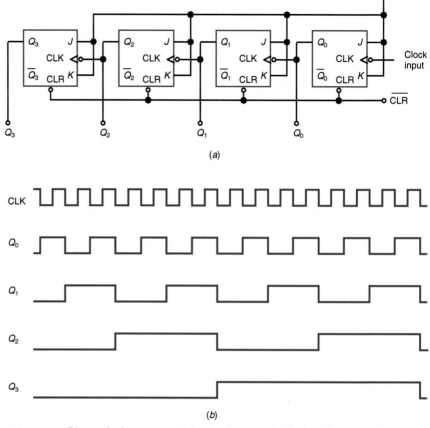

FIG. 31-48 Binary ripple counter. (*a*) Logic diagram. (*b*) Timing diagram to show the count for each negative-going clock pulse.

The modulus of a counter is the number of output states it has. A 4-bit ripple counter has a modulus of 16 because there are 16 different states ranging from 0000 to 1111. The modulus of a counter can be altered by connecting additional logic gates to the appropriate $Q$ and $\overline{Q}$ outputs, and to the preset and clear inputs of the flip-flops.

Several different counter chips are available in the 7400 series. The 7490 decade counter is a popular one. As the name implies (decade means 10), it divides the clock input by 10. Another popular counter is the 74193 presettable up/down counter. As its name implies, the 74193 can count up or down. It is called presettable because there are provisions for starting the count from some number other than 0000.

---

### TEST-POINT QUESTION 31-13

Answers at end of chapter.

Answer True or False.
**a.** *JK* flip-flops could be used individually to divide the clock input frequency by a factor of 2.
**b.** A 3-bit ripple counter has eight different output states.

# 31-14 NEW LOGIC SYMBOLS

The logic symbols used earlier in this chapter are the traditional logic symbols used by industry and educators for many years. In 1984 a new set of standard symbols was introduced by the Institute of Electrical and Electronics Engineers and the American National Standards Institute, abbreviated IEEE/ANSI. The new logic symbols are becoming accepted by the electronic industries and have been appearing in the literature published by the manufacturers of new electronic equipment. U.S. military contracts for the manufacture of electronic equipment require the use of the new symbols. Figure 31-49 shows both the traditional and new rectangular logic gate symbols. The rectangular symbols use a small right triangle to indicate inversion instead of the small bubble used on the traditional symbols. The presence or absence of a triangle on the new logic symbols indicates whether an input or output line is active HIGH or active LOW.

A special symbol inside the rectangle of each logic gate describes how the gate functions. The "1" inside the inverter gate rectangle denotes a gate with only one input. For the logic inverter in Fig. 31-49, the output $X$ will be active LOW when the input $A$ is active HIGH. The "&" symbol inside the AND gate rectangle means the output $X$ will go active HIGH only when all inputs are active HIGH. The "≥" symbol inside the OR gate rectangle means that the output $X$ will go active HIGH when one or more inputs are active HIGH.

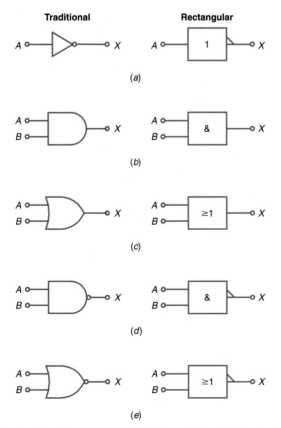

FIG. 31-49  Traditional and new rectangular logic symbols. (*a*) Inverter. (*b*) AND gate. (*c*) OR gate. (*d*) NAND gate. (*e*) NOR gate.

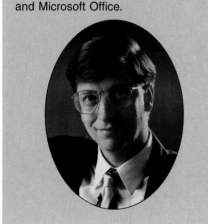
The rectangular symbols for the NAND and NOR gates are the same as for the AND and OR gates with the addition of the small triangle for inversion. The rectangular symbol for an XOR gate uses the "=1" symbol. This is shown in Fig. 31-50a. This indicates that the output will be active HIGH when only one input is HIGH. Notice that the rectangular symbol for the XNOR gate in Fig. 31-50b is the same as the XOR gate with a small triangle on the output.

Throughout this textbook and the rest of this chapter the traditional logic symbols, rather than the new rectangular logic symbols, are used. Most of the electronics industry is still using the traditional logic symbols. Also, most of the digital equipment already in the field still uses the standard traditional symbols. It is going to take several years before all electronics engineers and technicians, as well as manufacturers, convert to the new rectangular symbol. You should, however, be aware that the new symbols will become more and more commonplace in logic diagrams.

Complete ICs can be represented using the new rectangular symbol. Figure 31-51 shows the 7404 hex inverter IC. Notice that the notation "1" appears only in the top rectangle, but applies to all the inverters in the blocks below.

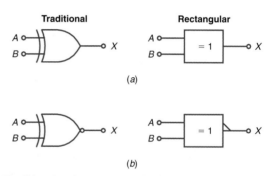

FIG. 31-50    (a) Traditional and new rectangular logic symbols for XOR gate. (b) Traditional and new rectangular logic symbols for XNOR gate.

### TEST-POINT QUESTION 31-14

Answers at end of chapter.

Answer True or False.
**a.** The new rectangular symbols use a small triangle instead of a bubble to indicate inversion.
**b.** Complete ICs can be represented using the new rectangular symbols.

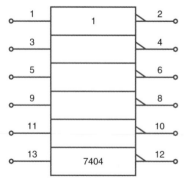

FIG. 31-51    New rectangular symbol for 7404 hex inverter.

# 31 SUMMARY AND REVIEW

Table 31-4 summarizes the basic logic gates used in digital circuits. Both the traditional and new rectangular symbols are shown, along with the boolean expression for each logic gate. Table 31-5 summarizes some of the different types of flip-flops found in digital machines.

The terminology used in the field of digital electronics is summarized in the following alphabetical list:

**AND gate**  A logic circuit with two or more inputs. The output is LOW if any or all inputs are LOW. The output is HIGH only when all inputs are HIGH.

**BCD**  Binary coded decimal. Each decimal digit is represented by a 4-bit nibble.

**binary**  A number system that is used in digital electronics. The digits used are 0 and 1. Binary 0 is used to represent a LOW voltage, and binary 1 is used to represent a HIGH voltage.

**bit**  A binary digit.

**byte**  A string of 8 bits.

**complement**  To change a binary digit to its opposite level, such as 0 to 1 or 1 to 0.

**decimal**  The most commonly used number system. The digits used are 0, 1, 2, 3, 4, 5, 6, 7, 8, 9.

## TABLE 31-4   SUMMARY OF LOGIC GATES

| TRADITIONAL | RECTANGULAR | BOOLEAN EXPRESSION |
|---|---|---|
| A ▷ X | A — [ 1 ] — X | $X = \overline{A}$ |
| A, B ▷ X | A, B — [ & ] — X | $AB = X$ |
| A, B ▷ X | A, B — [ ≥1 ] — X | $A + B = X$ |
| A, B ▷○ X | A, B — [ & ]○ X | $\overline{AB} = X$ |
| A, B ▷○ X | A, B — [ ≥ ]○ X | $\overline{A + B} = X$ |

## TABLE 31-5   SUMMARY OF FLIP-FLOPS

| LOGIC DIAGRAM | DESCRIPTION |
|---|---|
| S Q / R Q̄ | Set/reset flip-flop with active HIGH set, and reset inputs. |
| S̄ Q / R̄ Q̄ | Set/reset flip-flop with active LOW set and reset inputs. |
| S Q / CLK Q̄ / R Q̄ | Clocked set/reset flip-flop. Flip-flop is active only when clock input is HIGH. |
| D Q / CLK Q̄ | Edge-triggered D-type flip-flop. The data input D is stored on the positive-going clock edge. |
| J Q / CLK Q̄ / K Q̄ | Edge-triggered JK flip-flop. The J and K inputs determine what the flip-flop does when it receives a negative-going clock edge. |

**flip-flop** A digital circuit that can hold or store digital data.

**hexadecimal** A number system used in the microcomputer field. The digits used are 0, 1, 2, 3, 4, 5, 6, 7, 8, 9, A, B, C, D, E, and F.

**inverter** A logic gate with one input and one output. For a LOW input, the output will be HIGH, and for a HIGH input, the output will be LOW.

**NAND gate** A logic circuit with two or more inputs but only one output. The output is HIGH if any or all inputs are LOW. The output is LOW only when all inputs are HIGH.

**NOR gate** A logic circuit with two or more inputs but only one output. The output is LOW if any or all inputs are HIGH. The output is HIGH only when all inputs are LOW.

**OR gate** A logic circuit with two or more inputs but only one output. The output is HIGH if any or all inputs are HIGH. The output is LOW only when all inputs are LOW.

**radix** The number of digits used by a number system.

**truth table** A listing of input possibilities for a logic gate and the corresponding output for each input condition.

**XNOR gate** A logic circuit with two or more inputs but only one output. The output is HIGH when an even number of 1s is applied to its inputs. The output if LOW if an odd number of 1s is applied to its inputs.

**XOR gate** A logic circuit with two or more inputs but only one output. The output is HIGH when an odd number of 1s is applied to its inputs. The output is LOW when an even number of 1s is applied to its inputs.

**ANSWERS AT BACK OF BOOK.**

1. How many digits are used in the binary number system?
2. What number system has a base, or radix, of 16?
3. What is the decimal equivalent of binary 1011?
4. Which logic gate has a LOW output only when all inputs are HIGH?
5. Which logic gate has a HIGH output only when all inputs are LOW?
6. Which logic gate has a LOW output only when all inputs are LOW?
7. Which logic gate has a HIGH output only when an even number of 1s is applied to its inputs?
8. Which logic gate has a HIGH output when any or all inputs are LOW?
9. Which logic gate has a LOW output when any or all inputs are HIGH?
10. A logic gate has four inputs. When constructing the truth table, how many input combinations of 0s and 1s will there be?
11. Is a flip-flop set or reset when $Q = 0$ and $\overline{Q} = 1$?
12. Is a flip-flop set or reset when $Q = 1$ and $\overline{Q} = 0$?
13. A negative edge-triggered flip-flop has the following inputs: $J = 0$ and $K = 1$. What are the $Q$ and $\overline{Q}$ outputs after the clock input receives a negative-going clock pulse?

## QUESTIONS

1. List the next 10 counts after the hexadecimal number OAFC.
2. Define active LOW and active HIGH terminology for logic diagrams and boolean expressions.
3. With an ASCII keyboard, each keystroke produces the ASCII equivalent of the designated character. What is the output from the ASCII keyboard if you type "TWINS"?
4. Using boolean algebra express DeMorgan's theorems.
5. Explain the purpose of having standard and alternate logic symbols.
6. Explain what is meant by the toggle mode of a $JK$ flip-flop.

## PROBLEMS

**ANSWERS TO ODD-NUMBERED PROBLEMS AT BACK OF BOOK.**

1. Find the decimal equivalent for the following binary numbers: (a) 1011; (b) 10001; (c) 10000; (d) 10110101.
2. Find the binary equivalent for the following decimal numbers: (a) 15; (b) 20; (c) 54; (d) 63.
3. Convert the following hexadecimal numbers to their binary equivalents: (a) 100; (b) F06; (c) 75; (d) C33A.
4. Find the hexadecimal equivalent for the decimal number 894.
5. Convert the following binary numbers to their hexadecimal equivalents: (a) 1011111; (b) 01011111; (c) 110101; (d) 101100101001.

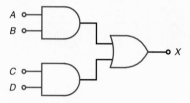

FIG. 31-52　Logic circuit for Probs. 10, 11, and 12.

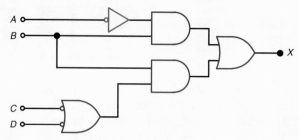

FIG. 31-53　Logic circuit for Prob. 17.

6. Find the decimal equivalent for the following BCD numbers: (**a**) 0010 0101; (**b**) 1001 1000 0111; (**c**) 0001 1001 1000 0010.

7. Draw the logic symbol and construct a truth table for a 2-input AND gate.

8. Draw the logic symbol and construct a truth table for a 3-input NAND gate.

9. Draw the logic symbol and construct a truth table for a 3-input NOR gate.

10. Write the boolean expression for the logic circuit shown in Fig. 31-52.

11. Construct a truth table for the logic circuit in Fig. 31-52.

12. Convert the logic circuit in Fig. 31-52 to a circuit that uses only NAND gates.

13. Draw the logic diagram that most clearly represents the boolean expression $A + B + C = \overline{X}$.

14. Simplify the boolean expression $\overline{A}\overline{B}C + \overline{A}BC + A\overline{B}C + ABC = X$. Draw the logic diagram (using only NAND gates) that will implement the simplified boolean expression.

15. Draw the new rectangular logic gate symbols for the following: (**a**) inverter; (**b**) AND; (**c**) OR; (**d**) NAND; (**e**) NOR; (**f**) XOR; and (**g**) XNOR gates.

16. Draw the logic diagram for the expression $AB + BCD$. Use the new rectangular logic symbols.

17. Write the boolean expression and construct a truth table for the logic circuit in Fig. 31-53.

18. Construct a truth table and logic diagram for the boolean expression $(A + \overline{B})(C + D) = X$.

19. Using $JK$ flip-flops, draw a binary ripple counter whose natural modulus is 32. Be sure to identify each $Q$ output and where the clock input is applied.

20. In Fig. 31-54, complete the $Q$ output column in the truth table using 0 and 1. Notice in the first row that $Q = 0$ when the clock input is receiving a positive clock edge and $D = 0$.

| CLK | D | Q |
|-----|---|---|
| ↑ | 0 | 0 |
| 1 | 1 | |
| ↓ | 1 | |
| 0 | 0 | |
| ↑ | 1 | |
| 1 | 0 | |
| ↓ | 0 | |
| 0 | 0 | |

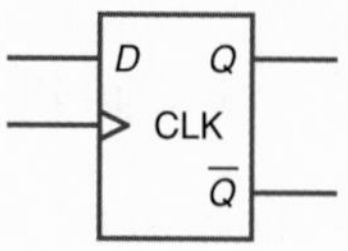

FIG. 31-54　Logic diagram and truth table for Prob. 20.

1. Using only NOR gates, draw the logic diagram for the boolean expression $(A + B)(\overline{C} + D) = X$.
2. Referring to Fig. 31-48, show how a 2-input NAND gate can be connected to alter the natural count sequence so that the modulus of the counter becomes 10.
3. Simplify the boolean expression $(\overline{A} + B)(A + B + D)\overline{D}$.

## ANSWERS TO TEST-POINT QUESTIONS

**31-1** a. 0 and 1
  b. 0, 1, 2, 3, 4, 5, 6, 7, 8, 9
  c. eight
  d. $(1000)_2$

**31-2** a. $(11110)_2$
  b. $(30)_{10}$
  c. $(111\ 1111)_2$

**31-3** a. 0, 1, 2, 3, 4, 5, 6, 7, 8, 9, A, B, C, D, E, F
  b. 53,508
  c. 10110000010100
  d. 173

**31-4** a. 0010 0100 0101
  b. 0001 0000 0101 0110
  c. 5874

**31-5** a. E
  b. 0111111

**31-6** a. T
  b. T
  c. F
  d. T
  e. T
  f. T
  g. T

**31-7** a. $A + B + C = X$
  b. $ABC = X$
  c. $\overline{A + B} = X$
  d. $\overline{AB} = X$
  e. $A + 0 = A$
  $A \cdot 0 = 0$
  $A + A = A$
  $A \cdot 1 = A$
  $A + \overline{A} = 1$
  $A \cdot \overline{A} = 0$
  $1 \oplus 1 \oplus 1 = 1$
  $0 \oplus 1 \oplus 1 = 1$

**31-8** a. T
  b. T
  c. T
  d. T
  e. T

**31-9** a. F
  b. T
  c. T
  d.
  e.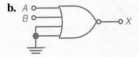

**31-10** a.

  b.

  c.

**31-11** a. T
  b. T
  c. F

**31-12** a. F
  b. T
  c. T
  d. T

**31-13** a. T
  b. T

**31-14** a. T
  b. T

# CHAPTER 32

# INTEGRATED CIRCUITS

Integrated circuits (ICs) have reduced the size, weight, and power requirements of today's electronic equipment. They are replacing transistors in electronic circuits just as transistors once replaced vacuum tubes. ICs are actually microelectronic circuits. Contained within the IC itself are microscopically small electronic components such as diodes, transistors, resistors, and capacitors. The actual IC is formed on a single piece of silicon about the size of a pin head.

ICs are classified as either digital or linear. Digital ICs are used in computers, calculators, and digital clocks as well as many other digital devices. Linear ICs are used in analog-type circuits such as audio amplifiers, voltage regulators, operational amplifiers, and radio frequency circuits to name just a few. Most linear ICs are low-power devices with power dissipation ratings less than 1 W. There are, however, some chips available that are capable of handling larger amounts of power such as 5 W or more. Most linear ICs manufactured today are designed so that they can be used in a wide variety of applications.

# CHAPTER OBJECTIVES

*Upon completion of this chapter, you should be able to:*

- *Understand* what is meant by the open-loop voltage gain of an op amp.
- *Define* the terms *slew rate* and *power bandwidth*.
- *Calculate* the voltage gain of an inverting amplifier.
- *Calculate* the voltage gain of a noninverting amplifier.
- *Explain* the usefulness of an op amp voltage-follower circuit.
- *Understand* the operation of an op amp summing amplifier.
- *Understand* the operation of an op amp differential amplifier.
- *Understand* the operation of a unity-gain active filter.

# IMPORTANT TERMS IN THIS CHAPTER

closed-loop voltage gain
common mode input
common mode rejection ratio
  (CMRR)
comparator
differential amplifiers
differential input voltage

input bias current
input offset current
inverting amplifier
noninverting amplifier
open-loop voltage gain
power bandwidth
saturation

slew rate
summing amplifier
unity-gain active filter
virtual ground
zero-crossing detector

# TOPICS COVERED IN THIS CHAPTER

**32-1**  Operational Amplifiers and Their
        Characteristics

**32-2**  Op Amp Circuits

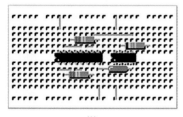

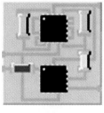

FIG. 32-1 Typical integrated circuit (IC). (*a*) Sample of 14-pin dual in-line package IC. (*b*) Two IC packages used in a circuit that is mounted on a lab prototype board. (*c*) Two surface-mount IC packages used in an SMT circuit.

Operational amplifiers (op amps) are the most commonly used type of linear integrated circuit (IC). (A typical IC package is shown in Fig. 32-1*a*.) By definition, an op amp is a high-gain, direct-coupled, differential amplifier. An op amp referred to as the 741 has become an industry standard. This op amp, which is contained in an 8-pin IC, is made by several different manufacturers. They are, however, all equivalent because the specifications are nearly identical from one manufacturer to another. Figure 32-1*b* shows two IC packages mounted on a lab prototype board. Figure 32-1*c* shows two surface-mounted IC packages on a printed circuit board.

Figure 32-2*a* shows the internal diodes, transistors, resistors, and capacitors for a 741 op amp. The base leads of *Q*1 and *Q*2 connect to pins on the IC unit and serve as the two inputs for the op amp. *Q*1 and *Q*2 form a differential amplifier circuit. This circuit is used because it can amplify the difference in voltage between the two input signals.

The output of the op amp is taken at the emitters of transistors *Q*8 and *Q*9. These transistors are connected in a push-pull configuration. As far as the output waveform is concerned, *Q*8 conducts during the positive half cycle, and *Q*9 conducts during the negative half cycle. This push-pull configuration allows the op amp to have a very low output impedance, which is analogous to a voltage source having a very low internal resistance.

When viewing the circuit in Fig. 32-2*a*, it is important to note that direct coupling is used between all stages. For this reason, the op amp can amplify signals all the way down to dc. Capacitor $C_C$ affects the operation of the op amp at higher frequencies. This capacitor is called a *compensating capacitor,* with a value of about 30 pF. $C_C$ is used to prevent undesirable oscillations from occurring within the op amp.

The schematic symbol commonly used for op amps is shown in Fig. 32-2*b*. Notice that the triangular schematic symbol shows only the pin connections to different points inside the op amp. Pin 7 connects to $+V_{CC}$, and pin 4 connects to $-V_{CC}$. Also, pins 2 and 3 connect to the op amp inputs, while pin 6 connects to the op amp output.

**OPEN-LOOP VOLTAGE GAIN $A_{VOL}$** The open-loop voltage gain $A_{VOL}$ of an op amp is its voltage gain when there is no negative feedback. The open-loop voltage gain of an op amp is the ratio of its output voltage $V_{out}$ to its differential input voltage $V_{id}$. The open-loop voltage gain $A_{VOL}$ of an op amp is expressed as:

$$A_{VOL} = \frac{V_{out}}{V_{id}} \tag{32-1}$$

where

$$A_{VOL} = \text{open-loop voltage gain of op amp}$$
$$V_{out} = \text{output voltage}$$
$$V_{id} = \text{differential input voltage}$$

The typical value of $A_{VOL}$ for a 741 op amp is 200,000.

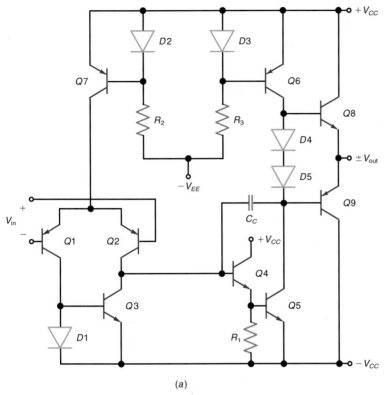

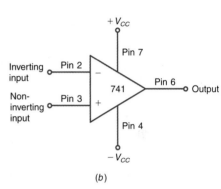

(a)                                                    (b)

FIG. 32-2   (a) Simplified schematic of a 741 op amp. (b) Schematic symbol for op amp.

Figure 32-3a shows the idea. Notice that $V_{id}$ is equal to $V_1 - V_2$, and that $V_{out}$ equals $A_{VOL} \times V_{id}$. Only the differential voltage $V_1 - V_2$ is amplified, not the individual values of $V_1$ and $V_2$.

As a numerical example, assume in Fig. 32-3b that the differential input $V_{id} = \pm 50 \ \mu V$ and that $A_{VOL} = 200,000$. Then

$$V_{out} = A_{VOL} \times V_{id}$$
$$= 200,000 \times (\pm 50 \ \mu V)$$
$$V_{out} = \pm 10 \ V$$

The answer is shown as $\pm 10$ V in Fig. 32-3b because the polarity of $V_{id}$ has not been specified. The polarity of output voltage $V_{out}$ for an op amp is determined using the following two rules.

1.  When the voltage at the noninverting (+) input is made positive with respect to its inverting (−) input, the output is positive.
2.  When the voltage at the noninverting (+) input is made negative with respect to its inverting (−) input, the output is negative.

Assume in Fig. 32-3c that $V_1 = 1$ V and $V_2 = 999.95$ mV. What will the output be? Simply multiply $V_{id}$ by $A_{VOL}$. But first find $V_{id}$.

$$V_{id} = V_1 - V_2$$
$$= 1 \ V - 999.95 \ mV$$
$$V_{id} = 50 \ \mu V$$

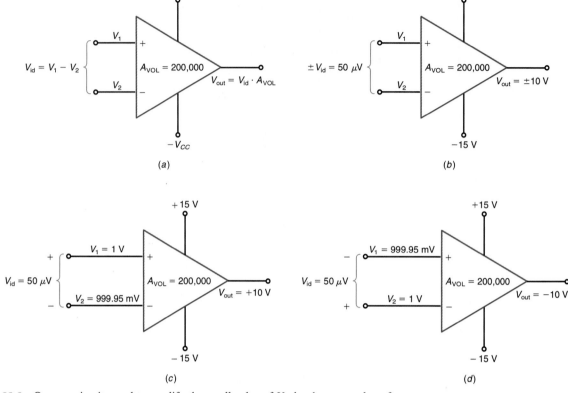

FIG. 32-3 Op amp circuits used to amplify the small value of $V_{id}$ by the HIGH value of $A_{VOL}$. See text for analysis.

To calculate $V_{out}$, proceed as follows:

$$V_{out} = A_{VOL} \times V_{id}$$
$$= 200,000 \times 50 \ \mu V$$
$$V_{out} = +10 \ V$$

Notice again that the actual values of $V_1$ and $V_2$ are not amplified, only the difference between them is. Notice also in Fig. 32-3c that $V_1$ is connected to the noninverting (+) input terminal and $V_2$ is connected to the inverting input terminal. Because $V_1$ is more positive than $V_2$, the output is positive.

In Fig. 32-3d, $V_1$ and $V_2$ are reversed. Here $V_1$ is negative with respect to $V_2$. $V_{id}$ is calculated as:

$$V_{id} = V_1 - V_2$$
$$= 999.95 \ mV - 1 \ V$$
$$V_{id} = -50 \ \mu V$$

To find $V_{out}$, multiply $V_{id}$ by $A_{VOL}$:

$$V_{out} = A_{VOL} \times V_{id}$$
$$= 200,000 \times -50 \ \mu V$$
$$V_{out} = -10 \ V$$

The key point demonstrated in all the circuits in Fig. 32-3 is that only the differential input voltage $V_{id}$ is amplified by the op amps HIGH value of open-loop voltage gain.

It should be pointed out that there are upper and lower limits for the output voltage $V_{out}$. The upper limit of $V_{out}$ is called the *positive saturation voltage* and is designated $+V_{sat}$. The lower limit of $V_{out}$ is called the *negative saturation voltage* and is designated $-V_{sat}$. For the 741, $\pm V_{sat}$ is usually within a couple volts of $\pm V_{CC}$. For example, if $\pm V_{CC} = \pm 15$ V, then $\pm V_{sat} = \pm 13$ V. Incidentally, the amount of differential input voltage $V_{id}$ required to produce positive or negative saturation in Fig. 32-3 is found as follows:

$$\pm V_{id} = \frac{\pm V_{sat}}{A_{VOL}} = \frac{\pm 13 \text{ V}}{200,000}$$

$$\pm V_{id} = \pm 65 \ \mu\text{V}$$

Remember that $V_{out}$ will be positive if the noninverting input $(+)$ is made positive with respect to the inverting $(-)$ input. Likewise, $V_{out}$ will be negative if the noninverting input $(+)$ is made negative with respect to the inverting $(-)$ input.

One more point. If the output voltage of any op amp lies between $\pm V_{sat}$, then $V_{id}$ will be so small that it can be considered zero. Realistically it is very difficult to measure a $V_{id}$ of 65 $\mu$V in the laboratory because of the induced noise voltages present. Therefore, $V_{id}$ can be considered zero, or $V_{id} = 0$ V, in most cases.

**INPUT BIAS CURRENTS**    In Fig. 32-2a, the base leads of Q1 and Q2 serve as the inputs to the op amp. These transistors must be biased correctly before any signal voltage can be amplified. In other words Q1 and Q2 must have external dc return paths to the power supply ground. Figure 32-4 shows current flowing from the noninverting and inverting input terminals when they're grounded. For a 741, these currents are very, very small, usually 80 nA (80 $\times$ 10$^{-9}$ A) or less. In Fig. 32-4 the $I_{B+}$ designates current flowing from the noninverting input terminal, and $I_{B-}$ designates the current flowing from the inverting input terminal. Manufacturers specify $I_B$ as the average of the two currents $I_{B+}$ and $I_{B-}$. This can be shown as:

▶  $$I_B = \frac{|I_{B+}| + |I_{B-}|}{2} \qquad (32\text{-}2)$$

where $\|$ means magnitude without regard to polarity. $I_{B+}$ and $I_{B-}$ may be different because it is difficult to match Q1 and Q2 exactly. The difference between these two currents is designated as $I_{OS}$ for input offset current. $I_{OS}$ can be expressed as:

▶  $$I_{OS} = |I_{B+}| - |I_{B-}| \qquad (32\text{-}3)$$

For a 741, $I_{OS}$ is typically 20 nA.

For most of our analysis, assume that the value of $I_{B+}$ and $I_{B-}$ are zero because they are so small. However, in some cases of high precision, the effects of $I_{B+}$ and $I_{B-}$ on circuit operation must be taken into account.

**FREQUENCY RESPONSE**    Figure 32-5 shows the frequency response curve for a typical 741 op amp. Notice that for frequencies below 10 Hz, $A_{VOL} =$

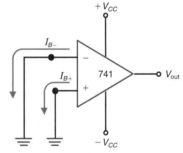

FIG. 32-4   Input bias currents flowing from op amp input terminals.

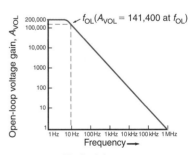

FIG. 32-5   Typical frequency response curve for a 741 op amp without negative feedback.

200,000, and at 10 Hz, $A_{VOL}$ is down to 70.7 percent of its maximum value. That is, at 10 Hz, $A_{VOL} = 141,400$. This frequency is designated $f_{OL}$, for open-loop cut-off frequency.

Beyond $f_{OL}$, the voltage gain decreases by a factor of 10 for each decade (factor of 10) increase in frequency. This drop in $A_{VOL}$ at higher frequencies is caused by capacitor $C_C$ inside the op amp. The frequency where $A_{VOL}$ equals 1 is designated $f_{unity}$. For a 741, $f_{unity}$ is approximately 1 MHz.

**SLEW RATE**   Another very important op amp specification is its slew rate, usually designated $S_R$. The slew-rate specification of an op amp tells how fast the output voltage can change. The slew rate of an op amp is specified in volts per microsecond, or V/$\mu$s. For a 741, the $S_R$ is 0.5 V/$\mu$s. This means that no matter how fast the input voltage to a 741 op amp changes, the output voltage can only change as fast as its slew rate allows—0.5 V/$\mu$s. Figure 32-6 illustrates the idea. Here the op amp's output waveform should be an amplified version of the sinusoidal input $V_{id}$. Waveform A would be the expected output. However, if the slope of the output sine wave exceeds the $S_R$ rating of the op amp, the waveform would appear triangular; that is, as waveform B. Therefore, slew-rate distortion of a sine wave produces a triangular wave.

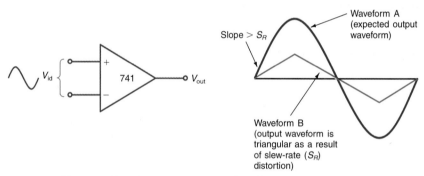

FIG. 32-6   Slew-rate distortion occurs when the initial slope of the output waveform exceeds the $S_R$ rating of the op amp.

**POWER BANDWIDTH**   There are two ways to avoid slew-rate distortion of a sine wave: either use an op amp with a faster slew rate or accept an output waveform with a lower peak voltage. Using an op amp with a faster slew rate seems like a logical solution because then the output waveform will be able to follow the sinusoidal input voltage $V_{id}$. But why would less peak voltage for the output waveform solve the problem? The answer is best illustrated in Fig. 32-7. Here, both waveforms A and B have exactly the same frequency but different peak values. Waveform A has a peak value of 1 V, while waveform B has a peak value of 10 V. If we compare the voltage change during the first 30° of each waveform, we see that the change in voltage $\Delta V$ for waveform A is 0.5 V during the first 30°, while $\Delta V$ for waveform B is 5 V during the same interval. Notice that the rate of voltage change for waveform B is 10 times that of waveform A during the same time interval even though both waveforms have exactly the same frequency! Therefore, it is true to say that two waveforms having identical frequencies, but different peak values have significantly different slopes during their positive and negative alternations.

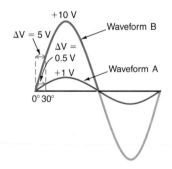

FIG. 32-7   Waveforms A and B have identical frequencies but different slopes during their positive and negative alternations.

The higher the peak voltage of a sine wave for a given frequency, the greater its initial slope. If the initial slope of the output waveform exceeds the $S_R$ rating of the op amp, slew-rate distortion will occur. The following formula shows the highest undistorted frequency out of an op amp for a given $S_R$ and peak voltage:

▶ 
$$f_{max} = \frac{S_R}{2\pi V_{pk}}$$
(32-4)

where

$$f_{max} = \text{Highest undistorted frequency}$$
$$S_R = \text{Slew rate}$$
$$V_{pk} = \text{Peak value of output sine wave}$$

Notice that $f_{max}$ can be increased by using an op amp with a higher slew rate or by accepting an output wave form with less peak voltage.

## Example

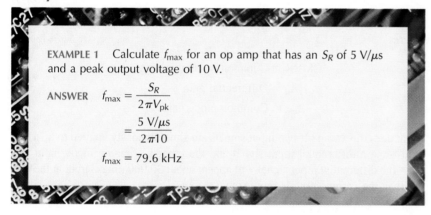

**EXAMPLE 1**  Calculate $f_{max}$ for an op amp that has an $S_R$ of 5 V/μs and a peak output voltage of 10 V.

**ANSWER**  $f_{max} = \dfrac{S_R}{2\pi V_{pk}}$

$= \dfrac{5\ \text{V/μs}}{2\pi 10}$

$f_{max} = 79.6\ \text{kHz}$

The frequency $f_{max}$ of 79.6 kHz is commonly called the 10-V power bandwidth. This means that slew-rate distortion for a 10-V peak sine wave will not occur for frequencies at or below 79.6 kHz.

If we try to amplify higher frequencies with the same peak value of 10 V, we get slew-rate distortion, meaning the output waveform gets triangular as described earlier.

**OUTPUT SHORT-CIRCUIT CURRENT**  An op amp, such as the 741, has short-circuit output protection. For a 741, the output short-circuit current is approximately 25 mA. This means that if the op amp output (pin 6) is tied directly to ground, the output current will not exceed 25 mA. It should be noted that small load resistances connected to the op amp output will usually have lower amplitudes of output voltage because the output voltage cannot exceed 25 mA $\times R_L$.

**COMMON MODE REJECTION RATIO**  As mentioned earlier, an op amp amplifies only the difference in voltage between its two inputs. This means that

if two identical signals are applied to the inputs of an op amp, each with exactly the same phasoral relationship and voltage values, the output will be zero. Such a signal is called a common mode signal because identical waveforms are applied to both inputs. In other words, the signal is common to both inputs. Unfortunately, even with a perfect common mode–type signal, the output from the op amp will not be zero. This is because op amps are not ideal. The rejection of the common mode signal, however, is very high. For a typical 741, the common mode rejection ratio (CMRR) is 90 db, which corresponds to a ratio of about 30,000. The CMRR of an op amp is defined as its ability to amplify differential input signals while attenuating or rejecting common mode signals. Expressed as an equation:

$$\text{CMRR} = \frac{A_d}{A_{cm}} \qquad\qquad \textbf{(32-5)}$$

where

$$\text{CMRR} = \text{Common mode rejection ratio}$$
$$A_d = \text{Differential gain}$$
$$A_{cm} = \text{Common mode gain}$$

What does this mean? If two input signals are simultaneously applied to a 741 op amp—one a differential input signal and the other a common mode input signal—the differential input signal will appear about 30,000 times larger at the output than the common mode input signal.

### TEST-POINT QUESTION 32-1

Answers at end of chapter.

Answer True or False.
a. The open-loop voltage gain $A_{VOL}$ of an op amp is very large for low frequencies.
b. For an op amp, $\pm V_{sat}$ is usually within a couple volts of $\pm V_{CC}$.
c. For a 741, the open-loop cut-off frequency $f_{OL}$ is 10 Hz.
d. The slew rate $S_R$ of an op amp tells how well the op amp can reject common mode signals.
e. In order to increase $f_{max}$ (the highest undistorted frequency out of an op amp), either accept less peak voltage for the output waveform or use an op amp with a higher $S_R$.
f. The output of an op amp will be positive if its noninverting (+) input is positive with respect to its inverting (−) input.
g. The output of an op amp will be negative if its inverting (−) input is positive with respect to its noninverting (+) input.

**h.** When the output voltage of an op amp is less than $\pm V_{sat}$, then $V_{id}$ is so small it can be considered zero.

## 32-2 OP AMP CIRCUITS

Most op amp circuits use negative feedback. As a general rule, op amp circuits without negative feedback are too unstable to be useful. Negative feedback reduces the overall voltage gain of the op amp circuit. In return for this loss of gain, however, we have a tremendously stable voltage gain over a very wide range of frequencies.

**INVERTING AMPLIFIER**   Figure 32-8 shows an op amp connected to work as an inverting amplifier. It is called an inverting amplifier because the input and output signals are 180° out of phase when $V_{in}$ is applied to the inverting $(-)$ input terminal, as shown.

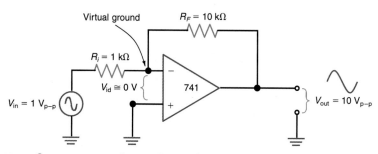

FIG. 32-8   Op amp connected to work as an inverting amplifier.

Resistors $R_F$ and $R_i$ provide the negative feedback, which in turn controls the circuit's overall voltage gain. The output signal $V_{out}$ is fed back to the inverting input of the op amp through resistors $R_F$ and $R_i$. The voltage between the inverting input and ground is $V_{id}$. The exact value of $V_{id}$ is determined by the values $A_{VOL}$ and $V_{out}$. For all practical purposes, $V_{id}$ is so small that it can be considered zero. This introduces little or no error in our circuit analysis. Because $V_{id}$ is so small (practically zero), the inverting input terminal of the op amp in Fig. 32-8 is said to be at virtual ground, because the voltage at the op amps inverting input is nearly the same as at ground, yet it can sink no current.

Since the inverting input is at virtual ground, $V_{in}$ is dropped across $R_i$. Therefore,

$$I = \frac{V_{in}}{R_i} \tag{32-6}$$

This says that all input current produced by $V_{in}$ flows through resistor $R_i$. Rearranging this equation, we have:

$$V_{in} = I \times R_i \tag{32-7}$$

Practically no current flows from the inverting input terminal, so all the current produced by $V_{in}$ must flow through $R_F$ to the op amp output terminal. Therefore,

$$V_{out} = I \times R_F \tag{32-8}$$

Since $V_{in} = I \times R_i$ and $V_{out} = I \times R_F$, we can calculate the voltage gain of the circuit as follows:

$$A_{CL} = \frac{V_{out}}{V_{in}} \tag{32-9}$$

$$= \frac{I \times R_F}{I \times R_i}$$

$$A_{CL} = \frac{R_F}{R_i}$$

where

$$A_{CL} = \text{Closed-loop voltage gain}$$

The closed-loop voltage gain of the circuit is the voltage gain with negative feedback. In Fig. 32-8, $A_{CL}$ is found as:

$$A_{CL} = \frac{R_F}{R_i}$$

$$= \frac{10 \text{ k}\Omega}{1 \text{ k}\Omega}$$

$$A_{CL} = 10$$

In Fig. 32-8, $V_{out}$ can be found by multiplying $A_{CL}$ by $V_{in}$:

$$V_{out} = A_{CL} \times V_{in} = 10 \times 1 \text{ V}_{p-p}$$

$$V_{out} = 10 \text{ V}_{p-p}$$

Remember that for an inverting amplifier, $V_{out}$ is 180° out of phase with $V_{in}$.

**NONINVERTING AMPLIFIER** Figure 32-9 shows an op amp circuit connected as a noninverting amplifier. It is a noninverting amplifier because the input signal $V_{in}$ drives the noninverting input terminal of the op amp. For this circuit, the input and output signals are always in phase. In Fig. 32-9, $V_{id}$ is again considered to be approximately 0 V. This means that the voltage across resistor $R_i$ must equal $V_{in}$. The current through $R_i$ is found as follows:

$$I = \frac{V_{in}}{R_i} \quad \text{or} \tag{32-10}$$

$$V_{in} = I \times R_i$$

All this current must flow through $R_F$, since virtually no current flows from the inverting input terminal. Therefore, the voltage across $R_F$ is:

$$V_{R_F} = I \times R_F \tag{32-11}$$

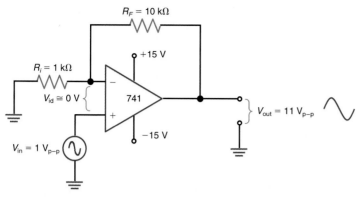

FIG. 32-9 Op amp connected to work as a noninverting amplifier.

Since the output voltage $V_{out}$ is taken with respect to ground, $V_{out}$ must be the sum of $V_{R_i}$ and $V_{R_F}$:

▶ $$V_{out} = IR_F + IR_i \quad \text{or}$$ (32-12)
$$V_{out} = I(R_F + R_i)$$

Therefore, the closed-loop voltage gain $A_{CL}$ can be expressed as:

▶ $$A_{CL} = \frac{V_{out}}{V_{in}}$$ (32-13)

$$= \frac{I(R_F + R_i)}{IR_i}$$

$$A_{CL} = \frac{R_F + R_i}{R_i} \quad \text{or}$$

$$A_{CL} = \frac{R_F}{R_i} + 1$$

For Fig. 32-9, $A_{CL}$ is:

$$A_{CL} = \frac{10 \text{ k}\Omega}{1 \text{ k}\Omega} + 1$$

$$A_{CL} = 11$$

And $V_{out}$ can be found by multiplying $A_{CL}$ by $V_{in}$:

$$V_{out} = A_{CL} \times V_{in}$$
$$= 11 \times 1 \text{ V}_{p-p}$$
$$V_{out} = 11 \text{ V}_{p-p}$$

Here is an important point. Since the voltage source has to supply virtually no current to the op amp's noninverting input, the voltage source $V_{in}$ sees a very high value of input impedance. For this reason there is virtually no loading of the voltage source $V_{in}$.

**VOLTAGE FOLLOWER**    Figure 32-10 shows the op amp connected to provide a voltage gain of one, or unity. Notice that the op amp output is connected

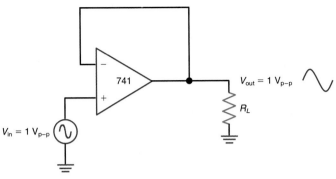

**FIG. 32-10** Op amp connected to work as a voltage follower. $A_{CL} = 1$; $V_{out} = V_{in} = 1$ Vpp.

directly to the inverting input terminal to obtain the maximum amount of negative feedback possible. For this circuit, $A_{CL} = 1$. Because $V_{id} = 0$ V, $V_{out}$ must equal $V_{in}$. But why use such a circuit if it provides no voltage gain? It is used because the op amp circuit will buffer, or isolate, the voltage source $V_{in}$ from the load $R_L$. This means that rather than connect a relatively low value of load resistance across the terminals of $V_{in}$, the op amp can be used to eliminate any loading that might occur. Since the voltage source $V_{in}$ is connected to the noninverting (+) input terminal of the op amp, it has to supply virtually no current to the circuit. Thus, the voltage source won't be loaded down. Also, because of negative feedback, the op amp circuit will have an output impedance that is close to zero. In effect, then, the load believes it is being driven by an ideal voltage source with zero internal impedance.

**SUMMING AMPLIFIER**  The circuit shown in Fig. 32-11 is called a summing amplifier or summer. When $R_1 = R_2 = R_3 = R_F$, the output voltage $V_{out}$ equals the negative sum of the input voltages. Because the right end of resistors $R_1$, $R_2$, and $R_3$ are at virtual ground, the input currents are calculated as

$$I_1 = \frac{V_1}{R_1}$$

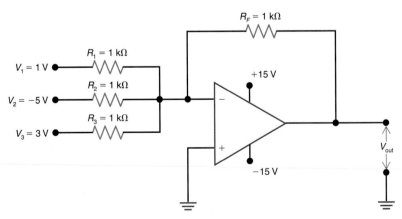

**FIG. 32-11**  Summing amplifier.

$$I_2 = \frac{V_2}{R_2}$$

$$I_3 = \frac{V_3}{R_3}$$

Because the inverting input has practically zero current, each of the input currents flow through the feedback resistor $R_F$. Because $R_1 = R_2 = R_3 = R_F$, the voltage gain of the circuit is 1 and the output voltage is calculated as

▶ $$V_{out} = -(V_1 + V_2 + V_3) \qquad \textbf{(32-14)}$$

If more inputs are necessary, additional resistors can be added at the input. This is possible because the inverting input is at virtual ground, thus effectively isolating each input from the other. Because of the virtual ground, each input sees its own input resistance and nothing else.

If each input is amplified by a different amount, the output voltage will equal the negative of the amplified sum of the inputs. When the voltage gain is different for each input, the formula for the output voltage becomes

▶ $$V_{out} = -\left(\frac{R_F}{R_1}V_1 + \frac{R_F}{R_2}V_2 + \frac{R_F}{R_3}V_3\right) \qquad \textbf{(32-15)}$$

## Example

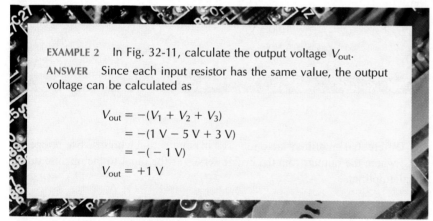

**EXAMPLE 2** In Fig. 32-11, calculate the output voltage $V_{out}$.

**ANSWER** Since each input resistor has the same value, the output voltage can be calculated as

$$V_{out} = -(V_1 + V_2 + V_3)$$
$$= -(1\ V - 5\ V + 3\ V)$$
$$= -(-1\ V)$$
$$V_{out} = +1\ V$$

**DIFFERENTIAL AMPLIFIERS** Differential amplifiers are circuits which have the ability to amplify differential input signals and severely attenuate common-mode signals. A typical op amp differential amplifier is shown in Fig. 32-12. The formula for calculating the output voltage is

▶ $$V_{out} = -\frac{R_F}{R_1}(V_X - V_Y) \qquad \textbf{(32-16)}$$

where $V_X$ and $V_Y$ represent the individual inputs being applied to the circuit. Note that if $V_X = V_Y$, the output voltage will be zero. Therefore, this circuit will amplify only the difference in voltage that exists between the inputs $V_X$ and $V_Y$.

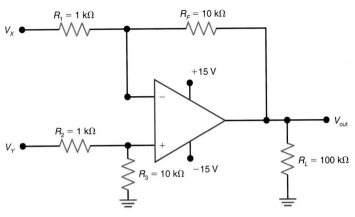

**FIG. 32-12** Op amp differential amplifier.

## Example

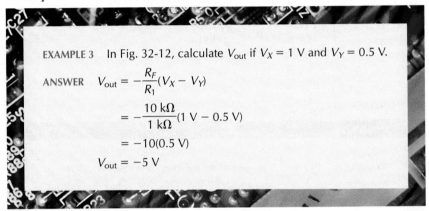

**EXAMPLE 3** In Fig. 32-12, calculate $V_{out}$ if $V_X = 1$ V and $V_Y = 0.5$ V.

**ANSWER**
$$V_{out} = -\frac{R_F}{R_1}(V_X - V_Y)$$

$$= -\frac{10 \text{ k}\Omega}{1 \text{ k}\Omega}(1 \text{ V} - 0.5 \text{ V})$$

$$= -10(0.5 \text{ V})$$

$$V_{out} = -5 \text{ V}$$

Differential amplifiers are often used in conjunction with resistive bridge circuits, where the output from the bridge serves as the input to the op amp differential amplifier.

**UNITY-GAIN ACTIVE FILTERS** An active filter is a type of filter that uses components or devices that have the ability to amplify, such as transistors or op amps. A passive filter is one that uses only passive components such as resistors, capacitors, and inductors.

Figure 32-13 shows a type of active filter that has unity gain in the passband. Figure 32-13*a* shows an active low-pass filter, whereas Fig. 32-12*b* shows an active high-pass filter. It is important to notice that, in each case, the op amp is wired to work as a voltage follower. The main reason for using the op amp is that the *RC* filter can be isolated from the load $R_L$, which may have a very low impedance. More specifically, because $Z_{in}$ is so high looking into the op amp and because $Z_{out}$ is approximately zero, the *RC* filter is effectively isolated from the load $R_L$.

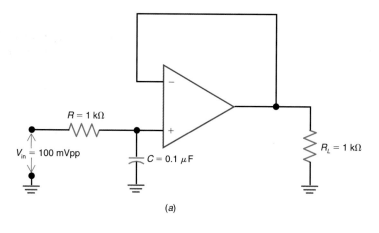

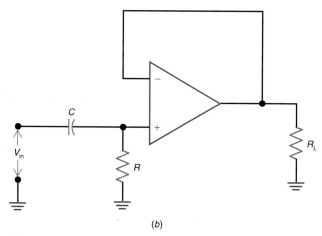

**FIG. 32-13** Unity-gain active filters. (*a*) Active low-pass filter with unity gain. (*b*) Active high-pass filter with unity gain.

For both circuits in Fig. 32-13, the cutoff frequency $f_c$ is calculated as

$$f_c = \frac{1}{2\pi RC} \tag{32-17}$$

For both filters, the voltage gain is 1 in the passband, which corresponds to a voltage gain of 0 db.

In Fig. 32-13*a*, the output voltage at any frequency can be calculated as

$$V_{\text{out}} = \frac{X_C}{Z_T} \times V_{\text{in}} \tag{32-18}$$

In Fig. 32-13*b*, $V_{\text{out}}$ can be calculated as

$$V_{\text{out}} = \frac{R}{Z_T} \times V_{\text{in}} \tag{32-19}$$

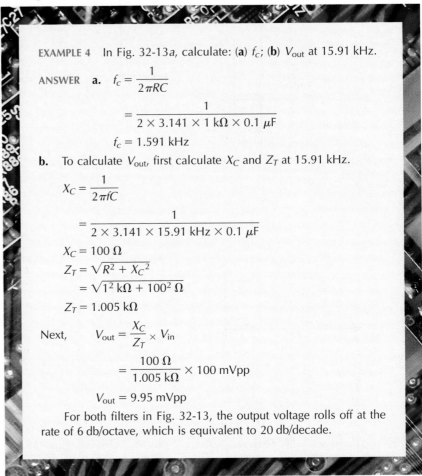

**EXAMPLE 4**  In Fig. 32-13*a*, calculate: **(a)** $f_c$; **(b)** $V_{out}$ at 15.91 kHz.

**ANSWER**  **a.**  $f_c = \dfrac{1}{2\pi RC}$

$$= \dfrac{1}{2 \times 3.141 \times 1\ k\Omega \times 0.1\ \mu F}$$

$$f_c = 1.591\ kHz$$

**b.**  To calculate $V_{out}$, first calculate $X_C$ and $Z_T$ at 15.91 kHz.

$$X_C = \dfrac{1}{2\pi fC}$$

$$= \dfrac{1}{2 \times 3.141 \times 15.91\ kHz \times 0.1\ \mu F}$$

$$X_C = 100\ \Omega$$
$$Z_T = \sqrt{R^2 + X_C^2}$$
$$= \sqrt{1^2\ k\Omega + 100^2\ \Omega}$$
$$Z_T = 1.005\ k\Omega$$

Next,  $V_{out} = \dfrac{X_C}{Z_T} \times V_{in}$

$$= \dfrac{100\ \Omega}{1.005\ k\Omega} \times 100\ mVpp$$

$$V_{out} = 9.95\ mVpp$$

For both filters in Fig. 32-13, the output voltage rolls off at the rate of 6 db/octave, which is equivalent to 20 db/decade.

**COMPARATORS**  A comparator is a circuit that compares the signal voltage on one input with a reference voltage on the other. An op amp comparator is shown in Fig. 32-14*a*. Notice that there is no feedback resistor to provide negative feedback. As a result, the op amp is running in the open-loop mode with a voltage gain equal to $A_{VOL}$.

In Fig. 32-14*a*, the inverting input of the op amp is grounded and the input signal is applied to the noninverting input. The comparator compares $V_{in}$ to the 0-V reference on the inverting input. When $V_{in}$ goes positive, the output is driven to $+V_{sat}$. When $V_{in}$ goes negative, the output is driven to $-V_{sat}$. Usually, $\pm V_{sat}$ is within a couple of volts of $\pm V_{CC}$.

Because of the op amp's extremely high open-loop voltage gain, even the slightest input voltage forces the output voltage to $\pm V_{sat}$. Figure 32-14*b* shows the transfer characteristic for the op amp comparator. Notice that $V_{out}$ switches to $+V_{sat}$ when $V_{in}$ is positive, and to $-V_{sat}$ when $V_{in}$ is negative. Because $V_{out}$ switches when $V_{in}$ crosses zero, the comparator in Fig. 32-14*a* is sometimes called a *zero crossing detector*.

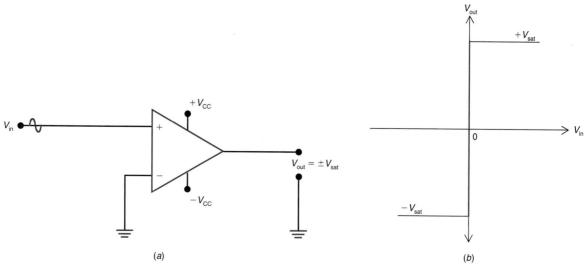

FIG. 32-14    Op amp comparator. (*a*) Circuit. (*b*) Transfer characteristic.

It should be noted that a comparator can use a reference voltage other than zero. For example, if the inverting input was a reference voltage of $+1$ V, then $V_{\text{out}}$ would switch between $\pm V_{\text{sat}}$ when $V_{\text{in}}$ crossed the $+1$-V reference value.

One final point. In some cases the noninverting input may be grounded or connected to a reference voltage rather than the inverting input. In this case, the output voltage switches to $+V_{\text{sat}}$ when $V_{\text{in}}$ is less than the reference voltage, and to $-V_{\text{sat}}$ when $V_{\text{in}}$ is greater than the reference voltage.

## TEST-POINT QUESTION 32-2

Answers at end of chapter.
**a.** In Fig. 32-8, calculate $A_{\text{CL}}$ if $R_F = 15$ k$\Omega$ and $R_i = 1.2$ k$\Omega$.
**b.** In Fig. 32-8, calculate $V_{\text{out}}$ if $R_F = 15$ k$\Omega$, $R_i = 1$ k$\Omega$, and $V_{\text{in}} = 0.5$ V$_{\text{p-p}}$.
**c.** In Fig. 32-9, calculate $A_{\text{CL}}$ if $R_F = 18$ k$\Omega$ and $R_i = 1.2$ k$\Omega$.
**d.** In Fig. 32-9, calculate $V_{\text{out}}$ if $R_F = 24$ k$\Omega$, $R_i = 1$ k$\Omega$, and $V_{\text{in}} = 250$ mV$_{\text{p-p}}$.
**e.** In Fig. 32-10, $V_{\text{in}} = 5$ V$_{\text{p-p}}$. What is $V_{\text{out}}$?
**f.** What is the approximate value of $V_{\text{id}}$ in Figs. 32-8, 32-9, and 32-10?
**g.** In Fig. 32-11, what is $V_{\text{out}}$ if $V_1 = -2$ V, $V_2 = +2$ V, and $V_3 = -4$ V?
**h.** In Fig. 32-12, what is $V_{\text{out}}$ if $V_X = +0.1$ V and $V_Y = +0.1$ V?

# 32 SUMMARY AND REVIEW

- Integrated circuits (ICs) are classified into two groups: digital or linear. Digital ICs process digital signals, and linear ICs process analog signals.
- Operational amplifiers (op amps) are the most commonly used type of linear IC. An op amp is a high-gain, direct-coupled, differential amplifier. The 741 op amp has become an industry standard.
- The open-loop voltage gain $A_{VOL}$ of an op amp is its voltage gain without negative feedback. For a 741, the typical value for $A_{VOL}$ is 200,000.
- For all practical purposes, the differential input voltage $V_{id}$ applied to an op amp is considered zero when $V_{out}$ is less than $\pm V_{sat}$.
- The input bias currents of a 741 are typically 80 nA. The input bias currents for the noninverting and inverting inputs are designated $I_{B+}$ and $I_{B-}$ respectively.
- The open-loop cut-off frequency of an op amp is designated $f_{OL}$. At this frequency, the op amps open-loop voltage gain $A_{VOL}$ is down to 70.7 percent of its maximum value. For a 741, $f_{OL} = $ 10 Hz.
- The slew rate of an op amp is designated $S_R$. The $S_R$ specification of an op amp tells how fast the output voltage can change. The $S_R$ of a 741 op amp is 0.5 V/μs.
- The power bandwidth (designated $f_{max}$) of an op amp circuit is the highest undistorted frequency out of an op amp for a given $S_R$ and peak voltage.
- The 741 has an output short-circuit current of approximately 25 mA.
- Most op amp circuits use negative feedback. When the op amp is connected to work as an inverting amplifier, the closed-loop voltage gain $A_{CL} = R_F/R_i$. For an inverting amplifier, the input and output signals are 180° out of phase.
- The op amp can also be connected to work as a noninverting amplifier. The closed-loop voltage gain $A_{CL} = R_F/R_i + 1$. For this circuit the input and output signals will be in phase with each other.
- An op amp circuit that has its output tied directly to the inverting input terminal is called a *voltage follower*. This circuit has a voltage gain of one, or unity.
- An op amp summer is a circuit whose output voltage is the negative sum of the input voltages.
- An op amp differential amplifier is a circuit which amplifies differential input signals and rejects common-mode signals.
- A unity-gain active filter has the advantage of isolating the $RC$ filter from a low-impedance load, $R_L$.
- An op amp comparator is a circuit that compares the signal voltage on one of its inputs with a reference voltage on the other.

Answer True or False.

1. Op amps can amplify both dc and ac signals.
2. An op amp comparator uses no negative feedback.
3. The open-loop voltage gain of an op amp is very high.
4. The $\pm V_{sat}$ for an op amp is usually 2 to 3 V higher than $\pm V_{CC}$.
5. To increase the power bandwidth of an op amp circuit, either accept less peak voltage $V_{pk}$ or use an op amp with a higher slew rate.
6. For the op amp circuit in Fig. 32-8, the voltage gain $A_{CL}$ could be increased by reducing the value of $R_i$.
7. For the op amp circuit in Fig. 32-8, $V_{id} = 1$ V$_{p-p}$.
8. Noninverting amplifier circuits have a very high input impedance.
9. A voltage follower has an input of 0.5 V$_{p-p}$. The output is also 0.5 V$_{p-p}$.
10. The slew rate of an op amp is of no concern when amplifying dc input signals.
11. Op amps will attenuate common mode input signals.

## QUESTIONS

1. Define what is meant by a common mode input signal.
2. What type of circuit is used for the input stage of an op amp?
3. What is meant by $f_{unity}$?
4. Define the term "input offset current" ($I_{OS}$).
5. Describe how slew-rate distortion affects the operation of an op amp circuit used to amplify sinusoidal signals.
6. What is meant by virtual ground?
7. Why are op amp circuits without negative feedback so unstable?

## PROBLEMS

1. Refer to Fig. 32-8. If $R_F = 10$ k$\Omega$, $R_i = 1.0$ k$\Omega$, and $V_{in} = -0.5$ Vdc, then calculate (**a**) $A_{CL}$; (**b**) $V_{out}$.
2. Refer to Fig. 32-9. If $R_F = 24$ k$\Omega$, $R_i = 1$ k$\Omega$, and $V_{in} = 0.25$ V$_{pp}$, then calculate (**a**) $A_{CL}$; (**b**) $V_{out}$.
3. An op amp has a slew rate of 0.5 V/$\mu$s. Calculate the 5-V power bandwidth.

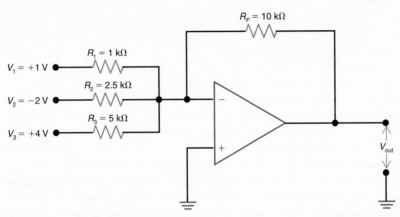

FIG. 32-15   Circuit for Prob. 9.

4. Refer to Fig. 32-11. If $V_1 = 2$ V, $V_2 = -3$ V, and $V_3 = -2$ V, calculate $V_{out}$.
5. In Fig. 32-12, calculate $V_{out}$ for the following values of $V_X$ and $V_Y$: **(a)** $V_X = +1$ V and $V_Y = -0.25$ V; **(b)** $V_X = -0.5$ V and $V_Y = +0.5$ V; **(c)** $V_X = +0.6$ V and $V_Y = +0.6$ V.
6. In Fig. 32-13a, calculate the cutoff frequency $f_c$ for $R = 1.5$ kΩ and $C = 0.047$ μF. Also, calculate $V_{out}$ at $f_c$ and $10f_c$.
7. In Fig. 32-13b, calculate the cutoff frequency $f_c$ for $R = 10$ kΩ and $C = 0.015$ μF. Also, calculate $V_{out}$ at $0.25f_c$. ($V_{in} = 100$ mVpp.)
8. In Fig. 32-14a, assume $\pm V_{sat} = \pm 13$ V and $A_{VOL} = 200{,}000$. Calculate the minimum value for $V_{id}$ which will drive the output to $\pm V_{sat}$.
9. In Fig. 32-15, calculate $V_{out}$.

---

## CRITICAL THINKING

1. In Fig. 32-12, assume $V_X = 100$ mVpp and $V_Y = 100$ mVpp. If the two waveforms are 180° out of phase, what is the value of $V_{out}$, and is $V_{out}$ in phase with $V_X$ or $V_Y$?

---

## ANSWERS TO TEST-POINT QUESTIONS

| 32-1 | | 32-2 | |
|---|---|---|---|
| **a.** | T | **a.** | 12.5 |
| **b.** | T | **b.** | 7.5 $V_{p-p}$ |
| **c.** | T | **c.** | 16 |
| **d.** | F | **d.** | 6.25 $V_{p-p}$ |
| **e.** | T | **e.** | 5 $V_{p-p}$ |
| **f.** | T | **f.** | 0 V |
| **g.** | T | **g.** | +4 V |
| **h.** | T | **h.** | 0 V |

# REVIEW: CHAPTERS 31 AND 32

## SUMMARY

- The basic logic gates used in digital electronic circuits are summarized in Table 31-4. Both the traditional and new rectangular symbols are shown, along with the boolean expression for each logic gate.
- The basic types of flip-flops used in digital electronic circuits are shown in Table 31-5.
- Digital circuits use a two-state design. For this reason, the binary number system is used when working with digital circuits. The binary digit 0 is used to represent a low voltage such as 0 V, whereas the binary digit 1 is used to represent a high voltage such as +5 V or +12 V.
- Truth tables are used to analyze the operation of a logic gate. The truth table lists all input possibilities and the corresponding output for each input.
- Table 31-1 compares the binary, decimal, and hexadecimal number systems. Memorize the binary and hexadecimal numbers that correspond to the decimal digits 0 through 15.
- DeMorgan's first theorem states that the complement of a sum equals the product of the complements. DeMorgan's second theorem states that the complement of a product equals the sum of the complements. The first and second theorems can be expressed as shown:

First Theorem:   $\overline{A + B} = \overline{A} \cdot \overline{B}$

Second Theorem:   $\overline{AB} = \overline{A} + \overline{B}$

- Operational amplifiers (op amps) are the most widely used type of linear IC. Op amps are high-gain, direct-coupled, differential amplifiers. The 741 is a very popular op amp and has become an industry standard.
- The open-loop voltage gain of an op amp is its voltage gain with no negative feedback. It is designated as $A_{VOL}$. If the output voltage of any op amp lies between $\pm V_{sat}$, then the differential input voltage $V_{id}$ will be so small that it can be approximated as zero. Typical values of $A_{VOL}$ are 200,000 or more at low frequencies. It should be realized, then, that $V_{id}$ will be very small for a given output voltage owing to the op amp's high value of $A_{VOL}$.
- Most op amp circuits use negative feedback. This is because op amp circuits without negative feedback are usually too unstable. When an op amp is connected to work as an inverting amplifier, $A_{CL} = R_F/R_i$. When the op amp is connected to work as a noninverting amplifier, $A_{CL} = R_F/R_i + 1$.
- The slew rate ($S_R$) specification of an op amp tells how fast the op amp's output voltage can change. For a 741, $S_R = 0.5$ V/$\mu$s. Slew-rate distortion of a sine wave produces a triangular wave.

## REVIEW SELF-TEST

### ANSWER TRUE OR FALSE.

1. The binary number system uses the digits 0 and 1.
2. The binary equivalent of decimal 21 is 10101.
3. The hexadecimal number F0 has a binary equivalent of 11110000.
4. An AND gate will have a high output only when all of its inputs are HIGH.
5. The output of an OR gate will be low if any or all inputs are LOW.
6. The output of an XOR gate is high only when an even number of input 1s are applied.
7. A NOR gate will have a high output only when all inputs are LOW.
8. A NAND gate will have a low output only when all inputs are HIGH.
9. The boolean expression for a 4-input XNOR gate would be $\overline{A \oplus B \oplus C \oplus D} = X$.
10. An open, or disconnected, input on a logic gate acts like a HIGH input.
11. The absence of a bubble on the output line of a logic gate indicates that it is an active HIGH output.
12. A flip-flop is set when $Q = 0$ and $\overline{Q} = 1$.
13. The differential input voltage $V_{id}$ for an op amp is usually 2 to 3 V in most cases.
14. Slew-rate distortion of a sine wave can be eliminated if we use an op amp with a higher $S_R$ rating or accept less peak voltage for the output waveform.
15. An op amp's output will be negative if the inverting ($-$) input terminal is positive with respect to the noninverting input terminal.
16. A voltage follower is often used to amplify common mode signals.

## REFERENCES

Malvino, A. P.: *Digital Computer Electronics,* Glencoe/McGraw-Hill, Columbus, Ohio.

Tokheim, R. L.: *Digital Principles,* Glencoe/ McGraw-Hill, Columbus, Ohio.

Couglin, R. F., and F. F. Driscoll: *Operational Amplifiers and Linear Integrated Circuits,* Prentice-Hall, Englewood Cliffs, New Jersey.

# APPENDIX A

## ELECTRICAL SYMBOLS AND ABBREVIATIONS

Table A-1 summarizes the letter symbols used as abbreviations for electrical characteristics and their basic units. All the metric prefixes for multiple and fractional values are listed in Table A-2. In addition, Table A-3 shows electronic symbols from the Greek alphabet. Table A-4 shows the preferred values for resistors having tolerances of $\pm20$ percent, $\pm10$ percent, and $\pm5$ percent.

### TABLE A-1   ELECTRICAL CHARACTERISTICS

| QUANTITY | SYMBOL* | BASIC UNIT |
|---|---|---|
| Current | $I$ or $i$ | ampere (A) |
| Charge | $Q$ or $q$ | coulomb (C) |
| Power | $P$ | watt (W) |
| Voltage | $V$ or $v$ | volt (V) |
| Resistance | $R$ | ohm ($\Omega$) |
| Reactance | $X$ | ohm ($\Omega$) |
| Impedance | $Z$ | ohm ($\Omega$) |
| Conductance | $G$ | siemens (S) |
| Admittance | $Y$ | siemens (S) |
| Susceptance | $B$ | siemens (S) |
| Capacitance | $C$ | farad (F) |
| Inductance | $L$ | henry (H) |
| Frequency | $f$ | hertz (Hz) |
| Period | $T$ | second (s) |

*Capital letters for $I$, $Q$, and $V$ are generally used for peak, rms, or dc value; small letters are used for instantaneous values. Small $r$ and $g$ are used for internal values, such as $r_p$ and $g_m$ of a tube.

### TABLE A-2   MULTIPLES AND SUBMULTIPLES OF UNITS*

| VALUE | PREFIX | SYMBOL | EXAMPLE |
|---|---|---|---|
| $1\,000\,000\,000\,000 = 10^{12}$ | tera | T | $THz = 10^{12}\,Hz$ |
| $1\,000\,000\,000 = 10^{9}$ | giga | G | $GHz = 10^{9}\,Hz$ |
| $1\,000\,000 = 10^{6}$ | mega | M | $MHz = 10^{6}\,Hz$ |
| $1\,000 = 10^{3}$ | kilo | k | $kV = 10^{3}\,V$ |
| $100 = 10^{2}$ | hecto | h | $hm = 10^{2}\,m$ |
| $10 = 10$ | deka | da | $dam = 10\,m$ |
| $0.1 = 10^{-1}$ | deci | d | $dm = 10^{-1}\,m$ |
| $0.01 = 10^{-2}$ | centi | c | $cm = 10^{-2}\,m$ |
| $0.001 = 10^{-3}$ | milli | m | $mA = 10^{-3}\,A$ |
| $0.000\,001 = 10^{-6}$ | micro | $\mu$ | $\mu V = 10^{-6}\,V$ |
| $0.000\,000\,001 = 10^{-9}$ | nano | n | $ns = 10^{-9}\,s$ |
| $0.000\,000\,000\,001 = 10^{-12}$ | pico | p | $pF = 10^{-12}\,F$ |

*Additional prefixes are exa $= 10^{18}$, peta $= 10^{15}$, femto $= 10^{-15}$, and atto $= 10^{-18}$.

## TABLE A-3 GREEK LETTER SYMBOLS*

| NAME | LETTER CAPITAL | LETTER SMALL | USES |
|------|---------|-------|------|
| Alpha | A | $\alpha$ | $\alpha$ for angles, transistor characteristic |
| Beta | B | $\beta$ | $\beta$ for angles, transistor characteristic |
| Gamma | $\Gamma$ | $\gamma$ | |
| Delta | $\Delta$ | $\delta$ | Small change in value |
| Epsilon | E | $\epsilon$ | $\epsilon$ for permittivity; also base of natural logarithms |
| Zeta | Z | $\zeta$ | |
| Eta | H | $\eta$ | |
| Theta | $\Theta$ | $\theta$ | Phase angle |
| Iota | I | $\iota$ | |
| Kappa | K | $\kappa$ | |
| Lambda | $\Lambda$ | $\lambda$ | $\lambda$ for wavelength |
| Mu | M | $\mu$ | $\mu$ for prefix micro, permeability, amplification factor |
| Nu | N | $\nu$ | |
| Xi | $\Xi$ | $\xi$ | |
| Omicron | O | $o$ | |
| Pi | $\Pi$ | $\pi$ | $\pi$ is 3.1416 for ratio of circumference to diameter of a circle |
| Rho | P | $\rho$ | $\rho$ for resistivity |
| Sigma | $\Sigma$ | $\sigma$ | Summation |
| Tau | T | $\tau$ | Time constant |
| Upsilon | $\Upsilon$ | $\upsilon$ | |
| Phi | $\Phi$ | $\phi$ | Magnetic flux, angles |
| Chi | X | $\chi$ | |
| Psi | $\Psi$ | $\psi$ | Electric flux |
| Omega | $\Omega$ | $\omega$ | $\Omega$ for ohms; $\omega$ for angular velocity |

*This table includes the complete Greek alphabet, although some letters are not used for electronic symbols.

## TABLE A-4 PREFERRED VALUES* FOR RESISTORS

| TOLERANCE 20% | TOLERANCE 10% | TOLERANCE 5% | TOLERANCE 20% | TOLERANCE 10% | TOLERANCE 5% |
|-----|-----|-----|-----|-----|-----|
| 10 | 10 | 10 | | | 36 |
| | | 11 | | 39 | 39 |
| | 12 | 12 | | | 43 |
| | | 13 | 47 | 47 | 47 |
| 15 | 15 | 15 | | | 51 |
| | | 16 | | 56 | 56 |
| | 18 | 18 | | | 62 |
| | | 20 | 68 | 68 | 68 |
| 22 | 22 | 22 | | | 75 |
| | | 24 | | 82 | 82 |
| | 27 | 27 | | | 91 |
| | | 30 | 100 | 100 | 100 |
| 33 | 33 | 33 | | | |

*Numbers and decimal multiples for ohms.

## SOLDER AND THE SOLDERING PROCESS*

# FROM SIMPLE TASK TO FINE ART

Soldering is the process of joining two metals together by the use of a low-temperature melting alloy. Soldering is one of the oldest known joining techniques, first developed by the Egyptians in making weapons such as spears and swords. Since then, it has evolved into what is now used in the manufacturing of electronic assemblies. Soldering is far from the simple task it once was; it is now a fine art, one that requires care, experience, and a thorough knowledge of the fundamentals.

The importance of having high standards of workmanship cannot be overemphasized. Faulty solder joints remain a cause of equipment failure, and because of that, soldering has become a *critical skill.*

The material contained in this appendix is designed to provide the student with both the fundamental knowledge and the practical skills needed to perform many of the high-reliability soldering operations encountered in today's electronics.

Covered here the fundamentals of the soldering process, the proper selection, and the use of the soldering station.

The key concept in this appendix is *high-reliability soldering.* Much of our present technology is vitally dependent on the reliability of countless, individual soldered connections. High-reliability soldering was developed in response to early failures with space equipment. Since then the concept and practice have spread into military and medical equipment. We have now come to expect it in everyday electronics as well.

# THE ADVANTAGE OF SOLDERING

Soldering is the process of connecting two pieces of metal together to form a reliable electrical path. Why solder them in the first place? The two pieces of metal could be put together with nuts and bolts, or some other kind of mechanical fastening. The disadvantages of these methods are twofold. First, the reliability of the connection cannot be assured because of vibration and shock. Second, because oxidation and corrosion are continually occurring on the metal surfaces, electrical conductivity between the two surfaces would progressively decrease.

A soldered connection does away with both of these problems. There is no movement in the joint and no interfacing surfaces to oxidize. A continuous conductive path is formed, made possible by the characteristics of the solder itself.

---

*This material is provided courtesy of PACE, Inc., Laurel, Maryland.

# THE NATURE OF SOLDER

Solder used in electronics is a low-temperature melting alloy made by combining various metals in different proportions. The most common types of solder are made from tin and lead. When the proportions are equal, it is known as 50/50 solder—50 percent tin and 50 percent lead. Similarly, 60/40 solder consists of 60 percent tin and 40 percent lead. The percentages are usually marked on the various types of solder available; sometimes only the tin percentage is shown. The chemical symbol for tin is Sn; thus Sn 63 indicates a solder which contains 63 percent tin.

Pure lead (Pb) has a melting point of 327°C (621°F); pure tin, a melting point of 232°C (450°F). But when they are combined into a 60/40 solder, the melting point drops to 190°C (374°F)—lower than either of the two metals alone.

Melting generally does not take place all at once. As illustrated in Fig. B-1, 60/40 solder begins to melt at 183°C (361°F), but it has not fully melted until the temperature reaches 190°C (374°F). Between these two temperatures, the solder exists in a plastic (semiliquid) state—some, but not all, of the solder has melted.

The plastic range of solder will vary, depending on the ratio of tin to lead, as shown in Fig. B-2. Various ratios of tin to lead are shown across the top of this figure. With most ratios, melting begins at 183°C (361°F), but the full melting temperatures vary dramatically. There is one ratio of tin to lead that has no plastic state and is known as *eutectic solder*. This ratio is 63/37 (Sn 63) and it fully melts and solidifies at 183°C (361°F).

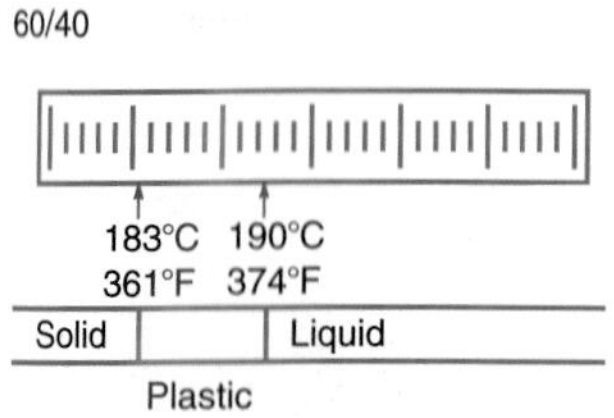

60/40

183°C  190°C
361°F  374°F

| Solid | Liquid |
| --- | --- |

Plastic

**FIG. B-1**  Plastic range of 60/40 solder. Melt begins at 183°C (361°F) and is complete at 190°C (374°F).

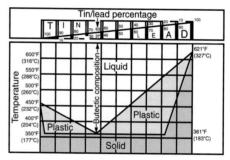

**FIG. B-2**  Fusion characteristics of tin/lead solders.

The solder most commonly used for hand soldering in electronics is the 60/40 type, but because of its plastic range, care must be taken not to move any elements of the joint during the cool-down period. Movement may cause a disturbed joint. Characteristically, this type of joint has a rough, irregular appearance and looks dull instead of bright and shiny. It is unreliable and therefore one of the types of joints that is unacceptable in high-reliability soldering.

In some situations, it is difficult to maintain a stable joint during cooling, for example, when wave soldering is used with a moving conveyor line of circuit boards during the manufacturing process. In other cases it may be necessary to use minimal heat to avoid damage to heat-sensitive components. In both of these situations, eutectic solder is the preferred choice, since it changes from a liquid to a solid during cooling with no plastic range.

# THE WETTING ACTION

To someone watching the soldering process for the first time, it looks as though the solder simply sticks the metals together like a hot-melt glue, but what actually happens is far different.

A chemical reaction takes place when the hot solder comes into contact with the copper surface. The solder dissolves and penetrates the surface. The molecules of solder and copper blend together to form a new metal alloy, one that is part copper and part solder and that has characteristics all its own. This reaction is called *wetting* and forms the intermetallic bond between the solder and copper (Fig. B-3).

Proper wetting can occur only if the surface of the copper is free of contamination and from oxide films that form when the metal is exposed to air. Also, the solder and copper surfaces need to have reached the proper temperature.

Even though the surface may look clean before soldering, there may still be a thin film of oxide covering it. When solder is applied, it acts like a drop of water on an oily surface because the oxide coating prevents the solder from coming into contact with the copper. No reaction takes place, and the solder can be easily scraped off. For a good solder bond, surface oxides must be removed during the soldering process.

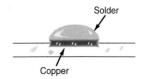

FIG. B-3  The wetting action. Molten solder dissolves and penetrates a clean copper surface, forming an intermetallic bond.

# THE ROLE OF FLUX

Reliable solder connections can be accomplished only on clean surfaces. Some sort of cleaning process is essential in achieving successful soldered connections, but in most cases it is insufficient. This is due to the extremely rapid rate at which oxides form on the surfaces of heated metals, thus creating oxide films which prevent proper soldering. To overcome these oxide films, it is necessary to utilize materials, called *fluxes,* which consist of natural or synthetic rosins and sometimes additives called activators.

It is the function of flux to remove surface oxides and keep them removed during the soldering operation. This is accomplished because the flux action is very corrosive at or near solder melt temperatures and accounts for the flux's ability to rapidly remove metal oxides. It is the fluxing action of removing oxides and carrying them away, as well as preventing the formation of new oxides, that allows the solder to form the desired intermetallic bond.

Flux must activate at a temperature lower than solder so that it can do its job prior to the solder flowing. It volatilizes very rapidly; thus it is mandatory that the flux be activated to flow onto the work surface and not simply be volatilized by the hot iron tip if it is to provide the full benefit of the fluxing action.

There are varieties of fluxes available for many applications. For example, in soldering sheet metal, acid fluxes are used; silver brazing (which requires a much higher temperature for melting than that required by tin/lead alloys) uses a borax paste. Each of these fluxes removes oxides and, in many cases, serves additional purposes. The fluxes used in electronic hand soldering are the pure rosins, rosins combined with mild activators to accelerate the rosin's fluxing

ypes of cored solder,
ng solder-flux percentages.

capability, low-residue/no-clean fluxes, or water-soluble fluxes. Acid fluxes or highly activated fluxes should never be used in electronic work. Various types of flux-cored solder are now in common use. They provide a convenient way to apply and control the amount of flux used at the joint (Fig. B-4).

## SOLDERING IRONS

In any kind of soldering, the primary requirement, beyond the solder itself, is heat. Heat can be applied in a number of ways—conductive (e.g., soldering iron, wave, vapor phase), convective (hot air), or radiant (IR). We are mainly concerned with the conductive method, which uses a soldering iron.

Soldering stations come in a variety of sizes and shapes, but consist basically of three main elements: a resistance heating unit; a heater block, which acts as a heat reservoir; and the tip, or bit, for transferring heat to the work. The standard production station is a variable-temperature, closed-loop system with interchangeable tips and is made with ESD-safe plastics.

## CONTROLLING HEAT AT THE JOINT

Controlling tip temperature is not the real challenge in soldering; the real challenge is to control the *heat cycle* of the work—how fast the work gets hot, how hot it gets, and how long it stays that way. This is affected by so many factors that, in reality, tip temperature is not that critical.

The first factor that needs to be considered is the *relative thermal mass* of the area to be soldered. This mass may vary over a wide range.

Consider a single land on a single-sided circuit board. There is relatively little mass, so the land heats up quickly. But on a double-sided board with plated-through holes, the mass is more than doubled. Multilayered boards may have an even greater mass, and that's before the mass of the component lead is taken into consideration. Lead mass may vary greatly, since some leads are much larger than others.

Further, there may be terminals (e.g., turret or bifurcated) mounted on the board. Again, the thermal mass is increased, and will further increase as connecting wires are added.

Each connection, then, has its particular thermal mass. How this combined mass compares with the mass of the iron tip, the "relative" thermal mass, determines the time and temperature rise of the work.

With a large work mass and a small iron tip, the temperature rise will be slow. With the situation reversed, using a large iron tip on a small work mass, the temperature rise of the work will be much more rapid—even though the *temperature of the tip is the same.*

Now consider the capacity of the iron itself and its ability to sustain a given flow of heat. Essentially, irons are instruments for generating and storing heat, and the reservoir is made up of both the heater block and the tip. The tip comes in various sizes and shapes; it's the *pipeline* for heat flowing into the work. For small work, a conical (pointed) tip is used, so that only a small flow of heat occurs. For large work, a large chisel tip is used, providing greater flow.

The reservoir is replenished by the heating element, but when an iron with a large tip is used to heat massive work, the reservoir may lose heat faster than it can be replenished. Thus the *size* of the reservoir becomes important: a large heating block can sustain a larger outflow longer than a small one.

An iron's capacity can be increased by using a larger heating element, thereby increasing the wattage of the iron. These two factors, block size and wattage, are what determine the iron's recovery rate.

If a great deal of heat is needed at a particular connection, the correct temperature with the right size tip is required, as is an iron with a large enough capacity and an ability to recover fast enough. *Relative thermal mass,* then, is a major consideration for controlling the heat cycle of the work.

A second factor of importance is the *surface condition* of the area to be soldered. If there are any oxides or other contaminants covering the lands or leads, there will be a barrier to the flow of heat. Then, even though the iron tip is the right size and has the correct temperature, it may not supply enough heat to the connection to melt the solder. In soldering, a cardinal rule is that a good solder connection cannot be created on a dirty surface. Before attempting to solder, the work should always be cleaned with an approved solvent to remove any grease or oil film from the surface. In some cases pretinning may be required to enhance solderability and remove heavy oxidation of the surfaces prior to soldering.

A third factor to consider is *thermal linkage*—the area of contact between the iron tip and the work.

Figure B-5 shows a cross-sectional view of an iron tip touching a round lead. The contact occurs only at the point indicated by the "X," so the linkage area is very small, not much more than a straight line along the lead.

The contact area can be greatly increased by applying a small amount of solder to the point of contact between the tip and workpiece. This solder heat bridge provides the thermal linkage and assures rapid heat transfer into the work.

From the aforementioned, it should now be apparent that there are many more factors than just the temperature of the iron tip that affect how quickly any particular connection is going to heat up. In reality, soldering is a very complex control problem, with a number of variables to it, each influencing the other. And what makes it so critical is *time.* The general rule for high-reliability soldering on printed circuit boards is to apply heat for no more than 2 s from the time solder starts to melt (wetting). Applying heat for longer than 2 s after wetting may cause damage to the component or board.

With all these factors to consider, the soldering process would appear to be too complex to accurately control in so short a time, but there is a simple solution—the *workpiece indicator* (WPI). This is defined as the reaction of the workpiece to the work being performed on it—a reaction that is discernible to the human senses of sight, touch, smell, sound, and taste.

Put simply, workpiece indicators are the way the work talks back to you—the way it tells you what effect you are having and how to control it so that you accomplish what you want.

In any kind of work, you become part of a closed-loop system. It begins when you take some action on the workpiece; then the workpiece reacts to what you did; you sense the change, and then modify your action to accomplish the result. It is in the sensing of the change, by sight, sound, smell, taste, or touch, that the workpiece indicators come in (Fig. B-6).

For soldering and desoldering, a primary workpiece indicator is *heat rate recognition*—observing how fast heat flows into the connection. In practice, this means observing the rate at which the solder melts, which should be within 1 to 2 s.

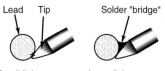

Lead   Tip        Solder "bridge"

Small linkage area    Large linkage area

**FIG. B-5**   Cross-sectional view (left) of iron tip on a round lead. The "X" shows point of contact. Use of a solder bridge (right) increases the linkage area and speeds the transfer of heat.

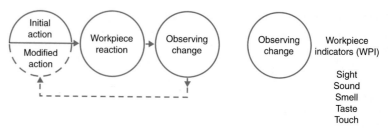

**FIG. B-6** Work can be viewed as a closed-loop system (left). Feedback comes from the reaction of the workpiece and is used to modify the action. Workpiece indicators (right)—changes discernible to the human senses—are the way the "work talks back to you."

This indicator encompasses all the variables involved in making a satisfactory solder connection with minimum heating effects, including the capacity of the iron and its tip temperature, the surface conditions, the thermal linkage between tip and workpiece, and the relative thermal masses involved.

If the iron tip is too large for the work, the heating rate may be too fast to be controlled. If the tip is too small, it may produce a "mush" kind of melt; the heating rate will be too slow, even though the temperature at the tip is the same.

A general rule for preventing overheating is "Get in and get out as fast as you can." That means using a heated iron you can react to—one giving a 1- to 2-s dwell time on the particular connection being soldered.

## SELECTING THE SOLDERING IRON AND TIP

A good all-around soldering station for electronic soldering is a variable-temperature, ESD-safe station with a pencil-type iron and tips that are easily interchangeable, even when hot (Fig. B-7).

The soldering iron tip should always be fully inserted into the heating element and tightened. This will allow for maximum heat transfer from the heater to the tip.

The tip should be removed daily to prevent an oxidation scale from accumulating between the heating element and the tip. A bright, thin tinned surface must be maintained on the tip's working surface to ensure proper heat transfer and to avoid contaminating the solder connection.

The plated tip is initially prepared by holding a piece of flux-cored solder to the face so that it will tin the surface when it reaches the lowest temperature at which solder will melt. Once the tip is up to operating temperature, it will usually be too hot for good tinning, because of the rapidity of oxidation at elevated temperatures. The hot tinned tip is maintained by wiping it lightly on a damp sponge to shock off the oxides. When the iron is not being used, the tip should be coated with a layer of solder.

## MAKING THE SOLDER CONNECTION

The soldering iron tip should be applied to the area of maximum thermal mass of the connection being made. This will permit the rapid thermal elevation of the parts being soldered. Molten solder always flows toward the heat of a properly prepared connection.

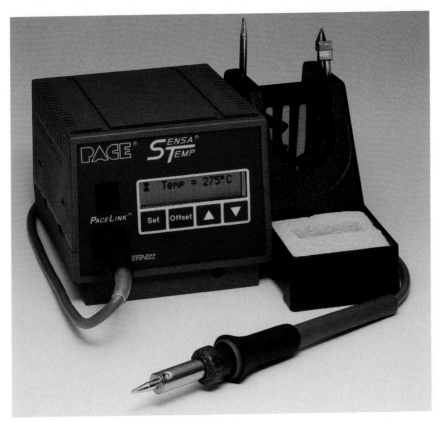

FIG. B-7   Pencil-type iron with changeable tips.

When the solder connection is heated, a small amount of solder is applied to the tip to increase the thermal linkage to the area being heated. The solder is then applied to the opposite side of the connection so that the work surfaces, not the iron, melt the solder. Never melt the solder against the iron tip and allow it to flow onto a surface cooler than the solder melting temperature.

Solder, with flux, applied to a cleaned and properly heated surface will melt and flow without direct contact with the heat source and provide a smooth, even surface, feathering out to a thin edge (Fig. B-8). Improper soldering will exhibit a built-up, irregular appearance and poor filleting. The parts being soldered must be held rigidly in place until the temperature decreases to solidify the solder. This will prevent a disturbed or fractured solder joint.

Selecting cored solder of the proper diameter will aid in controlling the amount of solder being applied to the connection (e.g., a small-gauge solder for a small connection; a large-gauge solder for a large connection).

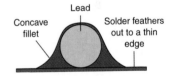

FIG. B-8   Cross-sectional view of a round lead on a flat surface.

## REMOVAL OF FLUX

Cleaning may be required to remove certain types of fluxes after soldering. If cleaning is required, the flux residue should be removed as soon as possible, preferably within 1 hour after soldering.

### TABLE C-1   GENERAL SYMBOLS

| DEVICE | SYMBOL | DEVICE | SYMBOL |
|---|---|---|---|
| AC voltage source | | Coil or inductance<br>  Air-core | |
| Amplifier | |   Iron-core | |
| Antenna<br>  General | |   Variable | |
|   Dipole | |   Powdered iron or<br>    ferrite slug | |
|   Loop | | Conductor<br>  General | |
| | |   Connection | |
| Battery, cell, or dc<br>voltage source | |   No connection | |
| Longer line positive | | Current source | |
| Capacitor<br>  General, fixed<br>  Curved electrode is<br>    outside foil, negative,<br>    or low-potential side | | Crystal, piezoelectric | |
| | | Fuse | |
|   Electrolytic | or | Ground, earth or metal frame<br>  Chassis or common return<br>    connected to one side of<br>    voltage source | |
|   Variable | or |   Chassis or common return not<br>    connected to voltage source | |
|   Ganged | |   Common return | |

TABLE C-1   GENERAL SYMBOLS (CONTINUED)

| DEVICE | SYMBOL | DEVICE | SYMBOL |
|---|---|---|---|
| Jack <br><br> Plug for jack | Tip <br> Sleeve | Resistor, fixed <br> Tapped <br><br> Variable | |
| Key telegraph | | Switch, SPST <br> SPDT <br><br> 2-pole (DPDT) | |
| Loudspeaker, general | | | |
| Phones or headset | | Shielding <br><br> Shielded conductor | |
| Magnet <br> Permanent <br><br> Electromagnet | PM | Transformer <br> Air-core <br><br> Iron-core | |
| Microphone | | Autotransformer | |
| Meters; letter or symbol to <br> indicate range or function | A   mA   V | | |
| Motor | M | Link coupling | |
| Neon bulb | | | |
| Relay, coil <br><br> Contacts | | | |

## THE OSCILLOSCOPE

## MAIN SECTIONS OF AN OSCILLOSCOPE

An oscilloscope is one of the most important types of test equipment for checking electronic circuits because the "scope" shows the waveform of an applied voltage (Fig. D-1). The fluorescent screen, usually green, of the cathode-ray tube (CRT) displays a graph of voltage amplitudes with respect to time. Examples of the oscilloscope display are shown in Fig. D-2 with sine waves in Fig. D-2a and square waves in Fig. D-2b. Actually, the pattern on the screen is produced by a small spot of light that is deflected vertically and horizontally to trace out the waveform.

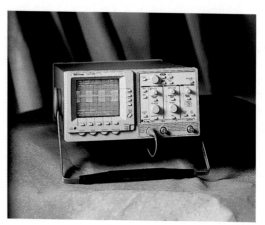

FIG. D-1    Oscilloscope.

The vertical axis represents voltage amplitudes. More voltage applied to the vertical input terminals of the oscilloscope results in a bigger trace pattern. For horizontal deflection, the oscilloscope has its own internal sawtooth voltage generator. No external connections are used for this function. A sawtooth waveform is needed for the internal horizontal sweep because of its linear increases in amplitude. Then the horizontal axis of the display is proportional to time. The screen pattern, therefore, displays a graph of the variations of the signal input voltage, with time on the horizontal axis and voltage on the vertical axis. It should be noted that for most measurements, only the vertical input terminal is used for connections to the circuit being tested.

The number of cycles you see depends on the frequency of the input signal and the timing of the internal sweep for horizontal deflection. Usually, the horizontal sweep frequency is set for a display of two or three complete cycles of the waveform, just for convenience.

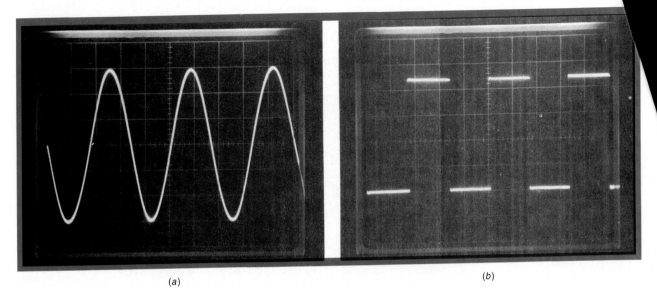

*(a)*        *(b)*

FIG. D-2   Examples of oscilloscope screen patterns. (*a*) Sine wave. (*b*) Square wave. Vertical lines are not visible because the spot moves too fast.

Not only does the oscilloscope show the amount of voltage, as the height of the trace pattern, but also the frequency can be checked in terms of the horizontal time base. Furthermore, any distortion of the signal is shown in the trace pattern.

The oscilloscope is a voltmeter. You connect the cable lead from the vertical input terminal *across* a component to check the voltage. Although the oscilloscope is generally used for ac voltages, it can also indicate dc values in terms of a steady displacement of the trace from the center position.

Figure D-3 shows the front panel of a typical dual-trace oscilloscope. The key functional controls are indicated with an emphasis on three basic functions:

1. The cathode-ray tube (or CRT) at the left, as the visual display, shows the signal waveform. The CRT provides a spot of light that can be deflected up or down and left or right.
2. The vertical (V) deflection sections (one for each of the two channels) amplify the signal applied to the V input terminals to provide enough signal voltage to the vertical deflection plates in the CRT.
3. The horizontal (H) deflection section has the internal sawtooth voltage generator that is used as a time base for horizontal deflection. The H deflection voltage is applied to the horizontal deflection plates in the CRT.

The combined functions of these three sections result in a trace pattern on the oscilloscope screen. From the waveform, you can measure voltage amplitude of the V input signal, determine the period or frequency, and observe any distortion.

**CRT SECTION**   In Fig. D-3, note the power on-off switch for the oscilloscope. The intensity control varies the brightness of the trace. Adjust the focus control for a sharp pattern at the desired brightness. Do not keep the brightness high with a stationary pattern for too long, as the screen phosphor may be "burned," which produces a permanent brown discoloration of the screen. In some cases, the power on-off switch may be part of the brightness control.

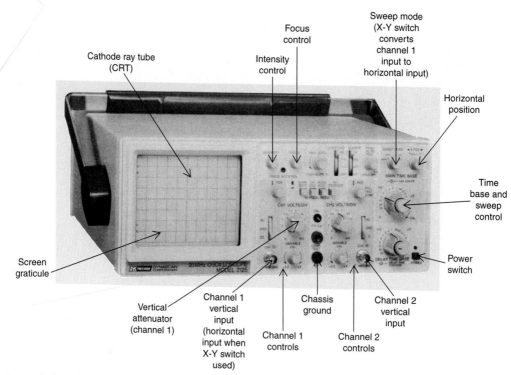

Cathode ray tube (CRT)

Focus control

Intensity control

Sweep mode (X-Y switch converts channel 1 input to horizontal input)

Horizontal position

Time base and sweep control

Power switch

Channel 2 vertical input

Channel 2 controls

Chassis ground

Channel 1 controls

Channel 1 vertical input (horizontal input when X-Y switch used)

Vertical attenuator (channel 1)

Screen graticule

**FIG. D-3** The main functional controls of a typical dual-trace oscilloscope.

The screen *graticule* is a plastic sheet over the face of the CRT to make measurements more convenient. A typical size for the graticule is 10 cm × 8 cm, with each box 1 cm high and wide. Calibrated values for the oscilloscope are often specified per centimeter.

Although not labeled in Fig. D-3, the oscilloscope also has provisions for centering the electron beam in the CRT, which positions the trace vertically and horizontally. The centering controls adjust dc voltages to leave the trace in a reference position for ac deflection by the signal voltage. If the beam should be off the screen, there will be no trace visible, but it can be returned to the screen with the V and H, or X and Y, positioning controls.

**V DEFLECTION** Figure D-3 shows a step attenuator and a variable gain control to adjust the height of the trace pattern. The trace can be adjusted to fit most of the screen height in order to see the waveform better. The step attenuator cuts down the amount of signal applied to the V input terminals, often in multiples of ½, ½.₅, or ¹⁄₁₀. The gain control is a variable adjustment for in-between values of vertical deflection. In many oscilloscopes, the step attenuator is calibrated in units of V/cm of vertical deflection at the maximum setting of the variable gain control.

**H DEFLECTION** The H deflection section is more complicated than the V section, because horizontal deflection involves timing of the internal H sweep, synchronizing the H timing to make the pattern remain still and the H amplification for the desired width of the trace pattern. For oscilloscopes with a calibrated time base, the step control is marked in μs/cm, ms/cm, or s/cm for the maximum setting of the variable timing control. Without the calibration, these controls just indicate approximate frequency for the internal time base.

The timing of the internal time base for horizontal deflection must be synchronized with the vertical input signal; otherwise, the pattern on the screen drifts to the left or right across the screen. The general procedure is to adjust the timing for two or three cycles, with as little drift as possible. Then adjust the synchronization (sync) control to make the pattern remain stationary. Always use as little sync as possible to avoid distortion of the pattern. Many oscilloscopes have an automatic sync or *trigger* level.

The pattern on the screen represents a spot of light that is moving so fast that you see the complete trace. Actually, the trace patterns are repeated one over the other, but it looks like a steady picture with the correct synchronization. Below about 30 Hz for the H sweep frequency, the brightness of the trace may flicker. At lower sweep frequencies, it is possible to see the spot moving.

In summary, then, for the general operation of using the oscilloscope to observe a signal waveform, connect the signal to the V input terminals and adjust the horizontal timing of the internal sweep generator to obtain the desired trace pattern. The H input terminals for an external input signal are only used for some special functions, such as the Lissajous patterns described at the end of this appendix. In some oscilloscopes, one of the two V inputs can be made an H input through the operation of an X-Y switch.

## *Y* AXIS FOR VOLTAGE AND *X* AXIS FOR TIME

Refer to Fig. D-4, which illustrates how oscilloscope waveforms are developed. In Fig. D-4*a*, the spot of light at the center of the screen is produced by the CRT. It has the required electrode voltages, including high voltage for the anode. The spot is focused for the smallest size and the intensity is set for the desired brightness. Also, the spot can be centered with the positioning controls. There is no vertical or horizontal deflection as yet.

In Fig. D-4*b*, horizontal deflection voltage is applied to the CRT to move the spot back and forth across the screen along the *x* axis. There is no vertical deflection. A horizontal line is displayed because the spot repeats its motion over the same area too fast for you to see movement. Horizontal deflection is provided by the internal sweep voltage, for most applications of the oscilloscope.

With vertical deflection, but without horizontal deflection, the spot moves up and down along the *y* axis. This action is shown in Fig. D-4*c*, without any horizontal deflection. You can obtain this display by turning off the internal horizontal sweep. The vertical deflection is provided by signal voltage at the vertical input terminal of the oscilloscope.

Both vertical and horizontal deflection are used for the trace pattern in Fig. D-4*d*. Two cycles of sine waves show the waveform of the vertical input signal. More cycles or less cycles can be displayed according to the frequency setting of the internal horizontal sweep voltage. The complete trace pattern results from the spot of light being deflected vertically by the input signal while the spot is deflected across the screen at a uniform rate of speed.

An example of oscilloscope waveforms for the video signal in a television receiver is shown in Fig. D-5. The oscilloscope is an important instrument for adjusting and troubleshooting television receivers.

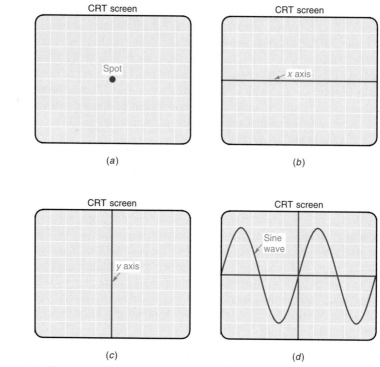

FIG. D-4 How an oscilloscope trace pattern is developed. (*a*) A spot of light at the center of the screen without V and H deflection. (*b*) A horizontal line produced by H deflection but no V deflection. (*c*) A vertical line produced by V deflection but no H deflection. (*d*) A sine-wave vertical input signal with V and H deflection.

**CALIBRATED VOLTAGES ON THE VERTICAL *Y* AXIS** In many oscilloscopes, the step attenuator that adjusts the amount of vertical input signal is calibrated so that you can read voltage amplitudes directly from the height of the trace on the oscilloscope screen. The variable gain control must stay set at its

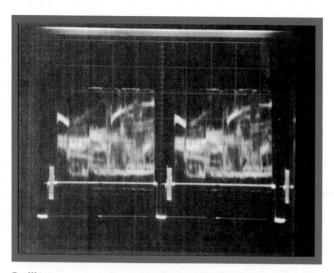

FIG. D-5 Oscilloscope pattern for a video signal in a television receiver. Two cycles shown.

maximum value. An example is illustrated in Fig. D-6 for a pattern with a height of six boxes equal to 6 cm. In Fig. D-6a, the horizontal deflection is turned off to show the vertical amplitude alone, whereas Fig. D-6b shows the complete trace pattern. Either way, the height of 6 cm represents the peak-to-peak voltage of the waveform. The measurement is peak-to-peak because it is between the two opposite peaks.

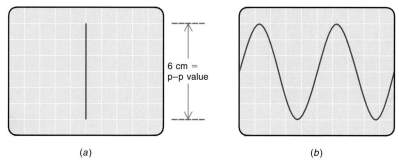

(a)   (b)

FIG. D-6  Voltage values on the vertical axis. (a) H deflection removed to show just the peak-to-peak amplitude on the y axis. (b) Complete waveform with V and H deflection.

Assume that the vertical attenuator is at 1 V/cm. This setting means that each 1-cm-high box represents 1 V of vertical input signal. For the six boxes equal to 6 cm, the amplitude is

$$6 \text{ cm} \times \frac{1 \text{ V}}{\text{cm}} = 6 \text{ V}$$

For this example, the amplitude of the vertical input signal is 6 V p-p.

Suppose that the height of the trace is 4 cm, instead of 6 cm. For the same 1-V/cm setting, the trace amplitude is

$$4 \times 1 = 4 \text{ V p-p}$$

As another example, let the V/cm setting be changed to 0.005 V/cm. For 6 cm of deflection, the V input signal then is

$$6 \text{ cm} \times \frac{0.005 \text{ V}}{\text{cm}} = 0.030 \text{ V or } 30 \text{ mV}$$

With 4 cm of vertical deflection, the amplitude is 20 mV. The 30 and 20 mV amplitudes are peak-to-peak values.

## CALIBRATED TIME VALUES ON THE HORIZONTAL X AXIS

Refer to Fig. D-7 with the x axis shown 10 cm wide. Also, the calibrated H time setting is taken here as 1 ms/cm. Each box horizontally represents 1 ms of time, as shown in Fig. D-7a. The two sine-wave cycles in Fig. D-7b, therefore, take 10 ms of time. For one cycle that takes 5 boxes or 5 cm, the period T for one cycle is 5 ms.

Remember that the frequency f is equal to 1/T. Therefore, the frequency for the sine waves in Fig. D-7b is as follows.

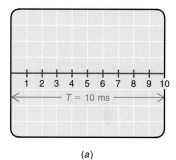

(a)

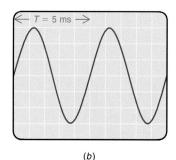

(b)

FIG. D-7  Time and frequency values on the x axis. (a) The period T of the horizontal sweep time is 10 ms. (b) One cycle of the vertical input signal has a period T of 5 ms, or f = 0.2 kHz = 200 Hz.

$$f = \frac{1}{T} = \frac{1}{5 \text{ ms}} = 0.02 \text{ kHz or } 200 \text{ Hz}$$

This value is the frequency of the vertical input signal.

Suppose that five cycles with the same time base of 10 ms were shown in Fig. D-7. One cycle would take $10/5 = 2$ ms. With $T$ of 2 ms, the $f$ is equal to 0.5 kHz or 500 Hz.

As another example, let the H time setting be 20 $\mu$s/cm. Then the width of 10 cm in Fig. D-7 represents $20 \times 10 = 200 \mu$s. For two cycles across the entire width of the screen, one cycle takes 100 $\mu$s for $T$ of the signal input. The frequency then is

$$f = \frac{1}{100 \ \mu\text{s}} = 0.01 \text{ MHz or } 10 \text{ kHz}$$

These calculations give the frequency of the signal applied to the vertical input terminals of the oscilloscope.

For a quick, simple check of the calibrated time values, you can apply a sample of the 60-Hz voltage from the ac power line, which is an accurate reference for frequency. With the horizontal $T$/cm control set on 5 ms/cm there should be exactly three cycles on the screen.

## COMPARISON OF H SYNC AND H SELECTOR SWITCHES

One of the most important problems in learning how to use the oscilloscope is to appreciate the difference between setting the type of deflection with the horizontal selector switch and choosing the type of sync with the sync selector switch to be used with internal sweep. The two switches have the same names for their three positions, but their functions are entirely different. In order to emphasize the comparison, Fig. D-8 shows the two switches with the name and function for each position.

**HORIZONTAL SELECTOR SWITCH**     In Fig. D-8*a* the horizontal selector switch turns on the internal sweep at the top position. This method supplies dc electrode voltages for the sawtooth generator used for H deflection. Then the sawtooth voltage output is fed to the H deflection amplifier for the horizontal deflection plates. This setting for internal sweep is the type of operation generally used for the oscilloscope to display the waveform of the vertical input signal.

On the 60-Hz position of the H selector switch, a sample of the 60-Hz ac line voltage is taken internally to be used for H deflection. The 60-Hz voltage is a sine wave.

On the "external" position of the H selector switch, the internal sweep is disconnected from the H amplifier. Without any signal connected to the H input terminals on the front panel of the oscilloscope, there is no horizontal deflection. However, any type of signal input can be connected to the external H terminals to provide signal for the H deflection amplifier.

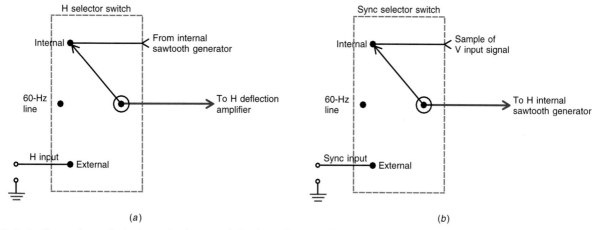

FIG. D-8 Comparison of a horizontal selector switch, shown in (a), with a sync selector switch, shown in (b).

## HOW A SAWTOOTH GENERATOR IS SYNCHRONIZED

Before we consider the different types of sync that can be chosen with the sync selector switch, an illustration of synchronization with the required sync pulses is shown in Fig. D-9. Keep in mind that the sync function only applies when the internal sawtooth generator is being used to provide the internal sweep. In general, any sawtooth generator is a pulse oscillator, like the bistable multivibrator (MV). An asymmetrical type of MV circuit is used with a waveshaping capacitor to provide sawtooth voltage in the output. This type of circuit is easily synchronized by injecting pulses at the input electrode to force the oscillator to run at the frequency of the synchronizing pulses. This value is the *forced frequency,* which is locked in by the sync pulses, compared with the *free-running frequency* without sync.

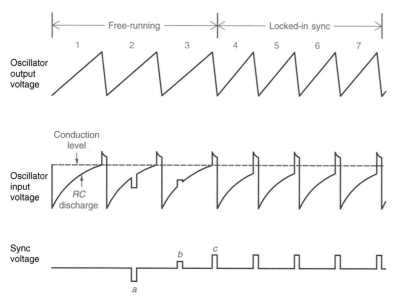

FIG. D-9 How synchronizing (sync) voltage is used to trigger a free-running pulse oscillator to lock it in at sync frequency.

The free frequency must be set a little lower than the sync frequency, thus allowing the input voltage of the oscillator to be ready for the sync voltage to produce the lock-in effect. Incidentally, synchronization of the deflection oscillator is also used in television receivers to hold the picture steady.

Refer to the waveforms in Fig. D-9. At the top is the sawtooth voltage output of the H deflection oscillator used for internal sweep. Just under the sawtooth waves are the waveforms of input voltage from the MV type of pulse oscillator. At the bottom of the figure, the pulses toward the end of the pulse train are able to lock in the oscillator at the sync frequency.

The trigger effect for controlling the oscillator occurs with the input voltage shown below the sawtooth waves in Fig. D-9. In the $RC$ discharge curve, this voltage is cutting off one stage of the MV, until the input voltage approaches the conduction level. Then when one stage conducts, it cuts off the other stage.

The sync voltage is able to control when the input voltage can reach the conduction level. Consider the sync pulses at the bottom of Fig. D-9, in sequence, from left to right. First, there is no sync. Now the oscillator is free-running. Next, is the sync pulse marked $a$, but it has the wrong polarity. It cannot force the input voltage to the conduction level, and the oscillator cannot be affected. Then comes sync pulse $b$ of the correct polarity but not enough amplitude. The oscillator is still free-running. During this time, the oscillator is free-running for the cycles marked 1, 2, and 3 at the top of the sawtooth waveform.

Finally, sync pulse $c$ in Fig. D-9 has the correct polarity and enough amplitude to force the oscillator input voltage to the conduction level. The start of conduction corresponds to the start of retrace on the sawtooth wave.

All the sync pulses that follow $c$ in Fig. D-9 also trigger the oscillator at the sync frequency, as shown for the sawtooth waves labeled 4, 5, 6, and 7 at the top of the figure. As long as the sync voltage is applied, it is able to hold the oscillator at the sync frequency.

**SYNC SELECTOR SWITCH**  We can now consider the different types of sync for the internal sawtooth generator. The sync section of the oscilloscope has waveshaping circuits to provide sharp pulses for exact synchronization. In many oscilloscopes, the polarity and slope of the sync pulses can be varied.

Most important is internal sync. It is used practically always with the internal sweep for horizontal deflection. The reason is that internal sync is automatically at the correct frequency for synchronizing the vertical input signal because this sync is a sample of the signal from the vertical deflection amplifier. In order to see complete cycles in the trace pattern, the sweep frequency must be at an exact submultiple of the signal frequency. As examples, for two cycles, the $V$ input signal is double the H scanning frequency, and for three cycles the ratio is $3:1$.

The 60-Hz position on the sync selector switch is seldom needed. One application is in the use of the oscilloscope in aligning tuned circuits.

The external sync also is used only for special applications. When necessary, though, the sync voltage must be connected to the external sync input terminal on the front panel of the oscilloscope. One application would be to display the pattern of an AM radio signal with an audio modulation envelope. In this case, the $V$ input is an RF signal, but to see the envelope, the audio modulating voltage must be used as external sync for the oscilloscope.

To summarize the functions for the selector switches in Fig. D-9, remember that the sync voltage does not produce deflection. Therefore, internal sync does not mean internal sawtooth scanning. The H selector switch determines when the internal sawtooth generator is used. Furthermore, selecting the type of sync has no meaning unless the internal sweep is on. The sync has its use only for the internal sawtooth generator. In other words, the H selector switch must be set for internal sweep in order to use any type of sync.

## OSCILLOSCOPE PROBES

Oscilloscope probes are the test leads used for connecting the vertical input signal to the oscilloscope. There are three types: a direct lead that is just a shielded cable, the low-capacitance probe (LCP) with a series-isolating resistor, and a demodulator probe. Figure D-10 shows a circuit for an LCP for an oscilloscope. The LCP usually has a switch to short out the isolating resistor so that the same probe can be used either as a direct lead or with low-capacitance.

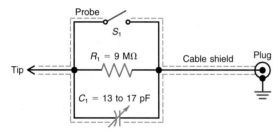

FIG. D-10    Circuit for low-capacitance probe (LCP) for an oscilloscope.

**DIRECT PROBE**    The direct probe is just a shielded wire without any isolating resistor. A shielded cable is necessary to prevent any pickup of interfering signals, especially with the high resistance at the vertical input terminals of the oscilloscope. The higher the resistance, the more voltage that can be developed by induction. Any interfering signals in the test lead produce distortion of the trace pattern. The main sources of interference are 60-Hz magnetic fields from the power line and stray RF signals.

The direct probe as a shielded lead has relatively high capacitance. A typical value is 90 pF for 3 ft (0.9 m) of 50-Ω coaxial cable. Also, the vertical input terminals of the oscilloscope have a shunt capacitance of about 40 pF. The total $C$ then is $90 + 40 = 130$ pF. This much capacitance can have a big effect on the circuit being tested. For example, it could detune a resonant circuit. Also, nonsinusoidal waveshapes are distorted. Therefore, the direct probe can be used only when the added $C$ has little or no effect. These applications include voltages for the 60-Hz power line or sine-wave audio signals in a circuit with a relatively low resistance of several kilohms or less. The advantage of the direct probe is that it does not divide down the amount of input signal, since there is no series isolating resistance.

**LOW-CAPACITANCE PROBE (LCP)**    Refer to the diagram in Fig. D-10. The 9-MΩ resistor in the probe isolates the capacitance of the cable and the oscilloscope from the circuit connected to the probe tip. With an LCP, the input capacitance of the probe is only about 10 pF. The LCP must be used for oscilloscope measurements when

1. The signal frequency is above audio frequencies.
2. The circuit being tested has $R$ higher than about 50 kΩ.
3. The waveshape is nonsinusoidal, especially with square waves and sharp pulses.

Without the LCP, the observed waveform can be distorted. The reason is that too much capacitance changes the circuit while it is being tested.

**THE 1:10 VOLTAGE DIVISION OF THE LCP**    Refer to the voltage divider circuit in Fig. D-11. The 9-MΩ of $R_P$ is a series resistor in the probe. Also, $R_S$ of 1 MΩ is a typical value for the shunt resistance at the vertical terminals of the oscilloscope. Then $R_T = 9 + 1 = 10$ MΩ. The voltage across $R_S$ for the scope equals $R_S/R_T$ or 1/10 of the input voltage. For the example in Fig. D-11 with 10 V at the tip of the LCP, 1 V is applied to the oscilloscope.

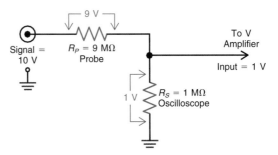

**FIG. D-11**    Voltage division of 1:10 with a low-capacitance probe.

Remember, when using the LCP, multiply by 10 for the actual signal amplitude. As an example, for a trace pattern on the screen that measures 2.4 V, the actual signal input at the probe is 24 V. For this reason, the LCP is generally called the "10 times" probe. Check to see whether or not the switch on the probe is on the direct or LCP position. Even though the scope trace is reduced by the factor of 1/10, it is preferable to use the LCP for almost all oscilloscope measurements to minimize distortion of the waveshapes.

**TRIMMER CAPACITOR OF THE LCP**    Referring back to Fig. D-10, note that the LCP has an internal variable capacitor $C_1$ across the isolating resistor $R_1$. The purpose of $C_1$ is to compensate the LCP for high frequencies. Its time constant with $R_1$ should equal the $RC$ time constant of the circuit at the vertical input terminals of the oscilloscope. When necessary, $C_1$ is adjusted for minimum tilt on a square-wave signal.

**DEMODULATOR PROBE**    The demodulator probe has an internal diode to detect an amplitude-modulated RF signal. The output of the probe is the envelope or modulation. Polarity of the rectified dc output is usually negative. The demodulator probe can be used for signal tracing in the RF circuits of an AM receiver, where the signal has the modulation envelope. There is usually a problem, however, in very low signal amplitudes.

**CURRENT MEASUREMENTS WITH OSCILLOSCOPE** Although it serves as an ac voltmeter, the oscilloscope can also be used for measuring current values indirectly. The technique is to insert a low $R$ in series where the current is to be checked. Use the oscilloscope to measure the voltage across $R$. Then the current is $I = V/R$. Keep the value of the inserted $R$ much lower than the resistance of the circuit being tested to prevent any appreciable change in the actual $I$. Besides measuring the current this way, the waveform of $V$ on the screen is the same as $I$ because $R$ does not affect the waveshape.

# SPECIAL OSCILLOSCOPE FEATURES

Many oscilloscopes have special features that make operation more convenient. Actually, most oscilloscopes are the dual-trace type and have triggered sweep with a horizontal time base calibrated in ms and μs. Some oscilloscopes even have three or four vertical input channels.

**DUAL-TRACE OSCILLOSCOPE** The dual-trace oscilloscope can show two traces at the same time, one above the other, for two vertical input signals. An example of the two traces is shown in Fig. D-1.

For dual-trace operation, the oscilloscope has two vertical amplifier channels, labeled either A and B or 1 and 2. An internal electronic switch changes the signals alternately from each vertical amplifier to the deflection plates. The switching is accomplished with a square-wave generator. The switching rate is fast enough to make the changes invisible.

The advantages of a dual trace is that it permits observation of two signals at the same time. They both have the same linear time base. As a result, time and amplitude comparisons can be viewed directly.

Also, many dual-trace oscilloscopes have provision for either adding or subtracting the two vertical input signals with one resultant trace pattern. This operation is labeled A + B or A − B. The subtraction is accomplished by inverting the trace for B and adding to A.

Furthermore, one channel can also be used as a horizontal deflection amplifier when the internal horizontal sweep is turned off. This is usually the B channel. Then it becomes an amplifier for the $x$ axis, whereas the A channel is for the $y$ axis. The $x$-$y$ operation is used for an external horizontal input signal, without the internal horizontal sweep.

**DUAL-BEAM OSCILLOSCOPE** The dual-beam oscilloscope can show two trace patterns also, but a special CRT is used that has two separate electron beams. One application of the dual-beam oscilloscope is in medical electronic equipment.

**TV POSITIONS FOR INTERNAL SWEEP** On the time or frequency switch for the internal horizontal sweep, many oscilloscopes have two positions marked V and H for television. At the H position, the internal sweep is set for two cycles of the horizontal scanning voltage in television receivers. This H frequency is exactly 5,734.26 Hz or the nominal value of 15,750 Hz. At the V position on the selector switch, the oscilloscope internal sweep is set for two cycles of 60-Hz signal at the vertical input terminal. This frequency is for the vertical scanning voltage in television receivers, which is exactly 59.94, but nominally 60 Hz. An example is the pattern in Fig. D-5, which shows the video signal for two horizontal scanning lines in a television receiver.

Do not confuse the abbreviation V for vertical deflection in television with V for the vertical input signal to an oscilloscope. The television V is 60 Hz for vertical deflection in the picture tube. The oscilloscope vertical input signal can have almost any frequency.

**TRIGGERED SWEEP**   The comparison here is with recurrent sweep, which uses a free-running sawtooth oscillator for internal sweep in the oscilloscope. In this method, horizontal deflection is produced by the internal sweep with or without the injection of pulses. With triggered sweep, though, the internal sawtooth generator produces one cycle of output only for each sync pulse as a trigger voltage at the input. As a result, the triggered sweep for internal horizontal deflection is produced only when the sawtooth generator has sync. The method of triggered sweep uses a monostable or one-shot multivibrator circuit to produce the sawtooth output voltage.

The advantages of triggered sweep are better synchronization and more exact control of the horizontal sweep time. Oscilloscopes with triggered sweep usually have the H sweep time calibrated. The time, rather than frequency, is calibrated because it applies for any number of cycles of the trace pattern on the screen.

**Z AXIS FOR INTENSITY MODULATION**   The $y$ and $x$ axes are for vertical and horizontal deflection in a CRT. In addition, though, the intensity of the electron beam can be varied by different values of the control grid voltage. The result is *intensity modulation* of the electron beam, which varies the light output from the screen. Such control is considered as $z$-axis modulation, because the effect is not vertical or horizontal.

In oscilloscopes, a separate $z$-axis external terminal may be provided for a connection to the control grid of the CRT. However, it is not used for the normal display of the vertical input signal.

When $z$-axis modulation is used in oscilloscopes, an amplitude of about 15 V p–p can vary the beam intensity between maximum light and zero. No light output is considered black, compared with bright illumination. The black level for control-grid voltage that cuts off the beam current can also be considered a blanking level. Any time the control-grid voltage is at the black level for zero beam current, the trace on the screen is blanked out, meaning it is not visible.

In television receivers, the picture is reproduced by $z$-axis modulation. The control-grid voltage of the picture tube is varied by the video signal, which corresponds to the picture information. Typical video signal amplitude is about 100 V p–p. More control-grid voltage is needed for TV picture tubes than for oscilloscopes because the anode voltage of 15 to 30 kV is much higher. It should be noted that for a television picture, horizontal and vertical deflection is used to fill the screen with scanning lines, whereas the video signal provides the visual information by varying the intensity of the electron beam.

**DIRECT CONNECTIONS TO DEFLECTION PLATES**   Direct connections to the deflection plates may be provided at the back of the oscilloscope, in order to bypass frequency limitations of the vertical and horizontal deflection amplifiers. However, appreciable deflection voltage is needed. Typically 30 V of potential difference between a pair of plates can deflect the beam 1 in.

**H TRACE MAGNIFIER**   The H trace magnifier expands the horizontal deflection to make the trace wider than the screen size. Then more details can be seen of the trace that is on the screen. The magnification is usually five times larger.

# LISSAJOUS PATTERNS FOR PHASE AND FREQUENCY COMPARISONS

Examples of Lissajous patterns are shown in Fig. D-12 for phase angles and in Fig. D-13 for frequency comparisons. In Fig. D-12, the phase comparisons are for two sine waves that have the same frequency but different phase angles. The patterns in Fig. D-13 can be used to check a sine wave of unknown frequency with another sine wave that has a frequency known to be accurate, like the 60-Hz power line.

The Lissajous patterns are only for sine-wave signals. One is applied to the oscilloscope vertical input and the other to the horizontal input. Turn off the oscilloscope internal sweep, as it is not used for this application. Lissajous patterns are named after the man who first used them, Jules A. Lissajous.

Both the vertical and horizontal deflection signals should have equal amplitude. This requirement can be checked by adjusting the gain until the same height and width are obtained for each signal alone without the other.

**PHASE-ANGLE COMPARISONS**   Assume two sine waves have the same frequency. The combined trace looks like one of the patterns in Fig. D-12. Consider the diagonal line for 0°. The two sine waves are in phase. At the start, the spot is at the center without any deflection. When the V signal increases in a positive direction to deflect the spot upward, the H signal also is positive and moves the spot the same amount to the right. Halfway to the peak voltage, the spot is halfway to the top, as shown by a dot in the figure. At the peak value for both the

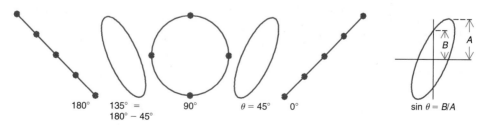

**FIG. D-12**   Lissajous patterns for phase angles on an oscilloscope screen. These patterns compare with the phases of two sine waves at the same frequency.

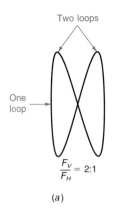

Two loops

One
loop

$$\frac{F_V}{F_H} = 2:1$$

(a)

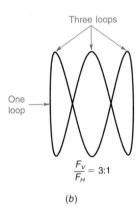

Three loops

One
loop

$$\frac{F_V}{F_H} = 3:1$$

(b)

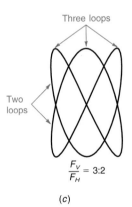

Three loops

Two
loops

$$\frac{F_V}{F_H} = 3:2$$

(c)

**FIG. D-13** Lissajous patterns for frequency comparisons on an oscilloscope screen. These patterns compare two sine waves of different frequencies. The frequency of the vertical signal is $F_V$. The frequency of the horizontal signal is $F_H$. The closed loops are counted to determine the frequency ratio of $F_V/F_H$.

V and H signals, the spot is at its extreme top right position shown at the end of the diagonal line. That action occurs during the first quarter-cycle for both signals.

On the next quarter-cycle the spot repeats the same positions on the way back to the center. In the same way, during the negative half-cycle the spot moves diagonally down to the bottom left. The spot repeating over this path produces a diagonal line. When the two waves are 180° out of phase, the line slopes in the opposite direction.

Consider the circle pattern produced by two waves 90° out of phase. One signal is at maximum when the other is at zero. When the vertical signal forces the spot to the extreme top or bottom position, the spot is in the center horizontally. Also, when the horizontal signal is maximum for the extreme left and right positions, the spot is in the center vertically. Then the spot traces a circle pattern for all the V and H values 90° out of phase.

For the pattern of an ellipse, the phase angle $\theta$ can be determined by calculating the ratio of the two lengths $B$ and $A$ shown at the right in Fig. D-12. As an example, when the $B$ intercept is seven-tenths of $A$, the ratio is 0.7. Since sine $\theta$ equals 0.707 for 45°, the phase angle is 45°.

**FREQUENCY COMPARISONS**  In practical terms, the patterns in Fig. D-12 show that the frequency is the same for the vertical and horizontal input signals. The pattern may drift between a diagonal line and the circle as the phase changes slowly. Even so, the pattern indicates a 1:1 frequency ratio.

When the vertical input signal has a higher frequency than the horizontal input signal, the patterns in Fig. D-13 are produced. To determine the frequency ratio, count the loops across either the top or bottom of the trace for $F_V$. Count only the closed loops; an open loop, such as a half-loop, is not counted at all. Similarly, count the closed loops at either side for $F_H$. The frequency ratio is then equal to $F_V/F_H$.

As an example, let the horizontal input be a 60-Hz ac voltage from the power line as a reference frequency. The vertical-input signal is from an audio signal generator. Its frequency calibration can be checked at the dial setting of 60 Hz. With a circle or line pattern, the frequency is exactly 60 Hz for the signal generator.

Next change the frequency dial to 120 Hz. Where the generator produces the pattern in Fig. D-13a, the frequency is exactly $2 \times 60 = 120$ Hz. The 3:1 pattern in Fig. D-13b shows the generator frequency is 180 Hz. Frequencies that are not exact multiples can also be compared, as in Fig. D-13c. The 3:2 ratio shows the generator frequency is $3/2 \times 60 = 90$ Hz. In that way the generator frequency can be checked for patterns up to about 10 loops which would represent 600 Hz.

After the generator is calibrated, it can be used as the reference for checking an unknown frequency. Use the generator for the horizontal-input signal and connect the other to the oscilloscope vertical input. The unknown frequency can be determined by seeing how many loops it produces compared with the generator frequency.

**ac**   Abbreviation for alternating current.

**active device**   One that can control voltage or current. Examples are transistor amplifier and diode rectifier.

**acute angle**   Less than 90°.

**A/D converter**   A device that converts analog input signals to digital output.

**admittance** $(Y)$   Reciprocal of impedance $Z$ in ac circuits. $Y = 1/Z$.

**air gap**   Air space between poles of a magnet.

**alkaline cell or battery**   One that uses alkaline electrolyte.

**alpha** $(\alpha)$   Characteristic of junction transistors. Ratio of collector current to emitter current. Value is 0.98 to 0.99.

**alternating current (ac)**   Current that reverses direction at a regular rate. Alternating voltage reverses in polarity. The rate of reversals is the frequency.

**alternator**   AC generator.

**ampere (A)**   Basic unit of electric current. Value of one ampere flows when one volt of potential difference is applied across one ohm of resistance.

**ampere-turn**   Unit of magnetizing force equal to 1 A × 1 turn.

**amplifier**   A device that increases the amplitude of a signal.

**amplitude modulation (AM)**   Changing the amplitude of an RF carrier wave in step with a lower-frequency signal that has the desired information.

**analog circuits**   Circuits that use continuous variations in voltage or current, compared with digital pulse circuits.

**AND gate**   Digital logic circuit. Produces HIGH output of 1 only when all inputs are at 1.

**antiresonance**   Term sometimes used for parallel resonance.

**apparent power**   The product of voltage and current $VA$ when $V$ and $I$ are out of phase.

**armature**   The part of a generator in which the voltage is produced. In a motor it is commonly the rotating member. Also, the movable part of a relay.

**astable MV**   Multivibrator that has no stable state. Used as an oscillator to generate clock timing pulses.

**audio frequency (AF)**   Within the range of hearing, approximately 16 to 16,000 Hz.

**autotransformer**   A single, tapped, winding used to step up or step down voltage.

**average value**   In sine-wave ac voltage or current, is 0.637 of peak value.

**back-off scale**   Ohmmeter readings from right to left.

**bandpass**   Filter that allows a band of frequencies to be coupled to the load.

**bandstop**   Filter that prevents a band of frequencies from being coupled to the load.

**bandwidth**   A range of frequencies that have a resonant effect in $LC$ circuits.

**bank**   Components connected in parallel.

**battery**   Group of cells connected in series or parallel.

**BCD**   Binary coded decimal. Converts a decimal number to a binary equivalent.

**beta** $(\beta)$   Current-gain characteristic of junction transistors. Ratio of collector current to base current.

**bias**   Average dc level of amplifier voltage or current to set operating characteristic.

**binary number system**   Uses only two digits, 0 and 1.

**bipolar transistor**   NPN or PNP type.

**bistable MV**   Multivibrator that has two stable states. Used as flip-flop circuit.

**bit**   One unit of information, either 0 or 1, in the binary number system.

**bleeder current**   Steady current from source, used to stabilize output voltage with changes in load current.

**boolean algebra**   Logical system of using binary information in digital circuits.

**branch**   Part of a parallel circuit.

**bridge**   Circuit in which voltages or currents can be balanced for a net effect of zero.

**brushes**   In a motor or generator, devices that provide stationary connections to the rotor.

**bypass capacitor**   One that has very low reactance in a parallel path.

**byte**   Digital word with a string of eight bits of 0 and 1.

$C$   Symbol for capacitance.

$C$   Abbreviation for coulomb, the unit of electric charge.

**calorie**   Amount of heat energy needed to raise the temperature of one gram of water by 1°C.

**capacitor**   Device used to store electric charge.

**capacitance**   The ability to store electric charge.

**carbon composition resistors**   Resistors made of finely divided carbon or graphite mixed with a powdered insulating material.

**carbon film resistors**   Resistors made by depositing a thin layer of carbon on an insulated substrate. The carbon film is cut in the form of a spiral.

**cascaded amplifiers**   Output terminal of one stage drives input terminal of next stage.

**CB circuit**   Common-base amplifier for junction transistors. Signal into emitter and output from collector.

**CB radio**   Citizen's band radio, 26.965 to 27.405 MHz.

**CC circuit**   Common-collector amplifier for junction transistors. Signal into base and output from emitter. Is emitter-follower stage.

**CD circuit**   Common-drain circuit for field-effect transistors. Is source-follower stage.

**CE circuit**   Common-emitter amplifier for junction transistors. Signal into base and output from collector.

**Celsius scale (°C)** Temperature scale that uses 0° for the freezing point of water and 100° for the boiling point. Formerly called centigrade.

**ceramic** Insulator with a high dielectric constant.

**chassis ground** Common return for all electronic circuits mounted on one metal chassis or PC board. Usually connects to one side of dc supply voltage.

**CG circuit** Common-gate amplifier for FETs.

**cgs** Centimeter-gram-second system of units.

**chip** Miniature semiconductor for integrated circuit.

**chip capacitor** A surface-mounted capacitor.

**choke** Inductance with high $X_L$ compared with the $R$ of the circuit.

**circuit breaker** A protective device that opens when excessive current flows in circuit. Can be reset.

**circular mil** Cross-sectional area of round wire with diameter of 1 mil or 0.001 in.

**clamp probe** Measures current without opening the circuit.

**clear** Same as reset on a flip-flop. Puts $Q$ output at logic 0.

**clock** A device that provides timing pulses for digital circuits; it is usually a multivibrator (MV) oscillator.

**closed circuit** A continuous path for current.

**coaxial cable** An inner conductor surrounded by an outer conductor that serves as a shield.

**coding of capacitors** The methods used to indicate the value of a capacitor.

**coil** Turns of wire conductor to concentrate the magnetic field.

**color code** System in which colors are used to indicate values in resistors and capacitors.

**commutator** Converts reversing polarities to one polarity.

**comparator** An op amp circuit that compares the signal voltage on one input with a reference voltage on the other.

**complex number** Has real and $j$ terms; uses form $A + jB$.

**conductance (G)** Ability to conduct current. It is the reciprocal of resistance, $G = 1/R$. The unit is the siemens (S).

**constant-current source** One that has high $r_i$ to supply constant $I$ with variations in $R_L$.

**constant-voltage source** One that has low $r_i$ to supply constant $V$ with variations in $R_L$.

**continuity** Continuous path for current. Reading of zero ohms with an ohmmeter.

**conventional current** Direction of flow of positive charges, opposite from electron flow.

**corona** Effect of ionization of air around a point at high potential.

**cosine** A trigonometric function of an angle, equal to the ratio of the adjacent side to the hypotenuse in a right triangle.

**cosine wave** One whose amplitudes vary as the cosine function of an angle. It is 90° out of phase with the sine wave.

**coulomb (C)** Unit of electric charge. $1 \text{ C} = 6.25 \times 10^{18}$ electrons.

**counter** Digital circuit using a flip-flop to accumulate the count of pulses.

**coupling capacitor** Has very low $X_C$ in series path.

**covalent bond** Pairing of atoms with electrical valence of $\pm 4$.

**cps** Cycles per second. Formerly used as unit of frequency. Replaced by hertz (Hz) unit where $1 \text{ Hz} = 1 \text{ cps}$.

**CRT** Cathode-ray tube. A device that converts electric signals to a visual display on a fluorescent screen.

**CS circuit** Common-source amplifier for field-effect transistors.

**current divider** A parallel circuit to provide branch $I$ less than the main-line current.

**current source** Supplies $I = V/r_i$ to load, with $r_i$ in parallel.

**cutoff** No current in an active device such as a transistor.

**cycle** One complete set of values for a repetitive waveform.

**D/A converter** Converts digital input to analog output.

**damping** Reducing the $Q$ of a resonant circuit to increase the bandwidth.

**Darlington pair** Combination of two transistor stages in cascade.

**D'Arsonval meter** A dc analog meter movement commonly used in ammeters and voltmeters.

**dB** Abbreviation for decibel. Equals 10 times the logarithm of the ratio of two power levels.

**dc** Abbreviation for direct current.

**decade** A 10:1 range of values.

**decade resistance box** A unit for providing any resistance within a wide range of values.

**decibels** A logarithmic expression that compares two power levels.

**degaussing** Demagnetizing by applying an ac field and gradually reducing it to zero.

**delta (Δ) network** Three components connected in series in a closed loop. Same as pi (π) network.

**detector diode** A device that rectifies a modulated signal to recover information in the modulation.

**diamagnetic** Material that can be weakly magnetized in the opposite direction from the magnetizing field.

**dicing** Cutting a slice of semiconductor material into tiny chips.

**dielectric** Insulating material. It cannot conduct current but does store charge.

**dielectric constant (k)** Ability to concentrate the electric field in a dielectric.

**differential amplifiers** An op amp circuit that amplifies differential signals but attenuates common-mode signals.

**differentiating circuit** An $RC$ circuit with a short time constant for pulses across $R$.

**digital circuit** One that uses only two amplitudes for a pulse of voltage or current, either HIGH at 1 or LOW at 0.

**digital IC** Abbreviation for digital integrated circuit.

**diode** Electronic device with two electrodes. Allows current flow in only one direction.

**DIP** Dual inline package for the pins of IC chip.

**direct current (dc)** Current that flows in only one direction. Dc voltage has a steady polarity that does not reverse.

**discrete component** A single individually packaged component usually with two or three leads.

**distributor** Digital circuit to convert serial data to parallel data. Also called demultiplexer.

**DMM** Digital multimeter. A piece of test equipment used to measure voltage, current, and resistance in an electronic circuit.

**doping**   Adding impurities to pure semiconductor material to provide free positive and negative charges.

**double subscripts**   An example is $V_{BA}$ to indicate voltage at point B with respect to point A.

**DPDT**   Double-pole double-throw switch or relay contacts.

**DPST**   Double-pole single-throw switch or relay contacts.

**dynamometer**   Type of ac meter, generally for 60 Hz.

**eddy current**   Circulating current induced in the iron core of an inductor by ac variations of magnetic flux.

**effective value**   For sine-wave ac waveform, 0.707 of peak value. Corresponds to heating effect of same dc value. Also called rms value.

**efficiency**   Ratio of power output to power input × 100%.

**EIA**   Electronic Industries Association.

**electricity**   Dynamic electricity is the effect of voltage in producing current in conductors. Static electricity is accumulation of charge.

**electrolyte**   Solution that forms ion charges.

**electrolytic capacitor**   Type with very high $C$ because electrolyte is used to form very thin dielectric. Must be connected with correct polarity in a circuit.

**electromagnet**   Magnet whose magnetic field is associated with electric current in a coil.

**electron**   Basic particle of negative charge, in orbital rings around the nucleus in an atom.

**electron flow**   Current of negative charges in motion. Direction is from the negative terminal of the voltage source, through the external circuit, and returning to the positive side of the source. Opposite to the direction of conventional current.

**electron volt**   Unit of energy equal to the work done in moving a charge of 1 electron through a potential difference of 1 V.

**electronics**   Based on electrical effects of the electron. Includes applications for amplifiers, oscillators, rectifiers, control circuits, and digital pulse circuits.

**emf**   Electromotive force, voltage to produce current in a circuit.

**emitter follower**   Circuit in which signal input is to base and output is from emitter. Same as common-collector circuit.

**F connector**   Solderless plug for coaxial cable.

**Fahrenheit scale (°F)**   Temperature scale that uses 32° for the freezing point of water and 212° for the boiling point.

**farad (F)**   Unit of capacitance. Value of one Farad stores one coulomb of charge with one volt applied.

**Faraday's law**   For magnetic induction, the generated voltage is proportional to the flux and its rate of change.

**FCC**   Federal Communications Commission.

**ferrite**   Magnetic material that is not a metal conductor.

**ferromagnetic**   Magnetic properties of iron and other metals that can be strongly magnetized in the same direction as the magnetizing field.

**FET**   Field-effect transistor.

**field**   Group of lines of force; magnetic or an electric field.

**field-effect transistor (FET)**   A device that depends on an electric field to control the current in a silicon channel.

**field winding**   The part of a motor or generator that supplies the magnetic field cut by the armature.

**film capacitor**   A capacitor which uses a plastic film for its dielectric.

**filter**   Circuit to separate different frequencies.

**fluctuating dc**   Varying voltage and current but no change in polarity.

**flux ($\phi$)**   Magnetic lines of force.

**flux density**   Amount of flux per unit area.

**flywheel effect**   Ability of an $LC$ circuit to continue oscillating after the energy source has been removed.

**forward voltage**   Polarity that allows current of majority carriers through a semiconductor junction.

**frequency ($f$)**   Number of cycles per second for a waveform with periodic variations. The unit is hertz (Hz).

**frequency modulation (FM)**   Changing the frequency of an RF carrier wave in step with a lower-frequency signal that has the desired information.

**function generator**   A piece of test equipment which produces sine, square, and triangular waveforms. It is used when designing or testing electronic circuitry.

**fuse**   Metal link that melts from excessive current and opens circuit.

**gain ($A$)**   Also amplification. Ratio of amplified output to input.

**galvanic cell**   Electrochemical type of voltage source.

**galvanometer**   Measures electric charge or current.

**gate**   Logic circuit with two or more inputs but one HIGH or LOW output for specific combinations of input pulses.

**gauss (G)**   Unit of flux density in cgs system, equal to one magnetic line of force per square centimeter.

**generator**   A device that produces voltage output. Is a source for either dc or ac V and I.

**germanium (Ge)**   Semiconductor element used for transistors and diodes.

**giga (G)**   Metric prefix for $10^9$.

**gilbert (Gb)**   Unit of magnetomotive force in cgs system. One gilbert equals 0.794 ampere-turn.

**graph cycle**   A 10:1 range of values on logarithmic graph paper.

**ground**   Common return to earth for ac power lines. Chassis ground in electronic equipment is the common return to one side of the internal power supply.

**half-power frequencies**   Define bandwidth with 70.7 percent response for resonant $LC$ circuit.

**Hall effect**   Small voltage generated by a conductor with current in an external magnetic field.

**harmonic**   Exact multiple of fundamental frequency.

**henry (H)**   Unit of inductance. Current change of one ampere per second induces one volt across an inductance of one henry.

**hertz (Hz)**   Unit of frequency. One hertz equals one cycle per second.

**hexadecimal**   Number system with radix of 16.

**$h_{FE}$**   Hybrid parameter for junction transistors that specifies current gain for common-emitter circuit.

**holding current** The minimum amount of current required to keep a relay energized.

**hole** Positive charge that exists only in doped semiconductors because of covalent bonds between atoms. Amount of hole charge is the same as a proton and an electron.

**hole current** Motion of hole charges. Direction is the same as that of conventional current, opposite from electron flow.

**hot resistance** The $R$ of a component with its normal load current. Determined by $V/I$.

**hot-wire meter** Type of ac meter.

**hybrid IC** A device that has discrete components with an integrated circuit.

**hypotenuse** Side of a right triangle opposite the 90° angle.

**hysteresis** In electromagnets, the effect of magnetic induction lagging in time behind the applied magnetizing force.

**Hz** Hertz unit of frequency, equal to one cycle per second.

**IC** Abbreviation for integrated circuit.

$I_{CB_O}$ Leakage current from collector to base with emitter open.

**IGFET** Insulated-gate field-effect transistor.

**imaginary number** Value at 90°, indicated by $j$ operator, as in the form $jA$.

**impedance matching** Occurs when a transformer is utilized for its impedance transformation properties. With impedance matching, maximum power is delivered to the load, $R_L$.

**inductance** ($L$) Ability to produce induced voltage when cut by magnetic flux. Unit of inductance is the henry (H).

**induction** Ability to generate $V$ or $I$ without physical contact. Electromagnetic induction by magnetic field; electrostatic induction by electric field.

**inductor** Coil of wire with inductance.

**insulator** A material that does not allow current to flow when voltage is applied, because of its high resistance.

**integrated circuit** Contains transistors, diodes, resistors, and capacitors in one miniaturized package. Can use bipolar transistor or FET technology.

**integration circuit** An $RC$ circuit with a long time constant. Voltage output across $C$.

**internal resistance** $r_i$ Limits the current supplied by the voltage source to $I = V/r_i$.

**inverse relation** Same as reciprocal function. As one variable increases, the other decreases.

**ion** Atom or group of atoms with net charge. Can be produced in liquids, gases, and doped semiconductors.

$IR$ **drop** Voltage across a resistor.

**iron-vane meter** Type of ac meter, generally for 60 Hz.

$j$ **operator** Indicates 90° phase angle, as in $j8\ \Omega$ for $X_L$. Also, $-j8\ \Omega$ is at $-90°$ for $X_C$.

**JFET** Junction field-effect transistor.

$JK$ **flip-flop** Type that has a clock input to toggle outputs between logic 1 and 0 when the $J$ and $K$ terminals are held HIGH.

**joule** (J) Practical unit of work or energy. One joule equals one watt-second of work.

$k$ Coefficient of coupling between coils.

**keeper** Magnetic material placed across the poles of a magnet to form a complete magnetic circuit. Used to maintain strength of magnetic field.

**Kelvin (K) scale** Absolute temperature scale, 273° below values on Celsius scale.

**kilo (k)** Metric prefix for $10^3$.

**Kirchhoff's current law (KCL)** The phasor sum of all currents into and out of any branch point in a circuit must equal zero.

**Kirchhoff's voltage law (KVL)** The phasor sum of all voltages around any closed path must equal zero.

**laminations** Thin sheets of steel insulated from one another to reduce eddy-current losses in inductors, motors, etc.

**latch** A device that remains in one stable state until activated to the opposite state. Can store binary information as logic 1 or 0. Is flip-flop in digital circuits.

**leakage current** Small reverse current of minority carriers across a PN junction.

**Leclanché cell** Carbon-zinc primary cell.

**LED** Light-emitting diode.

**Lenz's law** Induced current has magnetic field that opposes the change causing the induction.

**linear IC** A device that contains analog circuits, such as amplifiers, oscillators, rectifiers, and control circuits, rather than digital circuits.

**linear relation** Straight-line graph between two variables. As one increases, the other increases in direct proportion.

**load** Takes current from the voltage source, resulting in load current.

**loading effect** Source voltage is decreased as amount of load current increases.

**loop** In a circuit, any closed path.

**LSI** Large-scale integration for IC chips.

**magnetic pole** Concentrated point of magnetic flux.

**magnetism** Effects of attraction and repulsion by iron and similar materials without the need for an external force. Electromagnetism includes the effects of a magnetic field associated with an electric current.

**magnetomotive force (MMF)** Ability to produce magnetic lines of force. Measured in units of ampere-turns.

**magnitude** Value of a quantity regardless of phase angle.

**make and break** Occurs when contacts close and open.

**maxwell (Mx)** Unit of magnetic flux, equal to one line of force in the magnetic field.

**mega (M)** Metric prefix for $10^6$.

**memory device** Digital circuit that can store information as bits of logic 1 or 0. Often is flip-flop circuit.

**mesh current** Assumed current in a closed path, without any current division, for application of Kirchhoff's current law.

**metal film resistors** Resistors made by spraying a thin film of metal onto a ceramic substrate. The metal film is cut in the form of a spiral.

**micro** ($\mu$) Metric prefix for $10^{-6}$.

**microelectronics** Microscopic components used for IC chips to miniaturize size of equipment.

**milli (m)** Metric prefix for $10^{-3}$.

**miniDIP** Miniature IC package with eight pins in dual inline form.

**mks** Meter-kilogram-second system of units.

**monostable** Having one stable state, as in one-shot multivibrator.

**MOSFET** Metal-oxide semiconductor FET.

**motor** A device that produces mechanical motion from electric energy.

**multiplier** Resistor in series with a meter movement for voltage ranges.

**multivibrator (MV)** Astable type of oscillator circuit to produce pulses as a clock generator for timing in digital circuits.

**mutual induction ($L_M$)** Ability of one coil to induce voltage in another coil.

**NAND gate** Logic circuit that produces a LOW output of 0 only when all inputs are HIGH at 1.

**nano (n)** Metric prefix for $10^{-9}$.

**NC** Normally closed for relay contacts, or no connection for pinout diagrams.

**neutron** Particle without electric charge in the nucleus of an atom.

**nibble** Binary word with four bits, equal to one-half byte.

**node** A common connection for two or more branch currents.

**NOR gate** Logic circuit that produces a LOW output of 0 when any of the inputs is HIGH at 1.

**Norton's theorem** Method of reducing a complicated network to one current source with shunt resistance.

**NOT gate** Circuit to change binary 1 to 0 or 0 to 1. Same as inverter.

**obtuse angle** More than 90°.

**octal base** Eight pins for vacuum tubes. Eight digits for octal number system.

**octave** A 2:1 range of values.

**oersted (Oe)** Unit of magnetic field intensity; 1 Oe = 1 Gb/cm.

**ohm ($\Omega$)** Unit of resistance. Value of one ohm allows current of one ampere with potential difference of one volt.

**Ohm's law** In electric circuits, $I = V/R$.

**ohms per volt** Sensitivity rating for a voltmeter. High rating means less meter loading.

**open circuit** One that has infinitely high resistance, resulting in zero current.

**operational amplifier (op amp)** High-gain amplifier commonly used in linear IC chips for analog circuits.

**OR gate** Digital logic circuit that produces a HIGH output of 1 when any of the inputs is HIGH at 1.

**oscillator** Circuit that generates ac output from dc power input, without any ac signal input.

**oscilloscope** A piece of test equipment used to view and measure a variety of different ac waveforms.

**parallel circuit** One that has two or more branches for separate currents from one voltage source.

**paramagnetic** Material that can be weakly magnetized in the same direction from the magnetizing force.

**passive device** Components such as resistors, capacitors, and inductors. They do not generate voltage or control current.

**PC board** A device that has printed circuits.

**peak-to-peak value (p-p)** Amplitude between opposite peaks.

**peak value** Maximum amplitude, in either polarity; 1.414 times rms value for sine-wave $V$ or $I$.

**permanent magnet (PM)** It has magnetic poles produced by internal atomic structure. No external current needed.

**permeability** Ability to concentrate magnetic lines of force.

**permeance** Reciprocal of magnetic reluctance.

**phase angle** Angle between two phasors; denotes time shift.

**phasing dots** Used on transformer windings to identify those leads having the same instantaneous polarity.

**phasor** A line representing magnitude and direction of a quantity, such as voltage or current, with respect to time.

**pickup current** The minimum amount of current required to energize a relay.

**pico (p)** Metric prefix for $10^{-12}$.

**piezoelectric effect** Vibrations produced by some crystals compressed, expanded, or twisted, or when voltage is applied.

**pinout** Pin numbers for IC package.

**polar form** Form of complex numbers that gives magnitude and phase angle in the form $A \angle \theta$.

**polarity** Property of electric charge and voltage. Negative polarity is excess of electrons. Positive polarity means deficiency of electrons.

**potential** Ability of electric charge to do work in moving another charge. Measured in volt units.

**potentiometer** Variable resistor with three terminals connected as a voltage divider.

**power ($P$)** Rate of doing work. The unit of electric power is the watt.

**power factor** Cosine of the phase angle for a sine-wave ac circuit. Value is between 1 and 0.

**power supply** A piece of test equipment used to supply dc voltage and current to electronic circuits under test.

**preferred values** Common values of resistors and capacitors generally available.

**primary cell or battery** Type that cannot be recharged.

**primary winding** Transformer coil connected to the source voltage.

**printed wiring** Conducting paths printed on plastic board.

**proton** Particle with positive charge in the nucleus of an atom.

**pulsating dc value** Includes ac component on average dc axis.

**pulse** A sharp rise and decay of voltage or current of a specific peak value for a brief period of time.

**Q** Figure of quality or merit, in terms of reactance compared with resistance. The $Q$ of a coil is $X_L/r_i$. For an $LC$ circuit, $Q$ indicates sharpness of resonance. Also used as the symbol for charge: $Q = CV$.

**quadrature** A 90° phase angle.

**R** Symbol for resistance.

**radian (rad)** Angle of 57.3°. Complete circle includes $2\pi$ rad.

**radio** Wireless communication by electromagnetic waves.

**radio frequencies (RF)**   Those high enough to be radiated efficiently as electromagnetic waves, generally above 30 kHz. Usually much higher.

**radix**   Base for a number system; 10 for decimal numbers and 2 for binary numbers.

**ramp**   Sawtooth waveform with linear change in $V$ or $I$.

**reactance**   Property of $L$ and $C$ to oppose flow of $I$ that is varying. Symbol is $X_C$ or $X_L$. Unit is the ohm.

**read**   Take out digital information from a memory device.

**real number**   Any positive or negative number not containing $j$. $(A + jB)$ is a complex number but $A$ and $B$ by themselves are real numbers.

**real power**   The net power consumed by resistance. Measured in watts.

**reciprocal relation**   As one variable increases, the other decreases.

**rectangular form**   Representation of a complex number in the form $A + jB$.

**rectifier**   A device that allows current in only one direction.

**reflected impedance**   The value of impedance reflected back into the primary from the secondary.

**relay**   Automatic switch operated by current in a coil.

**relay chatter**   Describes the vibrating of relay contacts.

**reluctance ($R$)**   Opposition to magnetic flux. Corresponds to resistance for current.

**reset**   Put $Q$ output of flip-flop to logic 0.

**resistance ($R$)**   Opposition to current. Unit is the ohm ($\Omega$).

**resistance wire**   A conductor having a high resistance value.

**resonance**   Condition of $X_L = X_C$ in an $LC$ circuit to favor the resonant frequency for a maximum in $V$, $I$, or $Z$.

**reverse voltage**   Polarity that prevents forward current through a PN junction.

**rheostat**   Variable resistor with two terminals to vary $I$.

**ringing**   Ability of an $LC$ circuit to oscillate after a sharp change in $V$ or $I$.

**rms value**   For sine-wave ac waveform, 0.707 of peak value. Also called effective value.

**rotor**   Rotating part of generator or motor.

**saturation**   Maximum limit at which changes of input have no control in changing the output.

**sawtooth wave**   One in which amplitude values have a slow linear rise or fall and a sharp change back to the starting value. Same as a linear ramp.

**secondary winding**   Transformer coil connected to the load.

**secondary cell or battery**   Type that can be recharged.

**self-inductance ($L$)**   Inductance produced in a coil by current in the coil itself.

**series circuit**   One that has only one path for current.

**set**   Put $Q$ output of flip-flop at logic 1.

**shield**   Metal enclosure to prevent interference of radio waves.

**short-circuit**   Has zero resistance, resulting in excessive current.

**shunt**   A parallel connection. Also a device used to increase the range of an ammeter.

**SI**   Abbreviation for *Système International,* a system of practical units based on the meter, kilogram, second, ampere, kelvin, mol, and candela.

**siemens (S)**   Unit of conductance. Reciprocal of ohms unit.

**silicon (Si)**   Semiconductor chemical element used for transistors, diodes, and integrated circuits.

**sine**   Trigonometric function of an angle, equal to the ratio of the opposite side to the hypotenuse in a right triangle.

**sine wave**   One in which amplitudes vary in proportion to the sine function of an angle.

**slip rings**   In an ac generator, devices that provide connections to the rotor.

**solder**   Alloy of tin and lead used for fusing wire connections.

**solenoid**   Coil used for electromagnetic devices.

**source follower**   FET amplifier circuit in which input is to the gate and output from the source electrode. Same as common-drain circuit. Corresponds to emitter follower.

**spade lug**   A type of wire connector.

**SPDT**   Single-pole double-throw switch or relay contacts.

**specific gravity**   Ratio of weight of a substance with that of an equal volume of water.

**specific resistance**   The $R$ for a unit length, area, or volume.

**SPST**   Single-pole single-throw switch or relay contacts.

**square wave**   An almost instantaneous rise and decay of voltage or current in a periodic pattern with time and with a constant peak value. The $V$ or $I$ is on and off for equal times and at constant values.

**static electricity**   Electric charges not in motion.

**stator**   Stationary part of a generator or motor.

**steady-state value**   The $V$ or $I$ produced by a source without any sudden changes. Can be dc or ac value. Final value of $V$ or $I$ after transient.

**storage cell or battery**   Type that can be recharged.

**string**   Components connected in series.

**summing amplifier**   An op amp circuit whose output equals the negative sum of the inputs.

**superconductivity**   Very low $R$ at extremely low temperatures.

**superposition theorem**   Method of analyzing a network with multiple sources by using one at a time and combining their effects.

**supersonic**   Frequency above the range of hearing, generally above 16,000 Hz.

**surface-mount resistors**   Resistors made by depositing a thick carbon film on a ceramic base. Electrical connection to the resistive element is made by means of two leadless solder end electrodes which are C-shaped.

**surface-mount technology**   Components soldered directly to the copper traces of a printed circuit board. No holes need to be drilled with surface-mounted components.

**susceptance ($B$)**   Reciprocal of reactance in sine-wave ac circuits; $B = 1/X$.

**switch**   Device used to open or close connections of a voltage source to a load circuit.

**switching contacts**   The contacts which open and close when a relay is energized.

**tangent**   Trigonometric function of an angle, equal to the ratio of the opposite side to the adjacent side in a right triangle.

**tank circuit**   An $LC$ tuned circuit. Store energy in $L$ and $C$.

**tantalum**   Chemical element used for electrolytic capacitors.

**taper**   How $R$ of a variable resistor changes with the angle of shaft rotation.

**tapered control**   The manner in which the resistance of a potentiometer varies with shaft rotation. For a linear taper, one-half shaft rotation corresponds to a resistance change of one-half its maximum value. For a nonlinear taper, the resistance change is more gradual at one end, with larger changes at the other end.

**taut-band meter**   Type of construction for meter movement often used in VOM.

**temperature coefficient**   For resistance, how $R$ varies with a change in temperature.

**tesla (T)**   Unit of flux density, equal to $10^8$ lines of force per square meter.

**Thevenin's theorem**   Method of reducing a complicated network to one voltage source with series resistance.

**three-phase power**   AC voltage generated with three components differing in phase by $120°$.

**time constant**   Time required to change by 63 percent after a sudden rise or fall in $V$ and $I$. Results from the ability of $L$ and $C$ to store energy. Equals $RC$ or $L/R$.

**toggle**   For digital circuits, changing between HIGH at logic 1 and LOW at logic 0.

**toroid**   Electromagnet with its core in the form of a closed magnetic ring.

**transconductance**   Ratio of current output to voltage input.

**transformer**   A device that has two or more coil windings used to step up or step down ac voltage.

**transient**   Temporary value of $V$ or $I$ in capacitive or inductive circuits caused by abrupt change.

**transistor**   Semiconductor device used for amplifiers. Includes NPN and PNP junction types and FETs.

**trigonometry**   Analysis of angles and triangles.

**truth table**   Listing of all possible combinations of inputs and outputs for a digital logic circuit.

**tuning**   Varying the resonant frequency of an $LC$ circuit.

**turns ratio**   Comparison of turns in primary and secondary for a transformer.

**twin lead**   Transmission line with two conductors in plastic insulator.

**UHF**   Ultra high frequencies in band of 30 to 300 MHz.

**unity-gain amplifier**   An op amp circuit whose voltage gain is 1 or unity. It is used for buffering or isolating a low-impedance load from a high-impedance source.

**VAR**   Unit for voltamperes of reactive power, $90°$ out of phase with real power.

**Variac**   Transformer with variable turns ratio to provide different amounts of secondary voltage.

**vector**   A line representing magnitude and direction in space.

**VHF**   Very high frequencies, in band of 30 to 300 MHz.

**volatile memory**   Memory that loses its stored information when the power is turned off.

**volt (V)**   Practical unit of potential difference. One volt produces one ampere of current in a resistance of one ohm.

**voltage divider**   A series circuit to provide $V$ less than the source voltage.

**voltage drop**   Voltage across each component in a series circuit. The proportional part of total applied $V$.

**voltage regulator**   A device that maintains a constant output voltage with changes of input voltage or output load current.

**voltage source**   Supplies potential difference across two terminals. Has internal series $r_i$.

**voltampere (VA)**   Unit of apparent power, equal to $V \times I$.

**volt-ampere characteristic**   Graph to show how $I$ varies with $V$.

**voltmeter loading**   The amount of current taken by the voltmeter acting as a load. As a result the measured voltage is less than the actual value.

**VOM**   Volt-ohm-milliammeter.

**watt (W)**   Unit of real power. Equal to $I^2R$ or $VI \cos \theta$.

**watt hour**   Unit of electric energy, as power $\times$ time.

**wattmeter**   Measures real power as instantaneous value of $V \times I$.

**wavelength ($\lambda$)**   Distance in space between two points with the same magnitude and direction in a propagated wave.

**wavetrap**   An $LC$ circuit tuned to reject the resonant frequency.

**weber (Wb)**   Unit of magnetic flux, equal to $10^8$ lines of force.

**Wheatstone bridge**   Balanced circuit used for precise measurements of resistance.

**wire gage**   A system of wire sizes based on the diameter of the wire. Also, the tool used to measure wire size.

**wirewound resistors**   Resistors made with wire known as *resistance wire* which is wrapped around an insulating core.

**word**   In digital circuits, a group of bits of 0 and 1. Usually written in groups of four, eight, or sixteen bits.

**work**   Corresponds to energy. Equal to power $\times$ time, as in kilowatthour unit. Basic unit is one joule, equal to one volt-coulomb, or one watt-second.

**wye network**   Three components connected with one end in a common connection and the other ends to three lines. Same as T network.

$X_C$   Capacitive reactance, equal to $1/(2\pi fC)$.
$X_L$   Inductive reactance, equal to $2\pi fL$.
**XNOR gate**   Digital logic circuit for exclusive NOR gate.
**XOR gate**   Digital logic circuit for exclusive OR gate.

$Y$   Symbol for admittance in an ac circuit. Reciprocal of impedance $Z$; the $Y = 1/Z$.
**Y network**   Another way of denoting a wye network.

$Z$   Symbol for ac impedance. Includes resistance with capacitive and inductive reactance.

**zero-crossing detector**   An op amp comparator whose output switches between $\pm V_{sat}$ when $V_{in}$ crosses zero.

**zero-ohm resistors**   A resistor whose value is practically 0 $\Omega$. The 0-$\Omega$ value is denoted by a single black band around the center of the resistor body.

**zero-ohms adjustment**   Used with ohmmeter of VOM to set the correct reading at zero ohms.

# ANSWERS TO SELF-TESTS

| CHAPTER 1 | 1. T | 5. T | 9. T | 13. T | 17. T |
|---|---|---|---|---|---|
| | 2. T | 6. T | 10. T | 14. T | 18. T |
| | 3. T | 7. T | 11. T | 15. T | 19. F |
| | 4. T | 8. T | 12. T | 16. T | 20. F |

| CHAPTER 2 | 1. *b* | 3. *a* | 5. *c* | 7. *a* | 9. *c* |
|---|---|---|---|---|---|
| | 2. *d* | 4. *c* | 6. *a* | 8. *d* | 10. *c* |

| CHAPTER 3 | 1. 2 | 6. 25 | 10. 72 | 14. 0.83 | 18. 3 |
|---|---|---|---|---|---|
| | 2. 4 | 7. 25 | 11. 8 | 15. 144 | 19. 0.2 |
| | 3. 16 | 8. 10 | 12. 2 | 16. 2 | 20. 0.12 |
| | 4. 0.5 | 9. 0.4 | 13. 2 | 17. 1.2 | 21. *d* |
| | 5. 2 | | | | |

| CHAPTER 4 | 1. *d* | 3. *d* | 5. *c* | 7. *c* | 9. *b* |
|---|---|---|---|---|---|
| | 2. *c* | 4. *b* | 6. *d* | 8. *b* | 10. *d* |

| CHAPTER 5 | 1. *b* | 3. *a* | 5. *a* | 7. *c* | 9. *c* |
|---|---|---|---|---|---|
| | 2. *a* | 4. *d* | 6. *c* | 8. *b* | 10. *b* |

| CHAPTER 6 | 1. *c* | 3. *c* | 5. *d* | 7. *d* | 9. *d* |
|---|---|---|---|---|---|
| | 2. *c* | 4. *c* | 6. *b* | 8. *a* | 10. *d* |

| REVIEW: CHAPTERS 1 TO 6 | 1. *a* | 6. *c* | 10. *d* | 14. *b* | 18. *a* |
|---|---|---|---|---|---|
| | 2. *c* | 7. *b* | 11. *b* | 15. *a* | 19. *b* |
| | 3. *b* | 8. *c* | 12. *a* | 16. *a* | 20. *a* |
| | 4. *c* | 9. *b* | 13. *c* | 17. *a* | 21. *b* |
| | 5. *c* | | | | |

| CHAPTER 7 | 1. T | 3. T | 5. T | 7. T | 9. F |
|---|---|---|---|---|---|
| | 2. T | 4. F | 6. T | 8. T | 10. T |

| CHAPTER 8 | 1. *a* | 3. *a* | 5. *c* | 7. *a* | 9. *d* |
|---|---|---|---|---|---|
| | 2. *c* | 4. *a* | 6. *c* | 8. *c* | 10. *c* |

| REVIEW: CHAPTERS 7 AND 8 | 1. T | 4. T | 7. T | 9. T | 11. F |
|---|---|---|---|---|---|
| | 2. T | 5. F | 8. T | 10. F | 12. T |
| | 3. T | 6. F | | | |

| CHAPTER 9 | 1. T | 3. T | 5. T | 7. F | 9. T |
| | 2. F | 4. T | 6. T | 8. T | 10. T |

| CHAPTER 10 | 1. T | 3. T | 5. T | 7. T | |
| | 2. T | 4. T | 6. T | 8. F | |

| REVIEW: CHAPTERS 9 AND 10 | 1. T | 4. T | 7. F | 10. T | 13. T |
| | 2. T | 5. T | 8. T | 11. T | 14. T |
| | 3. T | 6. F | 9. T | 12. T | 15. T |

| CHAPTER 11 | 1. *a* | 3. *d* | 5. *b* | 7. *b* | 9. *c* |
| | 2. *d* | 4. *b* | 6. *a* | 8. *c* | 10. *c* |

| CHAPTER 12 | 1. *d* | 3. *b* | 5. *d* | 7. *a* | 9. *a* |
| | 2. *c* | 4. *a* | 6. *d* | 8. *c* | 10. *d* |

| REVIEW: CHAPTERS 11 AND 12 | 1. *d* | 3. *a* | 5. *b* | 7. *b* | 9. *a* |
| | 2. *c* | 4. *c* | 6. *d* | 8. *b* | 10. *d* |

| CHAPTER 13 | 1. T | 4. F | 7. T | 10. T | 13. T |
| | 2. T | 5. T | 8. T | 11. F | 14. T |
| | 3. T | 6. T | 9. T | 12. T | 15. F |

| CHAPTER 14 | 1. F | 4. F | 7. T | 9. T | 11. T |
| | 2. T | 5. T | 8. T | 10. T | 12. T |
| | 3. T | 6. T | | | |

| CHAPTER 15 | 1. T | 5. T | 9. T | 13. T | 17. F |
| | 2. T | 6. T | 10. T | 14. T | 18. T |
| | 3. T | 7. T | 11. T | 15. T | 19. F |
| | 4. T | 8. T | 12. T | 16. F | |

| CHAPTER 16 | 1. T | 11. 28.28 V | 21. 1000 Hz |
| | 2. T | 12. 1.2 A | 22. 180 Hz |
| | 3. T | 13. 70.7 V | 23. 11.1 Hz |
| | 4. T | 14. $3 \times 10^4$ cm | 24. 120 V |
| | 5. T | 15. 0.001 ms | 25. 240 Hz |
| | 6. T | 16. 60 Hz | 26. 240 V |
| | 7. F | 17. 0.01 $\mu$s | 27. 120° |
| | 8. F | 18. 0.25 MHz | 28. 208 V |
| | 9. T | 19. 7.07 V | |
| | 10. T | 20. 40 V | |

| REVIEW: CHAPTERS 13 TO 16 | 1. *b* | 3. *c* | 5. *b* | 7. *a* | 9. *c* |
| | 2. *a* | 4. *d* | 6. *d* | 8. *d* | 10. *a* |

| CHAPTER 17 | 1. *a* | 3. *b* | 5. *c* | 7. *c* | 9. *c* |
| | 2. *b* | 4. *c* | 6. *c* | 8. *b* | 10. *b* |

| CHAPTER 18 | 1. *b* | 3. *c* | 5. *d* | 7. *a* | 9. *b* |
|---|---|---|---|---|---|
| | 2. *c* | 4. *b* | 6. *a* | 8. *d* | 10. *a* |

| CHAPTER 19 | 1. *d* | 3. *a* | 5. *b* | 7. *c* | 9. *b* |
|---|---|---|---|---|---|
| | 2. *b* | 4. *b* | 6. *b* | 8. *c* | 10. *b* |

| REVIEW: CHAPTERS 17 TO 19 | 1. T | 7. T | 13. F | 19. T | 25. T |
|---|---|---|---|---|---|
| | 2. T | 8. T | 14. T | 20. T | 26. T |
| | 3. T | 9. F | 15. T | 21. T | 27. F |
| | 4. T | 10. T | 16. T | 22. T | 28. F |
| | 5. T | 11. T | 17. F | 23. T | 29. T |
| | 6. T | 12. F | 18. T | 24. T | 30. T |

| CHAPTER 20 | 1. *b* | 3. *c* | 5. *c* | 7. *b* | 9. *b* |
|---|---|---|---|---|---|
| | 2. *c* | 4. *d* | 6. *d* | 8. *d* | 10. *a* |

| CHAPTER 21 | 1. *a* | 3. *c* | 5. *a* | 7. *c* | 9. *d* |
|---|---|---|---|---|---|
| | 2. *c* | 4. *d* | 6. *c* | 8. *b* | 10. *c* |

| CHAPTER 22 | 1. *c* | 3. *c* | 5. *b* | 7. *c* | 9. *d* |
|---|---|---|---|---|---|
| | 2. *c* | 4. *c* | 6. *b* | 8. *c* | |

| CHAPTER 23 | 1. *a* | 3. *d* | 5. *d* | 7. *d* | 9. *d* |
|---|---|---|---|---|---|
| | 2. *c* | 4. *b* | 6. *c* | 8. *c* | 10. *c* |

| REVIEW: CHAPTERS 20 TO 23 | 1. *c* | 5. *d* | 8. *a* | 11. *c* | 14. *d* |
|---|---|---|---|---|---|
| | 2. *b* | 6. *d* | 9. *b* | 12. *a* | 15. *b* |
| | 3. *d* | 7. *c* | 10. *c* | 13. *c* | 16. *a* |
| | 4. *d* | | | | |

| CHAPTER 24 | 1. *b* | 3. *a* | 5. *c* | 7. *b* | 9. *c* |
|---|---|---|---|---|---|
| | 2. *c* | 4. *c* | 6. *a* | 8. *c* | 10. *a* |

| CHAPTER 25 | 1. d | 4. j | 7. c | 10. a | 12. f |
|---|---|---|---|---|---|
| | 2. m | 5. h | 8. k | 11. b | 13. g |
| | 3. i | 6. l | 9. e | | |

| REVIEW: CHAPTERS 24 AND 25 | 1. 300 | 9. 14.1 | 17. 5.66 $\angle 45°$ |
|---|---|---|---|
| | 2. 300 | 10. 1 | 18. 4 $\angle 10°$ |
| | 3. 300 | 11. 45° | 19. T |
| | 4. 250 | 12. −45° | 20. T |
| | 5. 250 | 13. 1 | 21. T |
| | 6. 200 | 14. 1.41 | 22. F |
| | 7. 200 | 15. 7.07 | |
| | 8. 14.1 | 16. 600 | |

| CHAPTER 26 | 1. *c* | 3. *d* | 5. *d* | 7. *d* | 9. *a* |
|---|---|---|---|---|---|
| | 2. *b* | 4. *c* | 6. *a* | 8. *d* | 10. *b* |

| CHAPTER 27 | 1. *d* | 4. *c* | 7. *b* | 10. *d* | 13. *d* |
| | 2. *a* | 5. *d* | 8. *b* | 11. *b* | 14. *a* |
| | 3. *b* | 6. *b* | 9. *a* | 12. *a* | 15. *c* |

| REVIEW: CHAPTERS 26 AND 27 | 1. 8 | 7. 5 | 12. −100 db | 17. T |
| | 2. 0.8 | 8. 0.08 | 13. octave, decade | 18. T |
| | 3. 0.4 | 9. 40 | 14. 70.7 | 19. T |
| | 4. 10 | 10. 150 | 15. F | 20. T |
| | 5. 10 | 11. $f_c = 31.83$ kHz | 16. T | 21. F |
| | 6. 1 | | | |

| CHAPTER 28 | 1. ±4 | 6. forward | 11. 100 mA | 15. higher |
| | 2. 0.7 V | 7. reverse | 12. source | 16. shorted |
| | 3. opposite | 8. positive | 13. N channel | 17. F |
| | 4. NPN | 9. cathode | 14. JFET, IGFET, | |
| | 5. base | 10. hole current | and MOSFET | |

| CHAPTER 29 | 1. active | 7. 30 to 300 MHz | 13. AM | 19. two |
| | 2. low | 8. AF | 14. video | 20. T |
| | 3. analog | 9. Hartley | 15. FM | 21. hum |
| | 4. $A_V = 100$ | 10. Multivibrator | 16. cathode | 22. T |
| | 5. $A_I = 50$ | 11. astable MV | 17. anode | 23. T |
| | 6. *C* | 12. T | 18. 60 Hz | |

| CHAPTER 30 | 1. CE | 7. A | 13. CD | 19. short-circuit |
| | 2. CE | 8. forward | 14. $\beta$ | 20. less |
| | 3. multiplied | 9. reverse | 15. $\alpha$ | 21. CC |
| | 4. CC | 10. positive | 16. 2.5 mA | 22. dc |
| | 5. CS | 11. NPN | 17. class A | 23. $R_E$ |
| | 6. Si | 12. $V_{CC}$ | 18. off | |

| REVIEW: CHAPTERS 28 TO 30 | 1. T | 6. T | 11. T | 16. T | 21. F |
| | 2. F | 7. T | 12. T | 17. T | 22. F |
| | 3. F | 8. T | 13. T | 18. F | 23. F |
| | 4. F | 9. T | 14. T | 19. T | 24. F |
| | 5. T | 10. T | 15. F | 20. T | 25. T |

| CHAPTER 31 | 1. 2 | 5. NOR | 8. NAND | 11. reset |
| | 2. hexadecimal | 6. OR | 9. NOR | 12. set |
| | 3. 11 | 7. XNOR | 10. $2^4$ or 16 | 13. $Q = 0, \overline{Q} = 1$ |
| | 4. NAND | | | |

| CHAPTER 32 | 1. T | 4. F | 7. F | 10. T |
| | 2. T | 5. T | 8. T | 11. T |
| | 3. T | 6. T | 9. T | |

| REVIEW: CHAPTERS 31 AND 32 | 1. T | 5. F | 9. T | 13. F |
| | 2. T | 6. F | 10. T | 14. T |
| | 3. T | 7. T | 11. T | 15. T |
| | 4. T | 8. T | 12. F | 16. F |

# ANSWERS TO ODD-NUMBERED PROBLEMS AND CRITICAL THINKING PROBLEMS

## ANSWERS TO ODD-NUMBERED CHAPTER PROBLEMS

### CHAPTER 1

**1.** $I = 5$ A
**3.** $Q = 9$ C
**5.** $Q = -3$ C
**7.** Since there are four electrons in the valence shell, the valence is $\pm 4$.
**9.** $T = 8$ s
**11.** (a) $R = 500\ \Omega$
(b) $R = 250\ \Omega$
(c) $R = 120\ \Omega$
(d) $R = 4\ \Omega$
**13.** (a) $G = 1$ S
(b) $G = 0.0001$ S
(c) $G = 0.025$ S
(d) $G = 2$ S
**15.** $V = 12$ V

### CHAPTER 2

**1.** (a) $1.5\ \text{k}\Omega \pm 10\%$
(b) $27\ \Omega \pm 5\%$
(c) $470\ \text{k}\Omega \pm 5\%$
(d) $6.2\ \Omega \pm 5\%$
(e) $91\ \text{k}\Omega \pm 10\%$
(f) $10\ \Omega \pm 5\%$
(g) $1.8\ \text{M}\Omega \pm 10\%$
(h) $1.5\ \text{k}\Omega \pm 20\%$
**3.** (a) $470\ \text{k}\Omega$
(b) $1.2\ \text{k}\Omega$
(c) $330\ \Omega$
(d) $10\ \text{k}\Omega$
**5.** Reading from left to right, the colors are:
(a) brown, black, orange, and gold
(b) red, violet, gold, and gold
(c) green, blue, red, and silver
(d) brown, green, green, and gold
(e) red, red, silver, and gold
**7.** (a) $680,225\ \Omega$
(b) $8250\ \Omega$
(c) $18,503\ \Omega$
(d) $275,060\ \Omega$
(e) $62,984\ \Omega$
**9.** See Fig. 2-19*b*

### CHAPTER 3

**1.** (b) $I = 15$ mA
(c) the same, 15 mA
(d) $I = 30$ mA
**3.** (a) $V = 36$ V
(b) $I = 150$ mA
**5.** (a) $V = 24$ V
(b) $P = 48$ W
(c) the same, 48 W
**7.** (a) $I = 300 \times 10^{-6}$ A $= 300\ \mu$A
(b) $I = 5 \times 10^{-6}$ A $= 5\ \mu$A
(c) $I = 200 \times 10^{-3}$ A $= 200$ mA
(d) $I = 300 \times 10^{-6}$ A $= 300\ \mu$A
(e) $I = 1 \times 10^{-3}$ A $= 1$ mA
(f) $I = 15 \times 10^{-3}$ A $= 15$ mA
**9.** (a) $R = 12 \times 10^3\ \Omega = 12\ \text{k}\Omega$
(b) $R = 3.75 \times 10^3\ \Omega = 3.75\ \text{k}\Omega$
(c) $R = 8.64 \times 10^3\ \Omega = 8.64\ \text{k}\Omega$
(d) $R = 18 \times 10^3\ \Omega = 18\ \text{k}\Omega$
**11.** (a) $R = 2.5\ \Omega$
(b) $V = 25$ V
(c) $P = 250$ W
**15.** $R = 240\ \Omega$
**17.** $I_{max} = 19.17$ mA
**19.** $I = 16.67$ mA
**21.** $P = 1.125$ W
**23.** Choose a resistor whose $R$ and $P$ values are $200\ \Omega$ and $\frac{1}{4}$ W respectively.
**25.** $R = 100\ \Omega$

### CHAPTER 4

**1.** $I = 2$ A, $R_2 = 10\ \Omega$
**3.** $V_2 = 1.2$ V
**5.** $I = 4$ mA
$V_1 = 8$ V
$V_2 = 32$ V
$P_1 = 32$ mW
$P_2 = 128$ mW
$P_T = 160$ mW $= 0.16$ W
**7.** $R_T = 2,573,470\ \Omega$
**9.** Each $R = 6\ \text{k}\Omega$
**11.** 20.7 V
**13.** $R_1 = 300\ \Omega$
$P_1 = 27$ W
$P_2 = 9$ W
**15.** $R_2 = 25\ \Omega$
**17.** $V_2 = 13$ V
**19.** (a) $V = 18$ V
(b) $V = 0$ V
**21.** $R = 60\ \Omega$
**23.** $V_1 = 0$ V
$V_2 = 36$ V
$V_3 = 0$ V
$V_4 = 0$ V
**25.** $R_T = 4.5\ \text{k}\Omega$
$I = 12$ mA
$V_1 = 1.2$ V
$V_2 = 2.64$ V
$V_3 = 8.16$ V
$V_4 = 14.4$ V
$V_5 = 21.6$ V
$V_6 = 1.32$ V
$V_7 = 4.68$ V
$P_T = 648$ mW
$P_1 = 14.4$ mW
$P_2 = 31.68$ mW
$P_3 = 97.92$ mW
$P_4 = 172.8$ mW
$P_5 = 259.2$ mW
$P_6 = 15.84$ mW
$P_7 = 56.16$ mW
**27.** $I = 20$ mA
$V_1 = 2.4$ V
$V_2 = 2$ V
$V_3 = 13.6$ V
$V_T = 18$ V
$R_3 = 680\ \Omega$
$P_T = 360$ mW
$P_2 = 40$ mW
$P_3 = 272$ mW

# CHAPTER 5

**1. (b)** 12 V
**(c)** $I_1 = 2$ A, $I_2 = 1$ A
**(d)** $I_T = 3$ A
**(e)** $R_{EQ} = 4$ $\Omega$
**3. (b)** 20 V
**(c)** $I_2 = 2$ A
$I_3 = 4$ A
**5. (a)** $I_2 = 0$ A
**(b)** $I_1 = 1$ A
**(c)** $I_T = 1$ A
**(d)** $R_{EQ} = 10$ $\Omega$
**(e)** $P_T = 10$ W
**7. (a)** 7.14 $\Omega$
**(b)** 2 k$\Omega$
**(c)** 250 $\Omega$
**(d)** 54.6 $\Omega$
**(e)** 714 $\Omega$
**(f)** 5 k$\Omega$
**9.** $G_T = 0.039$ S

**11. (a)** $R = 100$ k$\Omega$
**(b)** $R = 33.3$ k$\Omega$
**(c)** $R = 11.1$ k$\Omega$
**13. (a)** 8.8 V
**(b)** 8.8 V
**(c)** $I_2 = 2.26$ mA
**15.** $G_T = 0.5$ S
$R_{EQ} = 2$ $\Omega$
**17.** $I_1 = 200$ mA
$I_2 = 400$ mA
$I_3 = 600$ mA
$I_T = 1.2$ A
$R_{EQ} = 10$ $\Omega$
$P_1 = 2.4$ W
$P_2 = 4.8$ W
$P_3 = 7.2$ W
$P_T = 14.4$ W
**19.** $I_1 = 50$ mA
$I_2 = 25$ mA

$I_3 = 75$ mA
$I_T = 150$ mA
$R_{EQ} = 60$ $\Omega$
$P_1 = 450$ mW
$P_2 = 225$ mW
$P_3 = 675$ mW
$P_T = 1.35$ W
**21.** $I_1$ remains the same
(50 mA)
**23.** $R_{EQ} = 25$ $\Omega$
**25. (a)** 6 mA
**(b)** 30 mA
**27. (a)** 42.5 mA
**(b)** 157.5 mA
**29.** $I_T = 1.2$ A
$I_1 = 100$ mA
$I_2 = 900$ mA
$R_1 = 1.08$ k$\Omega$
$R_2 = 120$ $\Omega$

$R_3 = 540$ $\Omega$
$P_T = 129.6$ W
$P_2 = 97.2$ W
$P_3 = 21.6$ W
**31.** $R_{EQ} = 1.105$ k$\Omega$
$I_T = 190$ mA
$I_2 = 30$ mA
$I_3 = 50$ mA
$I_4 = 100$ mA
$R_1 = 21$ k$\Omega$
$R_3 = 4.2$ k$\Omega$
$P_T = 39.9$ W
$P_1 = 2.1$ W
$P_2 = 6.3$ W
$P_3 = 10.5$ W
$P_4 = 21$ W

# CHAPTER 6

**1. (a)** $R_T = 25$ $\Omega$
**(b)** $I_T = 4$ A
**3. (b)** $R_T = 15$ $\Omega$
**5. (a)** $R = 6$ $\Omega$
**(b)** $R = 24$ $\Omega$
**7. (a)** $V_1 = 2.23$ V
$V_2 = 0.74$ V
$V_3 = 6.7$ V
$V_4 = 22.3$ V
**(b)** $P_1 = 204$ mW
$P_2 = 69$ mW
$P_3 = 620$ mW
$P_4 = 2.08$ mW

**9.** $V_1 = V_X = 1$ V
$V_2 = V_S = 10$ V
$R_X = 4.2$ $\Omega$
**11.** $R_T = 10.45$ $\Omega$
**13. (a)** $V_2 = 20$ V
**(b)** $V_1 = V_2 = 22.5$ V
**15.** $R_T = 1$ k$\Omega$
$I_1 = 60$ mA
$I_2 = 44$ mA
$I_3 = 16$ mA
$V_1 = 7.2$ V
$V_2 = 52.8$ V
$V_3 = 52.8$ V

$V_{AB} = -52.8$ V
**17.** $V_{AB}$ increases. $I_T$ and $I_2$
both decrease, and $I_3$ is
zero.
**19.** $V_{AB}$ decreases to zero.
$I_T$ and $I_3$ both increase,
and $I_2$ is zero.
**21.** $R_T = 300$ $\Omega$
$I_1 = 120$ mA
$I_2 = 60$ mA
$I_3 = 60$ mA
$I_4 = 30$ mA
$I_5 = 30$ mA

$I_6 = 15$ mA
$I_7 = 15$ mA
$I_8 = 7.5$ mA
$I_9 = 7.5$ mA
$V_1 = 18$ V
$V_2 = 18$ V
$V_3 = 9$ V
$V_4 = 9$ V
$V_5 = 4.5$ V
$V_6 = 4.5$ V
$V_7 = 2.25$ V
$V_8 = 2.25$ V
$V_9 = 2.25$ V

# CHAPTER 7

**1.** $V_1 = 3$ V
$V_2 = 6$ V
$V_3 = 9$ V
**3.** $I_1 = 1$ A
$I_2 = 2$ A
**5.** $V_1 = 12$ V
$V_2 = 6$ V
$V_3 = 10.8$ V

$V_4 = 7.2$ V
$V_{CG} = 7.2$ V
$V_{BG} = 18$ V
$V_{AG} = 24$ V
**7.** $I_1 = 16$ mA
$I_2 = 8$ mA
**9.** $I_1 = 25$ $\mu$A
$I_2 = 37.5$ $\mu$A

$I_3 = 12.5$ $\mu$A
$I_4 = 75$ $\mu$A
**11.** $R_1 = 236.8$ $\Omega$
$R_2 = 333$ $\Omega$
$R_3 = 1.5$ k$\Omega$
$P_1 = 342$ mW
$P_2 = 108$ mW
$P_3 = 54$ mW

**13.** $R_1 = 500$ $\Omega$
$R_2 = 800$ $\Omega$
$R_3 = 1.6$ k$\Omega$
$P_1 = 1.8$ W
$P_2 = 1.62$ W
$P_3 = 360$ mW
**15.** $V_{load\ C} = 11.21$ V

# CHAPTER 8

**1. (a)** $R_S = 50$ $\Omega$
**(b)** $R_S = 5.55$ $\Omega$
**(c)** $R_S = 2.083$ $\Omega$
**(d)** $R_S = 0.505$ $\Omega$
(approximately)
**(e)** Half-scale current is
1 mA in **(a)**, 5 mA
in **(b)**, 12.5 mA in

**(c)**, and 50 mA in
**(d)**.
**3. (a)** $R_{mult} = 2.95$ k$\Omega$
**(b)** $R_{mult} = 9.95$ k$\Omega$
**(c)** $R_{mult} = 29.95$ k$\Omega$
**(d)** $R_{mult} = 99.95$ k$\Omega$
**(e)** $R_{mult} = 299.95$ k$\Omega$
**5. (a)** V = 4.8 V

**(b)** V = 3 V
**(c)** V = 4.77 V
**7.** $\dfrac{10\ k\Omega}{V}$
**9. (a)** $R_X = 0$ $\Omega$
**(b)** $R_X = 4.5$ k$\Omega$
**(c)** $R_X = 3$ k$\Omega$

**(d)** $R_X = 1.5$ k$\Omega$
**(e)** $R_X = 750$ $\Omega$
**(f)** $R_X = 500$ $\Omega$
**11.** $R_1 = 145$ $\Omega$
**13.** 10 $\Omega$
**15.** 1.1 V

# CHAPTER 9

1. (a) $I_3 = 8$ A
   (b) $I_5 = 16$ A
   (c) $I_6 = 11$ A
3. (a) $V_T = 36$ V
   $R_T = 4.5$ kΩ
   $I = 8$ mA
   $V_{R_1} = 8$ V
   $V_{R_2} = 12$ V
   $V_{R_3} = 16$ V
   (b) $V_{AG} = +12$ V
   $V_{BG} = +4$ V
   $V_{CG} = -8$ V

$V_{DG} = -24$ V
5. (a) $V_T = 30$ V
   $R_T = 25$ kΩ
   $I = 1.2$ mA
   $V_{R_1} = 12$ V
   $V_{R_2} = 6$ V
   $V_{R_3} = 12$ V
   (b) $V = +3$ V
   (c) $V = -3$ V
   (d) $V = 0$ V
7. $I_1 = 160$ mA
   $I_2 = 440$ mA

$I_3 = 600$ mA
$V_{R_1} = 19.2$ V
$V_{R_2} = 79.2$ V
$V_{R_3} = 10.8$ V
9. Answers are the same as for Prob. 7.
11. Left loop: CCW from negative terminal of $V_1$: $-10$ V $+ 16.875$ V $- 15$ V $+ 8.125$ V $= 0$. Right loop: CCW from positive terminal of $V_2$:

15 V $- 16.875$ V $+ 1.875$ V $= 0$. Outside loop: CCW from negative terminal of $V_1$: $-10$ V $+ 1.875$ V $+ 8.125$ V $= 0$.
13. $I_1 = 2$ A
    $I_2 = 3$ A
    $I_3 = 1$ A
    $V_{R_1} = 30$ V
    $V_{R_2} = 30$ V
    $V_{R_3} = 10$ V

# CHAPTER 10

1. $V_{TH} = 15$ V
   $R_{TH} = 3$ Ω
   $V_L = 6$ V
3. $I_S = 5$ A
   $R_S = 4$ Ω
   $I_L = 3$ A
5. $R_L$ not open
7. $V_P = 4.2$ V
9. $V_{R_2} = 16.8$ V

11. $V_{R_2} = 16.8$ V
13. $V_{R_3} = 10.6$ V
15. See Fig. 10-31
17. (a) $V_1 = 54$ V,
    $R_1 = 6$ Ω,
    $V_2 = 72$ V,
    $R_2 = 12$ Ω
    (b) $V_{AB} = V_{TH} = -18$ V,
    $R_{TH} = 18$ Ω

(c) $I_L = 500$ mA
(d) $I_N = 1$ A
    $R_N = 18$ Ω
19. $V_{AB} = V_{TH} = 36$ V
    $R_{TH} = 600$ Ω
    $V_L = 24$ V
21. $V_{TH} = 36$ V
    $R_{TH} = 600$ Ω
    $I_L = 20$ mA

$V_L = 24$ V
23. $I_N = 33.3$ mA
    $R_N = 300$ Ω
25. $I_1 = 890$ mA
    $I_2 = 522.5$ mA
    $I_3 = 1.41$ A
    $V_{R_1} = 8.9$ V
    $V_{R_2} = 20.9$ V
    $V_{R_3} = 21.1$ V

# CHAPTER 11

1. (a) 1024 cmil
   (b) gage no. 20
   (c) $R = 1.035$ Ω
3. (a) 1-A fuse
   (b) 0 V

(c) 120 V
5. $R = 96$ Ω
7. 10,000 ft
9. (a) 4.8 Ω
   (b) 4000 ft

11. 3 V
13. $I = 30$ A
15. (a) No. 14 gage
    (b) 0.25 Ω
    (c) 3.25 Ω

17. (a) 200 ft
    (b) 0.3185 Ω
    (c) 115 V approx.
    (d) 71.7 W approx.

# CHAPTER 12

1. 1.5 mA
3. 600 A
5. (a) $2.88 \times 10^5$ C
   (b) 40 h
7. 20 kΩ
9. 6 Ω
11. $R_L = 1$ Ω:
    $I = 2.5$ A
    $V_L = 2.5$ V
    $P_L = 6.25$ W
    $P_T = 37.5$ W
    % efficiency $= 16.67$
    $R_L = 3$ Ω:
    $I = 1.875$ A

$V_L = 5.625$ V
$P_L = 10.547$ W
$P_T = 28.125$ W
% efficiency $= 37.5$
$R_L = 5$ Ω:
$I = 1.5$ A
$V_L = 7.5$ V
$P_L = 11.25$ W
$P_T = 22.5$ W
% efficiency $= 50$
$R_L = 7$ Ω:
$I = 1.25$ A
$V_L = 8.75$ V
$P_L = 10.938$ W

$P_T = 18.75$ W
% efficiency $= 58.3$
$R_L = 10$ Ω:
$I = 1$ A
$V_L = 10$ V
$P_L = 10$ W
$P_T = 15$ W
% efficiency $= 66.7$
$R_L = 15$ Ω:
$I = 750$ mA
$V_L = 11.25$ V
$P_L = 8.438$ W
$P_T = 11.25$ W
% efficiency $= 75$

$R_L = 45$ Ω:
$I = 300$ mA
$V_L = 13.5$ V
$P_L = 4.05$ W
$P_T = 4.5$ W
% efficiency $= 90$
$R_L = 100$ Ω:
$I = 142.9$ mA
$V_L = 14.29$ V
$P_L = 2.04$ W
$P_T = 2.14$ W
% efficiency $= 95.3$
13. $r_i = 25$ Ω
15. $R_L = 150$ Ω

# CHAPTER 13

1. $5 \times 10^3$ Mx
   $5 \times 10^{-5}$ Wb
3. 0.4 T
5. $24 \times 10^3$ Mx

7. 300
9. 1 μWb $= 10^{-6} \times 10^8$ Mx
11. (a) 500 kG
    (b) 600 Mx

(c) 0.25 T
(d) 150 μWb
(e) 40 G

13. $B = 500$ G
15. $B = 80 \times 10^{-3}$ T or 80 mT

# CHAPTER 14

1. (a) 200
   (b) 500
3. (a) 300 G/Oe
   (b) $378 \times 10^{-6}$ T/(A · t/m)
   (c) 300
5. (a) $126 \times 10^{-6}$

(b) $88.2 \times 10^{-6}$
7. (b) 40 V
   (c) 1000 A · t/m
   (d) 0.378 T
   (e) $3.02 \times 10^{-4}$ Wb
   (f) $66 \times 10^4$ A · t/Wb

9. 14.4
11. $\mu_r = 133.3$
13. $B = 0.00189$ T or 1.89 mT
15. $\phi = 0.01$ Wb or 10 mWb

# CHAPTER 15

1. 8 kV
3. (a) 2 Wb/s
   (b) −2 Wb/s
5. (a) 0.2 A

(b) 80 ampere-turns
(c) 400 ampere-turns/m
(d) 0.252 T
(e) $1.512 \times 10^{-4}$ Wb

(f) See Fig. 15-7 for an example.
7. $v_{ind} = 1$ V
9. $N = 1600$ turns

# CHAPTER 16

1. (a) $I = 6$ A
   (b) $f = 60$ Hz
   (c) $0°$
   (d) 120 V
3. (a) $t = 0.25$ ms
   (b) $t = 0.0625$ $\mu$s
5. (a) $f = 20$ Hz
   (b) $f = 200$ Hz
   (c) $f = 0.2$ Hz
   (b) $f = 0.2$ Hz
7. (a) $+10$ and $-10$ V
   (b) $+10$ and $-10$ V
   (c) $+10$ and $-10$ V

(d) $+15$ and $-5$ V
9. $I_1 = 40$ $\mu$A
   $I_2 = 20$ $\mu$A
   $V_1 = V_2 = 200$ V
   $P_1 = 8$ mW
   $P_2 = 4$ mW
11. $I = 2.5$ A
13. (a) 27.15 V
    (b) 20.8 V
15. $I_1 = 2.553$ A
    $I_2 = 1.765$ A
    $I_3 = 5.455$ A
    $I_T = 9.773$ A

17. (a) 462.5 $\mu$V
    (b) 9.84 mV
    (c) 35.19 mV
19. (a) 7.93 $\Omega$
    (b) 1.55 W
21. (a) 42.42 $V_{rms}$
    (b) 60 V
    (c) 120 V
23. 7.5 MHz, first harmonic, first odd; 15 MHz, second harmonic, first even; 22.5 MHz, third harmonic, second odd;

30 MHz, fourth harmonic, second even.
25. (a) $\lambda = 113$ ft
    (b) $\lambda = 22.6$ ft
    (c) $\lambda = 4.52$ ft
    (d) $\lambda = 1.13$ ft
    (e) $\lambda = 0.0753$ ft
    (f) $\lambda = 0.0565$ ft
27. 1.6 kHz
29. 22.5°
31. $T = 6.67$ nS

# CHAPTER 17

1. $Q = 400$ $\mu$C
3. (a) $Q = 18$ $\mu$C
   (b) 9 V
5. $C = 1062$ pF
7. (a) 200 V
   (b) $Q = 200$ $\mu$C
   (c) $C = 1$ $\mu$F
9. (a) $2.5 \times 10^{-2}$ J
   (b) 12.5 J
   (c) 3.2 J

11. (a) 0.06 $\mu$F
    (b) 74.2 pF
13. (a) $C_T = 0.01334$ $\mu$F
    (b) $C_T = 0.047$ $\mu$F
15. (a) 4700 pF $\pm$ 20%
    (b) 10,000 pF $\pm$ 5%
    (c) 220,000 pF $\pm$ 10%
    (d) 820 pF $\pm$ 20%
    (e) 0.0033 $\mu$F + 80%, −20%
    (f) 0.022 $\mu$F + 100%, −0%

(g) 1800 pF $\pm$ 10%
(h) 0.0027 $\mu$F + 80%, −20%
17. (a) 56 pF
    (b) 12,000 pF
    (c) 560,000 pF
    (d) 22 pF
19. (a) 470,000 pF or 0.47 $\mu$F, $\pm$10%
    (b) 6,200,000 pF or 6.2 $\mu$F, $\pm$5%
    (c) 15,000,000 pF or 15 $\mu$F, $\pm$10%
    (d) 820,000,000 pF or 820 $\mu$F, $\pm$5%

# CHAPTER 18

1. 80 pF at 1 MHz
3. (b) $I = 4.5$ mA
   (c) $f = 1$ kHz
5. (b) $I = 2$ mA
   (c) $V_{C_1} = 2$ V
   (d) $V_{C_2} = 8$ V

7. $f = 3183$ Hz
9. (a) $X_{C_T} = 200$ $\Omega$
   (b) $C = 333.3$ pF
   $C_T = 1000$ pF
11. (a) $X_C = 300$ $\Omega$
    $C = 8.85$ $\mu$F

(b) $C = 17.7$ $\mu$F
13. $X_C = 206.5$ $\Omega$
15. $I = 0.78$ mA
17. $C = 422$ pF
19. See values in Prob. 21
21. See values in Prob. 19

23. (a) $X_{C_T}$ is halved
    (b) $I$ doubles
25. (a) $I_T$ is halved
    (b) $X_{C_{EQ}}$ doubles
27. $C = 100$ pF

# CHAPTER 19

1. (b) $Z = 50$ $\Omega$
   (c) $I = 2$ A
   (d) $V_R = 80$ V
   $V_C = 60$ V

(e) $\theta_Z = -37°$
3. $C = 0.08$ $\mu$F at 100 Hz
   $C = 80$ pF at 100 kHz
5. At 60 Hz, $C = 26.59$ $\mu$F

At 1 kHz, $C = 1.59$ $\mu$F
At 1 MHz, $C = 1590$ pF
7. $I_C = 15$ mA
   $I_R = 20$ mA

$I_T = 25$ mA
$Z_T = 1.2$ k$\Omega$
$\theta_I = 37°$
$V_R = V_C = 30$ V

# CHAPTER 19 (*cont.*)

**9.** For dc or ac,
  $V_1 = 400$ V
  $V_2 = 200$ V
  $V_3 = 100$ V
**11.** $Z_T = 583$ Ω
  $I = 0.2$ A
  $\theta_Z = -31°$
**13.** $I_T = 0.466$ A

$Z_{EQ} = 258$ Ω
$\theta_Z = 59°$
**15.** $C_1 = 66$ μF approx.
  $C_2 = 33$ μF approx.
**17.** $\theta_Z = -5.7°$
**19.** $C = 765$ pF
**21.** $X_C = 31.83$ kΩ
  $Z_T = 33.37$ kΩ

$I = 3.6$ mA
$V_C = 114.6$ V
$V_R = 35.6$ V
$\theta_Z = -72.6°$
**23.** $X_C = 965$ Ω
  $I_C = 10.36$ mA
  $I_R = 10$ mA
  $I_T = 14.4$ mA

$Z_{EQ} = 694$ Ω
$\theta_I = 55.2°$
**25.** $V_{AG} = 60$ V
  $V_{BG} = 12$ V
  $V_{CG} = 1.09$ V
**27.** (a) $C = 1.59$ μF
  (b) 0.0106 μF or
    10.61 nF

# CHAPTER 20

**1.** (a) 1.5 A/s
  (b) 10,000 A/s
  (c) 10,000 A/s
  (d) −10,000 A/s
**3.** (a) 7.5 mV
  (b) 50 V
  (c) 50 V
  (d) −50 V
**5.** (a) 60 Hz
  (b) 960 V
  (c) 96 mA

  (d) 0.768 A
**7.** (a) 300 μH
  (b) 66.7 μH
  (c) 320 and 280 μH
  (d) 0.0707
**9.** $R = 10.52$ Ω
**11.** $0.243 \times 10^{-3}$ J
**13.** (a) 80 percent
  (b) 500 W
**15.** 1.26 mH
**17.** (a) 12 V

  (b) 2.4 mA
  (c) 28.8 mW
  (d) 28.8 mW
**19.** $V_{S_1} = 120$ V
  $I_{S_1} = 50$ mA
  $P_{S_1} = 6$ W
  $V_{S_2} = 24$ V
  $I_{S_2} = 1$ A
  $P_{S_2} = 24$ W
  $P_P = 30$ W
  $I_P = 250$ mA

**21.** (a) $R_L = 3$ Ω
  (b) $I_P = 2.5$ A
**23.** (a) $Z_P = 200$ Ω
  (b) $Z_P = 12.5$ Ω
  (c) $Z_P = 6.25$ kΩ
  (d) $Z_P = 5$ kΩ
  (e) $Z_P = 5$ Ω
**25.** 11.18 : 1

# CHAPTER 21

**1.** At 100 Hz, $X_L = 314$ Ω
  At 200 Hz, $X_L = 628$ Ω
  At 1000 Hz, $X_L = 3140$ Ω
**3.** (b) $I = 21.4$ mA
  (c) $V_L = 16$ V
**5.** $X_L = 1.2$ kΩ
  $L = 3.18$ H
**7.** $L = 0.159$ H
  $X_L = 10$ kΩ
**9.** (a) $X_{L_T} = 5$ kΩ
  (b) $I = 2$ mA
  (c) $V_{L_1} = 2$ V

  $V_{L_2} = 8$ V
  (d) $L_1 = 2.65$ H
    $L_2 = 10.6$ H
**11.** (a) $f = 0.16$ kHz
  (b) $f = 1.27$ kHz
  (c) $f = 0.4$ MHz
  (d) $f = 1.6$ MHz
  (e) $f = 16$ MHz
**13.** $X_L = 1628.6$ Ω
**15.** $X_L = 754$ Ω
**17.** (d) At 500 Hz,
    $X_L = 785$ Ω

  $I = 12.7$ mA
**19.** (a) 250 μH
  (b) 125 μH
  (c) 500 μH
  (d) 25 μH
  (e) 2.5 mH
**21.** $X_{L_1} = 5$ kΩ
  $X_{L_2} = 10$ kΩ
  $X_{L_3} = 15$ kΩ
  $X_{L_T} = 30$ kΩ
  $I = 4$ mA
  $V_{L_1} = 20$ V

  $V_{L_2} = 40$ V
  $V_{L_3} = 60$ V
**23.** $X_{L_1} = 1.6$ kΩ
  $X_{L_2} = 6.4$ kΩ
  $X_{L_3} = 1.28$ kΩ
  $I_1 = 20$ mA
  $I_2 = 5$ mA
  $I_3 = 25$ mA
  $I_T = 50$ mA
  $X_{L_{EQ}} = 640$ Ω
**25.** (a) $X_{LT} = 5.34$ kΩ
  (b) $X_{LT} = 4.08$ kΩ

# CHAPTER 22

**1.** (a) $Z = 100$ Ω
  $I = 1$ A
  $\theta = 0°$
  (b) $Z = 100$ Ω
  $I = 1$ A
  $\theta = 90°$
  (c) $Z = 70.7$ Ω
  $I = 1.41$ A
  $\theta = 45°$
**3.** (b) $X_L = 377$ Ω
  (c) $Z = 390$ Ω
  (d) $I = 0.3$ A
  (e) $I = 47.8$ mA
**5.** $Z = 400$ Ω
  $X_L = 400$ Ω

**7.** $R_e = 94$ Ω
**9.** $Z = 566$ Ω
  $I = 0.177$ A
  $V_L = 70.7$ V
  $V_R = 70.7$ V
  $\theta_Z = 45°$
**11.** At 800 Hz,
  $I_R = 0.25$ A
  $I_L = 0.125$ A
  $\theta_I = -26.6°$
**13.** $X_L = 500$ Ω
  $L = 15.9$ mH
**15.** $Z_T = 583$ Ω
  $I = 0.2$ A
  $\theta_Z = 59°$

**17.** $v_L$ is a square wave,
  ±160 V p-p
**19.** (a) 45°
  (b) 63.4°
  (c) 84.3°
  (b) 63.4°
**21.** (a) −45°
  (b) −26.6°
  (c) −5.7°
  (b) −26.6°
**23.** $X_L = 6$ kΩ
  $Z_T = 7.62$ kΩ
  $I = 3.15$ mA
  $V_L = 18.9$ V
  $V_R = 14.8$ V

  $\theta_Z = 51.93°$
**25.** $X_L = 2$ kΩ
  $I_L = 12$ mA
  $I_R = 16$ mA
  $I_T = 20$ mA
  $Z_{EQ} = 1.2$ kΩ
  $\theta_I = -36.87°$
**27.** $L = 26.53$ mH
  $Z_T = 3.33$ kΩ
  $I = 4.51$ mA
  $V_L = 11.26$ V
  $V_R = 9.92$ V
  $\theta_Z = 48.6°$
**29.** (a) $L = 7.96$ mH
  (b) $L = 159.1$ μH

# CHAPTER 23

1. **(a)** 0.05 s
   **(b)** 0.05 $\mu$s
   **(c)** 1 ms
   **(b)** 20 $\mu$s
3. **(a)** 4 s
   **(b)** 100 V
5. $v_C = 86$ V
7. $v_C = 15$ V
9. 1.4 ms
11. **(a)** short
    **(b)** short
    **(c)** long
13. $C = 10\ \mu$F
15. 1.96 V
17. $0.05 \times 10^6$ V/s
19. Answer in instructor's manual.
21. **(a)** $V_C = 5$ V
    **(b)** $V_C = 10$ V
    **(c)** $V_C = 11.32$ V
    **(d)** $V_C = 13.65$ V
    **(e)** $V_C = 14.7$ V
    **(f)** $V_C = 14.93$ V

# CHAPTER 24

1. **(a)** 100 W
   **(b)** no reactance
   **(c)** 1
3. **(b)** $I = 10$ A, approx.
   **(c)** $Z = 10\ \Omega$
   **(d)** $\theta = 0°$
5. **(c)** $Z_T = 500\ \Omega$
   $I = 0.8$ A
   $\theta_Z = 53°$
7. **(a)** $X_L = 0$, approx.
   $X_C = 665\ \Omega$
   **(b)** $Z_T = 890\ \Omega$
   $I = 135$ mA
   $\theta_Z = -47.9°$
9. **(a)** $180°$
11. $R = 320\ \Omega$
13. $C = 300$ pF
15. $R = 9704\ \Omega$
17. $Z_T = 143\ \Omega$
   $I = 0.7$ A
   $\theta_Z = -36.5°$
   $\theta = 36.5°$
19. **(a)** $L_1 = 3$ mH
   $C_1 = 0.025\ \mu$F
   **(b)** same reactances
21. $I_L = 60$ mA
   $I_C = 120$ mA
   $I_R = 80$ mA
   $I_T = 100$ mA
   $Z_{EQ} = 120\ \Omega$
   $\theta_I = 36.87°$
   Real power = 960 mW; apparent power = 1.2 W; power factor = 0.8.

# CHAPTER 25

1. **(a)** $4 - j3$
   **(b)** $4 + j3$
   **(c)** $3 + j6$
   **(d)** $3 - j3$
3. **(a)** $5\ \angle -37°$
   **(b)** $5\ \angle 37°$
   **(c)** $3.18\ \angle 18.5°$
   **(d)** $4.24\ \angle -45°$
5. $Z_T = 65.36 + j23.48$
7. **(a)** $4.5\ \angle 14°$
   **(b)** $4.5\ \angle 34°$
   **(c)** $100\ \angle -84°$
   **(d)** $100\ \angle -60°$
9. $Z_T = 12.65\ \angle 18.5°$
11. $Z_T = 5.25\ \angle -13.7°$
13. $R = 5.08\ \Omega$
   $X_C = 1.27\ \Omega$
15. $R = 21.4\ \Omega$
   $X_L = 10.2\ \Omega$
17. $Z_T = 50\ \angle -37° = 40 - j30\ \Omega$
   $I = 2\ \angle 37° = 1.6 + j1.2$ A
   $V_R = 80\ \angle 37° = 64 + j48$ V
   $V_L = 120\ \angle 127° = -72 + j96$ V
   $V_C = 180\ \angle -53° = 108 - j144$ V
19. $Z_T = 2.07$ k$\Omega\ \angle 14.6°$ k$\Omega$
   $I = 3.88$ mA $\angle -14.6°$ mA
21. $Z_T = 13.4\ \angle 46.5°$
23. $Z_T = 1.28\ \angle -11.3°$ k$\Omega$
   $I_T = 18.75\ \angle 11.3°$ mA
   $V_{R_1} = 13.31\ \angle 56.3°$ V
   $V_{C_1} = 19.97\ \angle -33.7°$ V
   $V_{L_1} = 13.31\ \angle 56.3°$ V
   $V_{R_2} = 19.97\ \angle 33.7°$ V

# CHAPTER 26

1. $f_r = 5$ MHz
3. $f_r = 1.41$ MHz
5. $L = 35.08\ \mu$H
7. $f_r = 5$ MHz
9. $Q = 50$
   $\Delta f = 100$ kHz
   $f_1 = 4.95$ MHz
   $f_2 = 5.05$ MHz
11. **(a)** $C = 202.68$ pF
    **(b)** $X_L = 314.2\ \Omega$
    $X_C = 314.2\ \Omega$
    $Q = 25$
    $\Delta f = 100$ kHz
13. $X_L = 785.4\ \Omega$
   $X_C = 785.4\ \Omega$
   $I_L = 1.273$ mA
   $I_C = 1.273$ mA
   $Q = 100$
   $Z_{EQ} = 78.58$ k$\Omega$
   $I_T = 12.73\ \mu$A
15. **(a)** $Z_{EQ} = 55.55$ k$\Omega$
    $I_T = 18\ \mu$A
    $\theta_I = -45°$
    **(b)** $Z_{EQ} = 55.55$ k$\Omega$
    $I_T = 18\ \mu$A
    $\theta_I = 45°$
17. **(a)** $C = 253.5$ pF
    **(b)** $X_L = 628.3\ \Omega$
    $X_C = 628.3\ \Omega$
    $Q = 80$
    $\Delta f = 12.5$ kHz
    $Z_{EQ} = 50.26$ k$\Omega$
    $I_T = 19.9\ \mu$A
19. **(a)** Real power = 79.62 nW; apparent power = 79.62 nW; power factor = 1.
    **(b)** Real power = 39.8 nW; apparent power = 56.3 nW; power factor = 0.707.
    **(c)** Real power = 39.8 nW; apparent power = 56.3 nW; power factor = 0.707.
21. $f_r = 3$ MHz
23. $\Delta f = 60$ kHz
   $f_1 = 2.97$ MHz
   $f_2 = 3.03$ MHz
25. $R_S = 18.85\ \Omega$
27. $f_r = 1$ MHz
29. $\Delta f = 4$ kHz
   $f_1 = 998$ kHz
   $f_2 = 1.002$ MHz

# CHAPTER 27

1. **(a)** $C = 0.1\ \mu$F
   **(b)** $V_R \cong 0$ V
   $V_C = 20$ V
   **(c)** $V_R = 7.07$ V rms value
   $V_C \cong 0$ V
3. $C = 0.64\ \mu$F
5. **(a)** $f_c = 3.29$ kHz
   **(b)** $f_c = 5.305$ kHz
   **(c)** $f_c = 1.88$ kHz
   **(d)** $f_c = 2.39$ kHz
7. **(a)** $V_{out} = 10\ \angle 0°$ V
   **(b)** $V_{out} = 9.99\ \angle -2.16°$ V

## CHAPTER 27 (*cont.*)

(c) $V_{out} = 7.07 \angle{-45°}$ V
(d) $V_{out} = 2.2 \angle{-62°}$ V
(e) $V_{out} = 1 \angle{-84°}$ V
(f) $V_{out} = 53 \angle{-89.7°}$ mV
9. (a) $V_{out} = 1.05 \angle{88.8°}$ mV
   (b) $V_{out} = 26.58 \angle{57.9°}$ mV
   (c) $V_{out} = 35.35 \angle{45°}$ mV

(d) $V_{out} = 46.45 \angle{21.7°}$ mV
(e) $V_{out} = 49.94 \angle{2.74°}$ mV
(f) $V_{out} = 50 \angle{0°}$ mV
11. (a) $N_{db} = -27.6$ db
    (b) $N_{db} = -3$ db
    (c) $N_{db} = -0.17$ db
    (d) $N_{db} = 0$ db (approximately)

13. $f_N = 4.42$ kHz
15. (a) $N_{db} = 3$ db
    (b) $N_{db} = 10$ db
    (c) $N_{db} = 13$ db
    (d) $N_{db} = 20$ db
    (e) $N_{db} = 30$ db
    (f) $N_{db} = 33$ db

## CHAPTER 28

1. $R = 1.6\ \Omega$
3. $I_C = 5.7$ mA
5. $I_E = 50.3$ mA
7. $I = 20$ mA

## CHAPTER 29

1. $A_V = 300$
   $A_I = 90$
   $A_P = 27,000$
3. 10,000
5. $159\ \Omega$
7. (a) $C = 332\ \mu$F
   (b) $C = 166\ \mu$F
9. $f_r = 1.625$ MHz
11. $R_L = 2.5$ k$\Omega$

## CHAPTER 30

1. (a) 50
   (b) 80
   (c) 4000
3. 11.25
5. (a) 4 V
   (b) 2 mA
7. (a) 8 V
   (b) 2 mA
   (c) 1 k$\Omega$
9. (a) $\pm 2$ mA
   (b) 50

## CHAPTER 31

1. (a) 11
   (b) 17
   (c) 16
   (d) 181
3. (a) 100000000
   (b) 111100000110
   (c) 1110101
   (d) 1100001100111010
5. (a) 5F
   (b) 5F
   (c) 35
   (d) B29

7.

**Logic symbol for
2-input AND gate**

| A | B | X |
|---|---|---|
| 0 | 0 | 0 |
| 0 | 1 | 0 |
| 1 | 0 | 0 |
| 1 | 1 | 1 |

**Truth table for
2-input AND gate**

9.

**Logic symbol for
3-input NOR gate**

| A | B | C | X |
|---|---|---|---|
| 0 | 0 | 0 | 1 |
| 0 | 0 | 1 | 0 |
| 0 | 1 | 0 | 0 |
| 0 | 1 | 1 | 0 |
| 1 | 0 | 0 | 0 |
| 1 | 0 | 1 | 0 |
| 1 | 1 | 0 | 0 |
| 1 | 1 | 1 | 0 |

**Truth table for
3-input NOR gate**

11.

| A | B | C | D | X |
|---|---|---|---|---|
| 0 | 0 | 0 | 0 | 0 |
| 0 | 0 | 0 | 1 | 0 |
| 0 | 0 | 1 | 0 | 0 |
| 0 | 0 | 1 | 1 | 1 |
| 0 | 1 | 0 | 0 | 0 |
| 0 | 1 | 0 | 1 | 0 |
| 0 | 1 | 1 | 0 | 0 |
| 0 | 1 | 1 | 1 | 1 |
| 1 | 0 | 0 | 0 | 0 |
| 1 | 0 | 0 | 1 | 0 |
| 1 | 0 | 1 | 0 | 0 |
| 1 | 0 | 1 | 1 | 1 |
| 1 | 1 | 0 | 0 | 1 |
| 1 | 1 | 0 | 1 | 1 |
| 1 | 1 | 1 | 0 | 1 |
| 1 | 1 | 1 | 1 | 1 |

**Truth table for the boolean
expression: $AB + CD = X$**

## CHAPTER 31 (*cont.*)

**13.**

$$A + B + C = \overline{X}$$

**15.** See Fig. 31-49.

**17.**

| A | B | C | D | X |
|---|---|---|---|---|
| 0 | 0 | 0 | 0 | 0 |
| 0 | 0 | 0 | 1 | 0 |
| 0 | 0 | 1 | 0 | 0 |
| 0 | 0 | 1 | 1 | 0 |
| 0 | 1 | 0 | 0 | 1 |
| 0 | 1 | 0 | 1 | 1 |
| 0 | 1 | 1 | 0 | 1 |
| 0 | 1 | 1 | 1 | 1 |
| 1 | 0 | 0 | 0 | 0 |
| 1 | 0 | 0 | 1 | 0 |
| 1 | 0 | 1 | 0 | 0 |
| 1 | 0 | 1 | 1 | 0 |
| 1 | 1 | 0 | 0 | 1 |
| 1 | 1 | 0 | 1 | 1 |
| 1 | 1 | 1 | 0 | 1 |
| 1 | 1 | 1 | 1 | 0 |

**Truth table for the boolean expression:** $B(\overline{A} + \overline{C} + \overline{D}) = X$

**19.**

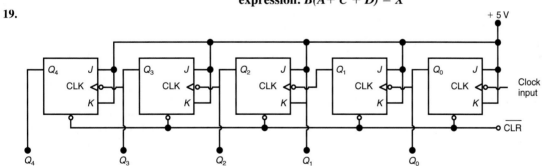

## CHAPTER 32

**1.** **(a)** $A_{CL} = 10$
**(b)** $V_{out} = 5$ V
**3.** $f_{max} = 15.92$ kHz

**5.** **(a)** $V_{out} = -12.5$ V
**(b)** $V_{out} = +10$ V
**(c)** $V_{out} = 0$ V

**7.** $f_c = 1.06$ kHz
$V_{out}$ at $0.25f_c = 24.25$ mVpp
**9.** $V_{out} = -10$ V

# ANSWERS TO ODD-NUMBERED CRITICAL THINKING PROBLEMS

## CHAPTER 1

**1.** $Q = 1.6 \times 10^{-16}$ C
**3.** $I = 0.0001$ A or $1 \times 10^{-4}$ A

## CHAPTER 2

**1.** $R = 250$ k$\Omega$

## CHAPTER 3

**1.** $I = 21.59$ A
**3.** Cost = $7.52
**5.** $I_{max}$ (120°C) = 13.69 mA

## CHAPTER 4

**1.** $R_1 = 300$ $\Omega$
$R_2 = 600$ $\Omega$
$R_3 = 1.8$ k$\Omega$
**3.** $I = 35.36$ mA
**5.** $R_1 = 250$ $\Omega$
$V_T = 1.25$ V

## CHAPTER 5

**1.** $I_T = 44.53$ mA
**3.** $R_1 = 2$ k$\Omega$
$R_2 = 6$ k$\Omega$
$R_3 = 3$ k$\Omega$
**5.** $R_1 = 15$ k$\Omega$
$R_2 = 7.5$ k$\Omega$
$R_3 = 3.75$ k$\Omega$
$R_4 = 1.875$ k$\Omega$

## CHAPTER 6

**1.** **(a)** $R_1 = 657$ $\Omega$
**(b)** $2 \times 12.9$ W = 25.8 W, approx.,
for a safety factor of 2.
**(c)** $R_T = 857$ $\Omega$
**3.** **(b)** $A(B + C) = X$

## CHAPTER 7

**1.** $R_1 = 1$ k$\Omega$
$R_3 = 667$ $\Omega$

## CHAPTER 8

**1.** $R_1 = 40$ $\Omega$
$R_2 = 9$ $\Omega$
$R_3 = 1$ $\Omega$
**3.** 10 k$\Omega/V$

## CHAPTER 9

**1.** $R_1 = 1.5$ k$\Omega$
$R_3 = 1$ k$\Omega$

## CHAPTER 10

**1.** $V_{TH} = 20$ V
$R_{TH} = 12$ $\Omega$
$I_L = 250$ mA
$V_L = 17$ V
**3.** $V_{TH} = 0$ V
$R_{TH} = 25$ $\Omega$

## CHAPTER 11

**1.** Drawing provided in instructor's manual.

## CHAPTER 12

**1.** **(a)** $V_L = 11.45$ V
**(b)** $I_L = 1.91$ A approx.
**(c)** $V_1$ supplies 550 mA approx.
$V_2$ supplies 275 mA approx.
$V_3$ supplies 1.1 A approx.

## CHAPTER 13

**1.** **(a)** $B = 1550$ G or 1.55 kG
**(b)** $B = 0.155$ T or 155 mT

## CHAPTER 14

**1.** $\mu_0 = B/H: 1 = 1$ G/10e
Since $1$ G $= \dfrac{1 \times 10^{-8} \text{ Wb}}{1 \times 10^{-4} \text{ m}^2}$
$= 1 \times 10^{-4}$ T
and $10$e $= 79.36 \dfrac{\text{A} \cdot \text{t}}{\text{m}^2}$ then
$\mu_0 = \dfrac{1 \times 10^{-4} \text{ T}}{79.36 \dfrac{\text{A} \cdot \text{t}}{\text{m}^2}}$
$= 1.26 \times 10^{-6} \dfrac{\text{T}}{\text{A} \cdot \text{t/m}^2}$

## CHAPTER 15

**1.** **(a)** $R_W = 1.593$ $\Omega$
**(b)** $R_T = 17.593$ $\Omega$
**(c)** $V_L = 218.3$ V
**(d)** $I^2R$ power loss = 296.5 W
**(e)** $P_L = 2.98$ kW
**(f)** $P_T = 3.27$ kW
**(g)** % efficiency = 91.1
**3.** With a relay, the 1000-ft length of wire does not carry the load current $I_L$ and thus the circuit losses are reduced significantly.

## CHAPTER 16

**1.** **(a)** 65 ft
**(b)** 1981 cm
**3.** $f = 3.9$ MHz

## CHAPTER 17

**1.** $C_1 = 8.08$ nF
$C_2 = 2.02$ nF
$C_3 = 161.6$ nF
**3.** **(a)** $\mathscr{E} = 500$ mJ
**(b)** $\mathscr{E} = 250$ mJ
**(c)** Yes. 250 mJ of energy was lost as heat energy ($I^2R$) in the wire conductors when the second 100 $\mu$F was connected in part **(b)**.

## CHAPTER 18

**1.** Connect the unmarked capacitor in series with an ac voltage source whose frequency and output voltage are known. Measure the ac current through the capacitor. Calculate $X_C$ as $V_C/I$. Next, solve for C as $C = 1/2\pi f X_C$.

## CHAPTER 19

1. $X_C = 300\ \Omega$
   $Z_T = 671\ \Omega$
   $I = 26.83\ \text{mA}$
   $f = 19.649\ \text{kHz}$
   $V_T = 18\ \text{V}$
   $V_R = 16.1\ \text{V}$
3. $I_C = 12\ \text{mA}$
   $I_R = 20.79\ \text{mA}$
   $I_T = 24\ \text{mA}$
   $X_C = 2\ \text{k}\Omega$
   $R = 1.154\ \text{k}\Omega$
   $C = 7960\ \text{pF approx.}$

## CHAPTER 20

1. Since $V_P = V_S \times N_S/N_P$ and $I_P = I_S \times N_S/N_P$ then $Z_P = V_P/I_P =$
   $$\frac{V_S \times N_S/N_P}{I_S \times N_S/N_P}$$
   since $Z_S = V_S/I_S$ then $Z_P = (N_P/N_S)^2 \times Z_S$.
3. (a) $Z_P = 800\ \Omega$
   (b) $Z_P = 200\ \Omega$

## CHAPTER 21

1. $L_1 = 60\ \text{mH}$
   $L_2 = 40\ \text{mH}$
   $L_3 = 120\ \text{mH}$
   $L_T = 90\ \text{mH}$
   $X_{L_1} = 1.2\ \text{k}\Omega$
   $X_{L_2} = 800\ \Omega$
   $X_{L_T} = 1.8\ \text{k}\Omega$
   $V_{L_1} = 24\ \text{V}$
   $V_{L_3} = 12\ \text{V}$
   $I_{L_2} = 15\ \text{mA}$
   $I_{L_3} = 5\ \text{mA}$
3. $L_1 = 10\ \text{mH}$
   $L_2 = 120\ \text{mH}$
   $L_3 = 40\ \text{mH}$

## CHAPTER 22

1. $X_L = 1.2\ \text{k}\Omega$
   $R = 2.08\ \text{k}\Omega$
   $L = 120\ \text{mH}$
   $I = 15\ \text{mA}$
   $V_L = 18\ \text{V}$
   $V_R = 31.2\ \text{V}$
3. $V_R = 6\ \text{Vpp}$
   $V_{R_1} = 5\ \text{Vpp}$
   $X_{L_1} = 833\ \Omega$
   $X_{L_2} = 500\ \Omega$
   $I = 6\ \text{mApp}$
   $Z_T = 1.67\ \text{k}\Omega$
   $L_1 = 41.67\ \text{mH}$
   $L_2 = 25\ \text{mH}$
   $\theta_Z = 53.13°$

## CHAPTER 23

1. (a) $V_C = 30\ \text{V}$
   (b) $7.5\ \text{ms}$
3. (a) $100\ \text{V}$
   (b) $0\ \text{V}$
   (c) $26.4\ \text{V}$
   (d) $55.37\ \text{V}$
   (e) $72.93\ \text{V}$

## CHAPTER 24

1. $L = 2.98\ \text{mH}$

## CHAPTER 25

1. $V_{in} = 24\ \angle 0°\ \text{V}$

## CHAPTER 26

1. $Q = 2\pi f_r L/r_S$
   $Qr_S = 2\pi L \times 1/2\pi\sqrt{LC}$
   $Qr_S = L/\sqrt{LC}$
   $Q^2 r_S^2 = L^2/LC$
   $Q^2 r_S^2 = L/C$
   $$\frac{X_L^2}{r_s^2} \times r_s^2 = L/C$$
   $X_L^2 = L/C$
   $X_L = \sqrt{L/C}$

## CHAPTER 27

1. (a) $f_c = 965\ \text{Hz}$
   (b) $V_{out} = 3.535\ \text{Vpp}$
   (c) $V_{out} = 68.2\ \text{mVpp}$
3. $L = 191\ \mu\text{H}$
   $C = 132.63\ \text{pF}$

## CHAPTER 28

1. $I_F = 150\ \text{mA}$

## CHAPTER 29

1. $V_{dc} = 27.68\ \text{V}$

## CHAPTER 30

1. $B = I_C/I_B$
   $= \alpha I_E/I_E - \alpha I_E$
   $= \alpha I_E/I_E\,(1 - \alpha)$
   $B = \alpha/1 - \alpha$

## CHAPTER 31

1.

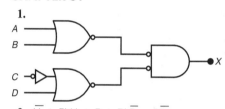

3. $(\overline{A} + B)(A + B + D)\overline{D} = B\overline{D}$

## CHAPTER 32

1. $V_{out} = 2\ \text{Vpp}$
   $V_{out}$ is in phase with $V_Y$.

# INDEX

A (ampere), 2, 29, 71, 74, 80, 384
Absorption losses in capacitors, 484
AC (alternating current), 2, 38–39, 423–424
    applications of, 416–417
    in capacitive circuit, 498–499
    combining direct current with, 760–763
    induction by, 542–543
    three-phase power, 447–449
    voltage divider, 528–529
AC circuits, 543, 664–685
    complex numbers for, 690–714
    negative and positive numbers, 692
    with resistance, 437–439
    with resistance but no reactance, 666–667
    types of ohms in, 682–683
    types of phasors in, 683–685
AC coupling, 527
AC effective resistance, 617–618
AC induction motor, 447
AC meters, 680–681
AC ripple, 762
AC voltage
    in amplifier circuit, 844–846
    checking input, 861
    comparison of, and dc voltage, 39
AC voltmeter, 861
Active components, 7, 255
Active devices, 842
Active filters, 772, 946–948
Admittance Y, 709–710
AF choke, 619–621
AF coupling capacitor, 527–528
Aging, 61
Air-core coils, 568
Air gap, magnet, 361–362
Alkaline cell, 325–326
Alnico magnets, 363
Alpha ($\alpha$) characteristic, 881
Alternating current. (*see* AC *entries*)
Alternating-voltage generator, 417–420
Alternation, 419–420
Alternators, 447
Amateur ("ham") radio, 4, 5
American National Standards Institute
        (ANSI), 925–926
American Standard Code for Information
        Interchange (ASCII) code, 901–902
Amp-clamp probe, 216
Ampère, André M., 2, 29, 80
Ampere (A), 2, 29, 71, 74, 80, 384
Ampere-turns (NI) of mmf, 372–373
Amplifier(s)
    components in, 842–844
    differential, 945–946
    FET, 882–884
    push-pull, 874
    signal frequencies in, 846–847
Amplifier circuits
    characteristics of, 841–847
    troubleshooting, 884–886
Amplifier class of operations, 873–875

Amplifier gain, 838–841
Amplitude modulation (AM), 3, 4, 854
Analog display, 219
Analog signals, 836–837
Analog-to-digital (A/D) converters, 217
AND gates, 112–113, 164–165, 903,
        907–908, 910, 914, 917–918
Angular measure, 420
Anode, 40
Antennas, 3, 4, 794
Antiresonance, 748
Apparent power, 680
Applied voltage(s), 103–104
    across open terminals, 111–112
    in parallel circuits, 122–123
Armature, 405, 445
Astable multivibrators, 852–853
Atom(s), 16–22
    covalent bonds, 309, 806
    electrons and protons in, 16–22
    structure of, 19–22
Atomic number, 20
Attenuation of filter, 771, 784–787
Audio frequencies, 428
Autorange function, 218
Autotransformers, 557
Axial leads, 49

Back emf, 547
Back-off ohmmeter scale, 211–212
Balanced filter circuit, 772
Balanced network, 279
Ballistic galvanometer, 197
Bandpass filters, 782, 791
Bandstop filters, 783, 791
Bandwidth of resonant circuit, 740–744
Bank(s)
    in parallel, 128–129
    in series, 151–152
Bank resistance, 128–129
Bank winding, 485
Bar magnet, solenoid as, 394
Bardeen, John, 3
Base bias voltage, 877
Baseband signal, 853
Bass tone, 428
Batteries, 318–345
    current drain, 338–339
    features of, 320–322
    internal resistance of generator, 339–340
    types of, 322–338
    voltage, 340–345
Beta ($\beta$) characteristic, 880
*B/H* magnetization curve, 375–378
Bias stabilization, 885
Bilateral components, 255
Binary coded decimal systems, 900
Binary counters, 922–924
Binary numbers, 894–896
    comparing to decimal, 894–895
    converting to decimal, 896
Bipolar transistors, 819

Bistable multivibrators, 853
Bit, 837
Bleeder current, 186
Bohr, Niels, 19
Boole, George, 906
Boolean algebra, 906–909, 915–918
Branch currents, 123–126, 130–133,
        150–151
    complex, 711–714
    division of, 183–184
    finding, 246
    formulas for, 180–181, 183–184
    method of, 237–241
Branch impedance, 710–711, 713
Brattain, Walter, 3
Bridge circuits
    simplifying, 278–279
    thevenizing, 260–262
Bridge rectifiers, 817
Brush discharge, 311
Brushes, 446
Bypass capacitors, 767–769
Byte, 837

C (coulomb), 22–25, 27, 384
Cable television technicians, 6
Capacitance, 458–489
    energy in electrostatic field of, 485–486
    of open circuit, 485
    parallel, 481
    series, 481–482
    stray effects, 483–485
    tolerance, 471
Capacitive circuit(s), 516–530
    alternating current in, 498–499
    capacitive reactance and resistance in se-
        ries, 519–522
    capacitive voltage dividers, 482, 528–529
    *RC* phase-shifter circuit, 522–523
    RF and AF coupling capacitors, 527–528
    sine-wave lags, 518–519
Capacitive coupling, 764–767
Capacitive current, 498–499, 530
Capacitive effects, 483–485
Capacitive reactance, 496–510
    applications of, 505–506
    calculation of ohms of, 499–503, 510
    circuits with, 668–669
    in parallel, 526
    in series, 519–522
Capacitive voltage dividers, 482, 528–529
Capacitor(s), 8–9, 460
    AF coupling, 527–528
    applications, 472
    bypass, 767–769
    *C* charges and discharges, 639–640, 641
    coding of, 474–480
    electrolytic, 471, 472–473
    functions of, 842–843
    inductance, 484
    RF coupling, 527–528
    troubles in, 487–489

Capacitor(s) (*cont.*):
  typical, 468–472
  voltage rating of, 471
Carbon-composition resistors, 49
Carbon control, 55
Carbon-film resistors, 49
Carbon resistor(s)
  choosing for circuit, 87
  color-coding of, 50–51
Carbon-zinc dry cell, 324–325
Carrier waves, 853
Cascade, 840–841, 878
Cathode, 11, 40
Center frequency, 855
Ceramic capacitors, 470, 476–477
Change, time rate of, 402–403
Charge(s)
  comparison of, and current, 29–30
  and discharge with short *RC* time constant, 645–646
  potential between different, 26
Charging
  of capacitor, 461–463
  of cell, 321
Chassis-ground
  connections, 159–160
  voltages measured to, 160–162
Chemical energy, 39
Chip capacitors, 470, 478–480
Chip resistors, 50, 53
Choke(s), AF and RF, 545, 619–621
Choke coils, 654
Chunking, 899
Circuit(s), 834–863
  AC. (*see* AC circuits)
  amplifier, 841–847, 884–886
  balanced filter, 772
  bridge, 260–262, 278–279
  capacitive. [*see* Capacitive circuit(s)]
  with capacitive reactance, 668–669
  characteristics of, 34
  choosing resistor for, 86–87
  closed, 34–36
  with current sources, 272–275
  filter, 770–771, 774–791
  inductive, 604–623, 653–654
  with inductive reactance, 667–668
  multiple units in, 75–76
  multivibrator, 852
  nortonizing, 263–265
  open. (*see* Open circuits)
  series-parallel, 146–165, 439
  short. (*see* Short circuit *entries*)
  tank, 732, 848
  thevenizing, 256–257, 259–262
Circuit breakers, 300
Circuit components, transistor amplifier, 876
Circuit configurations, 870–872
Circular mils (cmil), 292
Citizen's band (CB) radio, 4, 5
Class A operation, 873–874
Class B operation, 874
Class C operation, 874–875
Clockwise fields, 392–393
Closed circuit, 34–36
Coaxial cable, 293–294
Coercive force, 380
Coil(s), 8
  choke, 654

Coil(s) (*cont.*):
  distributed capacitance of, 485
  induced voltage across, 400–401
  magnetic polarity of, 394–395
  quality of, 617–618
  troubles in, 575–576
Collector, 822–823
Collector-base junctions, 820
Collector rings, 446
Color codes
  of capacitors, 477–478
  of resistors, 50–53
  of transformers, 558
Colpitts oscillators, 849
Common-base (CB) circuit, 871
Common-collector (CC) circuit, 872
Common-drain (CD) circuit, 883
Common-emitter (CE) amplifier, analysis of, 875–878
Common-emitter (CE) circuit, 871–872
Common-gate (CG) circuit, 883
Common-source (CS) circuit, 882–883
Communication electronics technicians, 6
Commutating, 857
Commutator, 446–447
Comparators, 948–949
Compensating capacitor, 934
Complex branch currents, 711–712, 714
Complex number(s), 694–695
  for ac circuits, 690–714
  magnitude and angle of, 700–701
  operations with, 698–699
  in parallel ac circuits, 708–710
  polar form of, 701–703
  rectangular form of, 694
  in series ac circuits, 705–708
Compound, 18–19
Compound winding, 446
Computer repair technicians, 5–6
Condensers, 460
Conductance(s), 33
  in parallel, 133–134
Conductor(s), 18
  function of, 290
  live, 88
  properties of, 302
  types of, 293–294
Conjugate complex numbers, 699
Connections, delta, 448
Connectors, 295–296
  troubleshooting hints for, 311–312
Constant-current generator, 343
Constant-current sources, 343
Constant-voltage sources, 343
Consumer electronics technicians, 5
Continuity, checking, with ohmmeter, 222–223
Controls, noise in, 60
Conventional current, 37
Core(s)
  losses, 567–568
  types of, 568–569
Corona effect, 311
Correct polarity, 199
Coulomb, Charles A., 23, 26
Coulomb (C), 22–25, 27, 384
Coulomb's law, 384
Counter emf, 547
Counterclockwise fields, 392–393

Counters, binary, 922–924
Coupling
  AC, 527
  capacitive, 764–767
  coefficient of, 549–550
  mutual, 550
  transformer, 763–764
Coupling capacitors, RF and AF, 527–528
Covalent bonds, 309, 806
Cross-coupling multivibrator, 850–851
Cryogenics, 306
Crystal filters, 793
Crystal oscillators, 849
Curie temperature, 363
Current(s) (*I*), 27–33
  alternating. (*see* AC *entries*)
  branch. (*see* Branch currents)
  calculating all, 243
  capacitive, 498–499, 530
  and charge in motion, 27–32
  comparison of
    and charge, 29–30
    with voltage, 34–35
  conventional, 37
  direct. (*see* DC *entries*)
  direction of, 36–37
  easy, 809
  effect of inductive reactance in reducing, 586–587
  electrode, 821–822
  electron, 30–31
  forward, 809
  induced voltage and change in, 547–548
  inside the cell, 323
  inverse relation between resistance and, 78
  leakage, 473, 809
  magnetic field around, 32, 392–394
  measurement of, 198–200
  nature of, 30–31
  in Ohm's law, 70–72
  outside the cell, 322–323
  path of, for $R_L$, 185–186
  reverse, 809, 815–816
  through the shunt, 201–202
  types of electric charges, 31
Current divider
  with parallel conductances, 183–184
  with two parallel resistances, 180–182
Current drain, load resistance as related to, 338–339
Current gain, 839–840
Current meter, connection of, 199, 220
Current ratings
  battery, 331–332
  transformer, 561
Current ratio, 555
Current sources
  circuits with, 272–275
  constant, 343
  conversion of, 268–270
Curves, collector characteristic, 879–881
Cutoff frequency, 771
Cycle, 418–420
Cycling of cell, 321

*D*-type flip-flops, 921
Dark current, 40
Darlington pair, 872

D'Arsonville movement, 197, 680, 681
DC (direct current), 38–39
    combining AC with, 760–763
    voltage divider, 529
DC circuits, 543
DC insertion, 762
DC meters, 194–223
    applications of, 219–221
    digital multimeter (DMM), 13, 215,
        217–219
    loading effect of voltmeter, 208–210
    measurement of current, 198–200
    meter shunts, 200–203
    moving-coil meter, 196–198
    multimeters, 196, 214–219
    ohmmeters. [see Ohmmeter(s)]
    voltmeters, 203–210, 861
DC resistance of a coil, 575
DC voltage
    in amplifier circuit, 844–846
    comparison of, and ac voltage, 39
    troubleshooting, 860–863
DC voltmeter, 861
Decade, 787–789
Decade resistance box, 55
Decay curve, equation of, 650
Decibels, 215, 784–787
Decimal
    comparing to binary, 894–895
    converting to binary, 896
    hexidecimal conversion to, 897–898
DeForest, Lee, 3
Degaussing, 380
Delta (Δ) connections, 448
Delta (Δ) networks, 275–279
Demagnetization, 380
DeMorgan's theorem, 909–911
Depletion mode, 825–826
Depletion zones, 812
Depolarizer, 325
Diamagnetic materials, 363
Dielectric
    capacitance, 466–467
    electric field in, 461
    insulating material, 18
Dielectric materials, 310, 460–461
Differential amplifiers, 945–946
Differentiation, 644
Digital electronics, 892–926
Digital logic gates, 817
Digital multimeter (DMM), 13, 217–219
    comparison of VOM of, 215
Digital signal(s), 836–837
Diode(s), 10–11
    semiconductor, 816–817
    as switches, 857
    testing, with ohmmeter, 827–829
Diode rectifiers, 857–860
Diode test, 218, 828
DIP switch, 298
Dipole magnet, 364
Direct current. (see DC entries)
Discharge
    brush, 311
    of capacitor, 462–463
    of cell, 321
    and charge with short RC time constant,
        645–646
    spark, 311

Discharge current and sine-wave charge,
    506–510
Domains, 364
Doping, 309, 806–807, 810
Double-dabble, 896
Double-pole double-throw (DPDT) switch,
    298
Drain electrode, 824
Dry cells, 321, 328
Dynamometer, 681

Easy current, 809
Eddy currents, 567
Edison, Thomas, 335
Edison cells, 335
Edison system, 444
Effective value, 426–427
Einstein, Albert, 19
Electric charge
    coulomb unit of, 22–25, 27, 384
    types of, for current, 31
Electric current. [see Current(s) (I)]
Electric fields, comparison of, with mag-
        netic fields, 383–385
Electric power. (see Power)
Electric shock, 88
Electricity, 14–40
    characteristics of, 16–39
    circuits, 34–36
    sources of, 39–40
Electrochemical series, 323–324
Electrode(s)
    drain, 824
    gate, 824
    source, 824
Electrode currents, 821–822
Electrolytes, 307
Electrolytic capacitors, 471, 472–473
Electromagnetic induction, 390–407
Electromagnetism, 2, 39, 362–363, 681
Electromotive force (emf), 27, 547
Electromotive series of elements, 323–324
Electron(s), 16–22
    charge of, 24–25, 31
Electron current, 30–31
Electron flow, 36–37
Electron valence, 21
Electron volt (eV), 80
Electronic circuits. [see Circuit(s)]
Electronic components, types of, 7–12
Electronic devices, 804–829
Electronic Industries Association (EIA), 37,
        51, 296, 826
Electronics
    applications of, 5–7
    career opportunities, 5–7
    development of, 2–3
    digital, 892–926
    tools of the trade, 13
Electrons, in semiconductors, 308–309
Electrostatic flux, 384
Electrostatic induction, 461
Electrostatics, 23
    capacitance, 485–486
Elements, 18
    electromotive series of, 323–324
    examples of, 19
Emitter-base junctions, 820
Emitter circuits, 886

Emitter-follower, 872
Energy
    in electrostatic field of capacitance,
        485–486
    levels of, 20–21
Enhancement mode, 825–826
Equivalent FM, 856
Eutectic solder, 958
Exclusive NOR (XNOR) gates, 905, 908
Exclusive OR (XOR) gates, 905, 908–909
External flux, conductor perpendicular to,
        398
Extrinsic semiconductors, 806–807

F connector, 295–296
Farad (F), 2, 6, 8, 384, 463–467
Faraday, Michael, 2, 6
Faraday screen, 485
Faraday's law of induced voltage, 402–404
Federal Communications Commission
        (FCC), 4
Ferrite core, 568–569
Ferrites, 364–365
Ferromagnetism, 354, 363
FET amplifiers, 882–884
Field-effect transistor (FET), 823–827
Field intensity, 373–375
Field lines, 354
Field winding, 446
Fields aiding, 393–394
Fields canceling, 393–394
Figure of merit, 736–737
Film capacitors, 470, 474–476
Film-type resistors, 49
Filter(s), 758–794
    active, 772, 946–948
    balanced, 772
    bandpass, 782, 791
    bandstop, 783, 791
    bypass capacitors, 767–769
    capacitive coupling, 764–767
    crystal, 793
    dc combined with ac, 760–763
    filter circuits, 770–771
    high-pass, 773–774, 780–781
    interference, 794
    L-type resonant, 792–793
    low-pass, 771–772, 774–779, 789–791
    parallel resonance, 792
    resonant, 791–793
    series resonance, 791
    transformer coupling, 763–764
Filter capacitors, checking, with an ohmme-
        ter, 862
Filter circuits, 770–771
    analyzing, 774–791
Filter section, 859
Flip-flops, 853, 918–922
Float charging, 333
Fluctuating direct current, 760–761
Flux
    comparison of, and flux density, 359
    electrostatic, 384
    external, 398
    magnetic, 355–359, 573–574
    in soldering, 959–960, 963
Flux density, 357–359
    calculating, 378

Flux density (*cont.*):
comparison of, and flux, 359
Flywheel effect, 732
Form factor, 427
Forward bias, 886
Forward current, 809
Free electrons, 17
Frequency, 4, 427–428
resonant, 724, 732–736
time factor in, 436–437
Frequency deviation, 855
Frequency modulation (FM), 4, 855–856
Frequency ratings, transformer, 562
Frequency reference, 60-Hz, 443
Frequency response curves, 787–791,
937–938
Frequency units, 428
Friction, static electricity by, 22, 39
Full-scale deflection current, 197
Full-wave rectifier, 859
Function generator, 13
Fuses, 221, 299–300
Fusible resistors, 50

Gain, calculation of, 877–878
Galvani, Luigi, 322
Galvanic cells, 322
Galvanometer, 196–197
Gases
ion current in, 306–308
ionization in, 307–308
Gate electrode, 824
Gates, William H., 926
Gauss, Karl F., 357
Gauss (G), 357–358
Generator(s), 445–447
alternating-voltage, 417–420
internal resistance of, 339–340
matching load resistance in, 343–345
Gilbert (Gb), 373
Graphs, plotting, 76–77, 787–789
Grounded tap, 162
Grounding, 444–445
chassis, 159–162

Hall, E. H., 366
Hall effect, 366
Hardware, 5
Harmonic frequencies, 442
Hartley oscillators, 849
Hayes, Dennis C., 820
Henry, Joseph, 2, 543
Henry (H), 2–3, 9, 384, 543–544
Hertz, Heinrich, 2, 3
Hertz (Hz), 2, 3, 428, 442–445
Hexadecimal values, 896–899
High current, production of, 640–641
High-pass filters, 773–774, 780–781
High-voltage probe, 216
Hole, 309, 808
Hole charges in semiconductors, 31,
308–309, 808
Honeycomb winding, 485
Horsepower units, 79
Hot resistance, 305–306
Hum, 863
Hybrid parameters, 882
Hydrate cells, 335
Hysteresis, 378–380

Hysteresis loop, 379–380
Hysteresis loss, 378–379, 568

*I.* (see Current *entries*)
Impedance, 294, 610
in complex form, 696–697, 714
matching, 565–567
reflected, 563
transformation, 563–567
Impedance $Z$ triangle, 610–612, 614–615
In-circuit tests, 885
Indirect FM, 856
Induced current, 398–399
Induced voltage
across coil, 400–401
analysis of, 403–404
and change in current, 547–548
Faraday's law of, 402–404
generating, 400–401
polarity of, 404
Inductance, 8–10, 540–576
of capacitor, 484
of coils, 544–545
energy in magnetic field of, 573–574
mutual, 548–551, 571–572
in series or parallel, 570–573
stray, 483–485, 573
typical coil values, 545–546
variable, 569–570
Induction, 398
by alternating current, 542–543
electromagnetic, 390–407
electrostatic, 461
by magnetic field, 360–361
residual, 380
Inductive capacitance, circuits with,
667–668
Inductive circuits, 604–623, 653–654
Inductive effects, 483–485
Inductive reactance ($X_l$), 584–598
applications of
for different frequencies, 593–594
Ohm's law in, 592
calculating, 587–591
effect of, in reducing current, 586–587
finding inductance from, 589–590
in parallel, 591–592, 613–616
and resistance in series, 607–609
Inductive voltage, 621–623
Inductive voltage pulses, applications of,
636
Inductors, 8–10
Industrial electronics technicians, 6
Institute of Electrical and Electronics Engi-
neers (IEEE), 925–926
Insulated-gate field-effect transistors
(IGFETs), 825–826
Insulator discharge current, 311
Insulators, 18, 310–311
Integrated circuits (ICs), 3, 932–949
operational amplifier characteristics,
934–949
operational amplifier circuits, 934–940
Integration, 645
Interference filters, 794
Internal resistance, 323
of generators, 339–340
measurement of, 342
Intrinsic semiconductors, 806

Inverted power supply, 859
Inverters, 902
Inverting amplifiers, 941–942
Ion(s), 31, 307
Ion current in liquids and gases, 306–308
Ionic bonds, 308
Ionization
in gases, 307–308
in liquids, 307
Ionization current, 307
*IR* drop, 102–106
voltage dividers, 179
zero, 111
Iron-vane meter, 681
Isolation transformer, 863

$j$ operator, 692–694
*JK* flip-flops, 922
Joule, James Prescott, 2, 79
Joule, 2, 27, 79, 80
Junction breakdown voltage, 816
Junction field-effect transistor (JFET),
826–827
Junction transistors, 819, 823–827

Keeper, magnet, 362
Kilohertz (kHz), 4
Kilowatthours (kWh), 80–81
Kirchhoff, Gustav R., 236
Kirchoff's current law (KCL), 234–235
Kirchoff's voltage law (KVL), 235–237

L-type resonant filter, 792–793
Laminated core, 568
Lead-acid wet cells, 330–334
Leakage current, 473, 809
Leakage flux, 549
Leclanché cell, 324–325, 326
LED (light-emitting diodes), 912–913
Lenz' law, 399–400, 547
Light current, 40
Light-emitting diodes (LED), 912–913
Linear components, 255
Linear proportion between V and I in
Ohm's law, 76–78
Linear resistance, 77
Liquid-crystal display (LCD), 217
Liquids
ion current in, 306–308
ionization in, 307
Lithium cells, 329
Lithium-iron sulfide cells, 335
Litz wire, 618
Load current, 35
effect of, on terminal voltage, 340–342
Load resistance, 35
matching to generator, 343–345
maximum power in, 344
maximum voltage across, 344–345
as related to current drain, 338–339
Loaded voltage, decrease in, 185
Loaded voltage divider, design of, 186–188
Loading down the circuit, 208
Loading effect
correction for, 210
of voltmeter, 208–210
Logic diagram, converting, to truth table,
903–905

Logic gate(s), 810, 902–918
  AND, 112–113, 164–165, 903, 907–908,
    910, 914, 917–918
  Boolean algebra, 906–909, 915–918
  digital, 817
  exclusive NOR (XNOR), 905, 908
  exclusive or (XOR), 905, 908–909
  NAND, 904, 910, 917–918, 920
  new logic symbols, 925–926
  NOR, 903, 908, 910
  OR, 138–139, 164–165, 902, 906–907,
    908
Loop equations, 236–241
  calculating voltages, 240
  checking solution, 240–241
  reasons for negative solution, 240
  solving for currents, 238–239
  writing, 238
Loose coupling, 549
Low-pass filters, 771–772, 774–779,
  789–791
$L/R$ time constant, 632–634

Magnet(s), 352–366
  air gap of, 361–362
  keeper for, 362
  permanent, 363
  types of, 362–364
Magnetic field(s), 39
  comparison of, with electric fields,
    383–385
  around electric current, 32, 392–394
  field lines, 354
  inductance in, 573–574
  induction by, 360–361
  motor action between, 395–397
  north and south magnetic poles, 354–355
Magnetic flux, 355–359, 573–574
Magnetic hysteresis, 378–380
Magnetic materials, classification of,
  363–364
Magnetic polarity, 394–395
Magnetic potential, 372–373
Magnetic shielding, 365–366
Magnetic tape recording, 363
Magnetic units, 370–385
  relations between, 382–383
  systems of, 356–357
Magnetizing force, 372–373
Magnetomotive force (mmf), ampere-turns
  of, 372–373
Main-line current, 124–126
Majority charges in semiconductors, 809
Manganese-zinc cells, 328
Marconi, Guglielmo, 3
Maxwell, James Clerk, 2, 356
Maxwell (Mx), 2, 356
Medical electronics technicians, 6
Megahertz (mHz), 4
Mercury cells, 327
Mesh currents, 244–247
Metal-film resistors, 49
Metal-oxide-semiconductor field-effect
  transistor (MOSFET), 825
Meter shunts, 200–203
Meters
  ac, 680–681
  dc, 194–223
Metric system, 384

Mho unit, 33
Mica capacitors, 468–469, 477
Microhenrys ($\mu$H), 545
Millihenrys (mH), 545
Millikan, Robert A., 24
Millman's theorem, 270–272
Minority charges in semiconductors, 809
Mistuning, 746–747
Modulation, 853–856
Modulation envelope, 854
Molecules, 18–19
Monostable multivibrator, 853
Motion, direction of, 398
Motor(s), 445–447
Motor action, 395–397
Moving-coil meters, 196–198
Multimeters, 196, 214–219
Multiple ohmmeter ranges, 212–213
Multiplier, 203, 474–475
Multiplier resistance, 204–205
Multitesters, 214
Multivibrators, 850–853
Mutual coupling, 550
Mutual inductance, 548–551, 571–572

N-type semiconductors, 31, 806–807
NAND gates, 904, 910, 917–918, 920
Negative polarities, 16, 23
Negative voltage, grounding of, 162
Network theorems, 252–279
  circuits with current sources, 272–275
  connections, 275–279
  Millman's theorem, 270–272
  Norton's theorem, 262–265
  superposition theorem, 254–255
  Thevenin-Norton conversions, 266–267
  Thevenin's theorem, 256–262
Nickel-cadmium (NiCd) cells, 334–335
Nickel-iron cells, 335
Nickel-zinc cells, 335
90° phase angles, 433–434, 510, 518–526,
  594–595, 598
Node(s), 241
Node equations
  calculating all voltage and currents, 243
  writing, 242–243
Node-voltage analysis, 241–243
Nonlinear resistance, 78–79
Nonsinusoidal ac waveforms, 440–441
NOR gates, 903, 908, 910
North magnetic poles, 354–355
Norton, E. L., 262
Norton equivalent circuits, 263
Norton's theorem, 262–265
NPN transistors, 818–823
Nucleus, 17, 21–22

Octave, 442, 787
Oersted, Hans Christian, 2
Oersted (Oe), 2, 374
Office equipment technicians, 7
Ohm, Georg Simon, 2, 33, 77
Ohm ($\Omega$), 2, 7, 33, 71, 74, 77, 184, 384,
  682–683
Ohm-centimeters, 303
Ohm's law, 68–89, 554
  applications of, 123–124
    branch current, 150–151
    to capacitive reactance, 504–505

Ohm's law, applications of (*cont.*):
    to inductive reactance, 592
    parallel resistance, 127
    series resistance, 101–102
  linear proportion between $V$ and $I$, 76–78
  for magnetic circuits, 380–381
  multiple units, 75–76
  use of, to define practical units, 74
Ohmic contact, 812–813
Ohmmeter(s), 210–214, 861–862
  testing capacitors with, 487–488
  testing continuity with, 222–223
  testing diodes with, 827–829, 862
  testing resistors with, 60–61
  testing semiconductors with, 827–829
Ohms-per-volt rating, 207–208
One-shot multivibrators, 853
Open circuits, 36
  capacitance of, 485
  effect of, 164
  in parallel circuits, 136–137
  in series-parallel circuits, 164
  in series paths, 110–112
  troubles in, 89
  voltage tests, 221
Open coils, 575–576
Open terminals, presence of applied voltage
  across, 111–112
Open winding, 575–576
Operational amplifier(s), 934–949
Operational amplifier circuits, 934–940
OR gates, 138–139, 164–165, 902,
  906–907, 908
Orbital rings, 20–21
Oscillators, 847–850
Oscilloscopes, 13, 966–980

P-type semiconductors, 31, 808
Paper capacitors, 469
Parallax, 197
Parallel
  capacitive reactance and resistance in,
    524–526
  conductances in, 133–134
  inductances in, 570–573
  inductive reactance in, 613–616
  resistance strings in, 149–151
  resistors in, 59
Parallel capacitances, 481
Parallel capacitive reactances, 503–504
Parallel cells, 337
Parallel circuits, 120–139
  analysis of, 135–136
  applied voltage in, 122–123
  with complex branches, 712–714
  complex numbers in, 708–710
  effect of, and open branch in, 136–137
  off resonance, 747
  with resistance, 438–439
  resistances in, 127–133, 524–526
  short circuits in, 137–138
  total power in, 134–135
  voltage sources in, 268
Parallel conductances, current division by,
  183–184
Parallel connections, 337
Parallel inductive reactances, 591–592,
  613–616

Parallel load current, series voltage divider with, 184–186
Parallel reactance, 503–504, 674–676
Parallel resistance, 666–667, 674–676
  current divider, 180–182
Parallel resonance, 728–732, 739–740
Parallel resonance filters, 792
Parallel resonant circuits, 739–740
  analysis of, 747–748
  damping of, 749–750
Paramagnetic materials, 363
Particles, stable, 21–22
Passbands, 772
Passive components, 7, 255
Passive devices, 842
Passive filters, 772
Percent modulation, 855
Period, 428–430
Periodic table, 20
Permanent magnets, 360, 363
Permeability, 360–361, 375–376
Permeance, 384
Permittivity, 384
Phase, time factor in, 436–437
Phase angle, 433–435, 440, 685
  capacitive, 510, 518–526
  inductive, 594–598, 606–607, 610–612, 615
  reactance, 653
Phase-angle diagrams, 434
Phase-angle reference, 434–435
Phase modulation, 856
Phase-shifter circuits, *RC*, 522–523
Phasor(s), 434, 683–685
Phasor current triangles, 615
Phasor voltage triangles, 608–609
Photoelectricity, 40
Photoelectrons, 40
Pi ($\pi$) network, 275–279
Pie, 485
Piezoelectric effect, 793
Planck, Max, 19
Plastic cells, 335–336
PN junction, 811–816
PNP transistors, 818–823
Polar form
  of complex numbers, 701–703
  conversions of, to rectangular, 703–705
Polarities
  attraction of opposite charges, 23
  capacitor, 472–473
  of charge, 23–24
  of induced poles, 360
  of induced voltage, 404
  magnetic, 394–395
  negative and positive, 16, 23
  repel of same charges, 23
  of voltage drops, 105–106
Polarization, 325
Positive polarities, 16, 23
Positive voltage, grounding of, 161–162
Potential, 25
  magnetic, 372–373
Potential difference, 25–27, 28–29, 39
Potentiometers, 56–58
Powdered-iron core, 568
Power, 78–86
  formulas of, 84–86
  in parallel circuits, 134–135

Power (*cont.*):
  practical units of, 79–80
  real, 677–680
  in secondary, 554
  in series circuit, 106–107
Power bandwidth, 938–939
Power dissipation in resistance, 81–83
Power factor
  of capacitor, 484
  real power, 678–680
Power gain, 840
Power-line filter, 794
Power ratings
  resistor, 48, 58–59
  transformer, 561–562
Power supply, 13, 859
Power-supply rectifier, 817
Primary cells, 320, 327
Primary power, equal to secondary power, 556
Primary winding, open, 576
Principal node, 241
Printed-circuit (PC) boards, 48, 296–297
Printed wiring (PW) boards, 296–297
Proportional voltage method, 178–179
Proton(s), 16–22
Pull-up resistors, 920
Pulsating direct current, 760–761
Pulse modulation, 856
Push-bottom switch, 298
Push-pull amplifier, 874

*Q* of coils, 617–618
*Q* magnification factor of resonant circuit, 736–740, 748
Quadrature phase, 434

Radian, 420
Radio broadcasting, 3–4, 4–5
Radio frequencies. (*see* RF *entries*)
Radio tuning dial, 745–746
Radio waves
  history of, 3–4
  wavelength of, 430–432
Ramp voltage, 440
Range overload, 218
Rationalization of fraction, 699
*RC* bandpass filters, 782
*RC* bandstop filters, 783
*RC* charge curve, 639–640
*RC* circuit, production of high-current by short-circuiting, 640–641
*RC* coupling circuit, long time constant for, 647–648
*RC* discharge curve, 640
*RC* feedback oscillators, 849
*RC* high-pass filters, 780
*RC* low-pass filters, 774–777, 789–791
*RC* phase-shifter circuits, 522–523
*RC* time constant, 636–639, 644–654
*RC* waveshapes, 642–644
Reactance
  ac circuits with resistance but no, 666–667
  cancellation of opposite, 669–671
  capacitive. (*see* Capacitive reactance)
  comparison of time constant and, 653–654
  inductive. (*see* Inductive reactance)

Reactance (*cont.*):
  parallel, 503–504, 674–676
  series, 503–504, 671–673
  series-parallel, 676–677
Real power, 677–680
Receivers, 3, 4
Reciprocal resistance formula, 128–129
Rectangular form
  of complex numbers, 694
  conversion of polar form to, 703–705
Rectifier(s)
  diode, 857–860
  movement, 681
  packaging, 817
  power-supply, 817
  ratings, 817
Reference clock, 850
Relative permeability, 360–361
Relative permittivity, 466–467
Relaxation oscillators, 850
Relays, 404–407
  applications of, 406–407
  specifications, 405–406
  troubles, 407
Reluctance, 380
Residential wiring, 443–444
Residual induction, 380
Resistance, 32–33
  ac circuits with, 437–439
    but no reactance, 666–667
  ac effective, 617–618
  bank, 128–129
  current meter, 199–200
  and inductive reactance
    in parallel, 613–616
    in series, 607–609
  internal. (*see* Internal resistance)
  inverse relation between current and, 78
  linear, 77
  load. (*see* Load resistance)
  measurement of, 217
  meter shunt, 201
  multiplier, 204–205
  nonlinear, 78–79
  in Ohm's law, 73–74
  parallel, 666–667, 674–676
  in parallel, 127–133, 524–526
  power dissipation in, 81–83
  response of, 632
  series, 100–102, 151–152, 666, 671–673
  series-parallel, 148–149, 676–677
  specific, 302–303
  temperature coefficient of, 304–306
  voltmeter, 207
  wire, 301–304
Resistance banks
  in series, 151–152
  in series-parallel, 153–154
Resistance movement, values of, 197
Resistance strings
  in parallel, 149–151
  in series, 101
  in series-parallel, 153–154
Resistance values, preferred, 52–53
Resistance wire, 48–49, 304
Resistor(s), 7–8, 46–61
  changed value of, 61
  characteristics of, 48
  checking, with ohmmeter, 60–61

Resistor(s) (*cont.*):
  choosing, for a circuit, 86–87
  color coding, 50–53
  power rating of, 48, 58–59
  preferred values, 956
  reactive effects in, 485
  series and parallel combinations of, 59
  shelf life of, 59
  tolerance, 51–52
  troubles, 60–61
  types of, 48–50
  variable, 54–55
Resonance, 722–751
  analysis of parallel resonant circuits, 747–748
  bandwidth of resonant circuits, 740–744
  mistuning, 746–747
  parallel, 728–732, 739–740
  resonant frequency, 732–736
  series, 725–728, 737–738
  tuning, 744–746
Resonance effect, 724
Resonant circuit, 724
  bandwidth of, 740–744
  choosing *L* and *C* for, 751
  *Q* magnification factor of, 736–740, 748
Resonant filters, 791–793
Resonant frequency, 724, 732–736
Retentivity, 380
Reverse current, 809, 815–816
RF (radio frequencies), 428
RF choke, 545, 619–621
RF coupling capacitor, 527–528
RF shielding, 567–568
Rheostats, 56–58
Ring magnets, 361–362
Ringing of current, 732
Ripple counters, 923
*RL* circuit, production of high voltage by opening, 634–636
*RL* high-pass filters, 780–781
*RL* low-pass filters, 777–779
Root-mean-square (rms) value, 426–427
Rotary switch, 298
Rotor, 445, 470
*RS* flip-flops, 918–920
Rutherford, Lord, 19

Saturation, 378
Schematic symbols, 8–12, 964–965
Schockley, William, 3
Sealed rechargeable cells, 322
Secondary
  isolation of, 557
  power in, 554, 556
Secondary cells, 321, 334–336
Secondary current, 554
Secondary winding
  open, 576
  short across, 576
Self-bias, 885
Self-excited generator, 446
Self-inductance, 543–547
Semiconductor(s), 3, 19, 806–810
  diodes, 816–817
  electrons and hole charges in, 31, 308–309, 808–809
  extrinsic, 806–807
  fixed ion charge in doped, 810

Semiconductor(s) (*cont.*):
  intrinsic, 806
  majority and minority charges in, 809
  N-type, 31, 806–807
  P-type, 31, 808
Series
  capacitive reactance and resistance in, 519–522
  current energy sources in, 274
  electromotive, 323–324
  inductances in, 570–573
  inductive reactance, 607–609, 610–612
  resistance banks in, 151–152
  resistors in, 59
  voltage dividers in, 178–180, 184–188
Series ac circuits, complex numbers in, 705–708
Series-aiding, 107, 571
Series capacitances, 481–482
Series capacitive reactances, 503–504
Series cells, 336
Series circuits, 96–113
  analysis of, 108–110
  complex numbers in, 705–708
  effect of open circuit in, 110–112
  equality of current in, 98–100
  off resonance, 747
  with resistance, 438
  resistance banks in, 151–152
  total power in, 106–107
  voltage sources in, 109–110, 269–270
Series connections, 336
Series inductive reactances, 591–592
Series ohmmeters circuit, 211
Series-opposing connection, 571
Series-opposing voltages, 107
Series-parallel
  current energy sources, 275
  open circuit in, 164
  resistance banks and strings in, 153–154
  short circuit in, 163–164
Series-parallel circuits, 146–165
  analysis of, 155–157
  logic functions, 164–165
  with resistance, 439
Series-parallel connections, 338
Series-parallel reactance, 676–677
Series-parallel resistance, 148–149, 676–677
Series reactance, 503–504, 671–673
Series resistance, 100–102, 151–152, 666, 671–673
Series resistors, 204–205
Series resonance, 725–728, 737–738
Series resonance filters, 791
Series string, 101
Series voltage-dropping resistors, 109
Shelf life, 59
Shells, 20–21
Shielding
  magnetic, 365–366
  RF, 567–568
Shock, electric, 88
Short circuit(s), 36
  effect of, 163–164
  in parallel circuits, 137–138
  in series-parallel circuits, 163–164
  troubles in, 89
Short-circuit current, 136, 265
Short-circuited capacitors, 488

Short-circuiting *RC* circuits, 640–641
Shunt current, 201–202
Shunt resistance, 202
Sidebands, 854–855
Siemens, Werner von, 2, 33, 384
Siemens (S), 2, 33, 184, 384
Sigma (Σ), 276
Signal detector, 817
Signal frequencies in amplifiers, 846–847
Silver oxide cell, 327
Sine wave, 420–423
  of applied voltage, 506–507
  voltage and current values for, 424–427
  waveshape of induced voltage as induced by, 594–598
Sine-wave charge and discharge current, 506–510
Sine-wave lags, 518–519, 606–607
Sine-wave voltage, 506–507
Single-pole, double-throw (SPDT) switch, 298
Single-pole, single-throw (SPST) switch, 298
Sinusoid(s), 420–423, 427, 434
Sinusoidal waves, 420–423
60-Hz ac power line, 442–445
Skin effect, 617
Slew rate, 938
Slip rings, 446
Slope, 622
Slow-blow fuses, 300
Sodium-sulphur cells, 335
Software, 5
Solar cells, 336
Solder and soldering, 296–297, 957–963
Solenoid, 362, 394
Solid-state devices, 3
Sonic frequencies, 428
Sound waves, wavelength of, 432
Source electrodes, 824
Source followers, 883
South magnetic pole, 354–355
Space-wound coils, 485
Spaghetti, 293
Spark discharge, 311
Specific gravity, 332–333
Specific resistance, 302–303
Stage, 840–841
Star connections, 448
Static electricity, 22, 25, 39
Stator, 446, 470
Stop band, 772
Stray effects, 483–485
Stray inductance, 573
String(s), 101, 130–133
Subshells, 21
Sum of (Σ), 276
Summing amplifiers, 944–945
Superconductivity, 306
Superposition, 272
Superposition method, 259–260
Superposition theorem, 254–255
Surface-mounted devices (SMDs), 11–12, 50
  capacitors, 470
  resistors, 50, 53
Susceptance *B*, 709–710
Switches, 297–298, 857
Système Internationale (SI) units, 357, 384–385

T networks, 275–279
Tank circuits, 732, 848
Tantalum capacitors, 473, 480
Tapered control, 55
Taut-band meters, 197
Television antenna filters, 794
Television broadcasting, 4
Temperature coefficient, 304–306, 471
Terminal voltage, effect of load current on, 340–342
Tesla, Nikola, 358
Tesla (T), 358–359, 385
Thermal emission, 40
Thermal movement, 680
Thermocouple, 681
Thevenin, M. L., 256
Thevenin-Norton conversions, 266–267
Thevenin's theorem, 256–262
Three-phase ac power, 447–449
Tight coupling, 549
Time, units of, 429–430
Time base, 440
Time constants
    charge and discharge with short *RC*, 645–646
    comparison of reactance and, 653–654
    *L/R*, 632–634
    *RC*, 636–639, 644–654
    universal graph, 648–652
Time factor in frequency and phase, 436–437
Tolerance
    capacitor, 471
    resistor, 51–52
Toroid magnets, 361–362
Torque, 397
Total-current method, 130
Total power
    in parallel circuits, 134–135
    in series circuits, 106–107
Transconductance, 884
Transformer(s), 10, 12, 552–567
    efficiency of, 557–558
    impedance, 563–567
    ratings, 558–562
Transformer coupling, 763–764
Transient response, 543, 632–634
Transistor(s), 11, 12
    bipolar, 819
    field-effect (FET), 823–827
    invention of, 3
    letter symbols for, 881–882
    testing, with ohmmeter, 827–829
Transistor action, 820–821
Transistor amplifiers, 868–886

Transistor-transistor logic (TTL), 917
Transmission lines, 293–294
Transmitters, 3, 4
Treble tone, 428
Triggering, 853
Triode(s), 819
Troubleshooting
    amplifier circuits, 884–886
    connectors, 311–312
    DC supply voltage, 860–863
    wires, 311–312
Truth tables, 113, 903–905, 915–916
TTL circuits, 917
Tuned RF feedback oscillators, 848–849
Tuning, 724, 744–746
Tuning ratio, 745
Turns ratio, 552–553

Ultrasonic frequencies, 428
Universal motors, 447
Universal time constant graphs, 648–652
Universal winding, 485

Valance, electron, 21
Variable capacitors, 470–471
Variable inductance, 569–570
Variable resistors, 54–55
Variac, 569–570
Variometer, 569
Vector, 434
Volt (V), 25–27, 71–72, 74, 384
Volt-ohm milliammeter (VOM), 215
Volt unit of potential difference, 25–27
Volta, Allesandro, 27
Voltage, 27
    ac, 39, 844–846, 861
    across resistance, 188
    applied, 103–104, 111–112, 122–123
    batteries, 340–345
    calculating, 240, 243
    comparison of, with current, 34–35
    generators, 417–420
    induced. (*see* Induced voltage)
    inductive, 621–623
    junction breakdown, 816
    measurement of, to chassis-ground, 160–162
    in Ohm's law, 70–73
    production of, by opening *RL* circuit, 634–636
    self-induced, 546–547
    series-aiding and series-opposing, 107
    for sine wave, 424–427
    source, 111
    tests, 221

Voltage dividers, 184–186, 254–255
    capacitive, 482, 528–529
    series, 178–180, 184–188
Voltage drops, 102–106, 109, 111, 246
Voltage followers, 943–944
Voltage gain, 838–839, 934–937
Voltage ratings
    capacitor, 471
    constant, 343
    transformer, 559–561
Voltage ratio, 553–554
Voltage source, 254–255
    circuit as load on, 35–36
    constant, 343
    conversion of, 268–270
    inverted, 162
    and maintenance of current, 35
    in series, 109–110, 269–270
    thevenizing circuits with two, 259–260
Voltaic cells, 322–324
Voltampere (VA), 77, 680, 814–815
Voltampere reactive (VAR), 680
Voltmeters, 203–210

Watt, James, 2, 49, 78
Watt (W), 3, 48, 49, 78, 79, 80
Wattmeters, 681–682
Waveforms, 434–435, 440–441
Wavelength, 430–432
Waveshape of induced voltage as induced by sine-wave current, 594–598
Weber, Wilhelm Eduard, 2, 356
Weber (Wb), 2, 356, 385
Wheatstone bridge, 158–159
Winding
    bank, 485
    field, 446
    open, 575–576
    universal, 485
Wire cable, 293
    troubleshooting hints for, 311–312
Wire gage, sizes of, 290–292
Wire links, 300
Wire resistance, 301–304
Wire-wound resistors, 48–49, 52, 87
Work, 79–80
Wye connection, 448

Y networks, 275–279

Zero-ohm adjustment, 214
Zero-ohm resistors, 53
Zinc-chloride cells, 326, 335

# Photo Credits

Cover and title page photos: Foreground: Larry Kennan Associates/The Image Bank; background: Simon Fraser/Welwyn Electronics/Science Photo Library/Photo Researchers

**Pages iii, xiv:** Stephen Simpson/FGP International; **Page 2:** Stephen Simpson/FPG International; **Page 3:** Bettmann Archive (Heinrich Hertz), Mark Steinmetz (Fig. S-1); **Page 5:** Science Photo Library/Photo Researchers; **Page 6:** Don Mason/The Stock Market (top), Bettmann Archive (Faraday), Courtesy of the Royal Institution (Faraday in lab); **Page 7:** Mark Steinmetz; **Page 9:** Mark Steinmetz; **Page 10:** Mark Steinmetz (Figs. S-5, S-6, and S-7); **Page 11:** Mark Steinmetz; **Page 12:** Mark Steinmetz; **Page 13:** Courtesy Fluke Corporation (Fig. S-10a), Courtesy of MCM Electronics (Fig. S-10b), Reproduced by permission of Tektronix, Inc. (Fig. S-11); **Page 14:** Phillip Hayson/Photo Researchers; **Page 18:** Bettmann Archive (Volta portrait), J-L Charmet/Science Photo Library/Photo Researchers (Volta with battery); **Page 21:** Sheila Terry/Science Photo Library/ Photo Researchers; **Page 26:** File photo; **Page 28:** Bettmann Archive (Millikan portrait and Millikan ray machine); **Page 33:** Mark Steinmetz; **Pages iv, 35:** Phillip Hayson/Photo Researchers; **Page 40:** Peter Aprahamian/Science Photo Library/Photo Researchers; **Page 45:** Mark Segal/Tony Stone Images; **Page 46:** Courtesy Harris Corporation; **Page 48:** Charles Krebs/Tony Stone Images (Fig. 2-1b), Mark Steinmetz (Fig. 2-2), P. R. Mallory (Fig. 2-3); **Page 49:** Bettmann Archive (Watt), Stackpole Corporation (Figs. 2-4 and 2-5); **Page 50:** Mark Steinmetz; **Page 55:** Mark Steinmetz; **Page 57:** Mark Steinmetz; **Page 60:** © Telegraph Colour Library/FPG International; **Page 66:** Courtesy Harris Corporation; **Page 67:** Charles Gupton/Stock Boston; **Pages v, 68:** Tom Tracy/The Stock Market; **Page 70:** Telegraph Colour Library/FPG International; **Page 77:** Bettmann Archive; **Page 79:** Bettmann Archive; **Page 82:** Telegraph Colour Library/FPG International; **Page 94:** Gabriel M. Covian/The Image Bank; **Page 95:** Matthew Borkoski/Stock Boston; **Page 96:** John Madere/The Stock Market; **Page 98:** Ben Swedowsky/The Image Bank; **Page 101:** File photo; **Page 103:** Metropolitan Museum of Art, Michael Friedsam Collection, 1931; **Page 111:** John Madere/The Stock Market; **Pages vi, 120:** Art Montes de Oca/FPG International; **Page 125:** Art Montes de Oca/FPG International; **Page 130:** Richard Pasley/Stock Boston; **Pages vii, 146:** Richard Nowitz/The Stock Market; **Page 151:** John Madere/The Stock Market; **Page 152:** Telegraph Colour Library/FPG International; **Page 157:** Richard Nowitz/The Stock Market; **Pages viii, 176:** Blair Seitz/Photo Researchers; **Page 188:** Geoff Tompkinson/Science Photo Library/Photo Researchers; **Pages xi, 194:** Joe Bator/The Stock Market; **Page 196:** Courtesy of MCM Electronics (Fig. 8-1a), Courtesy Fluke Corporation (Fig. 8-1a); **Page 197:** Weston Instrument Corp.; **Page 206:** Simpson Electric Company; **Page 215:** Courtesy of Simpson Electric Company; **Page 216:** Courtesy of Tektronix, Inc. (Fig. 8-20), Courtesy Fluke Corporation (Fig. 8-21); **Page 217:** Courtesy Fluke Corporation; **Page 223:** Alvis Upitis/The Image Bank; **Page 232:** Gary Gladstone/The Image Bank; **Page 236:** Bettmann Archive; **Page 239:** Rick Altman/Nawrock Stock Photo; **Page 240:** Charles Gupton/Stock Boston; **Page 243:** Gary Gladstone/The Image Bank; **Page 247:** Crown Studio; **Page 252:** Dick Luria/FPG International; **Page 261:** Dick Luria/FPG International; **Page 264:** SuperStock; **Pages xii, 288:** Gabe Palmer/The Stock Market; **Page 292:** L. S. Starrett; **Page 293:** Mark Steinmetz; **Page 294:** Hank Morgan/VHSID Lab/ECE Dept U of MA/Science Source/Photo Researchers; **Page 296:** Mark Steinmetz (Fig. 11-7a and b); **Page 299:** Mark Steinmetz; **Page 300:** Mark Steinmetz (Figs. 11-13, 11-14, and 11-15); **Page 305:** Bettmann Archive; **Page 306:** Gabe Palmer/The Stock Market; **Page 312:** Reproduced by permission of Tektronix, Inc.; **Page 317:** © Ken Biggs/Photo Researchers; **Page 318:** Mark Steinmetz; **Page 320:** Mark Steinmetz; **Page 321:** Mark Steinmetz; **Page 324:** Eveready Union Carbide Corporation; **Page 326:** Eveready Union Carbide Corporation; **Page 327:** Eveready Union Carbide Corporation; **Page 329:** Mark Steinmetz; **Page 330:** Exide Corporation; **Page 332:** © Ken Biggs/Photo Researchers; **Page 333:** Exide Corporation; **Page 334:** Doug Martin; **Page 335:** Mark Steinmetz; **Page 345:** Bob Daemmrick/Stock Boston; **Page 352:** Toshiba America Consumer Products, Inc.; **Page 363:** Mark Steinmetz; **Page 364:** © 1990 David A. Wagner/The Stock Market; **Page 365:** Toshiba America Consumer Products, Inc.; **Page 366:** Courtesy F. W. Bell; **Page 370:** Charles Thatcher/Tony Stone Images; **Page 375:** KS Studios; **Page 378:** Michael Gilbert/Science Photo Library/Photo Researchers; **Page 385:** Charles Thatcher/Tony Stone Images; **Page 389:** Gregory MacNicol/Photo Researchers; **Page 390:** Ralph Mercer/Tony Stone Images; **Page 402:** © Alvis Upitis/The Image Bank; **Page 405:** Mark Steinmetz; **Page 413:** Michael Rosenfeld/Tony Stone Images; **Page 414:** Tony Craddock/SPL/Photo Researchers; **Page 419:** Kim Steele/The Image Bank; **Page 445:** Mark Steinmetz (Fig. 16-22a and b; Fig. 16-23); **Page 449:** Courtesy Meteor Communications Corp., Kent, Washington; **Page 458:** Greg Pease/Tony Stone Images; **Page 469:** Mark Steinmetz (Figs. 17-4b and 17-5b); **Page 470:** Mark Steinmetz (Figs. 17-6 and 17-7); **Page 471:** Mark Steinmetz; **Page 472:** Mark Steinmetz; **Page 474:** Mark Steinmetz; **Page 483:** Bob Johnston/Texas State Technical College; **Page 489:** Bob Daemmrich/Uniphoto; **Pages x, 496:** Ken Cooper/The Image Bank; **Page 500:** Peter Scholey/Nawrocki Stock Photo; **Page 507:** Ken Cooper/The Image Bank; **Pages ix, 516:** Larry Keenan Associates/The Image Bank; **Page 523:** Larry Keenan Associates/The Image Bank; **Page 526:** © 1990 Joe Robbins/FGP International; **Page 540:** © 1990 Stephen Hunt/The Image Bank; **Page 543:** Bettmann Archive; **Page 545:** Mark Steinmetz; **Page 545:** Mark Steinmetz; **Page 553:** Mark Steinmetz; **Page 559:** Mark Steinmetz; **Page 570:** Sencore, Inc.; **Page 575:** Gabe Palmer/The Stock Market; **Page 576:** Hewlett-Packard/Peter Arnold; **Page 583:** Scott Eklund/Gamma Liaison; **Page 584:** American Honda Motor Company; **Page 597:** American Honda Motor Company; **Page 597:** American Honda Motor Company; **Page 604:** Stephen Ferry/Gamma Liaison; **Page 618:** Stephen Ferry/Gamma Liaison; **Page 619:** Mark Steinmetz; **Page 630:** Eric Sander/Gamma Liaison; **Page 637:** Eric Sander/Gamma Liaison; **Page 660:** Alfred Pasieka/Science Photo Library/Photo Researchers; **Page 664:** Yvonne Hemsey/Gamma Liaison; **Page 679:** Spencer Grant/Gamma Liaison; **Page 679:** Spencer Grant/Gamma Liaison; **Page 690:** Uniphoto; **Page 705:** Courtesy of Metatec; **Page 713:** Uniphoto; **Page 719:** File photo (top left), Fred Wilson/FPG International (top right), Courtesy Apple Computers (bottom left), Davies & Starr/Gamma Liaison (bottom right); **Page 722:** Remi Benali/Gamma Liaison; **Page 730:** Remi Benali/Gamma Liaison; **Page 757:** Robert Severi/Gamma Liaison; **Page 758:** Volker Steger/Peter Arnold; **Page 766:** Volker Steger/Peter Arnold; **Page 793:** Mark Steinmetz; **Page 794:** Mark Steinmetz; **Page 794:** Mark Steinmetz; **Page 804:** Eduardo Garcia/FPG International; **Page 807:** Texas Instruments, Inc.; **Page 810:** Eduardo Garcia/FPG International; **Page 812:** Leonard Lessin/Peter Arnold; **Page 820:** Hayes Microcomputer Products; **Page 829:** DISH Network; **Page 834:** Studiohio; **Page 843:** Mark Steinmetz; **Page 849:** Mark Steinmetz; **Page 852:** Studiohio; **Page 863:** Sencore, Inc.; **Page 868:** Robert Nickelsberg/Gamma Liaison; **Page 872:** Uniphoto; **Page 892:** C. Falco/Photo Researchers; **Page 920:** C. Falco/Photo Researchers; **Page 926:** Microsoft Corporation; **Page 932:** Michael Fairchild/Peter Arnold; **Page 934:** Mark Steinmetz; **Page 940:** Michael Fairchild/Peter Arnold; **Page 967:** Reproduced by permission of Tektronix, Inc.; **Page 969:** BK Precision

Photo for Did You Know? feature: Pete Saloutos/The Stock Market; photo for About Electronics feature: Dale O'Dell/The Stock Market

Circuit board frame: Steve Allen/The Image Bank

Appendix B: Courtesy of PACE, Inc., Laurel, Maryland